D1544747

FIELDS and WAVES in
MODERN RADIO

FIELDS and WAVES in MODERN RADIO

SIMON RAMO
Vice President, Hughes Aircraft Company
Research Associate, California Institute of Technology

JOHN R. WHINNERY
Professor of Electrical Engineering
University of California

SECOND EDITION

JOHN WILEY & SONS, INC. NEW YORK
LONDON

537.5
R175L
97979

SECOND EDITION

Sixth Printing, July, 1962

Library of Congress Catalog Card Number: 53-6615

Printed in the United States of America

PREFACE

The second edition differs from the first in the following major respects:

1. The rational mks system of units is used throughout.

2. Many problems have been added, particularly at the introductory level.

3. Much new material has been added, including an entirely new chapter on microwave networks; more simple examples in the chapters on static fields; the useful Smith chart in the simple transmission line treatment; several new aspects of propagating waves such as the principle of duality and slow-wave circuits; and new features in the chapter on radiation, such as discussions of horns, slot antennas, receiving antennas, and more on arrays.

4. Some of the material which seemed less useful has been eliminated, and nearly all has been revised for additional clarity.

Because the first edition found its place as a useful text of intermediate level, we have tried to maintain that level, and, although certain of the changes add more advanced material, others are concerned with additional examples in the beginning stages which will make the material easier to grasp. The general plan of the book has been changed little except for the added material, though there is some reorganization, and nearly every section has appreciable revision in the attempt to make the presentation clearer.

The need was obvious for additional problems and for the change of units in the one chapter of the first edition which used the classical systems. (We have retained definitions and conversion tables for these systems because the classical literature must still be consulted.) The question of added material was harder, for with the rapid development of microwave engineering additional important examples could be added without limit. The additions were consequently limited to those that introduced some new principle or point of view. For example, the helix as a guiding system was chosen because it illustrates the behavior of waves with phase velocities less than the velocity of light, the sectoral horn guide because it illustrates the phenomenon of a gradual cut-off, and the wedge guide because it illustrates the principle of duality. Some deletions were required to keep the book within reasonable length, and we hope that we have not eliminated material useful to people whose needs we do not know.

The book has been used continuously since its first appearance by both of us in teaching senior and first-year graduate courses on Electromagnetic Fields and Waves. The changes have been based primarily on this experience, on suggestions given us by our colleagues who are practicing engineers in organizations with which we have been affiliated, and on comments sent to us by many engineers and faculty members throughout the country. We wish to thank all persons who have taken the trouble to make comments and send suggestions. We also express our appreciation to the students, colleagues, and secretarial assistants who have helped with the labors of preparing and checking the manuscript and proof.

Simon Ramo

John R. Whinnery

May, 1953

CONTENTS

1 OSCILLATION AND
WAVE FUNDAMENTALS

1·01 INTRODUCTION

This text is concerned with electromagnetics, particularly that underlying oscillations and waves. Before introducing the laws of electricity and magnetism for serious study, it will be necessary to discuss some ideas and mathematics that have to do with oscillations and waves generally. This will be done by using simple circuits and conventional uniform transmission lines as examples. When this is done, the objective is not to present the theory of circuits and lines as such. Indeed the theory underlying both comprises a good part of the text. The purpose of this chapter is to illustrate (and for some readers to review) a point of view toward oscillations and waves needed for the rest of the text. Specifically the objectives are:

1. To present a clear picture of the energy relations in oscillating systems.

2. To point out criteria relating energy properties of a system to band width, impedance, etc., for later comparison purposes with cavity resonators.

3. To clarify the concepts of waves, particularly in regard to such properties as phase velocity, reflection, and characteristic impedance.

4. To point out common properties of transmission lines according to the conventional distributed constant approach for later comparison with properties of waves in space and in wave guides.

5. To present or review some fundamental mathematics necessary for the study of oscillations and waves throughout the book.

6. To develop approximate methods of analysis based upon the physical picture of the phenomena, so that these may be used in the later, more difficult problems.

1

Simple Circuits as Examples of Oscillating Systems

1·02 FREE OSCILLATIONS IN AN IDEAL SIMPLE CIRCUIT

Let us start with the simplest possible circuit for electrical oscillations, an ideal condenser connected across an ideal inductance. Consider first free oscillations, assuming that an amount of energy was
supplied to the combination at some instant (for example, by placing a
charge on the condenser) and that from that time on there is no connection to the outside. Energy may be stored
in the system in two forms:

1. Magnetic energy in the inductance. This
may be considered analogous to kinetic energy
in mechanics and has the value

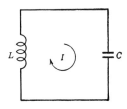

Fig. 1·02.

$$U_L = \tfrac{1}{2}LI^2 \tag{1}$$

where I is the current flowing through the inductance L.

2. Electric energy in the capacitance. This may be considered
analogous to potential energy in mechanics and has the value

$$U_C = \tfrac{1}{2}CV^2 \tag{2}$$

where V is the voltage across the condenser C.

The presence of energy in the condenser implies a voltage across the
condenser, and a consequent rate of change of current and stored magnetic energy in the inductance. Similarly, the presence of magnetic
energy requires a current flowing in the inductance, and a consequent
rate of change of voltage and stored electric energy in the condenser.
We are led then to expect oscillations, since the presence of energy in
one form requires a rate of change of energy in the other. It is also
necessary that the total energy in the system be a constant, the same
at all instants, since there is no connection to the outside and ideal
dissipationless conditions are assumed.

Before going further with purely physical reasoning, let us write an
equation for the instantaneous current in the circuit. By Kirchhoff's
laws, the sum of the induction voltage $L\, dI/dt$ and the condenser
voltage q/C must be zero:

$$L\frac{dI}{dt} + \frac{1}{C}\int I\, dt = 0 \tag{3}$$

If this equation is differentiated with respect to time, it becomes a true
differential equation.

$$L\frac{d^2I}{dt^2} + \frac{I}{C} = 0$$

or
$$\frac{d^2I}{dt^2} = -\frac{I}{LC} \tag{4}$$

The differential equation (4) is called the simple harmonic motion equation. This is probably the simplest and most common of all differential equations. It will probably be so familiar that the reader will wonder why we do not immediately write down the answer to the equation. The objectives here, however, are not to obtain answers to these simple and well-known problems, but rather to freshen up old techniques and to develop new ones for the much more interesting problems that lie ahead.

1·03   SOLUTION OF THE DIFFERENTIAL EQUATION BY ASSUMED SERIES

The differential equation to be solved is 1·02(4):

$$\frac{d^2I}{dt^2} = -\frac{I}{LC} \tag{1}$$

The method to be shown first for solution of this simple differential equation is one which will be necessary for later less familiar equations, such as the Bessel equation. The method merely recognizes that the solution to a given differential equation can often be expanded in a power series. Conversely, we may assume a general power series at the beginning, and determine what form its coefficients must have if the series is to be a solution for the equation. The required form may be recognizable as the expansion for a known function. At any rate the entire series, if convergent, may always be used as the solution.

Let us then assume that the solution to (1) will be some series of the form

$$I = a_0 + a_1 t + a_2 t^2 + a_3 t^3 + a_4 t^4 + \cdots \tag{2}$$

Differentiating,

$$\frac{dI}{dt} = a_1 + 2a_2 t + 3a_3 t^2 + 4a_4 t^3 + \cdots$$

$$\frac{d^2I}{dt^2} = 2 \cdot 1a_2 + 3 \cdot 2a_3 t + 4 \cdot 3a_4 t^2 + \cdots$$

These series forms may be substituted in (1) to determine the requirements on the coefficients in order that the series may satisfy that equation:

$$2 \cdot 1a_2 + 3 \cdot 2a_3 t + 4 \cdot 3a_4 t^2 + 5 \cdot 4a_5 t^3 + 6 \cdot 5a_6 t^4 + \cdots$$
$$= - \frac{1}{LC} (a_0 + a_1 t + a_2 t^2 + a_3 t^3 + a_4 t^4 + \cdots)$$

It may not be obvious at once, but a little study shows that, if the above equation is to be true for all values of t, coefficients of like powers of t must be equal on the two sides of the equation. That is,

$$a_2 = - \frac{a_0}{2 \cdot 1LC}$$

$$a_3 = - \frac{a_1}{3 \cdot 2LC}$$

$$a_4 = - \frac{a_2}{4 \cdot 3LC} = \frac{a_0}{4! \, (LC)^2}$$

$$a_5 = - \frac{a_3}{5 \cdot 4LC} = \frac{a_1}{5! \, (LC)^2}$$

and, generalizing,

$$a_{2n} = - \frac{a_{2n-2}}{(2n)(2n-1)LC} = \frac{(-1)^n a_0}{(2n)! \, (LC)^n}$$

$$a_{2n+1} = - \frac{a_{2n-1}}{(2n+1)(2n)LC} = \frac{(-1)^n a_1}{(2n+1)! \, (LC)^n}$$

Notice that the requirements placed upon the constants of the series by substituting in the differential equation have related all constants either to a_0 or to a_1, but there is nothing relating these two to each other or to anything else. This seems promising, for two independent solutions and two arbitrary constants are required for a second degree differential equation. Let us write now the assumed series (2), using these constants:

$$I = a_0 \left[1 - \frac{t^2}{2! \, LC} + \frac{t^4}{4! \, (LC)^2} - \frac{t^6}{6! \, (LC)^3} + \cdots \right]$$
$$+ (a_1 \sqrt{LC}) \left[\frac{t}{(LC)^{1/2}} - \frac{t^3}{3! \, (LC)^{3/2}} + \frac{t^5}{5! \, (LC)^{5/2}} - \frac{t^7}{7! \, (LC)^{7/2}} + \cdots \right] \quad (3)$$

Comparison with any tables of series shows that the first quantity in brackets has the form of the series expansion for a cosine function and the second for a sine. That is,

$$\cos x = 1 - \frac{x^2}{2!} + \frac{x^4}{4!} - \cdots \qquad (4)$$

$$\sin x = x - \frac{x^3}{3!} + \frac{x^5}{5!} - \cdots \qquad (5)$$

So (3) may be written

$$I = a_0 \cos\left(\frac{t}{\sqrt{LC}}\right) + a_1 \sqrt{LC} \sin\left(\frac{t}{\sqrt{LC}}\right)$$

Since a_1 is arbitrary, the entire quantity $a_1 \sqrt{LC}$ may be replaced by C_2 to stress the point that it is an arbitrary constant. Let us at the same time replace a_0 by C_1 and define

$$\omega_0 = \frac{1}{\sqrt{LC}} \qquad (6)$$

Then $\qquad I = C_1 \cos \omega_0 t + C_2 \sin \omega_0 t \qquad (7)$

This expression is a solution to the differential equation. It has two independent functions and two arbitrary constants. All is now known except the values of these constants. These cannot be determined until more information is given about the manner of starting oscillations in the circuit.

PROBLEMS

1·03a   Obtain a series solution for the equation

$$\frac{d^2y}{dx^2} - \frac{1}{x}\frac{dy}{dx} + \beta^2 y = 0$$

1·03b   Repeat a for the equation

$$\frac{d^2y}{dx^2} - \frac{1}{x}\frac{dy}{dx} + \left(\beta^2 + \frac{1}{x^2}\right) y = 0$$

1·04   SOLUTION OF THE DIFFERENTIAL EQUATION BY ASSUMED SINUSOIDS

The simple harmonic motion differential equation has been solved by assuming a series solution, determining the form required of that series by the differential equation, and identifying the resulting series as a sinusoidal function. Now, we might have guessed at the beginning that the solution would have been of a sinusoidal form. Although the frequency was not known, we might have assumed a solution of the form of Eq. 1·03(7), substituting in the differential equation 1·03(1) to determine the value of ω_0. If I is given by Eq. 1·03(7),

$$\frac{dI}{dt} = -\omega_0(C_1 \sin \omega_0 t - C_2 \cos \omega_0 t)$$

$$\frac{d^2I}{dt^2} = -\omega_0{}^2(C_1 \cos \omega_0 t + C_2 \sin \omega_0 t) \tag{1}$$

Substituting in the differential equation,

$$-\omega_0{}^2(C_1 \cos \omega_0 t + C_2 \sin \omega_0 t) = -\frac{1}{LC}(C_1 \cos \omega_0 t + C_2 \sin \omega_0 t)$$

If $$\qquad\qquad \omega_0{}^2 = \frac{1}{LC} \tag{2}$$

the equation is satisfied. This value of $\omega_0{}^2$ is exactly that defined in Eq. 1·03(6).

Thus it is demonstrated that, if we can guess the form of a solution to a differential equation, substitution of this form into the equation will determine whether or not it is a solution and will give values for any non-arbitrary constants, such as ω_0 above. This method is one of the most useful for solution of differential equations in engineering.

PROBLEM

1·04   The equations for a loss-free coupled circuit with input values L_1, C_1, output values L_2 and C_2, and mutual inductance M are

$$L_1 \frac{dI_1}{dt} + M \frac{dI_2}{dt} + \frac{1}{C_1} \int I_1 \, dt = 0$$

$$L_2 \frac{dI_2}{dt} + M \frac{dI_1}{dt} + \frac{1}{C_2} \int I_2 \, dt = 0$$

Assuming sinusoidal forms for I_1 and I_2, find values for the natural frequency ω_0.

1·05   SOLUTION OF THE DIFFERENTIAL EQUATION BY ASSUMED EXPONENTIALS

As a final attack on the differential equation for simple harmonic motion we shall attempt a solution in terms of exponentials. The wisdom of this will shortly be demonstrated. Suppose we try

$$I = A_1 e^{pt} + A_2 e^{-pt} \tag{1}$$

then $$\qquad\qquad \frac{d^2I}{dt^2} = p^2(A_1 e^{pt} + A_2 e^{-pt})$$

Substitute these in Eq. 1·03(1):

$$p^2(A_1 e^{pt} + A_2 e^{-pt}) = -\frac{1}{LC}(A_1 e^{pt} + A_2 e^{-pt})$$

or
$$p^2 = -\frac{1}{LC}$$

$$p = j\sqrt{\frac{1}{LC}} = j\omega_0$$

where $j \equiv \sqrt{-1}$.

This substitution indicates that (1) is a solution of the simple harmonic motion equation, provided that $p = j\omega_0$:

$$I = A_1 e^{j\omega_0 t} + A_2 e^{-j\omega_0 t} \tag{2}$$

Next let us remind ourselves of the identities

$$e^{jx} = \cos x + j \sin x \tag{3}$$

$$e^{-jx} = \cos x - j \sin x \tag{4}$$

These are most conveniently verified by considering the series expansion for an exponential:

$$e^y = 1 + y + \frac{y^2}{2!} + \frac{y^3}{3!} + \cdots$$

so
$$e^{jx} = 1 + jx - \frac{x^2}{2!} - j\frac{x^3}{3!} + \cdots$$

$$= \left(1 - \frac{x^2}{2!} + \frac{x^4}{4!} + \cdots\right) + j\left(x - \frac{x^3}{3!} + \frac{x^5}{5!} + \cdots\right)$$

By comparing with Eq. 1·03(4) and Eq. 1·03(5) the latter series are quickly identified as those for cosine and sine respectively, thus verifying (3). The corresponding demonstration for (4) is identical to this. If identities (3) and (4) are substituted in (2),

$$I = (A_1 + A_2) \cos \omega_0 t + j(A_1 - A_2) \sin \omega_0 t$$

Since A_1 and A_2 are both arbitrary, this may be written exactly in the previous forms:

$$I = C_1 \cos \omega_0 t + C_2 \sin \omega_0 t \tag{5}$$

For many purposes it will be convenient to use the solution in the form of (2) instead of changing to (5). This use of exponentials to replace sinusoids will be the subject of later discussion.

PROBLEMS

1·05a   Show that an alternative expression equivalent to Eq. 1·05(2) or Eq. 1·05(5) is

$$I = A \cos (\omega_0 t + \phi)$$

Relate A and ϕ to C_1 and C_2.

1·05b   Solve the equations for the coupled circuit, Prob. 1·04, using assumed exponentials.

1·06 NATURAL OSCILLATIONS WITH LOSSES—APPROXIMATE METHOD

The circuit analyzed previously was ideal. Suppose we now wish to consider the effect of the finite losses which must of necessity be present in the circuit. As will be shown in the next section, it is a simple matter to include these in the circuit equations rigorously; yet let us first use physical knowledge to develop an approximate method which will give the first order effect of the losses, provided that losses are small. The point of view will be extremely useful in later analyses of cavity resonators and wave guides.

If losses are small, physical intuition tells us that the natural period of oscillation will be changed little, and over a short period of time the solution will be very nearly that for the ideal circuit. The major correction will be a long-time decrease in the amplitude of oscillation due to the energy lost.

It is common experience to find exponential changes for a physical quantity which decreases (or increases) at a rate proportional to the amount of that quantity present. The power loss, or rate of energy decrease, for this example, is proportional to the amount of energy in the system. It would consequently be reasonable to expect an exponential damping factor to appear in the expressions for currents and voltages. As a first order correction, the expression for current obtained previously (Prob. 1·05a) might be assumed to be multiplied by some negative exponential:

$$I = Ae^{-\alpha t} \cos (\omega_0 t + \phi) \tag{1}$$

The energy in the circuit may be calculated at an instant when it is all in the inductance:

$$U = \tfrac{1}{2}L(I_{max})^2 = \frac{LA^2}{2} e^{-2\alpha t} \tag{2}$$

Within the limits of the assumption of relatively small losses, the negative rate of change of this stored energy over several cycles is merely the average power loss:

$$-\frac{dU}{dt} = W_L \tag{3}$$

From (2), $$\frac{dU}{dt} = -2\alpha \frac{LA^2}{2} e^{-2\alpha t} = -2\alpha U \tag{4}$$

So, by combining (3) and (4),

$$\alpha = \frac{W_L}{2U} \tag{5}$$

Define the quality factor or Q of the circuit as the quantity

$$Q = \frac{\omega_0(\text{energy stored in circuit})}{\text{average power loss}} = \frac{\omega_0 U}{W_L} \tag{6}$$

$$Q = \frac{\pi(\text{energy stored in circuit})}{\text{energy lost per half cycle}} \tag{7}$$

Then (5) may be written

$$\alpha = \frac{\omega_0}{2Q} \tag{8}$$

The exponential decay is thus expressible in terms of the quantity Q. The damping is also described sometimes as a logarithmic decrement, which is the relative amount by which the amplitude of oscillation decreases in one period.

$$\delta = \frac{Ae^{-\alpha t} - Ae^{-\alpha(t+T)}}{Ae^{-\alpha t}} = 1 - e^{-\alpha T} \cong \alpha T$$

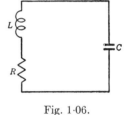

Fig. 1·06.

provided αT is small compared with unity, or

$$\delta = \frac{\omega_0}{2Q} T = \frac{2\pi f_0}{2Q} \times \frac{1}{f_0} = \frac{\pi}{Q} \tag{9}$$

Finally, let us interpret these results for a circuit with losses distributed as in Fig. 1·06. The current flow through the series combination of R and L is expressed by

$$I = A \cos (\omega_0 t + \phi)$$

(neglecting any exponential damping for a few cycles). The energy stored in the circuit is the maximum energy in the inductance,

$$U = \frac{L}{2} A^2$$

and the average power loss in resistance R is

$$W_R = \tfrac{1}{2}R(I_{\max})^2 = \frac{RA^2}{2}$$

So Q, defined by (6), is

$$Q_L = \frac{\omega_0(LA^2)}{RA^2} = \frac{\omega_0 L}{R} \tag{10}$$

This is the familiar expression for Q used to describe the excellence of an inductance, $\omega L/R$, calculated at resonance. It is to be used in (8) or (9) to give attenuation constant or logarithmic decrement.

PROBLEMS

1·06a If losses are present owing to a conductance $G = 1/R_1$ shunted across the condenser instead of a series resistance in the inductance, show that the Q to use in the general expressions Eq. 1·06(8) and Eq. 1·06(9) is

$$Q_C = \frac{\omega_0 C}{G} = \frac{R_1}{\omega_0 L}$$

1·06b If losses arise from both series resistance in L and shunt conductance across C, demonstrate that the Q to use in the general expressions may be found from the individual Q's defined previously.

$$\frac{1}{Q} = \frac{1}{Q_L} + \frac{1}{Q_C}$$

1·07 EXACT SOLUTION OF CIRCUIT EQUATION WITH LOSSES

The exact solution to the circuit of Fig. 1·06 will now be obtained to check the approximate results of the previous article.

$$L\frac{dI}{dt} + RI + \frac{1}{C}\int I\,dt = 0$$

is the exact equation of the circuit. Differentiating,

$$L\frac{d^2 I}{dt^2} + R\frac{dI}{dt} + \frac{I}{C} = 0 \tag{1}$$

Following the method of Art. 1·05, assume a solution of exponential form,

$$I = Ae^{pt} \tag{2}$$

If this is substituted in (1) and the resulting equation is solved for p, it is found that

$$p = -\frac{R}{2L} \pm \sqrt{\left(\frac{R}{2L}\right)^2 - \frac{1}{LC}} \tag{3}$$

Since for low-loss circuits $(R/2L)^2$ will be less than $1/LC$, it will be convenient to write (3) as

$$p = -\frac{R}{2L} \pm \frac{j}{\sqrt{LC}}\sqrt{1 - \frac{R^2C}{4L}} = -\alpha \pm j\omega_0' \qquad (4)$$

where $\qquad \alpha = \frac{R}{2L} = \frac{\omega_0}{2Q} \qquad\qquad\qquad\qquad (5)$

$$\omega_0' = \frac{1}{\sqrt{LC}}\sqrt{1 - \frac{R^2C}{4L}} = \omega_0\sqrt{1 - \left(\frac{1}{2Q}\right)^2} \qquad (6)$$

Q denotes ω_0L/R as in Eq. 1·06(10), and ω_0 is $1/\sqrt{LC}$.

The two possible values of p from (4) supply the two independent solutions needed for the second degree differential equation. Substitute these in (2):

$$I = A_1 e^{(-\alpha+j\omega_0')t} + A_2 e^{(-\alpha-j\omega_0')t}$$

$$= e^{-\alpha t}[A_1 e^{j\omega_0't} + A_2 e^{-j\omega_0't}]$$

By substitutions similar to those of Art. 1·05, an alternative expression is

$$I = e^{-\alpha t}[C_1 \cos \omega_0't + C_2 \sin \omega_0't] \qquad (7)$$

A comparison with the approximate analysis of Art. 1·06 shows that the same damping coefficient (5) is obtained. The natural frequency is different from ω_0 by (6), but this difference is small for low-loss (high-Q) circuits.

PROBLEM

1·07   Obtain exact results for the cases solved approximately in Probs. 1·06a and 1·06b, showing for these also that Q may be used as an indication of the usefulness of the approximate results.

1·08   FORCED OSCILLATIONS IN AN IDEAL L-C CIRCUIT

In previous examples, it was assumed that oscillations in the simple resonant circuit were free oscillations caused only by an initial deposit of energy in the circuit. In most practical cases, however, the circuit is continuously excited by a source of sinusoidal voltage. As the first example of such forced oscillations, consider the loss-free parallel L-C circuit excited by a sinusoidal voltage of constant magnitude (Fig. 1·08). The total current flow from the source is the sum of currents in the two impedances. The equations for these two currents are

$$L \frac{dI_1}{dt} = V \sin \omega t \qquad (1)$$

$$\frac{1}{C} \int I_2 \, dt = V \sin \omega t \qquad (2)$$

Current may be obtained from (1) by integrating directly and from (2) by differentiating:

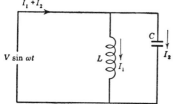

V sin ωt

Fig. 1·08.

$$LI_1 = -\frac{V}{\omega} \cos \omega t + C_1 \qquad (3)$$

$$\frac{I_2}{C} = \omega V \cos \omega t \qquad (4)$$

The constant term in (3) merely represents a possible constant d-c term flowing through the inductance, which is of no interest to the a-c problem so long as constant elements (linear systems) are assumed. Thus the total current

$$I = I_1 + I_2 = V \left(\omega C - \frac{1}{\omega L} \right) \cos \omega t \qquad (5)$$

The above relations, of course, check the well-known behavior of simple circuits. The current in the inductance has a phase lag of 90° with respect to its voltage, whereas the current in the capacitance has a 90° phase lead with respect to the voltage. The total current is leading (the total circuit acts as a capacitance) if $\omega C > 1/\omega L$, and is lagging (total circuit acts as an inductance) if $1/\omega L > \omega C$. If $\omega C = 1/\omega L$, there is no current to be supplied by the source; under this condition the current flow to the inductance is at every instant exactly equal and opposite to the current flow to the capacitance. The frequency for which this condition occurs is the natural frequency found previously,

$$\omega C = \frac{1}{\omega L} \quad \text{or} \quad \omega = \frac{1}{\sqrt{LC}} = \omega_0 \qquad (6)$$

At this natural frequency the energy inside the system is a constant and merely passes back and forth from inductance to capacitance, and no energy need be supplied by the source at any instant of time. For a frequency lower than this resonant frequency, the maximum energy stored in the inductance is greater than the maximum energy stored in the capacitance, so that this excess energy must be supplied from the source during one part of the cycle, but will be delivered back to it unharmed during another part.   This excess reactive energy from the inductance makes the circuit appear as an inductive load to the source. Similarly, for frequencies greater than the resonant frequency, the maximum energy in the capacitance is greater than the maximum energy in the inductance, and the excess reactive energy that must be supplied to the capacitance causes the circuit to appear as a capacitive load to the source.

At the resonant frequency the energy stored in the circuit is the maximum energy of the capacitance, or the maximum energy stored in the inductance, since both are equal:

$$U = \frac{1}{2} C V^2 = \frac{V^2}{2\omega_0} \sqrt{\frac{C}{L}} \tag{7}$$

1·09   APPROXIMATE INPUT IMPEDANCE AT RESONANCE

If the parallel circuit has losses in the coil or condenser, these may be taken into account from physical consideration of the energy relations, before attempting an exact analysis by the circuit equations.

At resonance the energy stored in the tuned circuit is given by Eq. 1·08(7).   From the definition of Q given in Eq. 1·06(6), the power loss at resonance is

$$W_L = \frac{\omega_0 U}{Q} = \frac{V^2}{2Q} \sqrt{\frac{C}{L}} \tag{1}$$

The source must supply to the circuit this amount of power.   The circuit then looks like a high-resistance R_i of value such that

$$W = \frac{V^2}{2R_i} \tag{2}$$

By comparing with (1),

$$R_i = Q \sqrt{\frac{L}{C}} \tag{3}$$

The approximations of reasonably low losses will be recognized in the above reasoning, for we have taken the expression for energy stored as that developed from the loss-free case.   In this picture, the major part of the energy is stored in the circuit and passes back and forth from the inductance to the capacitance.   Only the small amount of power lost in the process need be supplied by the source.   The resulting current flow to supply this loss component causes the circuit to have a high but finite input impedance in place of the infinite input impedance found previously.

PROBLEMS

1·09a Write alternative forms for Eq. 1·09(3) in terms of circuit reactances at resonance.

1·09b Write Eq. 1·09(3) in terms of: a series resistance in L, a shunt resistance across C, both series and shunt losses. For the first two cases, show that the resonant circuit can be considered an ideal transformer between the input terminals and the resistance R, and give the turns ratio n of the transformer for the two cases.

1·10 APPROXIMATE INPUT IMPEDANCE NEAR RESONANCE

The physical reasoning may be extended to give the approximate behavior of the circuit for a small departure from resonance. First it may be concluded that the major change will appear as a reactive component added to the admittance as frequency is changed to a value such that the capacitive and inductive reactive currents no longer cancel. To a first approximation, the input power supplied will be constant, so that the conductive portion of the admittance may be considered constant and equal to that calculated at resonance in Art. 1·09. We justify this by recognizing that any loss entering from a parallel conductance will not change at all with frequency, and, although that arising from a resistance in series with inductance will change with frequency, this is a uniform change, not comparable with the change in the differences of large quantities which affects the reactive current. The susceptance portion of the admittance is approximately that calculated without losses. The admittance may then be written

$$Y = G + jB \approx \frac{1}{Q}\sqrt{\frac{C}{L}} + j\left(\omega C - \frac{1}{\omega L}\right) \tag{1}$$

Let $\omega = \omega_0(1 + \delta)$, and make use of the approximation for small δ,

$$(1 + \delta)^{-1} \approx 1 - \delta$$

Then (1) becomes

$$Y = \sqrt{\frac{C}{L}}\left[\frac{1}{Q} + j2\delta\right] \tag{2}$$

From (2), the frequency shift for which susceptance becomes equal to conductance, a common measure of circuit "sharpness," is

$$\delta_1 = \frac{1}{2Q} \tag{3}$$

The Q of the circuit is consequently identified with the band width or sharpness of the circuit. For a frequency shift corresponding to (3),

$$| Y_1 | = \frac{1}{Q} \sqrt{\frac{C}{L}} | (1 + j) | = \frac{\sqrt{2}}{Q} \sqrt{\frac{C}{L}} \qquad (4)$$

In terms of impedance, the impedance at this frequency is $1/\sqrt{2}$ its magnitude at resonance.

Use of Complex Exponentials

1·11   SOLUTION OF THE CIRCUIT DIFFERENTIAL EQUATION IN TERMS OF COMPLEX EXPONENTIALS

The approximate results of the previous articles for the circuit relations when dissipation is included will now be verified by direct solution of the differential equation of the circuit. If a voltage $V \cos \omega t$ is applied to a circuit containing R, L, and C in series, the equation to be solved is

$$L \frac{dI}{dt} + RI + \frac{1}{C} \int I \, dt = V \cos \omega t \qquad (1)$$

But [see Eqs. 1·05(3), (4)]

$$\cos \omega t = \frac{e^{j\omega t} + e^{-j\omega t}}{2} \qquad (2)$$

If we assume that the current has the steady state solution,

$$I = Ae^{j\omega t} + Be^{-j\omega t} \qquad (3)$$

the result of substituting in (1) is

$$j\omega L(Ae^{j\omega t} - Be^{-j\omega t}) + R(Ae^{j\omega t} + Be^{-j\omega t}) + \frac{1}{j\omega C}(Ae^{j\omega t} - Be^{-j\omega t})$$

$$= \frac{V}{2}[e^{j\omega t} + e^{-j\omega t}] \qquad (4)$$

Following previous reasoning, this equation can be true for all values of time only if coefficients of $e^{j\omega t}$ are the same on both sides of the equation, and similarly for $e^{-j\omega t}$.

$$A \left[R + j \left(\omega L - \frac{1}{\omega C} \right) \right] = \frac{V}{2} \qquad (5a)$$

$$B \left[R - j \left(\omega L - \frac{1}{\omega C} \right) \right] = \frac{V}{2} \qquad (5b)$$

The complex quantity in the bracket of (5a) may be called Z and written in its equivalent form

$$Z = R + j \left(\omega L - \frac{1}{\omega C} \right) = |Z| e^{j\psi}$$

where

$$|Z| = \sqrt{R^2 + \left(\omega L - \frac{1}{\omega C} \right)^2} \tag{6}$$

and

$$\psi = \tan^{-1} \frac{\left(\omega L - \frac{1}{\omega C} \right)}{R} \tag{7}$$

Similarly,

$$R - j \left(\omega L - \frac{1}{\omega C} \right) = |Z| e^{-j\psi}$$

Then

$$A = \frac{V}{2|Z|} e^{-j\psi}$$

$$B = \frac{V}{2|Z|} e^{j\psi}$$

(A and B are conjugates: they have the same real parts and equal and opposite imaginary parts.)   Substituting in (3),

$$I = \frac{V}{|Z|} \left[\frac{e^{j(\omega t - \psi)} + e^{-j(\omega t - \psi)}}{2} \right] \tag{8}$$

By comparing with (2),

$$I = \frac{V}{|Z|} \cos (\omega t - \psi) \tag{9}$$

This final result gives the desired magnitude and phase angle of the current with respect to the applied voltage.   That information is contained in either constant A or constant B, and no information is given in one which is not in the other. B is of necessity the conjugate of A, since this is the only way in which the two may add up to a real current, and the final exact answer for current must be real.   It follows that half of the work was unnecessary.   We could have started only with $V e^{j\omega t}$ in place of the two-term expression which is exactly equivalent to $V \cos \omega t$.   For current, there would then be only

$$I = \frac{V}{|Z|} e^{j(\omega t - \psi)} \tag{10}$$

Although this cannot actually be the expression for current, since it is a complex and not a real quantity, it contains all the information we wish to know: magnitude of current, $V/|Z|$, and its phase with respect to applied voltage, ψ. This procedure may be made exact by writing

$$V(t) = \text{Re}\,[Ve^{j\omega t}] \tag{11}$$

$$I(t) = \text{Re}\left[\frac{V}{|Z|}e^{j(\omega t-\psi)}\right] \tag{12}$$

where Re denotes "the real part of." Because of the inconvenience of this notation, it is not commonly used, but it is useful to remember it when the instantaneous value of a quantity expressed in complex form is desired; that is, *if any single frequency sinusoid $f(t)$ is expressed by its magnitude and phase, $Me^{j\theta}$, or by its real (in-phase) and imaginary (out-of-phase) parts $A + jB$, the instantaneous expression may be found by multiplying by $e^{j\omega t}$ and taking the real part:*

$$f(t) = \text{Re}\,[Me^{j(\omega t+\theta)}] = \text{Re}\,[(A + jB)e^{j\omega t}] \tag{13}$$

PROBLEM

1·11 Utilizing the exact solution of this article, determine conditions for which the approximate solution of Art. 1·10 is a good approximation.

1·12 USE OF COMPLEX EXPONENTIALS IN POWER CALCULATIONS

The preceding article demonstrated the basis for the use of complex exponentials in the solution of problems involving steady state sinusoids. The consequent simplification of all linear problems in the steady state will be apparent throughout the book. More care must be exercised for non-linear expressions, the most common of which arises in the calculation of instantaneous power, requiring a product of terms.

Given a sinusoidal voltage across an impedance,

$$V(t) = V_m \cos\,(\omega t + \phi_1) \tag{1}$$

and a sinusoidal current flow through the impedance,

$$I(t) = I_m \cos\,(\omega t + \phi_2) \tag{2}$$

the expression for instantaneous power is certainly given by multiplying (1) and (2):

$$W(t) = V_m I_m \cos\,(\omega t + \phi_1) \cos\,(\omega t + \phi_2)$$

But $\cos A \cos B = \tfrac{1}{2}[\cos\,(A - B) + \cos\,(A + B)]$

$$\text{so}\quad W(t) = \frac{V_m I_m}{2}\cos{(\phi_1 - \phi_2)} + \frac{V_m I_m}{2}\cos{(2\omega t + \phi_1 + \phi_2)} \qquad (3)$$

This has an average part given by one-half the product of the peak amplitudes and the cosine of the difference in phase angles, and it has a double-frequency sinusoidal a-c part given by the last term in (3).

An expression identical with (3) is of course obtained if one utilizes the complex notation in the complete form of Eq. 1·11(13), since these are exact equivalents:

$$W(t) = \{\operatorname{Re}\,[V_m e^{j(\omega t + \phi_1)}]\}\,\{\operatorname{Re}\,[I_m e^{j(\omega t + \phi_2)}]\} \qquad (4)$$

However, after using the complex notation without the real part designated explicitly for a time, one may be tempted to form power in the same way. Let us ask if this will lead to the correct result.

$$W(t) \overset{?}{=} V_m e^{j(\omega t + \phi_1)} I_m e^{j(\omega t + \phi_2)} = V_m I_m e^{j(2\omega t + \phi_1 + \phi_2)} \qquad (5)$$

Even if one agrees to take the real part of the final answer in (5), it is clear that the power is not given correctly, for the average part is missing and the a-c part is twice the correct value.

The exact expression for instantaneous power may be written in complex notation. For the following demonstration, let us denote complex quantities by a wavy line above the symbol, and conjugates by an asterisk.

If $\qquad\qquad \tilde{V} = V_m e^{j\phi_1}$

and $\qquad\qquad \tilde{V}^* = V_m e^{-j\phi_1}$

then $\qquad\qquad \tilde{V}\tilde{I}^* = V_m I_m e^{j(\phi_1 - \phi_2)}$

and $\qquad\qquad \tilde{V}^*\tilde{I} = V_m I_m e^{-j(\phi_1 - \phi_2)}$

Then the exact equivalent of (3) in complex notation is

$$W = \tfrac{1}{2}\operatorname{Re}\,\{\tilde{V}\tilde{I}^* + [\tilde{V}e^{j\omega t}][\tilde{I}e^{j\omega t}]\} \qquad (6)$$

and the average power, or constant component of this, is

$$W_{\mathrm{av}} = \tfrac{1}{2}\operatorname{Re}\,[\tilde{V}\tilde{I}^*] = \tfrac{1}{2}\operatorname{Re}\,[\tilde{V}^*\tilde{I}] \qquad (7)$$

PROBLEM

1·12   An a-c voltage of 100 volts at frequency 1 mc/sec is applied across a parallel connection of 10 ohms resistance and a capacitance of 0.01 microfarad. Find the instantaneous power, utilizing (6), and check by first finding instantaneous expressions for voltage and current. Take phase of voltage as zero.

Fourier Series

1·13   FOURIER COEFFICIENTS FOR PERIODIC FUNCTIONS

All forced oscillations studied so far have consisted of sinusoids. Consider a more general oscillation which is periodic, returning once each cycle to any selected reference, or, stated mathematically,

$$f(t) = f(t - T)$$

This might be of any arbitrary form, such as is indicated by Fig. 1·13. Such a wave shape of voltage, if applied to a circuit, will act to that circuit as a superposition of a group of pure sinusoidal voltages.   The

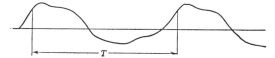

Fig. 1·13   Periodic wave of arbitrary shape.

wave may be replaced by a fundamental and its harmonics.   The method of finding the amplitudes of these is the classic method of Fourier analysis, and the theorem that proves the truth of the foregoing statements is the Fourier theorem, which it is assumed the reader has agreed with in another study.   What follows here is not a proof of the validity of a Fourier series expansion for a general periodic function, but merely a demonstration which shows the manner of obtaining the coefficients.   This will be extremely useful when we later add up series to represent known functions along boundaries in field problems.

We shall write the periodic function $f(t)$ as a series of sinusoids consisting of a fundamental and its harmonics:

$$f(t) = a_0 + a_1 \cos \omega t + a_2 \cos 2\omega t + a_3 \cos 3\omega t + \cdots$$
$$+ b_1 \sin \omega t + b_2 \sin 2\omega t + b_3 \sin 3\omega t \cdots \quad (1)$$

At the moment, the coefficients have not been determined.   The manner of finding them is based upon the so-called orthogonality property of sinusoids.   This property indicates that the integral of the product of any two sinusoids of different frequencies, over an interval in which they are commensurate (for example, from $-\pi$ to π, or 0 to 2π) shall be zero.   That is,

$$\int_{0 \; m \neq n}^{2\pi} \cos mx \cos nx \, dx = 0$$

$$\int_{0 \; m \neq n}^{2\pi} \sin mx \sin nx \, dx = 0 \quad (2)$$

$$\int_{0 \; m \neq n \text{ or } m = n}^{2\pi} \sin mx \cos nx \, dx = 0$$

However, $\int_0^{2\pi} \cos^2 mx \, dx = \int_0^{2\pi} \sin^2 mx \, dx = \pi$ (3)

Thus, if each term in (1) is multiplied by $\cos n\omega t$, and integrated from 0 to 2π, every term on the right will be zero except that term containing a_n. That is,

$$\int_0^{2\pi} f(t) \cos n\omega t \, d(\omega t) = \int_0^{2\pi} a_n \cos^2 n\omega t \, d(\omega t)$$

By (3), the integral on the right has the value $a_n \pi$, or

$$a_n = \frac{1}{\pi} \int_0^{2\pi} f(t) \cos n(\omega t) \, d(\omega t)$$ (4)

Similarly, to obtain b_n, each term in (1) is multiplied by $\sin n\omega t$ and integrated from 0 to 2π. Then,

$$b_n = \frac{1}{\pi} \int_0^{2\pi} f(t) \sin n(\omega t) \, d(\omega t)$$ (5)

Finally, to obtain the constant term a_0, every term is integrated directly over a period, and all terms on the right disappear, except that containing a_0:

$$\int_0^{2\pi} f(t) \, d(\omega t) = \int_0^{2\pi} a_0 \, d(\omega t) = 2\pi a_0$$

or $$a_0 = \frac{1}{2\pi} \int_0^{2\pi} f(t) \, d(\omega t)$$ (6)

This merely states that a_0 is the average of the function $f(t)$.

PROBLEM

1·13   Simplify the general expressions for Fourier coefficients found in Art. 1·13 for:
  (a) Even functions of t.
  (b) Odd functions of t.
  (c) Functions of a variable x, in terms of a period l.

1·14   FOURIER ANALYSIS OF A SQUARE WAVE VOLTAGE

Let us find by Fourier analysis the coefficients of the frequency components in the square wave shape of Fig. 1·14. Voltage is V over half the period T, and zero over the remaining half. The origin will be selected arbitrarily in the center of the constant portion as shown, in order to make the function even. Voltage then drops to zero at $t = T/4$, or $\omega t = \pi/2$.

The integral 1·13(6) shows that the constant term, a_0, is

$$a_0 = \frac{1}{2\pi} \int_{-\pi}^{+\pi} f(t) \, d(\omega t) = \frac{1}{2\pi} \int_{-\pi/2}^{+\pi/2} V \, d(\omega t) = \frac{V}{2} \tag{1}$$

This is clearly the average value of the wave. The integral 1·13(5) gives the coefficient b_n:

$$b_n = \frac{1}{\pi} \int_{-\pi}^{+\pi} f(t) \sin n(\omega t) \, d(\omega t) = \frac{1}{\pi} \int_{-\pi/2}^{+\pi/2} V \sin n(\omega t) \, d(\omega t) = 0 \tag{2}$$

Thus all coefficients of the sine terms are zero, as would be expected since sines are odd functions, and we have selected the origin to make $f(t)$ even.

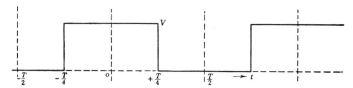

Fig. 1·14   Periodic wave of rectangular shape.

Finally, the a_n terms, by Eq. 1·13(4), are

$$a_n = \frac{1}{\pi} \int_{-\pi}^{+\pi} f(t) \cos n\omega t \, d(\omega t) = \frac{1}{\pi} \int_{-\pi/2}^{+\pi/2} V \cos n\omega t \, d(\omega t)$$

$$a_n = \frac{V}{n\pi} \left[\sin n(\omega t) \right]_{-\pi/2}^{+\pi/2} \tag{3}$$

The value of (3) is zero if n is even, is $+(2V/n\pi)$ if n is 1, 5, 9, etc., and is $-(2V/n\pi)$ if n is 3, 7, 11, etc. Thus the series expansion in sinusoids of the square wave voltage of Fig. 1·14 may be written

$$f(t) = \frac{V}{2} + \frac{2V}{\pi} \left[\cos \omega t - \frac{\cos 3\omega t}{3} + \frac{\cos 5\omega t}{5} - \frac{\cos 7\omega t}{7} + \cdots \right] \tag{4}$$

The current which flows when such a voltage is applied to a circuit is found by determining the currents due to the individual terms of (4) and superposing these. There will be, in general, a component of current of a frequency corresponding to each frequency component of the Fourier expansion. These, when added, give the wave shape of current. Such a procedure is straightforward and will not be carried further here.

Notice that it requires an infinite number of terms to represent truly the square wave shape of voltage. Often a high degree of approximation to the desired wave shape is obtained when only a finite number of terms is used. However, for functions with sharp discontinuities, many terms may be required near the sharp corners, and the theory of Fourier series shows that the series may not converge to the function in the neighborhood of the discontinuity (Gibbs phenomenon). The derivative of the series may not always converge to the derivative of the function, but the integral of the series does always converge to that of the function.

PROBLEM

1·14 Obtain Fourier series for the following periodic functions:

(a) A triangular wave defined by $f(t) = V_0[1 - (2t/T)]$ from 0 to $T/2$, and $V_0[(2t/T) - 1]$ from $T/2$ to T.

(b) A saw-tooth wave defined by $f(t) = V_0 t/T$ for $0 < t < T$.

(c) A sinusoidal pulse given by $f(t) = (V_m \cos \omega t - V_0)$ for $-\alpha < \omega t < \alpha$, $f(t) = 0$ for $-\pi < \omega t < -\alpha$ and also for $\alpha < \omega t < \pi$.

1·15 FOURIER SERIES TO REPRESENT A FUNCTION OVER AN INTERVAL

If a function $f(x)$ is defined over a finite interval $0 < x < l$, a Fourier series may be written for this even though it is not periodic. The point of view is that the interval of length l may be considered a period (or more commonly a half-period), and a periodic function defined to agree with the given function over the given interval, repeating itself outside of that interval. A Fourier series may then be written for this periodic function which will give desired values in the interval, and, although it also gives values outside of the interval, that is of no consequence since the original function is not defined there.

The interval is most commonly selected as a half-period since the function extended outside the interval may then be made either even or odd, and the corresponding Fourier series will then have respectively either cosine terms alone or sine terms alone. Thus a cosine series written to represent a function $f(x)$ over the interval $0 < x < l$ is

$$f(x) = a_0 + \sum_{n=1}^{\infty} a_n \cos \frac{n\pi x}{l} \qquad 0 < x < l \qquad (1)$$

$$a_0 = \frac{1}{l} \int_0^l f(x)\, dx \qquad (2)$$

$$a_n = \frac{2}{l} \int_0^l f(x) \cos \frac{n\pi x}{l}\, dx \qquad (3)$$

Or a sine series written to represent $f(x)$ over the interval $0 < x < l$ is

$$f(x) = \sum_{n=1}^{\infty} b_n \sin \frac{n\pi x}{l} \qquad 0 < x < l \tag{4}$$

$$b_n = \frac{2}{l} \int_0^l f(x) \sin \frac{n\pi x}{l} \, dx \tag{5}$$

As an example, to represent the simple function $f(x) = C$ over the interval $0 < x < l$ in a series of sines, (5) yields

$$b_n = \frac{2}{l} \int_0^l C \sin \frac{n\pi x}{l} \, dx = \frac{2C}{n\pi} \left[- \cos \frac{n\pi x}{l} \right]_0^l \tag{6}$$

$$f(x) = \frac{2C}{\pi} \left[2 \sin \frac{\pi x}{l} + \frac{2}{3} \sin \frac{3\pi x}{l} + \frac{2}{5} \sin \frac{5\pi x}{l} + \cdots \right] 0 < x < l \tag{7}$$

The series (7) actually represents a repeating square wave much like that in Fig. 1·14 (except for the constant term and the choice of origin), but properly agrees with the given function over the required interval.

PROBLEM

1·15   Suppose that a function is given over the interval 0 to l as $f(x) = \sin \pi x/l$. What do the cosine and sine representations yield?   Explain how this single sine term can be represented in terms of cosines.

Uniform Transmission Lines as Examples of Wave Systems

1·16   THE IDEAL TRANSMISSION LINE

To illustrate waves, we shall consider the uniform transmission line. The results developed are of importance themselves, since transmission lines are used in all modern high-frequency applications.   Results will also be used for later comparison with more general electromagnetic wave phenomena.   The approach used in this chapter is the conventional one, starting from distributed inductance and capacitance along the line.   It is true that this in a sense is jumping ahead of the story, for in a later chapter on guided waves the transmission line differential equations will be derived from rigorous considerations of electromagnetic theory.   Nevertheless, the approach to be used here is easy to visualize and is satisfactory for the present purpose.

A transmission line may be made up of parallel wires, of parallel plates, of coaxial conductors, or in general of any two conductors separated by a dielectric material. In conventional analyses, we think in terms of a current flowing in the conductors, equal and opposite in the two conductors if measured at any given transverse plane, and a voltage difference existing between the conductors. The current flow is affected by a distributed series inductance representing the back induced voltage effects of magnetic flux surrounding the conductors; the voltage between conductors acts across a distributed shunt capacitance. There are also loss terms which will be neglected for this first analysis of the ideal case. Incidentally, this does not relegate the results to a position of only academic interest, for many high-frequency transmission line problems have loss terms which are truly negligible.

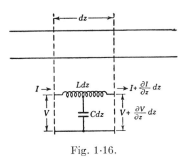

Fig. 1·16.

Consider a differential length of line, dz, including only the distributed inductance, L per unit length, and the distributed capacitance, C per unit length. The length dz then has inductance $L\,dz$ and capacitance $C\,dz$ (Fig. 1·16). The voltage drop or negative change in voltage across this length is then equal to the product of this inductance and the time rate of change of current. For such a differential length the voltage change along it at any instant may be written as the length multiplied by the rate of change of voltage with respect to length. Then

$$\text{voltage change} = \frac{\partial V}{\partial z}\,dz = -(L\,dz)\frac{\partial I}{\partial t} \tag{1}$$

Note that time and space derivatives are written as partial derivatives, since the reference point may be changed in space or time, in completely independent fashion.

Similarly, the decrease in current across the element at any instant is merely that current which is shunted across the distributed capacity. This is given by the capacity multiplied by time rate of change of voltage. Partial derivatives are again called for:

$$\text{current change} = \frac{\partial I}{\partial z}\,dz = -(C\,dz)\frac{\partial V}{\partial t} \tag{2}$$

The length dz may be canceled in (1) and (2):

$$\frac{\partial V}{\partial z} = -L\frac{\partial I}{\partial t} \tag{3}$$

$$\frac{\partial I}{\partial z} = -C\frac{\partial V}{\partial t} \tag{4}$$

Equations (3) and (4) are the fundamental differential equations for the analysis of the ideal transmission line. They may be combined to give equations containing voltage alone or current alone. To accomplish this, differentiate (3) partially with respect to distance, (4) with respect to time:

$$\frac{\partial^2 V}{\partial z^2} = -L\frac{\partial^2 I}{\partial z\,\partial t} \tag{5}$$

$$\frac{\partial^2 I}{\partial t\,\partial z} = -C\frac{\partial^2 V}{\partial t^2} \tag{6}$$

Since partial derivatives are the same taken in either order, (6) may be substituted directly in (5):

$$\frac{\partial^2 V}{\partial z^2} = LC\frac{\partial^2 V}{\partial t^2} \tag{7}$$

This differential equation is known as the wave equation. An exactly similar equation may be obtained in terms of current by differentiating (4) with respect to z, (3) with respect to t, and combining:

$$\frac{\partial^2 I}{\partial z^2} = LC\frac{\partial^2 I}{\partial t^2} \tag{8}$$

1·17 SOLUTIONS OF THE WAVE EQUATION

The differential equation to be solved, Eq. 1·16(7), may be written

$$\frac{\partial^2 V}{\partial z^2} = \frac{1}{v^2}\frac{\partial^2 V}{\partial t^2} \tag{1}$$

where

$$v = \frac{1}{\sqrt{LC}} \tag{2}$$

Unlike the differential equations met previously in this chapter, this is a partial differential equation. A direct attack on the equation to yield a general solution is not easy, but a simple check shows that any function whatever in the variable $t - (z/v)$ is a solution. That is,

$$V = F\left(t - \frac{z}{v}\right) \tag{3}$$

is a solution to (1). This may be verified by differentiating:

$$\frac{\partial V}{\partial t} = F'\left(t - \frac{z}{v}\right) \quad \text{and} \quad \frac{\partial V}{\partial z} = -\frac{1}{v}F'\left(t - \frac{z}{v}\right)$$

$$\frac{\partial^2 V}{\partial t^2} = F''\left(t - \frac{z}{v}\right) \quad \text{and} \quad \frac{\partial^2 V}{\partial z^2} = \frac{1}{v^2}F''\left(t - \frac{z}{v}\right)$$

(4)

In the above, the primes denote derivatives with respect to the entire variable, $t - (z/v)$. By comparing the two equations (4), (1) is verified.

It is necessary to show next what is meant by the statement that solution (3) represents a wave. This may be done by recognizing that we may stay on a particular reference value of the function (i.e., keep V constant) by keeping the argument, $t - (z/v)$, a constant. This is accomplished by moving in the positive z direction with velocity v as time increases. That is,

$$t - \frac{z}{v} = K$$

if $$z = vt - Kv \tag{5}$$

Only one solution of the second degree differential equation has been given. A second solution may be written as any function of $t + (z/v)$ and checked by methods exactly similar to those used for the first solution. This is identified as a wave traveling in the negative z direction with velocity v. A complete solution to (1) is then

$$V = F_1\left(t - \frac{z}{v}\right) + F_2\left(t + \frac{z}{v}\right) \tag{6}$$

where v is given by (2).

PROBLEMS

1·17a Differentiate the functions $\cos \omega[t - (z/v)]$, $e^{j\omega[t-(z/v)]}$, and $[t + (z/v)]^3$ to show that each satisfies (1).

1·17b Sketch the function $\cos \omega[t - (z/v)]$ versus $\omega z/v$ for values of $\omega t = 0$, $\pi/4, \pi/2, 3\pi/4, \pi$. Note how this demonstrates the interpretation as a propagating wave. Repeat for $\cos \omega[t + (z/v)]$.

1·18   RELATION BETWEEN VOLTAGE AND CURRENT IN THE IDEAL LINE

If the expression for voltage developed above, Eq. 1·17(6), is substituted in the transmission line equation, 1·16(3),

$$-L\frac{\partial I}{\partial t} = -\frac{1}{v}F_1'\left(t - \frac{z}{v}\right) + \frac{1}{v}F_2'\left(t + \frac{z}{v}\right) \tag{1}$$

This expression may be integrated partially with respect to t:

$$I = \frac{1}{Lv}\left[F_1\left(t - \frac{z}{v}\right) - F_2\left(t + \frac{z}{v}\right)\right] + f(z) \qquad (2)$$

If this result were substituted in the other transmission line equation, 1·16(4), it would be found that the function of integration, $f(z)$, could only be a constant. But we are not interested in possible superposed d-c solutions in studying the wave solution, so this will be ignored. Equation (2) may then be written

$$I = \frac{1}{Z_0}\left[F_1\left(t - \frac{z}{v}\right) - F_2\left(t + \frac{z}{v}\right)\right] \qquad (3)$$

where
$$Z_0 = Lv = \sqrt{\frac{L}{C}} \qquad (4)$$

The constant Z_0 as defined by (4) is called the *characteristic impedance* of the line, and is seen from (3) to be the ratio of voltage to current for a single one of the traveling waves at any given point and given instant. The negative sign for the negatively traveling wave would of course be expected since the wave propagates to the left, and by our convention current is positive if flowing to the right.

1·19 REFLECTION AND TRANSMISSION AT A DISCONTINUITY

Most transmission line problems are concerned with junctions between a given uniform line and a line of different characteristic impedance, a load impedance or some other element that introduces a discontinuity. By Kirchhoff's laws, total voltage and current must be continuous across the discontinuity. The total voltage in the line may be regarded as the sum of voltage in a positively traveling wave, equal to V_1 at the point of discontinuity, and a voltage in a reflected or negatively traveling wave, equal to V_1' at the discontinuity. The sum of V_1 and V_1' must be V_L, the voltage appearing across the load impedance Z_L:

$$V_1 + V_1' = V_L \qquad (1)$$

Similarly, the sum of currents in the positively and negatively traveling waves of the line, at the point of discontinuity, must be equal to the current flowing into Z_L:

$$I_1 + I_1' = I_L \qquad (2)$$

By utilizing the relations between voltage and current for the two traveling waves as found in the preceding article, (2) becomes

$$\frac{V_1}{Z_0} - \frac{V_1'}{Z_0} = \frac{V_L}{Z_L} \tag{3}$$

By eliminating between (1) and (3), the ratio of voltage in the reflected wave to that in the incident wave (*reflection coefficient*) and the ratio of the voltage in the load to that in the incident wave (*transmission coefficient*) may be found:

$$\rho = \frac{V_1'}{V_1} = \frac{Z_L - Z_0}{Z_L + Z_0} \tag{4}$$

$$\tau = \frac{V_L}{V_1} = \frac{2Z_L}{Z_L + Z_0} \tag{5}$$

The most interesting, and perhaps the most obvious, conclusion from the above relations is this: there is no reflected wave if the terminating impedance is exactly equal to the characteristic impedance of the line. All energy of the incident wave is then transferred to the load impedance, which cannot be distinguished from a line of infinite length and characteristic impedance $Z_0 = Z_L$.

Note that for arbitrary time functions the "impedance" used above should be a pure resistance in order for the ratio of instantaneous load voltage to instantaneous load current to be given by Z_L, as used above. The impedance form has, however, been utilized so that the equation will apply immediately to steady-state sinusoidal waves expressed in the complex form for later use.

PROBLEMS

1·19a For arbitrary time functions, assuming Z_L a pure resistance, find the fraction of the incident power reflected, and the fraction of the incident power transmitted to Z_L.

1·19b Calculate the reflection coefficient, transmission coefficient, and the power quantities of Prob. *a* for $Z_L = 0$, $\frac{1}{2}Z_0$, Z_0, $2Z_0$, and ∞.

1·20 SOME SIMPLE PROBLEMS ON TRAVELING WAVES

A. D-C Voltage Applied to an Infinite Line. Consider the case of a d-c voltage V, suddenly applied to an ideal line of infinite length (Fig. 1·20a). The line starts to charge to voltage V, the wave front traveling with the velocity $v = 1/\sqrt{LC}$. Since there is never any discontinuity, there is never any reflected wave, and the only current is that flowing in the positive wave, V/Z_0. This then is a d-c current flowing to the charges which appear on the line as voltage moves along. At any time t after the voltage is impressed, there is voltage V and current V/Z_0 in the line up to the point $z = vt$, and no voltage or current beyond.

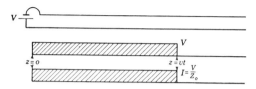

Fig. 1·20a Direct-current voltage suddenly applied to an infinite line.

B. D-C Voltage Applied to a Shorted Line. Suppose that the d-c voltage is applied to a line which is not infinite in length, but is shorted at some point, $z = l$ (Fig. 1·20b). We know that finally infinite current will flow if V is maintained. However, the mechanism of current build-up is interesting. After voltage is applied to the line, everything proceeds as in A until the time that the wave reaches the short

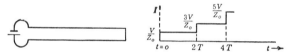

Fig. 1·20b Direct-current voltage suddenly applied to a shorted line.

circuit. At the time the incident wave with voltage V appears across the short circuit, which demands zero voltage, a reflected or negatively traveling wave of voltage $-V$ is sent back so that the sum of voltages in the two waves is indeed zero. Since current in the negative traveling wave is the negative of voltage divided by Z_0, this is $-(-V/Z_0)$ or $+V/Z_0$ and so adds directly to the current in the positive traveling wave. This reflected wave then moves to the left, leaving a wake of zero voltage and a current equal to $2V/Z_0$ behind it. As soon as the reflected wave has traveled back to the source, it brings the zero voltage condition back to this point so that the d-c voltage must send out a new wave of voltage V down the line, with associated current V/Z_0, making a total current in the line $3V/Z_0$ at this time. Current then builds up to infinity in the step manner indicated by Fig. 1·20b. T is the time l/v required for a wave to travel one way down the line.

C. Charged Line Connected to a Resistor. Consider an ideal line of length l initially charged to a d-c potential V, with a resistance R connected across the input at time $t = 0$.

The voltage across the resistance is the sum of the d-c voltage of the line and the voltage in the wave, V_1:

$$V_R = V + V_1 \tag{1}$$

The current flowing into the resistor is merely the negative of current for the positively traveling wave:

$$I_R = -I_1$$

or

$$\frac{V_R}{R} = -\frac{V_1}{Z_0} \tag{2}$$

By combining (1) and (2),

$$V_R = V\left(\frac{R}{R + Z_0}\right) = -V_1\frac{R}{Z_0} \tag{3}$$

For example, if $R = Z_0$, the voltage appearing across the resistance at the first instant is half the d-c voltage of the line, as is the voltage appearing in the traveling wave. When this wave reaches the open

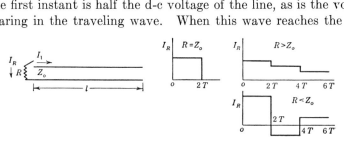

Fig. 1·20c   Charged line of length l suddenly connected to a resistor.

end, there must then be started a reflected wave such that total current is zero, so current in the reflected wave must be $-I_1$ or $V/2R$. Because current in the reflected wave is the negative of voltage divided by Z_0, this will require a voltage $-V/2$ for the reflected wave. Thus in the case of $R = Z_0$, the original wave wipes out half the voltage, and the corresponding current, $-V/2Z_0$, is that which flows through R. The reflected wave wipes out the remaining half of the voltage and, of course, reduces current to zero. When this wave reaches $R = Z_0$ there is no further reflection, so all is still. Current wave shape is shown in Fig. 1·20c. Also shown are currents for $R > Z_0$ and $R < Z_0$.

PROBLEMS

1·20a   An ideal line of length l is charged to d-c voltage V and shorted at its input at time $t = 0$. Sketch the current wave shape through the short as a function of time.

1·20b An ideal open-circuited line of length l, initially uncharged, has a d-c voltage V suddenly applied at its input at time $t = 0$. Sketch the current flow through the input source as a function of time.

1·21 IDEAL LINE WITH APPLIED SINUSOIDAL VOLTAGES

Much of the preceding discussion has involved little restriction on the type of variation with time of the voltages applied to the transmission lines. Most practical problems are concerned entirely or at least partially with sinusoidal time variations. If a voltage which is sinusoidal in time is applied at $z = 0$, it may be represented by the exponential (see Art. 1·11):

$$V\big|_{z=0} = F(t) = V_1 e^{j\omega t} \tag{1}$$

Then the corresponding positively traveling wave is written:

$$V_1 e^{j\omega[t-(z/v)]}$$

Similarly, a negatively traveling wave is written:

$$V_1' e^{j\omega[t+(z/v)]}$$

Or the total solution, made up of positive and negative traveling waves, is

$$V = e^{j\omega t}[V_1 e^{-j(\omega z/v)} + V_1' e^{j(\omega z/v)}] \tag{2}$$

The corresponding current, from Art. 1·18, is

$$I = \frac{e^{j\omega t}}{Z_0}[V_1 e^{-j(\omega z/v)} - V_1' e^{j(\omega z/v)}] \tag{3}$$

For problems in which we shall be concerned throughout with sinusoidal quantities, it is not necessary to write the factor $e^{j\omega t}$ explicitly each time, since it will always be understood that all terms are multiplied by this factor; we rewrite (2) and (3), omitting it:

$$V = V_1 e^{-j\beta z} + V_1' e^{j\beta z} \tag{4}$$

$$I = \frac{1}{Z_0}[V_1 e^{-j\beta z} - V_1' e^{j\beta z}] \tag{5}$$

where

$$\beta = \frac{\omega}{v} \tag{6}$$

The quantity β is called the phase constant of the line since βz measures the instantaneous phase at a point z with respect to $z = 0$. Moreover, if voltage and current are observed at any point z, they will be found exactly the same at points such that βz differs from that of the first point by multiples of 2π. The distance between points of like current and voltage is called a wavelength λ. By the above reasoning,

$$\beta\lambda = 2\pi$$

or $$\beta = \frac{2\pi}{\lambda} \tag{7}$$

The transformation of impedances by the ideal line is easily found from (4) and (5). Let us assume that the line is of length l and that the load impedance is Z_L. For convenience we take the origin $z = 0$ at the load, and the input then lies at $z = -l$. The ratio of (4) to (5) at $z = 0$ may be set equal to Z_L, and solved for the ratio V_1'/V_1. The result is in agreement with that already given in Eq. 1·19(4):

$$\rho = \frac{V_1'}{V_1} = \frac{Z_L - Z_0}{Z_L + Z_0} \tag{8}$$

The input impedance may be found by dividing (4) by (5) for $z = -l$:

$$Z_i = Z_0 \left[\frac{e^{j\beta l} + \rho e^{-j\beta l}}{e^{j\beta l} - \rho e^{-j\beta l}}\right] \tag{9}$$

Or, substituting the result of (8),

$$Z_i = Z_0 \left[\frac{Z_L \cos \beta l + jZ_0 \sin \beta l}{Z_0 \cos \beta l + jZ_L \sin \beta l}\right] \tag{10}$$

By defining admittances $Y_i = 1/Z_i$, $Y_L = 1/Z_L$ and $Y_0 = 1/Z_0$, we can find an exactly similar expression,

$$Y_i = Y_0 \left[\frac{Y_L \cos \beta l + jY_0 \sin \beta l}{Y_0 \cos \beta l + jY_L \sin \beta l}\right] \tag{11}$$

PROBLEMS

1·21a   Find the special cases of (10) for a shorted line; an open line; a half-wave line with impedance Z_L; a quarter-wave line with impedance Z_L.

1·21b   When two transmission lines are to be connected in cascade, a reflection of the wave to be transmitted from one to the other will occur if they do not have

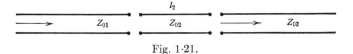

Fig. 1·21.

the same characteristic impedances. Show that a quarter-wave line matching transformer (Fig. 1·21) will cause the first line to see its characteristic impedance Z_{01} as a termination and thus eliminate reflection in transfer if $\beta l_2 = \pi/2$ and $Z_{02} = \sqrt{Z_{01}Z_{03}}$.

1·22   STANDING-WAVE RATIO

Of the two traveling-wave terms in the voltage equation, 1·21(4), the first becomes more negative in phase as z increases, and the second becomes more positive. There must consequently be some value of z for which the two terms are of the same phase. Their amplitudes will then add directly, and this point will give a maximum amplitude of voltage.

$$V_{max} = |V_1| + |V_1'| \tag{1}$$

A quarter wavelength from the position just discussed (say in a positive z direction), the first term will have decreased in phase by $\pi/2$, and the second will have increased by $\pi/2$, so that the two are then π apart in phase; they subtract and give a minimum amplitude of voltage:

$$V_{min} = |V_1| - |V_1'| \tag{2}$$

The *standing-wave ratio* is then defined as the ratio of the maximum voltage amplitude to the minimum voltage amplitude,

$$S = \frac{V_{max}}{V_{min}} \tag{3}$$

By substituting (1), (2), and the definition of reflection coefficient Eq. 1·21(8),

$$S = \frac{|V_1| + |V_1'|}{|V_1| - |V_1'|} = \frac{1 + |\rho|}{1 - |\rho|} \tag{4}$$

It is seen that standing-wave ratio is directly related to the magnitude of reflection coefficient ρ, giving the same information as this quantity. The inverse relation is

$$|\rho| = \frac{S - 1}{S + 1} \tag{5}$$

Because of the negative sign appearing in the current equation, 1·21(5), it is evident that, at the position where the two traveling-wave terms add in the voltage relation, they subtract in the current relation, and vice versa. The maximum voltage position is then a minimum current position:

$$I_{min} = \frac{|V_1| - |V_1'|}{Z_0}$$

At this position impedance is purely resistive and has the maximum value it will have at any point along the line:

$$Z_{\max} = Z_0 \left[\frac{|V_1| + |V_1'|}{|V_1| - |V_1'|} \right] = Z_0 \left[\frac{1 + |\rho|}{1 - |\rho|} \right] \tag{6}$$

At the position of the voltage minimum, current is a maximum, and impedance is a minimum and real:

$$I_{\max} = \frac{|V_1| + |V_1'|}{Z_0} \tag{7}$$

$$Z_{\min} = Z_0 \left[\frac{|V_1| - |V_1'|}{|V_1| + |V_1'|} \right] = Z_0 \left[\frac{1 - |\rho|}{1 + |\rho|} \right] \tag{8}$$

By comparing (6) and (8) with (4), the minimum and maximum values of impedance may be written in terms of the standing-wave ratio and the characteristic impedance of the line:

$$Z_{\max} = SZ_0 \tag{9}$$

$$Z_{\min} = \frac{Z_0}{S} \tag{10}$$

PROBLEMS

1·22a An impedance of $100 + j100$ ohms is placed as a load on a transmission line of characteristic impedance 50 ohms. Find the reflection coefficient in magnitude and phase and the standing-wave ratio for the line.

1·22b Suppose that reflection coefficient is given in magnitude and phase as $|\rho| e^{j\phi}$ at the load $z = 0$. Find the value of (negative) z for which voltage is a maximum. Show that current is in phase with voltage at this position, so that impedance there is real, as stated. Calculate the position of maximum voltage for the numerical values of Prob. a.

1·23 THE SMITH TRANSMISSION LINE CHART

Many graphical aids for transmission line computations have been devised. Of these, the most generally useful has been one presented by P. H. Smith,[1] which consists of loci of constant resistance and reactance plotted on a polar diagram in which radius corresponds to magnitude of reflection coefficient, and angle corresponds to phase of reflection coefficient referred to a general point along the line. The chart enables one to find simply how impedances are transformed along the line, or to relate impedance to reflection coefficient or to standing-wave ratio and position of a voltage minimum. By combinations of oper-

[1] P. H. Smith, "Transmission-Line Calculator," *Electronics*, **12**, 29–31 (Jan. 1939); "An Improved Transmission-Line Calculator," *Electronics*, **17**, 130 (Jan. 1944).

ations, it enables one to understand the behavior of complex impedance-matching techniques and to devise new ones.

The discussion of the chart will begin with Eq. 1·21(9), which gives
impedance in terms of reflection coefficient. If we define a per-unit
impedance

$$\zeta(l) = (r + jx) = \frac{Z_i}{Z_0} \tag{1}$$

and a complex variable w equal to the reflection coefficient at the end
of the line, shifted in phase to correspond to the input position l,

$$w = u + jv = \rho e^{-2j\beta l} \tag{2}$$

Equation 1·21(9) may then be written

$$\zeta(l) = \frac{1 + w}{1 - w} \tag{3}$$

or
$$r + jx = \frac{1 + (u + jv)}{1 - (u + jv)} \tag{4}$$

This equation may be separated into real and imaginary parts as
follows:

$$r = \frac{1 - (u^2 + v^2)}{(1 - u)^2 + v^2} \tag{5}$$

$$x = \frac{2v}{(1 - u)^2 + v^2} \tag{6}$$

or
$$\left(u - \frac{r}{1 + r}\right)^2 + v^2 = \frac{1}{(1 + r)^2} \tag{7}$$

$$(u - 1)^2 + \left(v - \frac{1}{x}\right)^2 = \frac{1}{x^2} \tag{8}$$

If we then wish to plot the loci of constant resistance r on the w
plane (u and v serving as rectangular coordinates), (7) shows that they
are circles with centers on the u axis at $[r/(1 + r), 0]$ and with radii
$1/(1 + r)$. The curves for $r = 0, \frac{1}{2}, 1, 2, \infty$ are sketched on Fig. 1·23a.
From (8), the curves of constant x plotted on the w plane are also
circles with centers at $(1, 1/x)$ and with radii $1/|x|$. Circles for $x = 0$,
$\pm\frac{1}{2}, \pm 1, \pm 2, \infty$ are sketched on Fig. 1·23a. Any point on a given
transmission line will have some impedance with positive resistance
part, and will then correspond to some particular point on the inside
of the unit circle of the w plane. Several uses of the chart will follow.

Many extensions and combinations of the ones to be cited will be obvious to the student. A chart with more divisions is given in Fig. 1·23b.

A. *To Find Reflection Coefficient Given Impedance, and Conversely.* The point within the unit circle of the Smith chart corresponding to a particular position on a transmission line may of course be located at

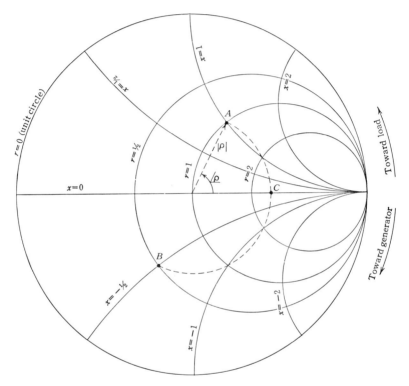

Fig. 1·23a   Polar transmission line chart.

once if the per-unit impedance corresponding to that position is known. This is done within a reasonable degree of accuracy by utilizing the orthogonal families of circles giving resistance and reactance as described above. Thus the point A of Fig. 1·23a is the intersection of the circles $r = 1$ and $x = 1$, and corresponds to a position with per-unit impedance $1 + j1$. The magnitude of reflection coefficient is the radius of that point from the origin, by the definition of the w variable in (2). The phase of reflection coefficient referred to that particular position (that is, the phase of the reflected wave voltage with respect to the incident wave voltage at that position) is the angle

measured counterclockwise from the right-hand u axis, by the definition of w. Thus, for a per-unit load impedance of $1 + j1$, the reflection coefficient in magnitude and phase referred to that position is found from the polar coordinates of A to be $0.45e^{j1.11}$. Of course, the reversal of this procedure to give impedance if ρ is known is obvious.

B. *To Transfer Impedances along the Line.* If one moves along an ideal line between points of discontinuity, the magnitude of reflection coefficient must remain constant since incident and reflected waves shift in phase but do not change amplitude. On the chart, one then follows a circle with center at the origin of the w plane. The angle through which one moves is proportional to the length of the line, and by (2) is just twice the electrical length of the line βl. (Most charts have a scale around the outside calibrated in fractions of a wavelength, so that the angle need not be computed explicitly.) Finally, the direction in which one moves is also defined by (2). If one moves toward the generator (increasing l), the angle of w becomes increasingly negative, which corresponds to clockwise motion about the chart. Motion toward the load corresponds to decreasing l in (2) and thus corresponds to counterclockwise motion about the chart. These directions are denoted by arrows on the chart.

As an example, if we are given a load impedance of $1 + j1$ per unit, we have seen that this corresponds to point A of Fig. 1·23a. If the line is a quarter-wave long (90 electrical degrees), we move through an angle of 180° at constant radius on the chart toward the generator (clockwise) to point B. The per-unit input impedance is then read as $0.5 - j0.5$ for point B. If input impedance is given and load impedance desired, the reverse of this procedure is obvious.

C. *To Find Standing-Wave Ratio and Position of Voltage Maximum from a Given Impedance, and Conversely.* If we wish the standing-wave ratio of an ideal transmission line terminated in a known load impedance, we make use of the information found in the last article (that the maximum impedance point along the line—which is also the voltage maximum and current minimum—is a pure resistance point, and this resistance is the standing-wave ratio times the characteristic impedance). That is, the per-unit resistance of this point is exactly the standing-wave ratio. Thus, in following about the circle on the chart determined by the given impedance, we note its crossing of the right-hand u axis of the w plane. The value of the per-unit resistance of this point is then the standing-wave ratio; the angle moved through to this position from the known impedance fixes the position of the voltage maximum.

As an example, for the given load impedance $1 + j1$ indicated by point A of Fig. 1·23a, one moves to the pure resistance point C by going 0.088 wavelength (31.7 electrical degrees) toward the generator from the load. The value of maximum per-unit resistance, which is the standing-wave ratio, is read as 2.6. The reversal of this procedure to determine the load impedance, if standing-wave ratio and position of a voltage maximum are given, is straightforward, as is the extension to finding position of voltage minimum, or finding input impedance in place of load impedance.

D. Use as an Admittance Diagram. Since admittance transforms along the ideal line in exactly the same manner as impedance, Eq. 1·21(11), it is evident that exactly the same chart may be used for transformation of admittances with the same procedure as for impedances described in (B) above. Admittance is read for impedance, conductance for resistance, and susceptance for reactance. The differences to remember are: the right-hand u axis now represents an admittance maximum, and therefore a current maximum instead of a voltage maximum; the phase of reflection coefficient read directly corresponding to a given per-unit admittance is that for current in the reflected wave compared with current in the incident wave and is therefore different by π from that based on voltages.

PROBLEMS

1·23a A 50-ohm line is terminated in a load impedance of $75 - j69$ ohms. The line is 3.5 meters long and is excited by a source of energy at 50 mc/sec. Velocity of propagation along the line is 3×10^8 meters/sec. Find the input impedance, the reflection coefficient in magnitude and phase, the value of standing-wave ratio, and the position of a voltage minimum.

1·23b The standing-wave ratio on an ideal 70-ohm line is measured as 3.2, and a voltage minimum is observed 0.23 wavelength in front of the load. Find the load impedance.

1·23c Repeat Prob. b, using the chart to determine load admittance. Check to see if the result is consistent with the impedance found in b.

1·23d A 70-ohm line is terminated in an impedance of $50 + j10$ ohms. Find the position and value of a reactance that might be added in series with the line at some point to produce a perfect match for waves incident from the left.

1·23e Repeat Prob. d to determine the position and value of a shunt susceptance to be placed on the line for matching.

1·24 TRANSMISSION LINES WITH LOSSES

If series resistance and shunt conductance are of importance in the transmission lines, the voltage drop along the line must include the resistance drop as well as the inductance drop of Eq. 1·16(3). Similarly, the leakage current must include the conductance as well as capacitance current shunted across the line. Instead of Eqs. 1·16(3) and 1·16(4) we then have

$$\frac{\partial V}{\partial z} = -L\frac{\partial I}{\partial t} - RI \tag{1}$$

$$\frac{\partial I}{\partial z} = -C\frac{\partial V}{\partial t} - GV \tag{2}$$

If steady-state sinusoidal conditions, of the form $e^{j\omega t}$, with respect to time are considered, time derivatives may be replaced by $j\omega$, and total derivatives written for distance since there are then no other derivatives:

$$\frac{dV}{dz} = -(R + j\omega L)I \tag{3}$$

$$\frac{dI}{dz} = -(G + j\omega C)V \tag{4}$$

Differentiate (3) with respect to z and substitute (4):

$$\frac{d^2V}{dz^2} = -(R + j\omega L)\frac{dI}{dz} = (R + j\omega L)(G + j\omega C)V$$

or

$$\frac{d^2V}{dz^2} = \gamma^2 V \tag{5}$$

where

$$\gamma^2 \equiv (R + j\omega L)(G + j\omega C) \tag{6}$$

The solution to (5) is in terms of exponentials,

$$V = Ae^{-\gamma z} + Be^{+\gamma z} \tag{7}$$

as can be verified by substituting (7) in (5).

An examination of (6) shows that γ must be complex in the general case. Let us write the real part as α, the imaginary part as β. By (6),

$$\gamma = \alpha + j\beta = \sqrt{(R + j\omega L)(G + j\omega C)} \tag{8}$$

If (7) is rewritten using α and β,

$$V = Ae^{-\alpha z}e^{-j\beta z} + Be^{\alpha z}e^{j\beta z} \tag{9}$$

This expression for voltage is quite similar to that of Eq. 1·21(4) for sinusoidal waves in ideal lines, except that there is now an attenuation term on both the forward and backward traveling waves. α is called the attenuation constant, β the phase constant, and γ the propagation constant.

As for current, solve by substituting (7) in (3):

$$I = \frac{\gamma}{R + j\omega L} [Ae^{-\gamma z} - Be^{\gamma z}]$$

or

$$I = \frac{1}{Z_0} [Ae^{-\alpha z}e^{-j\beta z} - Be^{\alpha z}e^{j\beta z}] \tag{10}$$

where

$$Z_0 = \frac{R + j\omega L}{\gamma} = \sqrt{\frac{R + j\omega L}{G + j\omega C}} \tag{11}$$

Z_0 may again be thought of as the characteristic or surge impedance of the line, since it relates voltage and current in a single wave and is the impedance of a line of infinite length.   However, it is now complex.

The formulas for reflection and transmission coefficients derived in Eqs. 1·19(4) and (5) apply to this case also, remembering of course that Z_0 is complex.   To find the input impedance at $z = -l$ in terms of a given reflection coefficient $\rho = B/A$ at $z = 0$, division of (7) by (10) yields

$$Z_i = Z_0 \left[\frac{Ae^{\gamma l} + Be^{-\gamma l}}{Ae^{\gamma l} - Be^{-\gamma l}} \right] = Z_0 \left[\frac{1 + \rho e^{-2\gamma l}}{1 - \rho e^{-2\gamma l}} \right] \tag{12}$$

This may be put in terms of load impedance by substituting Eq. 1·19(4):

$$Z_i = Z_0 \left[\frac{Z_L \cosh \gamma l + Z_0 \sinh \gamma l}{Z_0 \cosh \gamma l + Z_L \sinh \gamma l} \right] \tag{13}$$

The Smith transmission line chart may be utilized for lines with losses, with the same procedure as described in Art. 1·23 except that, in moving along the line toward the generator, one moves not along a circle but along a spiral of radius decreasing according to the exponential $e^{-2\alpha l}$.   The justification for this is provided by (12).

For low-loss lines, $R/\omega L \ll 1$ and $G/\omega C \ll 1$, it is interesting to note approximate values of attenuation constant, phase constant, and characteristic impedance.   The following results are obtained by retaining up to second order terms in the binomial expansions of (8) and (11):

$$\alpha \approx \frac{R}{2 \sqrt{L/C}} + \frac{G_0 \sqrt{L/C}}{2} \tag{14}$$

$$\beta \approx \omega \sqrt{LC} \left[1 - \frac{RG}{4\omega^2 LC} + \frac{G^2}{8\omega^2 C^2} + \frac{R^2}{8\omega^2 L^2} \right] \tag{15}$$

TABLE 1·24

Quantity	General Line	Ideal Line	Approximate Results for Low-Loss Lines
Propagation constant $\gamma = \alpha + j\beta$	$\sqrt{(R+j\omega L)(G+j\omega C)}$	$j\omega\sqrt{LC}$	(See α and β below)
Phase constant β	$Im(\gamma)$	$\omega\sqrt{LC} = \dfrac{\omega}{v} = \dfrac{2\pi}{\lambda}$	$\omega\sqrt{LC}\left[1 - \dfrac{RG}{4\omega^2 LC} + \dfrac{G^2}{8\omega^2 C^2} + \dfrac{R^2}{8\omega^2 L^2}\right]$
Attenuation constant α	$Re(\gamma)$	0	$\dfrac{R}{2Z_0} + \dfrac{GZ_0}{2}$
Characteristic impedance Z_0	$\sqrt{\dfrac{R+j\omega L}{G+j\omega C}}$	$\sqrt{\dfrac{L}{C}}$	$\sqrt{\dfrac{L}{C}}\left[1 + j\left(\dfrac{G}{2\omega C} - \dfrac{R}{2\omega L}\right)\right]$
Input impedance Z_i	$Z_0\left[\dfrac{Z_L\cosh\gamma l + Z_0\sinh\gamma l}{Z_0\cosh\gamma l + Z_L\sinh\gamma l}\right]$	$Z_0\left[\dfrac{Z_L\cos\beta l + jZ_0\sin\beta l}{Z_0\cos\beta l + jZ_L\sin\beta l}\right]$	$Z_0\left[\dfrac{\alpha l\cos\beta l + j\sin\beta l}{\cos\beta l + j\alpha l\sin\beta l}\right]$
Impedance of shorted line	$Z_0\tanh\gamma l$	$jZ_0\tan\beta l$	$Z_0\left[\dfrac{\cos\beta l + j\alpha l\sin\beta l}{\alpha l\cos\beta l + j\sin\beta l}\right]$
Impedance of open line	$Z_0\coth\gamma l$	$-jZ_0\cot\beta l$	$Z_0\left[\dfrac{Z_0 + Z_L\alpha l}{Z_L + Z_0\alpha l}\right]$
Impedance of quarter-wave line	$Z_0\left[\dfrac{Z_L\sinh\alpha l + Z_0\cosh\alpha l}{Z_0\sinh\alpha l + Z_L\cosh\alpha l}\right]$	$\dfrac{Z_0^2}{Z_L}$	$Z_0\left[\dfrac{Z_0 + Z_L\alpha l}{Z_L + Z_0\alpha l}\right]$
Impedance of half-wave line	$Z_0\left[\dfrac{Z_L\cosh\alpha l + Z_0\sinh\alpha l}{Z_0\cosh\alpha l + Z_L\sinh\alpha l}\right]$	Z_L	$Z_0\left[\dfrac{Z_L + Z_0\alpha l}{Z_0 + Z_L\alpha l}\right]$
Voltage along line $V(z)$	$V_i\cosh\gamma z - I_i Z_0\sinh\gamma z$	$V_i\cos\beta z - jI_i Z_0\sin\beta z$	
Current along line $I(z)$	$I_i\cosh\gamma z - \dfrac{V_i}{Z_0}\sinh\gamma z$	$I_i\cos\beta z - j\dfrac{V_i}{Z_0}\sin\beta z$	
Reflection coefficient K_R	$\dfrac{Z_L - Z_0}{Z_L + Z_0}$	$\dfrac{Z_L - Z_0}{Z_L + Z_0}$	
Standing wave ratio	$\dfrac{1+|K_R|}{1-|K_R|}$	$\dfrac{1+|K_R|}{1-|K_R|}$	

R, L, G, C Distributed resistance, inductance, conductance, capacitance per unit length.
l Length of line.
Subscript i denotes input end quantities.
Subscript L denotes load end quantities.

z Distance along line from input end.
λ Wavelength measured along line.
v Phase velocity of line equals velocity of light in dielectric of line for an ideal line.

$$Z_0 \approx \sqrt{\frac{L}{C}} \left[\left(1 + \frac{R^2}{8\omega^2 L^2} - \frac{3G^2}{8\omega^2 C^2} + \frac{RG}{4\omega^2 LC} \right) + j \left(\frac{G}{2\omega C} - \frac{R}{2\omega L} \right) \right] \quad (16)$$

In using the above approximate formulas, it is often sufficient to retain only first order correction terms, in which case β reduces to its ideal value of $2\pi/\lambda$ and α is computed from (14). It must then be remembered that Z_0 has a first order imaginary part, given by the last part of (16), which cannot in general be ignored.

Several of the important formulas for loss-free, low-loss, and general lines are summarized in Table 1·24.

1·25 PURELY STANDING WAVE ON AN IDEAL LINE

Suppose that a transmission line, shorted at one end, is excited by sinusoidal voltage at the other. Let us select the position of the short as the reference, $z = 0$. The short imposes the condition that, at $z = 0$, voltage must always be zero. From Eq. 1·21(4),

$$V\big|_{z=0} = V_1 + V_1'$$

For this to be zero, V_1' must be the negative of V_1. This result could be obtained as well from the general results for reflections at a discontinuity by setting $Z_L = 0$ in Eq. 1·19(4), or merely by physical reasoning which shows that no energy is absorbed by the short circuit, so all energy brought by the incident wave must appear in the reflected wave. The two waves of equal energy in the same line must have equal voltages. These must be in opposite directions at the short to add to the required zero voltage.

If $V_1' = -V_1$ is substituted in Eqs. 1·21(4) and 1·21(5),

$$V = V_1[e^{-j\beta z} - e^{j\beta z}] = -2jV_1 \sin \beta z \quad (1)$$

$$I = \frac{V_1}{Z_0} [e^{-j\beta z} + e^{j\beta z}] = 2 \frac{V_1}{Z_0} \cos \beta z \quad (2)$$

These results, typical for standing waves, show the following.

1. Voltage is always zero not only at the short, but also at multiples of $\lambda/2$ to the left. That is,

$$V = 0 \text{ at } -\beta z = n\pi \quad \text{or} \quad z = -n\frac{\lambda}{2}$$

2. Voltage is a maximum at all points for which βz is an odd multiple of $\pi/2$. These are at distances odd multiples of a quarter wavelength from the short circuit (Fig. 1·25).

3. Current is a maximum at the short circuit and at all points where voltage is zero; it is zero at all points where voltage is a maximum.

4. Current and voltage are not only displaced in their space patterns, but also are 90° out of time phase, as indicated by the j appearing in (1).

5. The ratio between the maximum current on the line and the maximum voltage is Z_0, the characteristic impedance of the line.

6. The total energy in any length of line a multiple of a quarter wavelength long is constant, merely interchanging between energy in

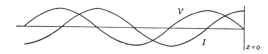

Fig. 1·25   Standing waves of voltage and current along shorted line.

the electric field of the voltages and energy in the magnetic field of the currents.

To check the energy relation stated above, calculate the magnetic energy of the currents at a time when the current pattern is a maximum and voltage is zero everywhere along the line.   Current is given by (2). The energy is calculated for a quarter wavelength of the line.

$$U_M = \frac{L}{2} \int_{-\lambda/4}^{0} |I|^2 \, dz = \frac{L}{2} \int_{-\lambda/4}^{0} \frac{4V_1^2}{Z_0^2} \cos^2 \beta z \, dz$$

$$= \frac{2V_1^2 L}{Z_0^2} \left[\frac{z}{2} + \frac{1}{4\beta} \sin 2\beta z \right]_{-\lambda/4}^{0}$$

Since $\beta = 2\pi/\lambda$ by 1·21(7), the above is simply

$$U_M = \frac{V_1^2 L\lambda}{4Z_0^2} \tag{3}$$

The maximum energy stored in the distributed capacity effect of the line is calculated for the quarter wavelength when the voltage pattern is a maximum and current is everywhere zero.   Voltage is given by (1).

$$U_E = \frac{C}{2} \int_{-\lambda/4}^{0} |V|^2 \, dz = \frac{C}{2} \int_{-\lambda/4}^{0} 4V_1^2 \sin^2 \beta z \, dz$$

$$= 2CV_1^2 \left[\frac{z}{2} - \frac{1}{4\beta} \sin 2\beta z \right]_{-\lambda/4}^{0} = \frac{CV_1^2 \lambda}{4} \tag{4}$$

By the definition of Z_0, (3) may also be written

$$U_M = \frac{V_1{}^2 L\lambda}{4L/C} = \frac{V_1{}^2 C\lambda}{4} = U_E \tag{5}$$

Thus the maximum energy stored in magnetic fields is exactly equal to that stored in electric fields 90° later in time. It could actually be shown that the sum of electric and magnetic energy at any other part of the cycle is equal to this same value.

PROBLEM

1·25 Write the instantaneous expressions for voltage and current represented by the complex values (1) and (2). For a general instant of time, make the integration of total energy, electric plus magnetic, for a quarter wavelength of the line and show that it is constant.

1·26 PHYSICAL APPROXIMATIONS FOR LOW-LOSS LINES

In Art. 1·06 we saw that, by certain physical approximations amounting to a small perturbation of the ideal solution, we could arrive at the approximate behavior of a resonant circuit with small but finite losses. We now wish to do the corresponding thing for transmission lines in order to arrive at approximate formulas for attenuation in a traveling wave, and impedance and quality factor of a standing wave. These techniques will be applied later in the book to the study of wave guides and cavity resonators.

If we take the formula for a traveling wave and assume that it is known that the major effect of small but finite losses in the line will be to produce an attenuating exponential multiplier,

$$V = V_1 e^{-\alpha z} e^{j(\omega t - \beta z)} \tag{1}$$

$$I = I_1 e^{-\alpha z} e^{j(\omega t - \beta z)} \tag{2}$$

The average power transfer at any position is then

$$W_T = \tfrac{1}{2} V_1 I_1 e^{-2\alpha z} \tag{3}$$

The factor $\frac{1}{2}$ in the above comes from the time average of a $\sin^2$ term [or, if preferred, use Eq. 1·12(7)]. The rate of decrease of this average power with distance along the line must correspond to the average power loss in the line per unit length.

$$\frac{\partial W_T}{\partial z} = -W_L = -2\alpha \left(\frac{1}{2} V_1 I_1 e^{-2\alpha z} \right) = -2\alpha W_T$$

or $$\alpha = \frac{W_L}{2W_T} \tag{4}$$

This is a very important approximate formula which, by the nature of the arguments used above, applies to the attenuation of a traveling wave along any uniform system.

To apply (4) to a transmission line with series resistance R and shunt conductance G, we first calculate the average power loss per unit length, part of which comes from the current flow through the resistance and another part from voltage appearing across the shunt conductance.

$$W_L = \frac{I_1{}^2 R}{2} + \frac{V_1{}^2 G}{2} = \frac{V_1{}^2}{2}\left[G + \frac{R}{Z_0{}^2}\right] \tag{5}$$

The average power transferred by the wave is

$$W_T = \frac{1}{2} V_1 I_1 = \frac{1}{2}\frac{V_1{}^2}{Z_0} \tag{6}$$

So (4) gives the result

$$\alpha = \frac{1}{2}\left[GZ_0 + \frac{R}{Z_0}\right]\text{nepers/meter} \tag{7}$$

which agrees with the value obtained by a mathematical approximation in Eq. 1·24(14).

We next want to ask about the effect of small losses on a quarter wavelength of the shorted line with standing waves, which was shown in Art. 1·25 to have the character of a resonant system. For the ideal line, the current a quarter wave in front of the short would be zero and voltage would be a maximum, so impedance would be infinite. When losses are present, there must be a high but finite resistance present representing energy dissipated in the losses of the line. To find these losses approximately, we shall use the expressions for voltage and current derived for the ideal line, Eqs. 1·25(1) and (2), assuming that they are not greatly changed by the small losses. The average power dissipated in the shunt conductance is then

$$W_G = \int_0^{\lambda/4} (2V_1 \sin \beta z)^2 \frac{G}{2}\, dz = \frac{4V_1{}^2 G}{4} \times \frac{\lambda}{4} \tag{8}$$

and the average power dissipated in the series resistance is

$$W_R = \int_0^{\lambda/4} \left(\frac{2V_1 \cos \beta z}{Z_0}\right)^2 \frac{R}{2}\, dz = \frac{4V_1{}^2 R}{4Z_0{}^2} \times \frac{\lambda}{4} \tag{9}$$

The input resistance must be such that the voltage appearing across this resistance will produce losses equal to the sum of (8) and (9). The magnitude of voltage at $z = -\lambda/4$ is $2V_1$. Thus

$$\frac{1}{2}\frac{(2V_1)^2}{R_i} = \frac{V_1{}^2\lambda}{4}\left(G + \frac{R}{Z_0{}^2}\right)$$

or
$$R_i = \frac{8Z_0}{\lambda[GZ_0 + (R/Z_0)]} \tag{10}$$

The approximate Q of the device describing its excellence as an energy storage device may be found by using the definition stated in Eq. 1·06(6). The stored energy is taken as that for the ideal line, Eq. 1·25(5), and the power loss is given by the sum of (8) and (9). The result is

$$Q = \frac{\omega_0 U}{W_L} = \frac{4\omega_0 C V_1{}^2\lambda}{4V_1{}^2\lambda\,[G + (R/Z_0{}^2)]} = \frac{\omega_0 C Z_0}{GZ_0 + (R/Z_0)} \tag{11}$$

PROBLEMS

1·26a   Find the input resistance and Q of a half wavelength of the shorted line having small but finite R and G.

1·26b   Use the formula for input impedance of a transmission line with losses to check (10), making approximations consistent with $R/\omega L \ll 1$ and $G/\omega C \ll 1$

1·26c   Suppose that frequency is varied by a small amount from the value giving resonance for the quarter-wave shorted line studied above.   For a line with $R/\omega L \ll 1$ and $G/\omega C \ll 1$, find the frequency shift for which impedance has decreased in magnitude to $1/\sqrt{2}$ its resonant value.   How is this related to the Q defined by (11)?

1·27   VELOCITIES OF WAVE PROPAGATION

The velocity $v_p = \omega/\beta$ for a single-frequency sinusoid has been shown to represent the velocity with which one must travel to keep instantaneous phase constant, for in the factor

$$e^{j(\omega t - \beta z)} = e^{j\omega[t - (z/v_p)]}$$

the instantaneous phase $(\omega t - \beta z)$ does remain constant if one travels with velocity v_p so that $z = v_p t + C$.   This velocity is thus known as the *phase velocity*.

A function of time with arbitrary wave shape may be expressed as a sum of sinusoidal waves by Fourier analysis.   If it happens that v_p is the same for each frequency component and there is no attenuation, the component waves will add in proper phase at each point along the line to reproduce the original wave shape exactly, but delayed by the time of propagation z/v_p.   The velocity v_p in this case describes the rate at which the wave moves down the line and could be said to be *the* velocity of propagation.   This case occurs, for example, in the ideal loss-free transmission line already studied for which

$$v_p = \frac{1}{\sqrt{LC}}$$

For transmission lines with losses and for general electromagnetic wave guides, phase velocity will vary with frequency.   In this case the individual sinusoidal components acting to make up a complex wave will shift in phase as they move down the line, the "faster" waves speeding ahead and the "slower" waves falling back.   In this phenomenon, known as *dispersion*, the waves at some point down the line may add to produce a wave shape quite different in appearance from that which went in.   It may then be very difficult to define any significant single velocity for this signal.   However, when there is relatively little dispersion over the frequency band of interest, the group velocity, to be defined in the following paragraph, is useful for this purpose.

The group velocity is most easily approached by considering the two-term combination:

$$\sin (\omega_0 - d\omega)t + \sin (\omega_0 + d\omega)t \tag{1}$$

If the above represents the transmitted voltage, the voltage everywhere along the path (assuming no amplitude change) is

$$\sin [(\omega_0 - d\omega)t - (\beta_0 - d\beta)x] + \sin [(\omega_0 + d\omega)t - (\beta_0 + d\beta)x] \tag{2}$$

in which β is to be regarded as a function of frequency as indicated by the use of $d\beta$ to go with $d\omega$.

Expression (2) may be changed to

$$2 \cos (d\omega t - d\beta x) \sin (\omega t - \beta x)$$

which shows that the resultant voltage on the line at any point may be pictured as a high-frequency wave whose amplitude varies at a low-frequency rate.   The envelope of the wave, in other words, is

$$\cos (d\omega t - d\beta x) \tag{3}$$

It varies sinusoidally with both time and distance and thus may be regarded as a traveling wave.   It is readily seen that the velocity of an imaginary observer who stays on the same point of the *envelope* is

$$v_g = \frac{d\omega}{d\beta} \tag{4}$$

This is called the group velocity. Since the phase velocity, Eq. 1·21(6), is

$$v_p = \frac{\omega}{\beta} \qquad (5)$$

the group velocity is seen to be

$$v_g = \frac{v_p}{1 - \frac{\omega}{v_p}\frac{dv_p}{d\omega}} \qquad (6)$$

Similarly for a signal made up of many sinusoidal components, so long as there is relatively small dispersion over the frequency band necessary to describe the signal, it may be shown that the group velocity v_g defined above expresses approximately the velocity of the composite envelope, and may thus be used as a "signal" velocity. For large dispersions, this is not a good approximation, but it is then usually impossible to give any single velocity describing the propagation of the wave since it changes shape so definitely as it goes. The group velocity is also not useful as a signal velocity in cases for which $dv_p/d\omega$ is positive (called anomalous dispersion), for then from (6) group velocity may become infinite or negative. An excellent discussion of the several velocities of propagation is made by Stratton.[2]

PROBLEMS

1·27a Is phase or group velocity the larger for normal dispersion ($dv_p/d\omega < 0$)? For anomalous dispersion ($dv_p/d\omega > 0$)?

1·27b Find the phase and group velocities for a transmission line with small but finite losses.

1·27c Consider a transmission line with very high leakage conductance G per unit length so that series resistance R and shunt capacitance C are negligible. Find phase and group velocities.

1·28 ANALYSIS OF TRANSMISSION LINE IN TERMS OF NATURAL MODES

In this article we shall demonstrate a technique which will be one of the most widely useful methods for solution of field and wave problems to come later. The method makes use of a summation or series of harmonic solutions to a wave problem to fit imposed boundary or initial conditions, just as in Art. 1·13 a series of sinusoids was used to fit any arbitrary periodic functions.

As the example, let us consider a problem quite similar to those solved by consideration of the traveling waves in Art. 1·20. For this

---

[2] J. A. Stratton, *Electromagnetic Theory*, McGraw-Hill, 1941, pp. 330–340.

problem, imagine the open-circuited transmission line, first charged to a d-c voltage V_0, and then shorted at both ends simultaneously at a specified instant of time. The voltage distribution at the instant of shorting is then known (zero at each end and a constant equal to V_0 at all other points). It is desired to find the current and voltage behavior at all later times.

In Art. 1·25 it was noted that natural sinusoidal oscillations for a line of length l, shorted at both ends, occur at all frequencies for which the line is a multiple of a half-wave long. From the results of that article one of these natural sinusoidal modes of oscillation may be written. For voltage,

$$V_m = A_m e^{j\omega_m t} \sin \frac{m\pi z}{l} \tag{1}$$

where
$$\omega_m = 2\pi f_m = \frac{m\pi v}{l} = \frac{m\pi}{\tau} \tag{2}$$

τ is the time of travel of a wave down the line, l/v. The results of Art. 1·25 also reveal that the corresponding current for each natural frequency is 90° out of time and space phase with voltage and has the magnitude of voltage divided by Z_0. That is,

$$I_m = \frac{jA_m}{Z_0} e^{j\omega_m t} \cos \frac{m\pi z}{l} \tag{3}$$

Now, let us form a solution to the transmission line equations from the sum of all solutions of the form of (1). The basis for this step may be traced to the fact that the sum of solutions to a linear differential equation is also a solution. The transmission line differential equations are linear, and (1) is a solution. Adding,

$$V = A_1 e^{j\omega_1 t} \sin \frac{\pi z}{l} + A_2 e^{j\omega_2 t} \sin \frac{2\pi z}{l} + A_3 e^{j\omega_3 t} \sin \frac{3\pi z}{l} + \cdots \tag{4}$$

and the corresponding sum of (3) for current,

$$I = \frac{j}{Z_0} \left[A_1 e^{j\omega_1 t} \cos \frac{\pi z}{l} + A_2 e^{j\omega_2 t} \cos \frac{2\pi z}{l} + A_3 e^{j\omega_3 t} \cos \frac{3\pi z}{l} + \cdots \right] \tag{5}$$

The amplitudes A_1, A_2, $\cdots$, A_m are still arbitrary. They may be determined from the known initial condition by expanding the known initial voltage distribution with distance as a Fourier series.

At $t = 0$, the voltage is known to be a constant V_0 over the interval $0 < z < l$. Such a function has been expanded in a Fourier series of sines in Eq. 1·15(7).

$$V \bigg|_{t=0} = \frac{4V_0}{\pi} \left[\sin \frac{\pi z}{l} + \frac{1}{3} \sin \frac{3\pi z}{l} + \frac{1}{5} \sin \frac{5\pi z}{l} + \cdots \right] \qquad (6)$$

But, at $t = 0$, the series (4) reduces to

$$V \bigg|_{t=0} = A_1 \sin \frac{\pi z}{l} + A_2 \sin \frac{2\pi z}{l} + A_3 \sin \frac{3\pi z}{l} + \cdots \qquad (7)$$

By a term-by-term comparison of (6) and (7) it is seen that all the even coefficients, A_2, A_4, etc., must be zero; for the odd coefficients,

$$A_1 = \frac{4V_0}{\pi} \qquad A_3 = \frac{4V_0}{3\pi} \qquad \cdots \qquad A_n = \frac{4V_0}{n\pi}$$

Now that the coefficients are determined, the complete series expressions for voltage and current at any time may be written

$$V = \frac{4V_0}{\pi} \left[e^{j(\pi t/\tau)} \sin \frac{\pi z}{l} + \frac{e^{j(3\pi t/\tau)}}{3} \sin \frac{3\pi z}{l} + \frac{e^{j(5\pi t/\tau)}}{5} \sin \frac{5\pi z}{l} + \cdots \right]$$
$$(8)$$

$$I = \frac{4jV_0}{Z_0\pi} \left[e^{j(\pi t/\tau)} \cos \frac{\pi z}{l} + \frac{e^{j(3\pi t/\tau)}}{3} \cos \frac{3\pi z}{l} + \frac{e^{j(5\pi t/\tau)}}{5} \cos \frac{5\pi z}{l} + \cdots \right]$$
$$(9)$$

It must be remembered that, to find instantaneous values, we must take the real part of the above expressions (Art. 1·11), and voltage or current could then be calculated approximately at any point along the line for any time by retaining a number of terms from the above infinite series. It is especially interesting to note the current through the short circuit by letting $z = 0$.

$$I \bigg|_{z=0} = \mathrm{Re} \left\{ \frac{4jV_0}{Z_0\pi} \left[e^{j(\pi t/\tau)} + \frac{1}{3} e^{j(3\pi t/\tau)} + \frac{1}{5} e^{j(5\pi t/\tau)} + \cdots \right] \right\}$$

$$= \frac{-4V_0}{Z_0\pi} \left[\sin \frac{\pi t}{\tau} + \frac{1}{3} \sin \frac{3\pi t}{\tau} + \frac{1}{5} \sin \frac{5\pi t}{\tau} + \cdots \right] \qquad (10)$$

This can be shown to be the Fourier series of a step function which

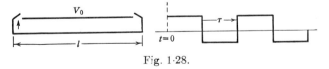

Fig. 1·28.

changes from V_0/Z_0 to $-V_0/Z_0$ at intervals of τ, as sketched in Fig. 1·28. The same result would have been found by a traveling-wave analysis as in Art. 1·20.

2 THE EQUATIONS OF
STATIONARY ELECTRIC
AND MAGNETIC FIELDS

2·01 INTRODUCTION

The discussion of field concepts will begin in this book with the study of static electric and magnetic fields. The main reason for this is that the laws and physical pictures for such fields are probably somewhat more familiar to the student than the more general laws of time-varying electricity and magnetism, so that the mathematical tools required for a discussion of all fields and the physical pictures required for the acceptance of field concepts may be more easily introduced at this stage. In other words, the material of static fields is used here primarily as a training ground for the important tools and concepts to be used throughout the book, with the belief that this will make the all-important general laws (Maxwell's equations) more meaningful for the student when they are introduced in a later chapter.

It is true that the present approach involves some risk. By concentrating on the special case of statics first, there is danger that the student will become too strongly imbued with certain laws and concepts which are not complete when the currents and charges are functions of time. For example, the use of a voltage defined along a path as synonymous with a difference in potential of the end points of that path is valid for static electric fields, but not for time-varying fields when any significant part of the electric field is generated by a changing magnetic field. Yet the incorrect use of the potential concept for a-c fields is fairly common among engineers. To minimize the risk, the student must remind himself from time to time that the discussion of this and the following chapter is for statics only, and that additions necessary when the electric and magnetic quantities change with time will follow. In fact, it is this opportunity to contrast the time-varying laws with the more simple ones of statics that can make the discussion of the general laws more meaningful, especially since the mathematical tools and the philosophy behind the use of field concepts will be somewhat familiar by that time.

If we begin the study of fields from some observed law which may be regarded as fundamental, the statement of the law should be made as general as possible so that it will be useful to describe a variety of conditions. We should always be critical of this procedure, since these "laws" represent generalizations from several experiments, all of which are special in nature; there is nothing to assure us, in extending them from the range of magnitudes and conditions in which they were determined to an entirely new set of magnitudes and conditions, that the phenomena predicted will actually ever be observed until these too are checked by special experiment. Once checked, the derived form of the relation might just as well have been the fundamental law. In fact, we might have started from that point had we thought of it first. In applied physics it is particularly necessary to find a large number of these derived relations, since it is seldom convenient to use the law in its original form for all design or analysis. There are often so many of these forms that the engineer in using a dozen different relations for as many separate problems may be quite unaware that many of these relations are in reality equivalent.

To study static fields some experimental "laws" will be taken as fundamental. By transformations, definitions, and generalizations, other forms of the law will be obtained, which may be more general or more convenient to use for certain problems. We shall extend the laws developed from macroscopic systems to the infinitesimal, and so obtain differential equations with which we may study continuous variations from point to point, as well as discrete systems. Once this extension has been justified, the differential equation will be the most valuable tool for the study of fields.

As the discussion proceeds, it will be noticed that directions appear as frequently as magnitudes in the statement of the laws, so that quite naturally it will be necessary to use a short-cut vector notation to save time, space, and many words. It will soon be discovered that this notation permits many short cuts in manipulation and, most important of all, leads to a very superior way of thinking about electric and magnetic effects.

Static Electric Fields

2·02 THE PROBLEM OF STATIC ELECTRIC FIELDS

The problem which must be solved in static electric field theory is that of obtaining relations which involve the geometrical configurations of conductors and dielectrics, the distribution of charges on the conductors and in the dielectric medium separating them, the potential differences between conductors, and the field distribution in the dielectric. Several or all of these factors will enter into the determination of capacitance between conductors, the maximum gradient in insulation, the amount of field between deflecting plates in an oscilloscope, the amount of shielding which a grid provides in a vacuum tube, or the accelerating force on an electron in an electron gun.

Essentially, the problem is one of equilibrium. We require a knowledge of the forces that act on charges, thus making them move to eventual equilibrium positions, and we must know the manner in which conductors and dielectrics affect the charge distribution and the field distribution.

2·03   FORCE BETWEEN ELECTRIC CHARGES

We shall take as the starting point for electrostatics the experimental law of Coulomb, which gives the force between two electric charges. The law includes the following information:

1. Like charges repel, opposites attract.

2. Force is proportional to the product of charge magnitudes.

3. Force is inversely proportional to the square of the distances between charges.

4. Force is dependent upon the medium in which the charges are placed.

5. Force acts along the line joining the charges.

This information may be written as an equation:

$$f = k \frac{q_1 q_2}{\epsilon r^2} \tag{1}$$

In this equation, f is defined as the force of attraction acting on the line between charges, q_1 and q_2 represent the charges in magnitude and sign, r is the distance between charges, ϵ is a property of the medium which may be called the dielectric constant, and k is a constant of proportionality which must be included for the present, since we have not as yet defined units.

The equation may be written so that the direction of the force is included:

$$\bar{f} = k \frac{q_1 q_2}{\epsilon r^2} \bar{a}_r \tag{2}$$

The bar above f denotes that force is a directed quantity, or vector; that is, it has both magnitude and direction. The direction of $\bar{f}$ is given by $\bar{a}_r$, a vector of unit length pointing from one charge directly away from the other, and the sign of q_1q_2. Thus, if q_1 and q_2 have opposite signs, q_1q_2 is negative and the force has the opposite direction to $\bar{a}_r$, or is from one charge toward the other. If q_1 and q_2 have the same signs, $\bar{f}$ has the same direction as $\bar{a}_r$ and is hence from one charge directly away from the other. This is merely the statement of opposite charges attracting, like charges repelling. Vectors such as $\bar{a}_r$ are known as unit vectors and will be useful throughout the study of fields, since they serve to indicate direction without interfering with magnitudes.

2·04 THE ELECTROSTATIC SYSTEM OF UNITS

Equation 2·03(1) may be used to define systems of units. Originally, the most common system of units used for electric quantities in discussing the physical laws was a centimeter-gram-second system of units known as the electrostatic system of units (esu). Although it is not the system to be used throughout the remainder of the book, it will be defined briefly in this article. Since it is a cgs system, the unit of force appearing in Eq. 2·03(1) is the dyne, and the unit of distance is the centimeter. A unit charge is defined as that charge which repels an exactly similar charge with a force of 1 dyne when the two are placed 1 centimeter apart in vacuum, so that $k/\epsilon = 1$. In this system of units the dielectric constant of vacuum is further defined as unity, so that k is also unity. The unit of charge defined in this system is known as the statcoulomb, and it is very nearly $\frac{1}{3} \times 10^{-9}$ of the practical unit of charge, the coulomb.

The dielectric constant of a material based upon vacuum as unity is known as the relative dielectric constant, or specific inductive capacity. In this text the relative dielectric constant will be denoted by ϵ' to distinguish it from the dielectric constant in the mks system of units, to be described below, which will be denoted simply as ϵ.

2·05 THE RATIONAL MKS SYSTEM OF UNITS

The system of units that has come to be used almost universally in applied electromagnetic theory is the system of units introduced by Giorgi[1] in 1901. It is an mks system, so that lengths are in meters, mass in kilograms, and time in seconds, but the significant advantage so far as its use in electricity and magnetism is concerned lies in the fact that the units of all primary electric quantities are those actually measured. Thus, current is in amperes, potential in volts, an impedance derived at any stage of the discussion is in ohms, power is in

[1] Giorgi, *Elettricità* (Milan), **20**, 787–788 (Dec. 1901).

watts, etc. These and other advantages will become clearer as the various laws are introduced and studied.

The unit of force in any meter-kilogram-second system of units, defined as the product of mass and acceleration, has the units of kilogram-meters per (second)^2 and is known as a newton:

$$1 \text{ newton} = 1 \text{ kilogram-meter (second)}^{-2} = 10^5 \text{ dynes} \qquad (1)$$

The unit of energy, the product of force and distance, is in newton-meters, and is the well-known unit of physics and engineering called the joule:

$$1 \text{ joule} = 1 \text{ newton-meter} = 10^7 \text{ ergs} \qquad (2)$$

For later purposes, it is also well to note that, from elementary circuit theory for a simple condenser, the energy in joules can be written in terms of charge in coulombs and capacitance in farads:

$$\text{energy in joules} = \frac{\frac{1}{2} \text{ (charge in coulombs)}^2}{\text{(capacitance in farads)}} \qquad (3)$$

The unit of charge appearing in Eq. 2·03(1) is selected as the practical unit, the coulomb. All dimensions in the basic force equation have now been selected except for the constant k and the dielectric constant ϵ. In this system the dielectric constant is allowed to absorb the conversion factors between units so that it has a value other than unity for free space, and definite dimensions. The remaining dimensionless factor k is selected either as $1/4\pi$ or as unity, depending upon whether a "rational" or an "irrational" system of units is desired. The relative advantages of these choices cannot be discussed intelligently until the entire set of electromagnetic equations has been presented, but, since the choice in the literature has been predominantly in favor of the rational system, that system will be used in this text. The constant k is therefore chosen as $1/4\pi$, and the force equation in rational mks units reads

$$\bar{f} = \frac{q_1 q_2}{4\pi \epsilon r^2} (\bar{a}_r) \qquad (4)$$

The units of ϵ may now be found from (4) in conjunction with (2) and (3):

$$\epsilon = \frac{\text{(coulombs)}^2}{\text{newtons (meter)}^2} = \frac{\text{(coulombs)}^2}{\text{joules-meter}} = \frac{\text{farads}}{\text{meter}}$$

To find the value of ϵ for free space, which will be denoted ϵ_0, we may refer to the known result from the force equation in esu: two charges of 1 statcoulomb each placed 1 centimeter apart in vacuum yield a force of 1 dyne. If these data are converted to the mks system and substituted in (4), the result is

$$\epsilon_0 = \frac{q_1 q_2}{4\pi r^2 f} = \frac{(\tfrac{1}{3} \times 10^{-9})^2}{4\pi (10^{-2})^2 10^{-5}} = \frac{1}{36\pi} \times 10^{-9} \text{ farads/meter} \quad (5)$$

The use of the approximate conversion between statcoulombs and coulombs, as in the above, results in the easily remembered value shown. A more accurate value is 8.854×10^{-12} farads per meter. The dielectric constant of other materials may then be written as the product of ϵ_0 and the relative dielectric constant ϵ' defined in the previous article:

$$\epsilon = \epsilon' \epsilon_0 \quad (6)$$

ϵ' is the quantity commonly listed in tables for dielectric materials.

PROBLEMS

2·05a Compute the force between two charges of 1 coulomb each placed 1 meter apart in vacuum. Use Coulomb's force law in both esu and mks units, and show that the results are equivalent.

2·05b Calculate the ratio of the electrostatic force of repulsion between two electrons to the gravitational force of attraction, assuming that Newton's law of gravitation holds. The electron's charge is 1.602×10^{-19} coulombs, its mass is 9.11×10^{-28} grams, and the gravitational constant K is 6.66×10^{-8} dyne cm^2 g^{-2}

2·06 ELECTRIC FIELD INTENSITY

Coulomb's force law gives the force that will be exerted on a charge when placed in the vicinity of another point charge. In the more general case, any charge placed in the vicinity of a system of charges experiences a force whose magnitude and direction are functions of the amounts and positions of all charges of the system. A region so influenced by charges is called a region of electric field. The force per unit charge on a positive test charge at a point is defined as the strength of electric field or electric intensity at the point, provided that the test charge is so small that it does not disturb the original charge distribution of the system. Since the force on the test charge has direction as well as magnitude, the electric intensity is a vector. The electric intensity or electric field vector is then defined by

$$\bar{E} = \frac{\bar{f}}{\Delta q} \quad (1)$$

where $\bar{f}$ is the force acting upon the infinitesimal test charge Δq.

The electric field arising from a point charge q in a homogeneous dielectric is then given by the force law, Eq. 2·05(4):

$$\bar{E} = \frac{q}{4\pi\epsilon r^2}\,(\bar{a}_r) \qquad (2)$$

Since $\bar{a}_r$ is the unit vector directed from the point in a direction away from the charge, the electric field vector is seen to point away from positive charges and toward negative charges. The units of electric field in the mks system are in volts per meter, as may be found by substituting units in (2):

$$E = \frac{\text{coulombs meter}}{\text{farads (meter)}^2} = \frac{\text{volts}}{\text{meter}}$$

For a system of point charges, the total electric field may be found by adding vectorially the forces from the individual charges, as is illustrated at point P of Fig. 2·06 for the charges q and $-q$ separated by distance d. In this manner the electric field vector could be found for any point in the vicinity of the two charges. An electric field line is defined as a line drawn tangent to the electric field vector at each point in space. If the vector is constructed for enough points of the region, the electric field lines can be drawn in roughly by following the direction of the vectors as illustrated in the figure. Easier methods of constructing the electric field will be studied in later articles, but the present method, although laborious, demonstrates clearly the meaning of the electric field lines.

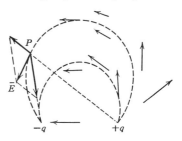

Fig. 2·06   Construction of field lines about point charges.

PROBLEMS

2·06a   Construct the electric field vector for several points in the x-y plane for like charges q at $(d/2,0,0)$ and $(-d/2,0,0)$, and draw in roughly a few electric field lines.

2·06b   Repeat Prob. a for charges of $2q$ and $-q$ at $(d/2,0,0)$ and $(-d/2,0,0)$, respectively.

2·07   ELECTRIC FLUX DENSITY

Equation 2·06(2) shows that the electric intensity is dependent upon the medium in which the charge is placed. Suppose that a new vector quantity independent of the medium is defined. Define the quantity $\bar{D}$ by

$$\bar{D} = \epsilon \bar{E} \tag{1}$$

This quantity for a point charge then becomes [Eq. 2·06(2)]

$$\bar{D} = \frac{q}{4\pi r^2} (\bar{a}_r) \tag{2}$$

The vector $\bar{D}$ at any point is thus a function of charge and position only, and is called an electric flux density. It is true that the justification for this name and the use of the concept of flux in connection with it cannot be appreciated fully at this stage but must gradually be built up over the next few articles. The name implies that each charge may be considered a source of flux or lines of flow in the medium, each charge giving rise to a certain amount of that flux. For example, if an imaginary spherical surface of radius r is chosen with center at the point charge of strength q, Eq. (2) shows that at each point on the surface of this sphere the vector which we have called electric flux density points radially outward and has strength $q/(4\pi r^2)$. If this is multiplied by the surface of the sphere, $4\pi r^2$, to obtain the total electric flux passing through the surface, it is found to be exactly equal to the charge q, and is independent of the radius of the sphere chosen for the calculation. It will be demonstrated that this same result is obtained for any surface surrounding the charge, leading to the very important statement of Gauss's law.

For reasons which are largely historical, the vector $\bar{D}$ is also sometimes called the "displacement vector," and the flux associated with it is called "displacement flux." The terms electric flux density and electric flux give a better physical picture at this stage of the discussion. In (2), q has the dimensions of coulombs and r has the dimensions of meters, so D has the dimensions of coulombs per square meter in the mks system.

PROBLEM

2·07 If (1) were used to define dielectric constant, with D in coulombs per meter^2 and E in volts per meter, show that ϵ has the units stated: farads per meter.

2·08 GAUSS'S LAW

In Art. 2·07 it was shown that the electric flux passing through a spherical surface centered about a point charge q is exactly equal to the charge q. It is now desirable to generalize the demonstration to a surface of arbitrary shape containing any number of charges. If one of these point charges, q, is considered first (Fig. 2·08), the field intensity and electric flux density can be calculated for any point on the surface by equations of previous articles. Thus, at point P, D is $q/(4\pi r^2)$. (When a quantity normally a vector appears without the bar, it signifies that magnitude alone is being considered.) If we continue the interpretation of $\bar{D}$ as a flux or flow density vector, analogous to the flow vector for a fluid passing through a surface, it is the component of the vector normal to the surface at each point which determines the flow through the surface. Thus,

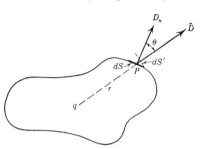

Fig. 2·08   Charge q and arbitrary surrounding surface.

if θ is the angle between $\bar{D}$ and the normal to the surface at P, the amount of flux passing through an elemental surface dS is

$$d\psi = \frac{q}{4\pi r^2}\, dS\, \cos\,\theta$$

$dS \cos \theta$ is the area dS', the component of dS normal to $\bar{D}$. But in solid geometry the element of solid angle $d\Omega$ is defined as the ratio of the surface subtended to the square of the radius:

$$d\Omega = \frac{dS'}{r^2} = \frac{dS\,\cos\,\theta}{r^2}$$

Hence the amount of flux flowing through the elemental surface can be written as $qd\Omega/4\pi$. To obtain the total electric flux, this expression is integrated over all the surface, which amounts to integrating $d\Omega$. Since the total solid angle subtended by a closed surface is 4π steradians, the result is again simply q:

$$\oint_S D \cos \theta \, dS = q \tag{1}$$

D is the magnitude of the electric flux density at any point on the surface, dS is an·elemental area at that point, and θ is the angle between $\bar{D}$ and the normal to the surface. $\int_S$ is used to denote the integral over a general surface, and the circle through the integral signifies that the surface is a closed one.

If there are a number of point charges inside the region considered, there will be an integration similar to the above for each of the charges and the flux will add linearly, since the total force on a test charge at any point will be the vector sum of the forces from the individual charges considered separately. Hence the q on the right side of Eq. (1) may be considered the total charge inside the surface under consideration.

The above is a statement of Gauss's law. In words, it is

flux out of a surface = charge enclosed

It has been derived from Coulomb's force law by the introduction of new definitions and concepts, but without any further experimental information. It is more useful than the original law for much general thinking, and also for a variety of simple problems, some of which will be demonstrated in the next articles.

2·09 EXAMPLES OF THE USE OF GAUSS'S LAW

The simple but important examples to be discussed below demonstrate that Gauss's law enables one to obtain the field strength immediately in problems with certain kinds of symmetry. This symmetry allows one to tell the direction of the electric field by physical reasoning, and then allows one to write the flux as the product of area and flux density, since the flux density does not vary over the surface.

A. Field about a Line Charge or between Coaxial Cylinders. A line charge is defined as one for which the charge per unit length, q_l, is given along an axis, and its radial extent is assumed to be very small but is not otherwise specified. Unless stated, it is assumed to extend to infinity in each direction along the axis with uniform strength, and is hence the two-dimensional equivalent of the point charge. Practically, a long thin charged wire is a good approximation. The symmetry of this problem reveals that the force on a test charge, and hence the electric field, can only be radial. Moreover, this electric field will not vary with angle about the line charge, or with distance along it. If the strength of the radial electric field is desired at distance r from the line charge, Gauss's law may be applied to an imaginary cylindrical surface of radius r and any length l (Fig. 2·09a). Since the electric field (and hence the electric flux density $\bar{D}$) is radial, there is no normal component at the ends of the cylinder and hence no flux flow through them. However, $\bar{D}$ is exactly normal to the cylindrical part of the surface, and does not vary with either angle or distance along the axis, so that the flux out is the surface $2\pi r l$ multiplied by the electric flux density D_r. The charge enclosed is the length l multiplied by the charge per unit length, q_l. By Gauss's law, flux out equals the charge enclosed:

$$2\pi r l D_r = l q_l$$

If the dielectric surrounding the wire has constant ϵ, D_r is ϵE_r, and

$$E_r = \frac{q_l}{2\pi \epsilon r} \tag{1}$$

Hence the electric field about the line charge has been obtained by the use of Gauss's law and the special symmetry of the problem.

The same symmetry applies to the coaxial transmission line formed of two coaxial conducting cylinders of radii a and b with dielectric ϵ between them (Fig. 2·09b). Hence the result (1) applies for radius r between a and b. As a static problem, it is probably better to think of this as a cylindrical condenser.

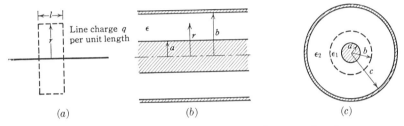

(a) (b) (c)

Fig. 2·09   Line charge, coaxial cylinders, and concentric spheres.

B. Field inside an Electron Beam.   Next imagine a long cylindrical beam of electrons moving with velocity v_0 carrying a direct current I_0 in vacuum. Since the charges are in motion, it might appear that this is not a static problem, but, although the individual charges move through the beam, there is always the same total amount of charge (except for statistical fluctuations) in a given part of the beam. Again, because of the cylindrical symmetry, the imaginary surface for the application of Gauss's law is selected as a cylinder of length l and radius r. The electric field is radial, independent of angle and axial distance, and the flux out is again $2\pi r l \epsilon E_r$. The charge per unit length to produce the current I_0 is I_0/v_0 coulombs per meter. If it is assumed here that this charge is distributed uniformly over the cross section, the total charge inside the cylinder of radius r and length l may be found and set equal to the outgoing flux by Gauss's law. For r taken inside the beam radius, a,

$$2\pi r l \epsilon E_r = l \frac{r^2}{a^2} \frac{I_0}{v_0}$$

or
$$E_r = \frac{r I_0}{2\pi \epsilon a^2 v_0} \qquad r < a \tag{2}$$

If the field is desired outside the beam, the Gaussian surface is selected with radius greater than a, and the total charge per unit length for the beam is used:

$$2\pi r l \epsilon E_r = \frac{l I_0}{v_0}$$

$$E_r = \frac{I_0}{2\pi \epsilon r v_0} \qquad r > a \qquad (3)$$

C. Field in a Spherical Condenser with Two Dielectrics. Figure 2·09c shows a condenser formed of two conducting spheres of radii a and c, with one dielectric ϵ_1 extending from $r = a$ to $r = b$, and a second, ϵ_2, from $r = b$ to $r = c$. This problem has spherical symmetry about the center, which reveals that the electric field will be radial, and independent of the angular direction about the sphere. If the charge on the inner sphere is Q and that on the outer sphere is $-Q$, the charge enclosed by an imaginary spherical surface of radius r selected anywhere between the two conductors is only that charge Q on the inner sphere. The flux passing through it is the surface $4\pi r^2$ multiplied by the radial component of flux density, D_r. Hence, using Gauss's law,

$$D_r = \frac{Q}{4\pi r^2} \qquad (4)$$

The form of the equation for the flux density is the same for either dielectric, since the flux passes from the positive charge on the center conductor continuously to the negative charge on the outer conductor. However, the electric field has a different form in the two regions, since in each dielectric D and E are related by the corresponding dielectric constant:

$$E_r = \frac{Q}{4\pi \epsilon_1 r^2} \qquad a < r < b \qquad (5)$$

$$E_r = \frac{Q}{4\pi \epsilon_2 r^2} \qquad b < r < c \qquad (6)$$

The radial flux density is continuous at the dielectric discontinuity at $r = b$, but the radial electric field is discontinuous there.

PROBLEMS

2·09a   A coaxial transmission line has an inner conducting cylinder of radius a, and an outer conducting cylinder of radius c. Charge q_l per unit length is uniformly distributed over the inner conductor and $-q_l$ over the outer. If dielectric ϵ_1 extends from $r = a$ to $r = b$ and dielectric ϵ_2 from $r = b$ to $r = c$, find the electric field for $r < a$, for $a < r < b$, for $b < r < c$, and for $r > c$. Take the conducting cylinders as infinitesimally thin.

2·09b In the electron beam example, find electric field for $r < a$ and for $r > a$ if the velocity as a function of radius is $v_z = v_0[1 - (r^2/a^2)]$ and the charge density is $\rho = \rho_0[1 + (r^2/a^2)]$ coulombs/meter^3.

2·09c Imagine that a sphere of charge of radius a and uniform density ρ_0 coulombs/meter^3 can be considered static over a certain time interval. Find the electric field for $r < a$ and for $r > a$.

2·10 SURFACE AND VOLUME INTEGRALS; GAUSS'S LAW IN VECTOR NOTATION

The general notation for a surface integral used in the statement of Gauss's law in Eq. 2·08(1) is very useful, but frequently confusing to students on first introduction. Once the integral sign is sighted, it is felt that the process of integration should be performed as the next step. However, the actual evaluation of the integral cannot take place until the particular surface and the particular way in which the flux density $\bar{D}$ varies over that surface are specified. Nevertheless, the general notation is of great usefulness in writing a general law such as Gauss's which says that, no matter what surface is selected, and no matter how the flux density varies over that surface, the net result of the integration, when performed, will always yield the charge enclosed. The actual evaluation of the surface integral will require a double integration in the general case.

The surface integral can also be written in a still more compact form if vector notation is employed. Define the unit vector normal to the surface under consideration, for any given point on the surface, as $\bar{a}_n$. Then replace $D \cos \theta$ by $\bar{D} \cdot \bar{a}_n \, dS$. This particular product of the two vectors $\bar{D}$ and $\bar{a}_n$ denoted by the dot between the two is known as the dot product of two vectors, or the scalar product, since it results by definition in a scalar quantity equal to the product of the two vector magnitudes and the cosine of the angle between them. Also the combination $\bar{a}_n \, dS$ is frequently abbreviated further by writing it $\overline{dS}$. Thus the elemental vector $\overline{dS}$, representing the element of surface in magnitude and orientation, has a magnitude equal to the magnitude of the element dS under consideration, and the direction of the outward normal to the surface at that point. The surface integral in Eq. 2·08(1) may then be written in any of the equivalent forms,

$$\oint_S D \cos \theta \, dS = \oint_S \bar{D} \cdot \bar{a}_n \, dS = \oint_S \bar{D} \cdot \overline{dS} \tag{1}$$

All of these say that the normal component of the vector $\bar{D}$ is to be integrated over the general closed surface S.

If the charge inside the region is given as a density of charge per unit volume in coulombs per cubic meter for each point of the region, the total charge inside the region must be obtained by integrating this density over the volume of the region. This is of course exactly analogous to the process of finding the total mass inside a region when the variable mass density is given for each point of a region. This process may also be denoted by a general integral. The symbol $\int_V$ is used to denote this, and, as with the surface integral, the particular volume and the variation of density over that volume must be specified before the integration may be performed. Then, in the general case, it will have to be performed as a triple integral.

Gauss's law may then be written in this notation:

$$\oint_S \bar{D} \cdot \overline{dS} = \int_V \rho \, dV \tag{2}$$

The notation is cryptic enough so that it may at first appear to conceal the physical meaning of the law rather completely, yet, after a bit of practice, the contrary will be found to be true. The left-hand side will reveal at once that the normal component of a vector $\bar{D}$ is to be integrated over a closed surface, yielding the flux out of the region, and the right side will show that the volume density ρ is to be integrated over the volume surrounded by that surface, yielding the total charge inside the region.

PROBLEM

2·10   A point charge q is located at the origin of coordinates. Express the electric field vector in its rectangular coordinate components, and evaluate the surface integral for S chosen as the surface of a cube of sides $2a$ centered on the charge.

2·11   SCALAR OR DOT PRODUCT OF VECTORS

The vector operation defined in the last article is important since there is often occasion to multiply one vector by the projection of the other upon it. That is, if $\bar{A}$ and $\bar{B}$ are vectors (of magnitudes A and B) with an angle of θ between them, $AB \cos \theta$ is of interest. This has been written as $\bar{A} \cdot \bar{B}$. (Read A dot B.) This product may now be expressed in terms of the components of $\bar{A}$ and $\bar{B}$ along the coordinate axes, not only for the calculation of flux flow through a surface, as in preceding articles, but also in the computation of the work done by a vector force moving through a vector distance.

A unit vector has already been defined in the statement of Eq. 2·03(2). If $\bar{a}_x$, $\bar{a}_y$, $\bar{a}_z$ are three such unit vectors having the directions of the three axes in rectangular coordinates, and if A_x, A_y, and A_z

are the magnitudes of the components of $\bar{A}$ along these axes, $\bar{A}$ may be written

$$\bar{A} = A_x \bar{a}_x + A_y \bar{a}_y + A_z \bar{a}_z$$

The addition of the three component vectors to obtain $\bar{A}$ is performed according to the definition of vector addition, which states that the beginning of one vector is placed in coincidence with the

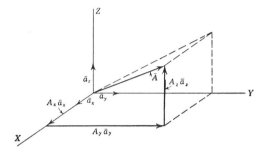

Fig. 2·11   Vector $\bar{A}$ and its rectangular components.

terminus of another, and the resultant drawn from the starting point to the final point (Fig. 2·11).   The dot product is

$$\bar{A} \cdot \bar{B} = (A_x \bar{a}_x + A_y \bar{a}_y + A_z \bar{a}_z) \cdot (B_x \bar{a}_x + B_y \bar{a}_y + B_z \bar{a}_z)$$

If the multiplication is carried through term by term, with the dot product between component vectors retained,

$$\bar{A} \cdot \bar{B} = A_x B_x \bar{a}_x \cdot \bar{a}_x + A_x B_y \bar{a}_x \cdot \bar{a}_y, \text{ etc.}$$

The terms $\bar{a}_x \cdot \bar{a}_x$, $\bar{a}_y \cdot \bar{a}_y$, $\bar{a}_z \cdot \bar{a}_z$ are unity by definition of the unit vectors and the dot product.   The terms $\bar{a}_x \cdot \bar{a}_y$, $\bar{a}_y \cdot \bar{a}_z$, etc., are zero since the angle between any of these unit vectors and either of the other two is 90°.   The scalar product then reduces to

$$\bar{A} \cdot \bar{B} = A_x B_x + A_y B_y + A_z B_z \tag{1}$$

PROBLEMS

2·11a   If $\bar{A}$, $\bar{B}$, and $\bar{C}$ are vectors, show

$$\bar{B} \cdot \bar{A} = \bar{A} \cdot \bar{B}$$

$$(\bar{A} + \bar{B}) + \bar{C} = \bar{A} + (\bar{B} + \bar{C})$$

$$\bar{A} \cdot (\bar{B} + \bar{C}) = \bar{A} \cdot \bar{B} + \bar{A} \cdot \bar{C}$$

2·11b   Vector $\bar{A}$ makes angles α_1, β_1, γ_1 with the x, y, and z axes respectively, and $\bar{B}$ makes angles α_2, β_2, γ_2 with the axes.   If θ is the angle between the vectors, make use of the scalar product $\bar{A} \cdot \bar{B}$ to show that

$$\cos \theta = \cos \alpha_1 \cos \alpha_2 + \cos \beta_1 \cos \beta_2 + \cos \gamma_1 \cos \gamma_2$$

2·12   TUBES OF FLUX

The concept of flux passing through an area does not have to be limited to electric phenomena.   If $\bar{D}$ is any vector function of space, the product of the magnitude of $\bar{D}$ at any point by an element of area perpendicular to $\bar{D}$ at that point may be called the flux of $\bar{D}$ passing through that area.   The total flux flowing through a surface is given by the surface integral

$$\psi = \int_S \bar{D} \cdot d\bar{S} \tag{1}$$

Consider a surface (Fig. 2·12a), bounded by two planes, S_1 and S_2, perpendicular to the field vector at two points, and a surface S_3 always parallel to the direction of the field vector.   If there is no charge enclosed, Gauss's law gives

$$\int_{S_1} \bar{D} \cdot d\bar{S} + \int_{S_2} \bar{D} \cdot d\bar{S} + \int_{S_3} \bar{D} \cdot d\bar{S} = 0 \tag{2}$$

Since S_3 is always parallel to $\bar{D}$, there is no flux flowing out through S_3. So

$$\int_{S_1} \bar{D} \cdot d\bar{S} = - \int_{S_2} \bar{D} \cdot d\bar{S} \tag{3}$$

This equation states that the flux passing through the plane S_1 is that which comes out of the plane S_2, so that total flux across any cross section of the tube is a constant.   Such a tubular region may be called a tube of flux.   To study the field intensity distribution, it is sometimes helpful to draw out many of these tubes, the size of area being so selected that the flux through the area is one unit.   Lines are often used to represent the tubes, and the tubes loosely called lines.   Thus, the closer the spacing of these lines, the stronger is the flux density at that point.

The electrostatic tubes of flux emanate from positive charges, are continuous in regions without charge, and end on negative charges. The boundaries of the flux tubes, as have been shown, follow the direction of the flux density vector $\bar{D}$ and therefore the direction of the electric field $\bar{E}$.   This fact is sometimes useful in drawing the electric field lines about charges.   For example, consider two line charges, q_l at $x = -1$ and $-q_l$ at $x = 1$ (Fig. 2·12b).   If the flux is to be computed passing through a surface between a general point P and the line BC, it may be broken up into the part from the charge at A and that from the charge at B, since the effects are superposable.   The flux due to the charge at A alone would come out radially from its center, so that the amount (per unit length) between P and BC would be

$q_l\alpha_1/2\pi$.   That from the charge at B alone would pass radially inward toward the negative line charge at $x = 1$, and would therefore cause flux $-q_l\alpha_2/2\pi$ to pass through the portion of the surface under con-

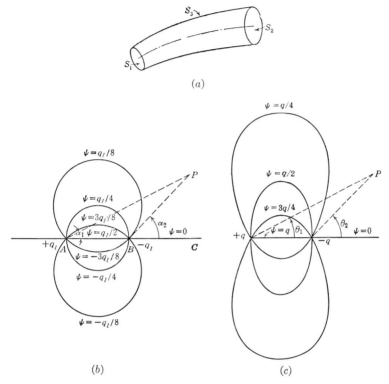

Fig. 2·12   (a) Tube of flux; (b) electric field lines about line charges found from flux function; (c) same for point charges.

sideration.   Thus the net flux between P and the reference is

$$\psi = \frac{q_l}{2\pi}(\alpha_1 - \alpha_2) \tag{4}$$

To trace out a boundary of a flux tube, and therefore a field line, the locus of α_1 versus α_2 is found to keep the total flux ψ a constant.   Thus, from (4), this is a locus of $(\alpha_1 - \alpha_2)$ a constant, which turns out to be a circle passing through the points ± 1 and with center on the y axis. The circular field lines shown were plotted by choosing the flux per tube to be $q_l/8$.

Similarly, the field lines about two equal and opposite point charges may be obtained.   If q is located at $x = -1$, and $-q$ at $x = 1$, the flux from each of these point charges passes radially in or out from the charges in a spherical sense. The flux from the charge at A passing through a spherical cap bounded by a circle through P is $q\Omega_1/4\pi$, where Ω_1 is the solid angle subtended by the cap at the charge, and the flux due to the negative charge at B is $-q\Omega_2/4\pi$. The relation between solid angle subtended by a spherical cap centered about the axis and the angle θ measured from the axis is

$$\Omega = 2\pi(1 - \cos \theta) \tag{5}$$

Hence the total flux for this problem may be written

$$\psi = \frac{q}{4\pi}(\Omega_1 - \Omega_2) = \frac{q}{2}(\cos \theta_2 - \cos \theta_1) \tag{6}$$

To plot field lines, the flux function may again be maintained constant as the angles θ_1 and θ_2 are varied. Figure 2·12c shows the results when the flux per tube is selected as $q/4$. In comparing Figs. 2·12b and c, it should be remembered that the flux tubes in c are figures of revolution, whereas those in b are cylinders.

PROBLEMS

2·12a Plot the field from like charges q distance d apart (Prob. 2·06a) by making use of the flux function.

2·12b Plot the field of charges $2q$ and $-q$ distance d apart (Prob. 2·06b) by this method.

2·13 THE DIVERGENCE OF AN ELECTROSTATIC FIELD

Gauss's law was derived from Coulomb's law, which was determined by experiment on systems of finite size. Let us extend it to an infinitesimally small system. Equation 2·10(2) may be divided by the volume element ΔV, and the limit taken:

$$\lim_{\Delta V \to 0} \frac{\oint_S \bar{D} \cdot d\bar{S}}{\Delta V} = \lim_{\Delta V \to 0} \frac{\int_V \rho dV}{\Delta V} \tag{1}$$

The right side is, by inspection, merely ρ. The left side is the amount of electric flux per unit volume flowing out of an infinitesimal volume. This will be defined as the divergence of flux density, abbreviated div $\bar{D}$. Then

$$\text{div } \bar{D} = \rho \tag{2}$$

To make the picture clearer, consider the infinitesimal volume as a rectangular parallelepiped of dimensions Δx, Δy, Δz as shown in Fig. 2·13a. To compute the amount of flux leaving such a volume element as compared with that entering it, note that the flux passing through any face of the parallelepiped can differ from that which passes through the opposite face only if the flux density perpendicular to those faces varies from one face to the other. If the distance between the two faces is small, then to a first approximation the difference in any vector function on the two faces will simply be the rate of change of the function with distance times the distance between faces. According to the basis of calculus, this is exactly correct when we pass to the limit, since the higher order differentials are then zero.

If the vector at the center has components D_x, D_y, D_z,

$$D_x \bigg|_{x+(\Delta x/2)} = D_x + \frac{\Delta x}{2} \frac{\partial D_x}{\partial x}$$

$$D_x \bigg|_{x-(\Delta x/2)} = D_x - \frac{\Delta x}{2} \frac{\partial D_x}{\partial x}$$

(3)

The flux flowing out the front face is $\Delta y \, \Delta z \, D_x \big|_{x+(\Delta x/2)}$, and that flowing in the back face is $\Delta y \, \Delta z \, D_x' \big|_{x-(\Delta x/2)}$, leaving a net flow out of $\Delta x \, \Delta y \, \Delta z \, \dfrac{\partial D_x}{\partial x}$, and similarly for the y and z directions, so that net flux flow out of all the parallelepiped is

$$\Delta x \, \Delta y \, \Delta z \, \frac{\partial D_x}{\partial x} + \Delta x \, \Delta y \, \Delta z \, \frac{\partial D_y}{\partial y} + \Delta x \, \Delta y \, \Delta z \, \frac{\partial D_z}{\partial z}$$

By Gauss's law, this must be $\rho \, \Delta x \, \Delta y \, \Delta z$. So, in the limit,

$$\frac{\partial D_x}{\partial x} + \frac{\partial D_y}{\partial y} + \frac{\partial D_z}{\partial z} = \rho$$

(4)

An expression for div $\bar{D}$ in rectangular coordinates is obtained by comparing (2) and (4):

$$\text{div } \bar{D} = \frac{\partial D_x}{\partial x} + \frac{\partial D_y}{\partial y} + \frac{\partial D_z}{\partial z}$$

(5)

It will be convenient to define a vector operator ∇ (pronounced del) in rectangular coordinates as

$$\nabla = \bar{a}_x \frac{\partial}{\partial x} + \bar{a}_y \frac{\partial}{\partial y} + \bar{a}_z \frac{\partial}{\partial z}$$

(6)

Consider the expansion for the dot or scalar product, Eq. 2·11(1), and the definition of ∇ above. Then (5) indicates that div $\bar{D}$ can correctly be written as $\nabla \cdot \bar{D}$. It should be remembered that ∇ is not a true vector but rather a vector operator. We need not worry about its meaning except when it is operating on another quantity in a defined manner. The divergence represents the first of several of these operations to be defined:

$$\nabla \cdot \bar{D} = \frac{\partial D_x}{\partial x} + \frac{\partial D_y}{\partial y} + \frac{\partial D_z}{\partial z} \tag{7}$$

Finally $\nabla \cdot \bar{D} \equiv \operatorname{div} \bar{D} = \rho$ (8)

The divergence is made up of space derivatives of the field, so (8) is evidently a differential equation derived by generalizing from the previous laws for comparatively large systems. It will be so important that we should become accustomed to looking at it as an expression for

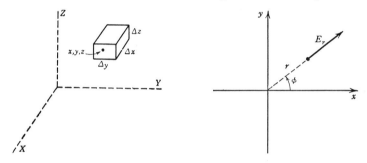

Fig. 2·13a.   Fig. 2·13b.

Gauss's law generalized to a point in space. The physical significance of the divergence must be clear. It is, as defined, a description of the manner in which a field varies at a point. It is the amount of flux per unit volume emerging from an infinitesimal volume at a point. With this picture in mind, (8) seems a logical extension of Gauss's law.

As an example of the way in which this equation shows the relation between the charge density at a point and the way in which the field varies about that point, consider the cylindrical electron beam, example B of Art. 2·09. Since we have for the present an expression for divergence only in rectangular coordinates, let us convert the radial electric field inside the beam, Eq. 2·09(2), into rectangular coordinate components. Referring to the coordinate system of Fig. 2·13b,

$$D_x = \epsilon E_r \cos \phi = \epsilon \left(\frac{r I_0}{2\pi \epsilon a^2 v_0} \right) \frac{x}{r}$$

$$D_y = \epsilon E_r \sin \phi = \epsilon \left(\frac{r I_0}{2\pi \epsilon a^2 v_0} \right) \frac{y}{r}$$

If the divergence of $\bar{D}$ is taken according to Eq. (7), the result is

$$\nabla \cdot \bar{D} = \frac{\partial D_x}{\partial x} + \frac{\partial D_y}{\partial y} = \frac{I_0}{\pi a^2 v_0}$$

This is exactly the charge density ρ, as it should be by (8). Similarly, the field components outside the beam may be found and the divergence computed. Here the result is zero, as it should be since the charge density is zero for each point outside the beam.

PROBLEMS

2·13a   Evaluate the divergence of $\bar{D}$ in the remaining examples of Art. 2·09, and in the results of Probs. 2·09a, b, and c, comparing results with the known charge densities for those problems.

2·13b   Evaluate $\nabla \cdot \bar{F}$, where $\bar{F} = \bar{a}_x x^3 + \bar{a}_y xyz + \bar{a}_z yz^2$.

2·14   DIVERGENCE THEOREM

If Eq. 2·13(2) is integrated over any volume,

$$\int_V \operatorname{div} \bar{D} \, dV = \int_V \rho \, dV \tag{1}$$

Replace the last term by its equivalent from Gauss's law, Eq. 2·10(2):

$$\int_V \operatorname{div} \bar{D} \, dV = \int_S \bar{D} \cdot d\bar{S} \tag{2}$$

Although this relation has been derived from a consideration of $\bar{D}$, a little thought will show that it is a direct consequence of the definition of divergence and so must hold for any vector field. For, if divergence of any vector is considered a density of outward flux flow from a point for that vector, then it seems that the total outward flux flow from a closed region must be obtained by integrating the divergence throughout the volume. If $\bar{F}$ is any vector,

$$\int_V \operatorname{div} \bar{F} \, dV = \int_V \nabla \cdot \bar{F} \, dV = \int_S \bar{F} \cdot d\bar{S} \tag{3}$$

This relation is known as the divergence theorem or Gauss's theorem (as distinguished from Gauss's law of Art. 2·08) and will be useful later in manipulating vector equations in order to arrive at their most useful forms. Note that the theorem is true for any continuous vector function of space, regardless of the physical significance of that vector.

PROBLEM

2·14   Given a vector $\bar{F} = \bar{a}_x x$. Evaluate $\oint_S \bar{F} \cdot \overline{dS}$ for S taken as the surface of a cube of sides $2a$ centered about the origin. Then evaluate the volume integral of $\nabla \cdot \bar{F}$ for this cube and show that the two results are equivalent, as they should be by the divergence theorem.

2·15   CONSERVATIVE PROPERTY OF ELECTRIC FIELDS

Before proceeding very far in attempts to build up pictures and quantitative relations for electrostatic fields, we should pause to look into the very important matter of energy.   The field may be checked with ideas of conservation of energy, to determine, for example, whether the energy of the electrostatic field is a function merely of its

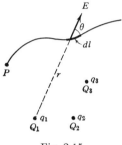

Fig. 2·15.

state at any given time, or whether it depends upon the manner in which that state occurred. We no doubt already feel certain that the energy of an electrostatic field depends only upon the amounts and positions of the charges, and not upon how they grew; the inverse square law tells us that this must be so.

The force on a small charge Δq moved from infinity to a point P in the vicinity of a system of charges: q_1 at Q_1, q_2 at Q_2, q_3 at Q_3, etc., may be calculated at any point along its path.

Consider, for example, the work integral arising from q_1.   The work is the integral of force component in the direction of the path, multiplied by differential path length (Fig. 2·15):

$$U_1 = - \int \frac{\Delta q q_1 \cos \theta \, dl}{4\pi\epsilon r^2}$$

But $dl \cos \theta$ is dr, so the integral is simply

$$U_1 = - \int_{\infty}^{PQ_1} \frac{\Delta q q_1 \, dr}{4\pi\epsilon r^2}$$

and similarly for contributions from other charges, so that the total work integral is

$$U = - \int_{\infty}^{PQ_1} \frac{\Delta q q_1}{4\pi\epsilon r^2} \, dr - \int_{\infty}^{PQ_2} \frac{\Delta q q_2}{4\pi\epsilon r^2} \, dr - \int_{\infty}^{PQ_3} \frac{\Delta q q_3}{4\pi\epsilon r^2} \, dr \ \cdots$$

Integrating,

$$U = \frac{(\Delta q) q_1}{4\pi\epsilon P Q_1} + \frac{(\Delta q) q_2}{4\pi\epsilon P Q_2} + \frac{(\Delta q) q_3}{4\pi\epsilon P Q_3} + \ \cdots \tag{1}$$

Equation (1) shows that the work done is only a function of final positions and not of the path of the charge.   This conclusion leads to another: if a charge is taken around any closed path, no net work is done.   Mathematically this is written

$$\oint \bar{E} \cdot \overline{dl} = 0 \tag{2}$$

This general integral signifies that the component of electric field in the direction of the path is to be multiplied by the element of distance along the path, and the sum taken by integration as one moves about the path. The circle through the integral sign signifies that a closed path is to be considered. As with the designation for a general surface or volume integral, the actual integration cannot be performed until there is a specification of a particular path and of the variation of $\bar{E}$ about that path.

In the study of magnetic fields and time-varying electric fields, we shall find corresponding line integrals which are not zero.

PROBLEM

2·15   A point charge q is located at the origin of a system of rectangular coordinates. Evaluate $\int \bar{E} \cdot \overline{dl}$ in the x-y plane first along the x axis from $x = 1$ to $x = 2$, and next along a rectangular path as follows: along a straight line from the point $(1,0)$ on the x axis to the point $(1,\frac{1}{2})$; along a straight line from $(1,\frac{1}{2})$ to $(2,\frac{1}{2})$; along a straight line from $(2,\frac{1}{2})$ to $(2,0)$.

2·16   ELECTROSTATIC POTENTIAL

To solve the differential field equations, it is often convenient to introduce mathematical tools known as potential functions, which may aid materially during the solution but which need not appear in the final result. It is never necessary to give these mathematical tools physical significance, though it often may be desirable. We are already quite familiar with the potential function of electrostatics, and in this case it may easily have more significance for us than the fields, which were themselves only defined concepts to describe the situation in a region containing charges.

The common potential function in electrostatics is a scalar quantity defined so that the difference in this function between two points P and Q is given by the integral

$$\Phi_P - \Phi_Q = - \int_Q^P \bar{E} \cdot \overline{dl} \tag{1}$$

The physical significance that may be attached to it is now apparent, for (1) is an expression for the work done on a unit charge in moving it from P to Q. The conclusion of the preceding article that the work in moving around any closed path is zero shows that the potential function defined is single valued; that is, corresponding to each point of the field there is only one value of potential, though the potential may, of course, vary from point to point.

Only a *difference* of potential has been defined. The potential of any point can be arbitrarily fixed, and then the potentials of all other points in the field found by application of the definition to give potential differences between all points and the base. This base is quite arbitrary since the potential differences alone have significance. For example, in certain cases it may be convenient to define the potential at infinity as zero and then find the corresponding potentials of all points in the field; for the determination of the field between two conductors, it will be more convenient to select the potential of one of these as zero.

If the potential at infinity is taken as zero, it is evident that the potential at the point P in the system of charges, Art. 2·15, is given by U of Eq. 2·15(1) divided by Δq, so

$$\Phi = \frac{q_1}{4\pi\epsilon PQ_1} + \frac{q_2}{4\pi\epsilon PQ_2} + \frac{q_3}{4\pi\epsilon PQ_3} + \cdots = \sum_{i=1}^{n} \frac{q_i}{4\pi\epsilon r_i} \qquad (2)$$

Generalizing to the case of continuously varying charge density,

$$\Phi = \int_V \frac{\rho \, dV}{4\pi\epsilon r} \qquad (3)$$

ρ is the charge density, and the integral signifies that a summation should be made similar to that of (2) but continuous over all space. There are, of course, arbitrary added constants if the potential at infinity is not taken as zero.

At once there is evidence of the usefulness of the potential tool, for Φ is obtained by simple scalar addition; it would have been necessary to perform corresponding vector additions to obtain fields directly. Since the fields can be obtained simply from the potential, the work of obtaining electric fields from charges is simplified. We shall show in the next article how this may be done.

As an example of the relations between potential and electric field, consider first the problem of the line charge used as an example in Art. 2·09, with electric field given by Eq. 2·09(1). By (1) we integrate this from some radius r_0 chosen as the reference of zero potential to radius r:

$$\Phi = -\int_{r_0}^{r} E_r \, dr = -\int_{r_0}^{r} \frac{q_l \, dr}{2\pi\epsilon r} = -\frac{q_l}{2\pi\epsilon} \ln\left(\frac{r}{r_0}\right) \qquad (4)$$

Or this expression for potential about a line charge may be written

$$\Phi = -\frac{q_l}{2\pi\epsilon} \ln r + C \qquad (5)$$

Note that it is not desirable to select infinity as the reference of zero potential for the line charge, for then by (4) the potential at any finite point would be infinite.

In a similar manner, the potential difference between the coaxial cylinders of Fig. 2·09b may be found:

$$\Phi_a - \Phi_b = - \int_b^a \frac{q_l \, dr}{2\pi\epsilon r} = \frac{q_l}{2\pi\epsilon} \ln \left(\frac{b}{a} \right)$$

The electrostatic capacitance of a two-conductor capacitor is defined as the charge on one conductor divided by the potential difference. So the capacitance per unit length for the coaxial cylindrical example is

$$C = \frac{q_l}{\Phi_a - \Phi_b} = \frac{2\pi\epsilon}{\ln \, (b/a)} \text{ farads/meter} \tag{6}$$

PROBLEMS

2·16a   Derive the expression for electrostatic capacitance of a spherical condenser formed of concentric spherical conductors of radii a and b ($a < b$), with dielectric ϵ between the spheres.

2·16b   Find the expression for electrostatic capacitance of the spherical condenser with two dielectrics used as an example in Art. 2·09.

2·16c   A circular insulating disk of radius a is charged with a uniform surface density of charge ρ_s coulombs/meter^2. Find an expression for electrostatic potential Φ at a point on the axis distance z from the disk.

2·16d   A charge of surface density ρ_s is spread uniformly over the surface of a sphere of radius a. Find the potential for $r < a$ and for $r > a$ by integrating contributions from the differential elements of charge. Check the results by making use of Gauss's law and the symmetry of the problem.

2·16e   Check the result of (4) or (5) for the potential about a line charge by integrating contributions from the differential elements of charge. Note that the problem is one of handling properly the infinite limits.

2·17 GRADIENT

If the definition of potential difference is applied to two points a distance dl apart,

$$d\Phi = -\bar{E} \cdot \overline{dl} \tag{1}$$

$\overline{dl}$ may be written in terms of its components and the defined unit vectors (Art. 2·11):

$$\overline{dl} = dx \, \bar{a}_x + dy \, \bar{a}_y + dz \, \bar{a}_z \tag{2}$$

Expand the dot product according to Eq. 2·11(1)

$$d\Phi = -(E_x \, dx + E_y \, dy + E_z \, dz)$$

Since Φ is a function of x, y; and z, the total derivative may also be written

$$d\Phi = \frac{\partial \Phi}{\partial x} dx + \frac{\partial \Phi}{\partial y} dy + \frac{\partial \Phi}{\partial z} dz$$

From a comparison of the two expressions,

$$E_x = -\frac{\partial \Phi}{\partial x}, \quad \text{etc.} \tag{3}$$

$$\bar{E} = -\left(\bar{a}_x \frac{\partial \Phi}{\partial x} + \bar{a}_y \frac{\partial \Phi}{\partial y} + \bar{a}_z \frac{\partial \Phi}{\partial z} \right) \tag{4}$$

or $\qquad\qquad \bar{E} = -\text{grad } \Phi \tag{5}$

where grad Φ, an abbreviation of the gradient of Φ, is a vector showing the direction and magnitude of the maximum space variation in the scalar function Φ, at any point in space. It is the maximum variation that is represented because the gradient is the vector sum of the variations in all three directions. That is, substituting back in (1),

$$d\Phi = (\text{grad } \Phi) \cdot \overline{dl}$$

Thus the change in Φ is given by the scalar product of the gradient and the vector $\overline{dl}$, so that, for a given element of length dl, the maximum value of $d\Phi$ will be obtained when that element is oriented to coincide with the direction of the gradient vector.

The vector operator ∇ was defined by Eq. 2·13(6). Then grad Φ may be written as $\nabla\Phi$ if the operation is interpreted

$$\nabla\Phi = \bar{a}_x \frac{\partial \Phi}{\partial x} + \bar{a}_y \frac{\partial \Phi}{\partial y} + \bar{a}_z \frac{\partial \Phi}{\partial z} \tag{6}$$

and $\qquad\qquad \bar{E} = -\text{grad } \Phi \equiv -\nabla\Phi \tag{7}$

PROBLEMS

2·17a Given a scalar function $M = \sin \alpha x \cos \beta y \sinh \gamma z$; find the gradient of M.

2·17b For two point charges q and $-q$ at $(d/2,0,0)$ and $(-d/2,0,0)$, respectively, find the potential for any point (x,y,z) and from this derive the electric field. Check the result by adding vectorially the electric field from the individual charges.

2·17c For two line charges q_l and $-q_l$ at $(d/2,0)$ and $(-d/2,0)$, respectively, find the potential for any point (x,y) and from this derive the electric field.

2·17d Find the electric field along the axis for Prob. 2·16c.

2·17e Utilize the rectangular coordinate form to prove the vector equivalences

$$\nabla(\psi\Phi) = \psi\nabla\Phi + \Phi\nabla\psi$$

$$\nabla \cdot (\psi\bar{A}) = \psi\nabla \cdot \bar{A} + \bar{A} \cdot \nabla\psi$$

where ψ and Φ are any scalar functions, $\bar{A}$ any vector function of space.

2·18 EQUIPOTENTIALS

All points of a field having the same potential may be thought of as connected by equipotential surfaces. The distribution and spacing of these equipotential surfaces can be used to describe the field. The electric field vector must be perpendicular to these surfaces at every point, for if there were the slightest component tangential to the surface, say E_t, then two points $d\xi$ apart would have a potential difference $E_t\,d\xi$ which would violate the condition for an equipotential surface. Since the flux tubes were shown in Art. 2·12 to have the same direction as the field lines, these also are at right angles to the equipotential surfaces.

If the potential were to vary in one direction only, say x, as in a potential difference applied between two infinite parallel conducting planes perpendicular to the x axis, the electric field, or negative gradient of potential, would be entirely in the x direction. The equipotential surfaces would be perpendicular to the x axis, or parallel to the conducting planes, as would be expected from symmetry. The equipotential surfaces about a point charge would be spheres centered on the charge, and the equipotentials about a line charge or between coaxial cylinders would be cylindrical surfaces of constant radius from the axis. In the general case, potential may be a function of all coordinates, the gradient will have components in all three component directions, and the equipotential surfaces will be more complex than those of the above simple examples.

PROBLEM

2·18 Show that the equipotential surfaces for the two line charges of Prob. 2·17c are cylinders whose traces in the x-y plane are circles.

2·19 CONDUCTING BOUNDARIES IN ELECTROSTATICS

If expressions for the field in differential equation form are to be obtained, it is important that boundary conditions for application to their solutions be well understood. Conducting metal surfaces will often form these boundaries.

Conductors are defined as those materials which readily permit a current flow, or motion of charges. So, if charges are placed on or in conductors, they will move about as long as there is the slightest electric field producing a force upon them. After they have reached equilibrium, the necessary condition for a static field to exist, all the electric field inside the conductor or tangential to its surface must have disappeared. If there were charges in the body, Gauss's law would require an electric field in the vicinity of these charges, so that this is an impossible condition for the static case. All the charge in electrostatics must then reside on the surface and must be distributed so that the component of electric field intensity tangential to the surface and the total electric field intensity inside the material surface of the conductor are zero.

Since the tangential component of electric field is zero along the conducting surface, it follows that the conducting surface must be an equipotential surface. Moreover, since the field is zero inside the conductor, the entire conducting body will be at a constant potential in electrostatics.

To obtain the charge induced on the conducting surface by the field ending on it, we may make use of Gauss's law. For, since all the electric flux lines must end on the surface of the conductor, they must end on a surface distribution of charge there, with the charge per unit area equal to the flux per unit area at each point of the surface. To make this more convincing, consider an imaginary infinitesimal pillbox located at the boundary, as sketched in Fig. 2·19. There can be no flux through the bottom surface embedded in the conductor, since field is zero there. There will also be zero flux flow through the sides marked h, since there is no component of electric field tangential to the conducting surface. This leaves the total flux to pass through the surface dS just outside the conductor, so that this flux is $D_n\, dS$, where D_n represents the component of electric flux density normal to the conducting surface. By Gauss's law this flux must be equal to the charge enclosed, which may be written $\rho_s\, dS$, where ρ_s is defined as the charge per unit area in coulombs per square meter:

$$\rho_s\, dS = D_n\, dS$$

or $$D_n = \epsilon E_n = \rho_s \tag{1}$$

As a simple example showing the relation between the field ending on a conductor and the charge which it induces there, let us find the charge induced on the anode of an idealized parallel-plane space-charge-limited diode if we take as given the fact that the potential varies as the $\frac{4}{3}$ power of distance across the diode:

$$\Phi = V_0 \left(\frac{x}{d}\right)^{4/3} \tag{2}$$

In the above, x is the distance from the cathode, d is the anode-cathode spacing, and V_0 is the anode potential with respect to the cathode. To find the electric field, we must take the gradient of Φ, which has an x component only:

$$E_x = -\frac{\partial \Phi}{\partial x} = -\frac{4}{3} V_0 \frac{x^{1/3}}{d^{4/3}} \tag{3}$$

The (outward) normal electric field at the anode is $-E_x$ evaluated at $x = d$, so the charge per unit area there is

$$\rho_s = -\epsilon_0 E_x \Big|_{x=d} = \frac{4\epsilon_0}{3} \frac{V_0}{d} \text{ coulombs/meter}^2 \qquad (4)$$

The dielectric constant has been written ϵ_0, since the dielectric in the ideal diode is assumed to be vacuum.

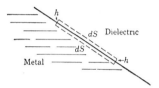

Fig. 2·19   Cross section showing surface separating a dielectric and a conductor.

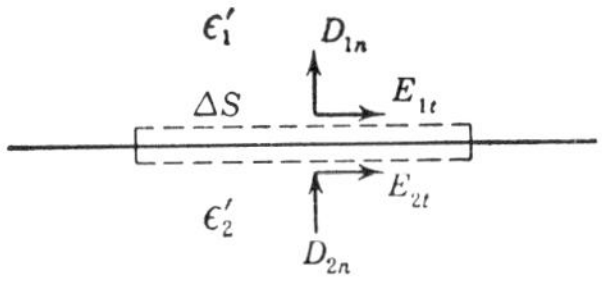

Fig. 2·20   Cross section showing surface separating two dielectrics.

2·20 DIELECTRIC BOUNDARIES IN ELECTROSTATICS

The charge-free boundary between two dielectrics may first be investigated by Gauss's law, as was done for the conducting boundary in Art. 2·19.   An imaginary pillbox as indicated in Fig. 2·20 contains no charge, so the flux flowing in on one side must equal that flowing out on the other.   If subscript n denotes components normal to the element of surface ΔS,

$$D_{n1} \Delta S = D_{n2} \Delta S$$

or $\qquad\qquad\qquad D_{n1} = D_{n2} \qquad\qquad\qquad (1)$

A second relation may be found by taking a line integral about a closed path of length Δl on one side of the boundary, returning on the other side.   By Eq. 2·15(2), any closed line integral of electric field must be zero:

$$\oint \bar{E} \cdot \overline{dl} = E_{t1} \Delta l - E_{t2} \Delta l = 0$$

or $\qquad\qquad\qquad E_{t1} = E_{t2} \qquad\qquad\qquad (2)$

The subscript t denotes components tangential to the surface.

Thus normal components of electric flux density and tangential components of electric field are continuous across a charge-free boundary between two dielectrics.   It is also true that the electrostatic potential is continuous across such a boundary:

$$\Phi_1 = \Phi_2 \qquad\qquad\qquad (3)$$

However, condition (3) is not independent of (2), but may be derived from (2) by integrating tangential electric field along the boundary, for the two sides of the boundary. Conditions (1) and either (2) or (3) are then the required continuity conditions to be applied to problems with dielectric discontinuities. Note that, as a consequence of (1) and (2), the electric field or flux lines will change direction in crossing the boundary between dielectrics of different dielectric constant.

PROBLEM

2·20 If the field vector makes an angle θ with the normal in region 1 of the above example, what angle does it have in region 2?

2·21 THE USE OF IMAGES

A. Point Image in a Plane.   The method of images is useful when it is desired to find the field arising from point charges or line charges

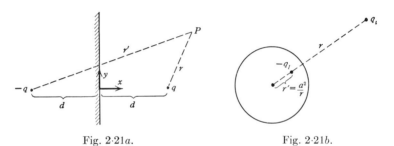

Fig. 2·21a.   Fig. 2·21b.

in the vicinity of conductors of certain simple shapes. The most simple case is that of a point charge near a grounded conducting plane (Fig. 2·21a). Boundary conditions require that the potential along the plane be zero. The requirement is met if in place of the conducting plane an equal and opposite image charge is placed at $x = -d$. Potential at any point P is then given by

$$\Phi = \frac{1}{4\pi\epsilon}\left(\frac{q}{r} - \frac{q}{r'}\right)$$

$$= \frac{q}{4\pi\epsilon}\{[(x - d)^2 + y^2 + z^2]^{-\frac{1}{2}} - [(x + d)^2 + y^2 + z^2]^{-\frac{1}{2}}\} \quad (1)$$

This reduces to the required zero potential along the plane $x = 0$, so that (1) gives the potential for any point to the right of the plane. The expression of course does not apply for $x < 0$, for inside the conductor the potential must be everywhere zero.

If the plane is at a potential other than zero, the value of this constant potential is simply added to (1) to give the expression for potential at any point for $x > 0$.

B. Image of a Line Charge in a Plane.   If there is a line charge of strength q_l coulombs per meter parallel to a conducting plane and distance d from it, one proceeds as above, placing an image line charge of strength $-q_l$ at $x = -d$.   The potential at any point $x > 0$ is then

$$\Phi = -\frac{q_l}{2\pi\epsilon}\ln\left(\frac{r}{r'}\right) = \frac{q_l}{4\pi\epsilon}\ln\left[\frac{(x+d)^2 + y^2 + z^2}{(x-d)^2 + y^2 + z^2}\right] \tag{2}$$

C. Image of a Line Charge in a Cylinder.   For a line charge of strength q_l parallel to the axis of a conducting circular cylinder, and at radius r from the axis, the image line charge of strength $-q_l$ is placed

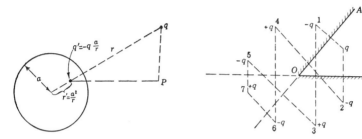

Fig. 2·21c   Image of a point charge   Fig. 2·21d   Multiple images in inter-
        in a conducting sphere.   secting planes.

at radius $r' = a^2/r$, where a is the radius of the cylinder (Fig. 2·21b). The combination of the two line charges can be shown to produce a constant potential along the given cylinder of radius a.   Thus the potential for any point outside the cylinder may be computed from the original line charge and its image.   If the original line charge is within a hollow cylinder of radius a, the rule for finding the image is the same, and potential for any point inside may be computed from the two line charges.

D. Image of a Point Charge in a Sphere.   For a point charge q placed distance r from the center of a conducting sphere of radius a, the image is a point charge of value $(-qa/r)$ placed at a distance (a^2/r) from the center (Fig. 2·21c).   This combination gives the required zero potential along the spherical surface of radius a, and may be used to compute potential at any point P outside of radius a.   (Or, if the original charge is inside, the image is outside, and the pair may be used to compute potential inside.)

E. Multiple Imagings.   For a charge in the vicinity of the intersection of two conducting planes, as q in the region of AOB of Fig.

2·21d, there might be a temptation to use only one image in each plane, as 1 and 2 of Fig. 2·21d. Although $+q$ at Q and $-q$ at 1 alone would give constant potential as required along OA, and $+q$ at Q and $-q$ at 2 alone would give constant potential along OB, the three charges together would give constant potential along neither OA nor OB. It is necessary to image these images in turn, repeating until further images coincide, or until all further images are too far distant from the region to influence potential. It is possible to satisfy exactly the required conditions with a finite number of images only if the angle AOB is an exact submultiple of 360°, as in the 45° case illustrated by Fig. 2·21d.

PROBLEMS

2·21a   Prove that the line charge and its image as described for a conducting cylinder of radius a will give constant potential along the cylinder of radius a.

2·21b   Prove that the point charge and its image as described for the spherical conductor gives zero potential along the sphere of radius a.

2·21c   A circularly cylindrical electron beam of radius a and uniform charge density ρ passes near a conducting plane which is parallel to the axis of the beam and distance s from it. Find the electric field acting to disperse the beam for the edge near the plane and for the edge farthest from the plane.

2·21d   For a point charge q lying in a dielectric ϵ_1 distance $x = d$ from the plane boundary between ϵ_1 and a second dielectric ϵ_2, an image charge $q(\epsilon_1 - \epsilon_2)/(\epsilon_1 + \epsilon_2)$ placed at $x = -d$ in a homogeneous dielectric of constant ϵ_1 may be used to compute the potential for any point $x > 0$. To find the potential for a point $x < 0$, a single charge of value $2q\epsilon_2/(\epsilon_1 + \epsilon_2)$ is placed at the position of q in a homogeneous dielectric of constant ϵ_2. Show that these images satisfy the required continuity relations at a dielectric boundary.

2·21e   Find and plot the surface charge density induced on the conducting plane as a function of y when the point charge q is at $x = d$. Repeat for a line charge at $x = d$.

2·22   LAPLACE'S AND POISSON'S EQUATIONS

For many problems that do not have the simple geometrical configurations of the examples used up to now, it is most convenient to begin the solution from differential equations. In Art. 2·13 a differential equation relating the electric flux density $\bar{D}$ to charge density ρ was derived. It will often be more convenient to work directly with potentials instead of fields, since the specified boundary conditions on the problem will be more often given in terms of potentials. If the dielectric constant ϵ is constant throughout the region, the substitution of $\bar{E}$ from Eq. 2·17(7) in Eq. 2·13(2) yields

$$\text{div (grad } \Phi) \equiv \nabla \cdot \nabla \Phi = -\frac{\rho}{\epsilon}$$

But, from the equations for divergence and gradient in rectangular coordinates [Eqs. 2·13(7) and 2·17(6)],

$$\nabla \cdot \nabla \Phi = \frac{\partial^2 \Phi}{\partial x^2} + \frac{\partial^2 \Phi}{\partial y^2} + \frac{\partial^2 \Phi}{\partial z^2} \tag{1}$$

so

$$\frac{\partial^2 \Phi}{\partial x^2} + \frac{\partial^2 \Phi}{\partial y^2} + \frac{\partial^2 \Phi}{\partial z^2} = -\frac{\rho}{\epsilon} \tag{2}$$

This is a differential equation relating potential variation at any point to the charge density at that point. It is known as Poisson's equation and is often written

$$\nabla^2 \Phi = -\frac{\rho}{\epsilon} \tag{3}$$

where $\nabla^2 \Phi$ (del-squared of Φ) is known as the Laplacian of Φ.

$$\nabla^2 \Phi \equiv \nabla \cdot \nabla \Phi \equiv \text{div (grad } \Phi) \tag{4}$$

In the special case of a charge-free region, Poisson's equation reduces to

$$\frac{\partial^2 \Phi}{\partial x^2} + \frac{\partial^2 \Phi}{\partial y^2} + \frac{\partial^2 \Phi}{\partial z^2} = 0$$

or

$$\nabla^2 \Phi = 0 \tag{5}$$

which is known as Laplace's equation.

Any number of possible configurations of potential surfaces will satisfy the requirements of (3) and (5). All are called solutions to these equations. It is necessary to know the conditions existing around the boundary of the region in order to select the particular solution which applies to a given problem. It can be shown mathematically that, once ρ is given at every point in a region and Φ is given at every point on the surface surrounding the region, only one potential distribution is possible.

Equations exactly similar in form to (3) and (5) are found in many branches of physics. In fact, we shall discover later that they are true not only when the function is a static potential; for example, the function may be the static field strength vectors or certain of their components. Laplace's and Poisson's equations are of first importance in getting answers to all problems in which static electric and magnetic effects are involved. The ability to choose solutions of these equations is fundamental in arriving at the final solutions to the common problems discussed in Art. 2·02. For that reason the next chapter will be devoted almost entirely to a discussion of the techniques of building up solutions to these equations to fit boundary conditions that are likely to occur in practical problems.

PROBLEMS

2·22a   Find the gradient and Laplacian of a scalar field varying as $1/r$ in two dimensions and in three dimensions.

2·22b   Find the electric field and charge density as functions of x, y, and z if potential is expressed as

$$\Phi = C \sin \alpha x \sin \beta y \, e^{\gamma z} \qquad \gamma = \sqrt{\alpha^2 + \beta^2}$$

2·22c   Find the electric field and charge density as a function of x for a space-charge-limited, parallel-plane diode with potential variation given by Eq. 2.19(2).

2·23   ENERGY OF AN ELECTROSTATIC SYSTEM

The work required to move a charge in the vicinity of a system of charges was discussed in the study of the electrostatic potential. The work done must appear as energy stored in the system, and consequently the potential energy of a system of charges may be computed from the amount and position of the charges. If a charge q' is brought from infinity to a point at distance r from charge q, the work done was shown to be

$$U_E = \frac{qq'}{4\pi\epsilon r}$$

Then, for a large number of charges,

$$U_E = \frac{1}{2} \sum_m \sum_n \frac{q_n q_m}{4\pi\epsilon r_{nm}} \tag{1}$$

The factor $\frac{1}{2}$ appears since n and m are each summed over all the particles, and by this convention each contribution of energy is included twice.

In (1) it is apparent that the term for which $q_n = q_m$ will cause difficulty. It is the energy of an isolated point charge, and the value of r_{nm} is zero. This says that the energy required to locate any finite amount of charge at a point is infinite. Such a conclusion is not incorrect; rather, it is an expected result since to build up charge at a point involves infinite repelling forces between the additional charge being introduced and the amount already there. Actually (and, in fact, almost for this very reason) we do not have charges concentrated at points; instead, there always is a certain amount of space distribution. Recognition of this suggests that an expression for energy more useful than (1) may be obtained.

If it is noted from Eq. 2·16(2) that the potential at the mth charge is

$$\Phi_m = \sum_n \frac{q_n}{4\pi\epsilon r_{nm}}$$

then (1) may be written

$$U_E = \tfrac{1}{2} \sum_n \Phi_m q_m \tag{2}$$

Or, extending to a system with continuously varying charge density ρ per unit volume,

$$U_E = \tfrac{1}{2} \int_V \rho\Phi \, dV \tag{3}$$

The charge density ρ may be replaced by the divergence of $\bar{D}$ by Eq. 2·13(8):

$$U_E = \frac{1}{2} \int_V (\nabla \cdot \bar{D})\Phi \, dV$$

Using the vector equivalence of Prob. 2·17e (and Art. 2·39),

$$U_E = \frac{1}{2} \int_V \nabla \cdot (\Phi\bar{D}) \, dV - \frac{1}{2} \int_V \bar{D} \cdot (\nabla\Phi) \, dV$$

The first volume integral may be replaced by the surface integral of $\Phi\bar{D}$ over the closed surface surrounding the region, by the divergence theorem (Art. 2·14). But, if the region is to contain all fields, the surface should be taken at infinity. Since Φ dies off as $1/r$ at infinity, D as $1/r^2$, and area only increases as r^2, this surface integral approaches zero as the surface approaches infinity.

$$\int_V \nabla \cdot (\Phi\bar{D}) \, dV = \oint_{S_\infty} \Phi\bar{D} \cdot \overline{dS} = 0$$

Then there remains

$$U_E = -\frac{1}{2} \int_V \bar{D} \cdot (\nabla\Phi) \, dV = \frac{1}{2} \int_V \bar{D} \cdot \bar{E} \, dV \tag{4}$$

This result seems to say that the energy is actually in the electric field, each element of volume dV appearing to contain the amount of energy

$$dU_E = \frac{1}{2} \bar{D} \cdot \bar{E} \, dV \tag{5}$$

The right answer is obtained if this "energy density" picture is used. Actually, we know only that the total energy stored in the system will be correctly computed by the total integral of (4).

It is interesting to check these results against a case with which we are already familiar. Consider a parallel plate condenser of capacity C and a voltage between plates of V. The energy is known to be $\frac{1}{2}CV^2$, which is commonly obtained by integrating the product of instantaneous current and instantaneous voltage over the time of charging. The result may also be obtained by integrating the energy distribution in the field throughout the volume between plates according to (4). For plates of area A closely spaced so that the end effects may be neglected, the magnitude of field at every point in the dielectric is $E = V/d$ (d = distance between plates).

Hence

$$D = \frac{\epsilon V}{d}$$

$$\text{Stored energy } = \frac{1}{2} A d \left(\frac{\epsilon V}{d}\right) \left(\frac{V}{d}\right)$$

$$= \frac{1}{2} \left(\frac{\epsilon A}{d}\right) V^2 = \frac{1}{2} C V^2 \tag{6}$$

PROBLEMS

2·23a For a given potential difference V_0 between conductors of a coaxial condenser, evaluate the stored energy in the electrostatic field per unit length. By equating this to $\frac{1}{2}CV^2$, evaluate the capacitance per unit length.

2·23b Evaluate the total energy stored in the space-charge-limited, parallel-plane diode of Prob. 2.22c when there is potential V_0 between the plates. Is there any meaning in equating this to $\frac{1}{2}CV^2$?

Static Magnetic Fields

2·24   THE CONCEPT OF A MAGNETIC FIELD

In the first part of this chapter the concept of the electric field has been developed starting from the experimental observation that a charge brought into the vicinity of other charges experiences a force. It can also be experimentally determined that a current element (e.g., a small loop carrying current) will be acted on by a force if it is brought in the vicinity of another current or system of currents. The region in which such forces exist is spoken of as a region of magnetic field. This concept may appear to exclude the well-known magnetic effects arising from permanent magnets, but these effects may be included conceptually if we think of them as arising from groups of atomic currents in the ferromagnetic material. Although it may not be convenient to make specific calculations for permanent magnets from the laws developed for current paths of finite size, there will be a real advantage in developing the theory of magnetic fields from the concept that it is an effect due to current flow.

The force arising from two current elements depends upon the magnitude of the currents, the medium, and the distance between currents in a similar manner to the force between electric charges already studied. However, current has direction and so is a vector. The force between the two currents will be more complex than that for charges. It is consequently convenient to proceed by first defining the quantity which we will call the magnetic field, and then give in another section the law (Ampère's) which describes how currents contribute to that magnetic field. A vector field quantity $\bar{B}$, usually known as the magnetic flux density, is defined in terms of the force $\overline{df}$ produced on a small current element of length $\overline{dl}$ carrying current I, such that

$$df = I \, dl \, B \sin \theta \tag{1}$$

θ is the angle between $\overline{dl}$ and $\bar{B}$. The direction relations of the vectors are so defined that the vector force $\overline{df}$ is along a perpendicular to the plane containing $\overline{dl}$ and $\bar{B}$, and has the sense determined by the advance of a right-hand screw if $\overline{dl}$ is rotated into $\bar{B}$ through the smaller angle. It is convenient to define a vector product which expresses this information in a more compact manner, and which will be useful in a manner similar to the dot or scalar product defined early in the chapter. If we define the vector product of two vectors (denoted by a cross) as a vector having a magnitude equal to the product of the magnitudes of the two vectors and the sine of the angle between them, a direction perpendicular to the plane containing the two vectors, and a sense given by the advance of a right-hand screw if the first is rotated into the second through the smaller angle, (1) may be written

$$\overline{df} = I \, \overline{dl} \times \bar{B} \tag{2}$$

The quantity which is known as the magnetic field vector or magnetic field intensity is denoted $\bar{H}$ and is related to the vector $\bar{B}$ defined by the force law (2) through a constant of the medium known as the permeability, μ.

$$\bar{H} = \frac{\bar{B}}{\mu} \tag{3}$$

The units in the equations of this article will be discussed later (Art. 2·27).

2·25   VECTOR OR CROSS PRODUCT OF VECTORS

The relation between vectors met in the definition of the force law of the last article will be met in many other types of situations, and has consequently been denoted by the convenient notation of the cross product.   In terms of two vectors $\bar{A}$ and $\bar{B}$ (Fig. 2·25a), the vector product or cross product $\bar{C} = \bar{A} \times \bar{B}$ is defined as a vector having a magnitude equal to the product of one by the normal component of the other,

$$C = AB \sin \theta \qquad (1)$$

The direction of $\bar{C}$ lies along the perpendicular to the plane containing $\bar{A}$ and $\bar{B}$, and the sense is that of a right-hand screw's sense of advance

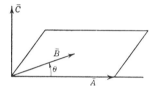

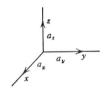

Fig.   2·25a   Demonstration   of   cross   Fig. 2·25b.
product, $\bar{C} = \bar{A} \times \bar{B}$.

if $\bar{A}$ is rotated into $\bar{B}$ through the smaller angle.   From the sense definition, it is clear that

$$\bar{B} \times \bar{A} = -\bar{A} \times \bar{B} \qquad (2)$$

This vector product may be expressed in terms of the rectangular coordinate components as was the scalar product of Art. 2·11.   For, if $\bar{A}$ and $\bar{B}$ are given in terms of the unit vectors and the components along the three coordinate axes,

$$\bar{A} \times \bar{B} = (A_x\bar{a}_x + A_y\bar{a}_y + A_z\bar{a}_z) \times (B_x\bar{a}_x + B_y\bar{a}_y + B_z\bar{a}_z) \qquad (3)$$

From the definition of the vector product and a consideration of the coordinate system, Fig. 2·25b, it should be evident that

$$\bar{a}_x \times \bar{a}_y = \bar{a}_z = -\bar{a}_y \times \bar{a}_x$$

$$\bar{a}_y \times \bar{a}_z = \bar{a}_x = -\bar{a}_z \times \bar{a}_y$$

$$\bar{a}_z \times \bar{a}_x = \bar{a}_y = -\bar{a}_x \times \bar{a}_z$$

$$\bar{a}_x \times \bar{a}_x = 0 = \bar{a}_y \times \bar{a}_y = \bar{a}_z \times \bar{a}_z$$

Notice that coordinates were purposely selected so that the sign of the unit vectors resulting from the product of one unit vector and the succeeding unit vector, in the order xyz, is positive. Such coordinate systems, known as right-handed systems, should always be selected to prevent confusion in signs. To check for a right-handed system, rotate one axis into the succeeding axis in order of writing; a right-hand screw given that motion should then progress in the positive direction along the third axis. Then

$$\bar{A} \times \bar{B} = \bar{a}_x(A_yB_z - A_zB_y) + \bar{a}_y(A_zB_x - A_xB_z) + \bar{a}_z(A_xB_y - A_yB_x) \tag{4}$$

Note that this quantity may also be written as the determinant:

$$\bar{A} \times \bar{B} = \begin{vmatrix} \bar{a}_x & \bar{a}_y & \bar{a}_z \\ A_x & A_y & A_z \\ B_x & B_y & B_z \end{vmatrix} \tag{5}$$

PROBLEMS

2·25a Write the torque about an axis in terms of vector notation (suitably defining a vector to represent torque) when a force $\bar{F}$ acts at distance $\bar{r}$ from the axis.

2·25b Show the following:

$$\bar{A} \times (\bar{B} + \bar{C}) = \bar{A} \times \bar{B} + \bar{A} \times \bar{C}$$

$$\bar{A} \times (\bar{B} \times \bar{C}) = \bar{B}(\bar{A} \cdot \bar{C}) - \bar{C}(\bar{A} \cdot \bar{B})$$

$$\bar{A} \cdot (\bar{B} \times \bar{C}) = \bar{B} \cdot (\bar{C} \times \bar{A}) = \bar{C} \cdot (\bar{A} \times \bar{B})$$

2·26 AMPÈRE'S LAW; FIELD ON THE AXIS OF A CIRCULAR LOOP

Ampère's law, deduced experimentally from a series of ingenious experiments,[2] describes how the magnetic field vector defined in Art. 2·24 is calculated from a system of direct currents. The contribution to magnitude of magnetic field from a small element dl' of the current path carrying current I' is

$$dH = \frac{I'\, dl'\, \sin \phi}{4\pi r^2}$$

where r is the distance from the current element to the point P at which field is to be computed (Fig. 2·26a), and ϕ is the angle between $\overline{dl'}$ and the radius vector from $\overline{dl'}$ to P. The direction of $\overline{dH}$ is perpendicular to the plane containing $\overline{dl'}$ and the radius vector, and the sense is determined by the sense of advance of a right-hand screw if $\overline{dl'}$ is rotated into the radius vector. It is immediately recognized that the

[2] See Maxwell, *Electricity and Magnetism*, Oxford, 3rd ed., 1892, Part II, Chapter 2.

cross product defined in the last article may be used for writing this law:

$$\overline{dH} = \frac{I' \, \overline{dl'} \times \bar{a}_r}{4\pi r^2} \tag{1}$$

$\bar{a}_r$ is a unit vector pointing in the direction of the radius from $\overline{dl'}$ to P. To obtain the total magnetic field, expression (1) is integrated over all the current path:

$$\bar{H} = \int \frac{I' \, \overline{dl'} \times \bar{a}_r}{4\pi r^2} \tag{2}$$

As an example of the application of the law, the magnetic field will be computed for a point on the axis of a circular loop of wire carrying

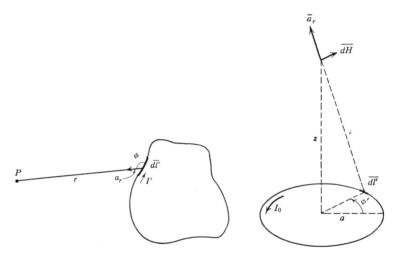

Fig. 2·26a.   Fig. 2·26b   Magnetic field from
                               element of a circular current loop.

d-c current I_0 (Fig. 2·26b). The element $\overline{dl'}$ has magnitude $ad\phi'$ and is always perpendicular to the radius $\bar{r}$. Hence the contribution to dH from an element is

$$dH = \frac{I_0 a \, d\phi'}{4\pi(a^2 + z^2)} \tag{3}$$

As one integrates about the loop, the direction of $\bar{a}_r$ changes, and so the direction of $\overline{dH}$ changes, generating a conical surface as one moves about the loop. The radial components of the various contributions all cancel, and the axial components add directly:

$$dH_z = dH \sin \theta = \frac{dH a}{(a^2 + z^2)^{1/2}}$$

So
$$H_z = \frac{I_0 a^2}{2(a^2 + z^2)^{3/2}} \tag{4}$$

Note that for a point at the center of the loop, $z = 0$,

$$H_z \Big|_{z=0} = \frac{I_0}{2a} \tag{5}$$

Although the matter of units has not been mentioned in this article, the forms used are suitable for the rational mks system, which will be discussed in detail for magnetic quantities in the next article.

PROBLEMS

2·26a   Find from Ampère's law the magnetic field at a point distance r from an infinite straight wire carrying d-c current I_0.

2·26b   D-c current I_0 flows in a square loop of wire having sides $2a$.   Find the magnetic field on the axis at a point z from the plane of the loop.

2·27   UNITS FOR MAGNETIC FIELD QUANTITIES

In the rational mks system of units, current is chosen in the practical units of amperes, and distance is of course in meters.   Hence magnetic field, which by Eq. 2·26(2) [or more clearly from the example, Eq. 2·26(5)] is seen to have the dimensions of a current divided by length, has dimensions of amperes per meter in this system.

The magnetic flux density B defined in Art. 2·24 is chosen in the mks system to have units of webers per square meter, where a magnetic flux of one weber is 10^8 maxwells or "lines."   This choice is made for convenience in the study of time-varying fields, for a rate of change of magnetic flux of one weber per second will generate an emf of one volt.   That is, a weber may also be written as a volt-second, and B could be said to have dimensions of volt-seconds per square meter.

With the units of B and H chosen by separate considerations, the permeability μ, defined as the ratio of B to H, will have definite units and a value other than unity for free space.   As for the units,

$$\mu = \frac{B}{H} = \frac{\text{volt sec meter}^{-2}}{\text{amp meter}^{-1}} = \frac{\text{volt sec}}{\text{amp meter}} = \frac{\text{henry}}{\text{meter}}$$

The above equivalence utilized between a henry and a volt-second per ampere may be checked from the well-known circuit equation for an inductance, $V = L\, dI/dt$. The value of μ for free space, denoted μ_0, may be shown to be

$$\mu_0 = 4\pi \times 10^{-7} \text{ henry/meter} \tag{1}$$

Then, if μ' is a relative permeability (the value of permeability commonly given in tables), the value of μ for any material may be written

$$\mu = \mu'\mu_0 \tag{2}$$

The above system may be compared with the electromagnetic system of units (emu), which was the most common system used for the discussion of the physical laws concerning magnetic quantities until a few years ago. This is a cgs system, and is an irrational system, so that the factor of 4π is absent from the denominator of Ampère's law, Eq. 2·26(2). Unit magnetic field and unit current are then defined so that unit current (1 abampere) flowing in a loop of radius 1 centimeter produces a magnetic field of 2π oersteds at the center. Permeability of space is defined as unity, so that the numerical value of B is equal to that of H in vacuum. The units of B are maxwells per square centimeter, or gauss. Values of current in abamperes and flux density in gauss substituted in the force equation, 2·24(2), give force in dynes. One ampere is equal to 0.1 abampere, and a magnetic field of 1 ampere per meter is equal to $4\pi \times 10^{-3}$ oersteds.

PROBLEM

2·27 Utilizing the above conversion factors, and the fact that B/H is unity for vacuum in the emu system, show that μ_0 is $4\pi \times 10^{-7}$ in the rational mks system as given in (1) above.

2·28 THE LINE INTEGRAL OF MAGNETIC FIELD

Although Ampère's law describes the way in which magnetic field may be computed from a given system of currents, other derived forms of the law may be more easily applied to certain types of problems. In this and the following articles, certain of these forms will be presented, with examples of their application. The sketch of the derivations of these forms, because they are more complex than for the corresponding electrostatic forms, will be postponed to a later article.

One of the most useful of the forms of the magnetic field laws is that sometimes known as the law of Biot and Savart. This states that a line integral of static magnetic field taken about any given closed path must equal the current enclosed by that path. In the vector notation,

$$\oint \bar{H} \cdot \overline{dl} = I \qquad (1)$$

Obviously this law cannot be independent of Ampère's law, for, since the latter gives the magnetic field in the vicinity of the currents producing it, a line integral of that field could be taken about a closed path giving a result related to current in some way. That it actually does lead to the result (1) will be shown later.

Although line integrals were met previously in the study of electric fields, a few additional comments may make the notation more meaningful. As with the general notations for surface and volume integrals, the actual integration cannot be performed until the path of integration is specified, and the variation of the vector over that path. Then, for each element of that path, the length of element dl is multiplied by the component of the vector in the direction of that element (as denoted by the dot product), and the results added by integration as one moves about the path. As a very simple example, consider the integral $\oint \bar{F} \cdot \overline{dl}$, where $\bar{F} = \bar{a}_x xy$, taken about a rectangular path from $(0,1)$ to $(1,1)$ to $(1,2)$ to $(0,2)$ back to $(0,1)$. Along the vertical sides, $\bar{F}$ is perpendicular to $\overline{dl}$, so that there is no contribution to the dot product. Along the lower side, $\bar{F}$ and $\overline{dl}$ are in the same direction, so that a positive contribution will result, and along the upper side, in moving from $(1,2)$ to $(0,2)$, the direction of $\bar{F}$ and $\overline{dl}$ are opposite so that a negative contribution will result. Note that this negative relation may be taken care of by putting in the sign explicitly and integrating from the lower limit in x to the upper, or by letting the sign take care of itself by putting in limits in the order of moving about the path, but the two methods must not be confused. Then for this example

$$\oint \bar{F} \cdot \overline{dl} = \int_0^1 F_x(x,1)\, dx + \int_1^0 F_x(x,2)\, dx$$

$$= \int_0^1 F_x(x,1)\, dx - \int_0^1 F_x(x,2)\, dx$$

$$= \int_0^1 x\, dx - \int_0^1 2x\, dx = -\tfrac{1}{2}$$

Note that the result of the line integration may give either a positive or a negative result. The sign convention for current on the right side of (1) is taken so that it is positive if it has the sense of advance of a right-hand screw rotated in the direction of circulation chosen for the line integration. This is simply a statement of the well-known right-hand rule relating direction of current and magnetic field.

PROBLEMS

2·28a   Evaluate $\oint \bar{F} \cdot \overline{dl}$ for a vector $\bar{F} = \bar{a}_x x + \bar{a}_y x^2 y^2$ for a path as described in the example above.   Also evaluate the integral for a triangular path from (0,0) to (0,1) to (1,1) back to (0,0).

2·28b   If $\bar{F}$ is derivable as the gradient of some scalar function $\bar{F} = -\nabla U$, show that $\oint \bar{F} \cdot \overline{dl}$ is always zero.

2·29   FIELD ABOUT A LINE CURRENT OR BETWEEN COAXIAL CYLINDERS

The form of the law given in the preceding article is especially useful in problems with a symmetry such that the line integral may be written as a product of path length and magnetic field strength.   An important example is that of a long line conductor carrying current I. If an integration is made about a circular path of radius r centered on the axis of the wire, the symmetry reveals that magnetic field will be circumferential and will not vary with angle as one moves about the path.   Hence the line integral is just the product of circumference and the value of H_ϕ.   This must equal the current enclosed:

$$\oint \bar{H} \cdot \overline{dl} = 2\pi r H_\phi = I$$

or
$$H_\phi = \frac{I}{2\pi r} \text{ amp/meter} \tag{1}$$

The sense relations are shown in Fig. 2·29a, agreeing with the sense convention described in the preceding article.

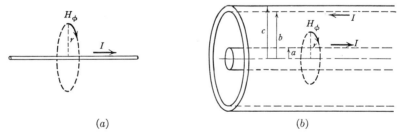

(a) (b)

Fig. 2·29   Magnetic field about line current and between coaxial cylinders.

A coaxial line (Fig. 2·29b) carrying current I on the inner conductor, and $-I$ on the outer (the return current), has the same type of symmetry, and a path taken between the two conductors encloses just current I, so that the result (1) applies directly for the region between conductors:

$$H_\phi = \frac{I}{2\pi r} \qquad a < r < b \tag{2}$$

Outside the outer conductor, a circular path encloses both the going and return current, or a net current of zero. Hence the magnetic field outside is zero.

PROBLEMS

2·29a For the coaxial line of Fig. 2·29b, find the magnetic field for $r < a$, and for $b < r < c$, assuming that current is distributed uniformly over the cross section of both conductors.

2·29b Express the magnetic field about a long line current in rectangular coordinate components, taking the wire axis as the z axis, and evaluate $\oint \bar{H} \cdot \overline{dl}$ about a square path from $(-1,-1)$ to $(1,-1)$ to $(1,1)$ to $(-1,1)$ back to $(-1,-1)$. Also evaluate the integral about the path from $(-1,1)$ to $(1,1)$ to $(1,2)$ to $(-1,2)$ back to $(-1,1)$. Comment on the two results.

2·29c An infinitely long solenoid has n turns/meter and carries current I. Given that the magnetic field is zero outside the solenoid and does not vary with distance along the axis, show that the magnetic field for any point inside the solenoid has a value

$$H_z = nI$$

2·30 THE CURL OF A VECTOR FIELD

In order to write differential equation forms for laws having to do with line integrals, it will be necessary to define a new vector operation. This operation, called the curl, is defined in terms of a line integral taken around an infinitesimal path, divided by the area enclosed by that path. It is seen to have some similarities to the operation of divergence of Art. 2·13, which was defined as the surface integral taken about an infinitesimal surface divided by the volume enclosed by that surface. However, unlike the divergence, the curl operation results in a vector because the orientation of the surface element about which the integral is taken must be described in some way. This is the only additional complication in the curl over the divergence, but it seems to be just enough to make it enormously more difficult for the beginning student to grasp. The student should attempt to obtain as much physical significance as possible from the definitions to be given, but at the same time should recognize that full appreciation of the operation will come only with practice in its use.

The curl of a vector field is defined as a vector function whose component at a point in a particular direction is found by orienting an infinitesimal area normal to the desired direction at that point, and finding the line integral per unit area:

$$[\text{Curl } \bar{F}]_i = \lim_{\Delta S_i \to 0} \frac{\oint \bar{F} \cdot \overline{dl}}{\Delta S_i} \qquad (1)$$

where i denotes a particular direction, ΔS_i is normal to that direction, and the line integral is taken in the right-hand sense with respect to the positive i direction. In rectangular coordinates for example, to compute the z component of the curl the infinitesimal area is selected in the x-y plane in order to be normal to the z direction (Fig. 2·30).

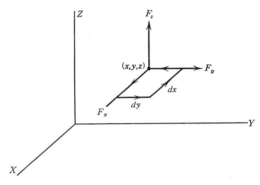

Fig. 2·30.

The right-hand sense of integration about the path with respect to the positive z direction is as shown by the arrows of the figure. The line integral is then

$$\oint \bar{F} \cdot \overline{dl} = dy\, F_y \Big|_{x+dx} - dx\, F_x \Big|_{y+dy} - dy\, F_y \Big|_{x} + dx\, F_x \Big|_{y}$$

We have implied the limit of infinitesimals by writing the elements of length as dx and dy. Then

$$F_x \Big|_{y+dy} = F_x \Big|_{y} + dy\, \frac{\partial F_x}{\partial y}\Big|_{y} \quad ; \quad F_y \Big|_{x+dx} = F_y \Big|_{x} + dx\, \frac{\partial F_y}{\partial x}\Big|_{x}$$

and
$$\oint \bar{F} \cdot \overline{dl} = \left(\frac{\partial F_y}{\partial x} - \frac{\partial F_x}{\partial y}\right) dx\, dy$$

Then, using the definition (1),

$$[\text{Curl } \bar{F}]_z = \frac{\oint \bar{F} \cdot \overline{dl}}{dx\, dy} = \frac{\partial F_y}{\partial x} - \frac{\partial F_x}{\partial y} \qquad (2)$$

Similarly, by taking the elements of area in the y-z plane and x-z plane, respectively, we would find

$$[\mathrm{Curl}\ \bar{F}]_x = \frac{\partial F_z}{\partial y} - \frac{\partial F_y}{\partial z} \tag{3}$$

$$[\mathrm{Curl}\ \bar{F}]_y = \frac{\partial F_x}{\partial z} - \frac{\partial F_z}{\partial x} \tag{4}$$

These components may be multiplied by the corresponding unit vectors and added to form the vector representing the curl:

$$\mathrm{Curl}\ \bar{F} = \bar{a}_x \left[\frac{\partial F_z}{\partial y} - \frac{\partial F_y}{\partial z} \right] + \bar{a}_y \left[\frac{\partial F_x}{\partial z} - \frac{\partial F_z}{\partial x} \right] + \bar{a}_z \left[\frac{\partial F_y}{\partial x} - \frac{\partial F_x}{\partial y} \right] \tag{5}$$

If this form is compared with the form of the cross product, Eq. 2·25(4) or (5), and the definition of the vector operator ∇, Eq. 2·13(6), it is noted that the above can logically be written as "del cross $\bar{F}$":

$$\mathrm{Curl}\ \bar{F} \equiv \nabla \times \bar{F} = \begin{vmatrix} \bar{a}_x & \bar{a}_y & \bar{a}_z \\ \dfrac{\partial}{\partial x} & \dfrac{\partial}{\partial y} & \dfrac{\partial}{\partial z} \\ F_x & F_y & F_z \end{vmatrix} \tag{6}$$

This way of writing in terms of the del operator may be thought of as defining a new notation for the curl operation, and no other significance need be read into it. The name "curl" (or "rotation" as it has been called in the German literature) has some physical significance in the sense that a finite value for the line integral taken in the vicinity of a point is obtained if the curl is finite. However, the name should not be associated with the curvature of the field lines, for a field consisting of closed circles may have zero curl nearly everywhere, and a straight line field varying in certain ways may have a finite curl.

Finally, we want to write the line integral for magnetic field for a differential path, using this curl operation. It is clear that, if the line integral is made about an infinitesimal rectangle in the x-y plane, it should be equal to the current enclosed by Art. 2·28. But this is just the current density (current per unit area) in the z direction, multiplied by the area $dx\ dy$. So

$$[\mathrm{Curl}\ \bar{H}]_z = \frac{\oint \bar{H} \cdot \overline{dl}}{dx\ dy} = \frac{i_z\ dx\ dy}{dx\ dy} = i_z$$

and similarly for the x and y components. If these component equations are multiplied by the corresponding unit vectors and added, we get the vector equation

$$\mathrm{Curl}\ \bar{H} \equiv \nabla \times \bar{H} = \bar{\imath} \tag{7}$$

This is simply the equivalent of Eq. 2·28(1) for a differential path taken in the vicinity of a point. As a very simple example, if we wish to know the current distribution required to produce a magnetic field $\bar{H} = \bar{a}_z x^2$, from (7) and (5) the current density should be

$$\bar{\imath} = \nabla \times \bar{H} = -\bar{a}_y \frac{\partial H_z}{\partial x} = -2x\bar{a}_y \qquad (8)$$

PROBLEMS

2·30a   Find the curl of a vector field $\bar{F} = \bar{a}_x x^2 z^2 + \bar{a}_y y^2 z^2 + \bar{a}_z x^2 y^2$.

2·30b   For the coaxial line of Fig. 2·29b, express the magnetic field found in Art. 2·29 and Prob. 2·29a in rectangular coordinates and find the curl in the four regions, $r < a, \ a < r < b, \ b < r < c, \ r > c$. Comment on the results.

2·30c   By using the rectangular coordinate forms show that

$$\nabla \times (\psi\bar{F}) = \psi \nabla \times \bar{F} - \bar{F} \times \nabla\psi$$

where $\bar{F}$ is any vector function and ψ any scalar function.

2·30d   Show that $\nabla \times \nabla\psi \equiv 0$.

2·31   STOKES'S THEOREM

Just as the divergence should be thought of as a flux flow per unit volume, the curl should be thought of as a line integral per unit area, at a point in space. Just as the divergence theorem (Art. 2·14) states

Fig. 2·31.

that the total flux flow out of any volume may be obtained by integration of the divergence throughout that volume, there is another theorem which states that the line integral around any surface may be obtained by integrating the normal components of the curl over that surface. If the surface is broken up into a large number of infinitesimal areas as shown in Fig. 2·31, it is known from the definition of curl that for each of these infinitesimal areas

$$\oint \bar{F} \cdot \overline{dl} = \operatorname{curl} \bar{F} \cdot \overline{dS} \qquad (1)$$

If contributions from infinitesimal areas are summed over all the surface, the line integral must disappear for all internal areas, since a boundary is first traversed in one direction and then later in the opposite direction in determining the contribution from an adjacent area. The only places where these contributions do not disappear are along the outer boundary, so that the result of the summation is then the line integral of the vector around the boundary:

$$\oint \bar{F} \cdot \overline{dl} = \int_S \operatorname{curl} \bar{F} \cdot \overline{dS} \equiv \int_S \nabla \times \bar{F} \cdot \overline{dS} \qquad (2)$$

This relation is known as Stokes's theorem, and, as with the divergence theorem, it holds for any continuous vector field.

This theorem may be used, for example, in going back from the differential form of the law, Eq. 2·30(7), to the integral form from which it was derived. Writing Stokes's theorem for magnetic field,

$$\oint \bar{H} \cdot \overline{dl} = \int_S (\nabla \times \bar{H}) \cdot \overline{dS}$$

But, by Eq. 2·30(7), the curl may be replaced by the current density:

$$\oint \bar{H} \cdot \overline{dl} = \int_S \bar{\imath} \cdot \overline{dS} \tag{3}$$

The right side represents the current flow through the surface of which the path for the line integration on the left is a boundary. Hence (3) is exactly equivalent to Eq. 2·28(1).

PROBLEM

2·31   Prove the result of Problem 2·30d by integrating over an arbitrary surface and applying Stoke's theorem.

2·32   VECTOR MAGNETIC POTENTIAL; FIELD OF A PARALLEL-WIRE LINE

It will be shown in Art. 2·35 that Ampère's law of Art. 2·26 may be broken into two steps by making use of certain vector equivalences. The result gives

$$\bar{B} = \nabla \times \bar{A} \tag{1}$$

where

$$\bar{A} = \int \frac{\mu I' \, \overline{dl}'}{4\pi r} \tag{2}$$

Or, if the current is given as a vector density $\bar{\imath}$ in current per unit area spread over a volume, V, the equivalent to (2) is

$$\bar{A} = \int_V \frac{\mu \bar{\imath} \, dV}{4\pi r} \tag{3}$$

In both (2) and (3), r is the distance from a current element of the integration to the point at which $\bar{A}$ is to be computed.

Equations (1) and (2) together are equivalent to Eq. 2·26(2). The function $\bar{A}$, introduced as an intermediate step, is computed as an integral over the given currents from (2) or (3) and then differentiated in the manner defined by (1) to yield the magnetic field. $\bar{A}$ may be thought of as a potential function in an analogous but different way to the potential function of electrostatics which is found in terms of an integral over the charges and then differentiated in a certain way to yield the electric field. Unlike the potential of electrostatics, the vector magnetic potential does not have any very simple physical significance beyond that given by the definitions above. Some physical pictures can be developed, but the student should not worry about these until more familiarity with the function has been developed through certain examples.

The example to be given in this article will be that of a parallel-wire transmission line of infinite length carrying current I in one conductor and its return in the other distance $2a$ away. The coordinate system is set up as in Fig. 2·32. Since the field quantities will not vary with

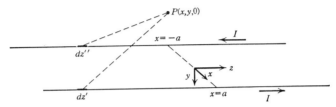

Fig. 2·32   Parallel-wire line.

z, it will be convenient to calculate them in the plane $z = 0$. The line will first be taken as extending from $z = -L$ to $z = L$ to avoid indeterminacies in the integrals. Since current is only in the z direction, $\bar{A}$ by (2) will be in the z direction also. The contribution to A_z from both wires is

$$A_z = \int_{-L}^{L} \frac{\mu I \, dz'}{4\pi \sqrt{(x-a)^2 + y^2 + z'^2}} - \int_{-L}^{L} \frac{\mu I \, dz''}{4\pi \sqrt{(x+a)^2 + y^2 + z''^2}}$$

$$= \frac{2\mu}{4\pi} \left[\int_{0}^{L} \frac{I \, dz'}{\sqrt{(x-a)^2 + y^2 + z'^2}} \right.$$

$$\left. - \int_{0}^{L} \frac{I \, dz''}{\sqrt{(x+a)^2 + y^2 + z''^2}} \right]$$

The integrals may be evaluated (e.g., Dwight, 200.01)

$$A_z = \frac{I\mu}{2\pi} \{ \ln [z' + \sqrt{(x-a)^2 + y^2 + z'^2}]$$

$$- \ln [z'' + \sqrt{(x+a)^2 + y^2 + z''^2}] \}_0^L$$

Now, as L is allowed to approach infinity, the upper limits of the two terms cancel. Hence

$$A_z = \frac{I\mu}{4\pi} \ln \left[\frac{(x+a)^2 + y^2}{(x-a)^2 + y^2} \right] \tag{4}$$

If (1) is then applied, using the expression for curl in rectangular coordinates,

$$H_x = \frac{1}{\mu} \frac{\partial Az}{\partial y} = \frac{I}{2\pi} \left[\frac{y}{(x+a)^2 + y^2} - \frac{y}{(x-a)^2 + y^2} \right] \tag{5}$$

$$H_y = -\frac{1}{\mu} \frac{\partial Az}{\partial x} = \frac{I}{2\pi} \left[\frac{(x-a)}{(x-a)^2 + y^2} - \frac{(x+a)}{(x+a)^2 + y^2} \right] \tag{6}$$

PROBLEMS

2·32a Check the results (5) and (6) by adding vectorially the magnetic field from the individual wires, using the result of Art. 2·29.

2·32b A square loop of thin wire lies in the x-y plane extending from $(-a, -a)$ to $(a, -a)$ to (a, a) to $(-a, a)$ back to $(-a, -a)$ and carries current I in that sense of circulation. Find $\bar{A}$ and $\bar{H}$ for any point (x, y, z).

2·32c A circular loop of thin wire carries current I. Find $\bar{A}$ for a point distance z from the plane of the loop, and radius r from the axis, for $r/z \ll 1$. Use this to find the expression for magnetic field on the axis.

2·32d For a current-free region, show that it would be possible to derive the magnetic field as the gradient of some scalar magnetic potential,

$$\bar{H} = \nabla \Phi_m$$

Why would this not be possible within a region carrying currents?

2·32e Show that $\bar{B}$ would also be given by $\nabla \times \bar{A}'$, where $\bar{A}'$ is obtained by adding to $\bar{A}$ the gradient of any scalar function,

$$\bar{A}' = \bar{A} + \nabla \psi$$

2·33   DIVERGENCE OF MAGNETIC FIELD

Magnetic flux density has been written as the curl of a vector, $\bar{A}$. Its divergence is then

$$\nabla \cdot \bar{B} = \nabla \cdot \nabla \times \bar{A} \tag{1}$$

The result, in rectangular coordinates, is

$$\nabla \cdot \bar{B} = \frac{\partial^2 A_z}{\partial x \, \partial y} - \frac{\partial^2 A_y}{\partial x \, \partial z} + \frac{\partial^2 A_x}{\partial y \, \partial z} - \frac{\partial^2 A_z}{\partial y \, \partial x} + \frac{\partial^2 A_y}{\partial z \, \partial x} - \frac{\partial^2 A_x}{\partial z \, \partial y} \tag{2}$$

since partials may be taken in either order,

$$\nabla \cdot \bar{B} = 0 \tag{3}$$

Notice that the evaluation of the divergence of the curl of $\bar{A}$ was independent of the value of $\bar{A}$, so then the divergence of the curl of any vector is identically zero.

A major difference between electric and magnetic fields is here apparent, for, unlike the electric field, the magnetic field must have zero divergence everywhere. That is, when the magnetic field is due to currents, there are no sources of magnetic flux which correspond to the electric charges as sources of electric flux. Fields with zero divergence such as these are consequently often called source-free fields.

Magnetic field concepts are often developed from an exact parallel with electric fields by considering the concept of isolated magnetic poles as sources of magnetic flux, corresponding to the charges of electrostatics. The result of zero divergence still seems entirely applicable, since such poles have never been isolated, but seem to appear in nature as equal and opposite pairs.

PROBLEM

2·33 Express the magnetic field in rectangular coordinates for the coaxial line of Fig. 2·29b, and differentiate to form the divergence both for $r < a$ and for $a < r < b$.

2·34 DIFFERENTIAL EQUATION FOR VECTOR MAGNETIC POTENTIAL

The differential equation for magnetic field in terms of current density was developed in Art. 2·30:

$$\nabla \times \bar{H} = \bar{\imath}$$

If the relation for $\bar{B}$ as the curl of vector potential $\bar{A}$ is substituted,

$$\nabla \times \nabla \times \bar{A} = \mu \bar{\imath} \tag{1}$$

This may be considered a differential equation relating $\bar{A}$ to current density. It is more common to write it in a different form utilizing the Laplacian of a vector function defined in rectangular coordinates as the vector sum of the Laplacians of the three scalar components:

$$\nabla^2 \bar{A} = \bar{a}_x \nabla^2 A_x + \bar{a}_y \nabla^2 A_y + \bar{a}_z \nabla^2 A_z \tag{2}$$

It may then be verified that, for rectangular coordinates,

$$\nabla \times \nabla \times \bar{A} = -\nabla^2 \bar{A} + \nabla(\nabla \cdot \bar{A}) \tag{3}$$

For other than rectangular coordinate systems, (3) may be taken as the definition of ∇^2 of a vector.

If $\bar{A}$ is defined by Eq. 2·32(3), it may be shown that its divergence is zero (Art. 2·35). Hence (1) may be written

$$\nabla^2 \bar{A} = -\mu \bar{\imath} \tag{4}$$

This is a vector equivalent of the Poisson type of equation first met in

Art. 2·22. It includes three component scalar equations which are exactly of the Poisson form.

For an example, take a case in which $\bar{A}$ has only a z component given by

$$A_z = -\frac{\mu i_0}{4}(x^2 + y^2) \tag{5}$$

From (4) and (2),

$$i_z = -\frac{1}{\mu}\nabla^2 A_z = -\frac{1}{\mu}\left(\frac{\partial^2 A_z}{\partial x^2} + \frac{\partial^2 A_z}{\partial y^2}\right) = i_0 \tag{6}$$

Going backwards, we can see that (5) is the appropriate form for vector potential in a cylindrical conductor carrying a current of constant density i_0. The corresponding magnetic field is

$$\bar{B} = \nabla \times \bar{A} = \frac{\mu i_0}{2}(\bar{a}_x y - \bar{a}_y x) \tag{7}$$

The differential equation (4) is more useful in determining the vector potential $\bar{A}$ when the current density $\bar{i}$ is given. This requires solution of the differential equation; this phase of the subject will be reserved for the following chapter.

PROBLEMS

2·34a Deduce the appropriate form for vector potential outside a long straight wire carrying current I, and show that $\nabla^2\bar{A}$ is equal to zero there.

2·34b Use the rectangular coordinate forms to prove (3).

2·34c Show that the magnetic field given by (7) is circumferential and can be written

$$H_\phi = \frac{i_0 r}{2}$$

Obtain this result also by the methods of Art. 2·29.

2·35 SKETCH OF THE DERIVATION OF MAGNETIC FIELD LAWS

In presenting various forms for the laws of static magnetic fields, many of the less obvious steps have been left out, and the order has been chosen as that most convenient for presentation of the laws rather than that of the logical development. It is the purpose of this article to sketch the omitted steps.

We wish to start from Ampère's law, Eq. 2·26(2), which may be written

$$\bar{H} = \int \frac{I'\,d\bar{l}' \times \bar{r}}{4\pi r^3} \tag{1}$$

I' is the current in a contributing element $\overline{dl}'$ at point (x', y', z'), and $\bar{r}$ is the vector running from $\overline{dl}'$ to point (x,y,z) at which $\bar{H}$ is to be computed.

$$\bar{r} = \bar{a}_x(x - x') + \bar{a}_y(y - y') + \bar{a}_z(z - z')$$

$$r = \sqrt{(x - x')^2 + (y - y')^2 + (z - z')^2}$$

It may be shown that

$$\frac{\overline{dl}' \times \bar{r}}{r^3} = \nabla \left(\frac{1}{r}\right) \times \overline{dl}' \tag{2}$$

And also, using the vector identity of Prob. 2·30c,

$$\nabla \left(\frac{1}{r}\right) \times \overline{dl}' = \nabla \times \left(\frac{\overline{dl}'}{r}\right) - \frac{1}{r} \nabla \times \overline{dl}' \tag{3}$$

But ∇ represents derivatives with respect to x, y, and z, which are not involved in $\overline{dl}'$, so the last term is zero. Therefore

$$\bar{B} = \mu \int \frac{I'}{4\pi} \nabla \times \left(\frac{\overline{dl}'}{r}\right) = \nabla \times \bar{A} \tag{4}$$

where

$$\bar{A} = \mu \int \frac{I' \, \overline{dl}'}{4\pi r} \tag{5}$$

The curl operation in (4) could be taken outside of the integral since it is with respect to x,y,z, and the integration is with respect to x',y',z'. Thus the vector potential forms of Art. 2·32 have been derived from Ampère's law.

For the next step, let us note the x component of (5):

$$A_x = \mu \int \frac{I_x' \, dx'}{4\pi r} = \mu \int_V \frac{i_x \, dV}{4\pi r} \tag{6}$$

This may be compared with Poisson's equation and the integral expression for electrostatic potential:

$$\nabla^2 \Phi = -\frac{\rho}{\epsilon} \qquad \Phi = \int_V \frac{\rho \, dV}{4\pi\epsilon r} \tag{7}$$

Although these equations were obtained from a consideration of the properties of electrostatic fields, the second of the two equations (7) may be considered a solution in integral form for the first, for any continuous scalar functions Φ and ρ/ϵ. Consequently, by direct analogy between (6) and (7), we write

$$\nabla^2 A_x = -\mu i_x \tag{8}$$

$$\nabla^2 \bar{A} = -\mu \bar{i} \tag{9}$$

This was the differential equation relating $\bar{A}$ to current density discussed in Art. 2·34. By reversing the steps of that article, the differential equation for magnetic field may be derived from it:

$$\nabla \times \bar{H} = \bar{\imath} \tag{10}$$

And as was shown in Art. 2·31, the integral form may be derived from this by use of Stoke's theorem:

$$\oint \bar{H} \cdot \overline{dl} = I \tag{11}$$

There remains the argument for $\nabla \cdot \bar{A} = 0$ used in Art. 2·34. In this it is necessary to make use of the del operator both with respect to the variables x,y,z and with respect to the variables x',y',z'. The former will be denoted ∇, and the latter ∇'. Recall that the integration is with respect to the primed variables. Then

$$\frac{1}{\mu} \nabla \cdot \bar{A} = \nabla \cdot \int_V \frac{\bar{\imath}' \, dV'}{4\pi r} = \int_V \nabla \cdot \left(\frac{\bar{\imath}'}{r}\right) \frac{dV'}{4\pi} \tag{12}$$

Use the vector equivalence of Prob. 2·17e:

$$\frac{1}{\mu} \nabla \cdot \bar{A} = \int_V \left[\frac{\nabla \cdot \bar{\imath}'}{r} + \bar{\imath}' \cdot \nabla \left(\frac{1}{r}\right)\right] \frac{dV'}{4\pi}$$

The first term is zero since $\bar{\imath}'$ is not a function of the x,y,z coordinates. In the latter term, from the definition of r, we can write

$$\nabla \left(\frac{1}{r}\right) = -\nabla' \left(\frac{1}{r}\right)$$

Then

$$\frac{1}{\mu} \nabla \cdot \bar{A} = -\int_V \bar{\imath}' \cdot \nabla' \left(\frac{1}{r}\right) \frac{dV'}{4\pi} = \int_V \left[\frac{1}{r} \nabla' \cdot (\bar{\imath}') - \nabla' \cdot \left(\frac{\bar{\imath}'}{r}\right)\right] \frac{dV'}{4\pi}$$

In the last step we have again used the vector equivalence referred to above. The first term is zero, but this time because we are concerned with direct currents which have as much flow out as in any volume by continuity, or $\nabla' \cdot (\bar{\imath}') = 0$. The second term is transformable to a surface integral by the divergence theorem:

$$\frac{1}{\mu} \nabla \cdot \bar{A} = \oint_{S'} \left(\frac{\bar{\imath}'}{4\pi r}\right) \cdot \overline{dS'} \tag{13}$$

But, if the surface encloses all the current, as it must, there can be no current flow through the surface and the result in (13) is seen to be zero.

Thus all the major laws given have been shown to follow from the original experimental law of Ampère. It should be noted that the argument given is for a homogeneous medium (permeability not a function of position). For an inhomogeneous medium, equations (10) and 2·33(3) are found to form the fundamental starting point:

$$\nabla \times \bar{H} = \bar{\imath} \qquad \nabla \cdot \bar{B} = 0 \tag{14}$$

For an inhomogeneous medium, certain of the other forms given are then found not to apply.

PROBLEMS

2·35a   Supply the proof of $\nabla(1/r) \times \overline{dl}' = (\overline{dl}' \times \bar{r})/r^3$ used above.

2·35b   If μ is a function of position and $\nabla \cdot \bar{B} = 0$, show that in general $\nabla \cdot \bar{H}$ will not be zero.

2·36   ENERGY OF A STATIC MAGNETIC FIELD

An expression similar to that of Art. 2·23 for an electrostatic system may be derived to give the energy in a magnetostatic system. This is

$$U_H = \int_V \frac{\bar{B} \cdot \bar{H}}{2} \, dV = \int_V \frac{\mu H^2}{2} \, dV \tag{1}$$

The derivation will not be given for static magnetic fields, but will be given in a later chapter for magnetic fields with arbitrary time variations. As in the corresponding expression for electric fields, an interpretation of this is that the energy of the system is stored in the field, with an energy density of $\mu H^2/2$ joules per cubic meter for all parts of the volume for which fields are significant. This is not the only possible interpretation, but it is a convenient one from a field theory point of view.

PROBLEM

2·36   Find the energy stored per unit length between the conductors of a coaxial line carrying current I in the inner conductor and return current in the outer.

Coordinate Systems and Vector Relations

2·37   THE RECTANGULAR, CYLINDRICAL, AND SPHERICAL COORDINATE SYSTEMS

When it was necessary to refer to a coordinate system in the preceding articles, rectangular coordinates were used exclusively. There was actually no loss in generality in the results obtained, since, if it had been necessary to transfer to a new coordinate system at any point, it could have been done by an ordinary transformation of variables. However, it is evident that the physical boundaries of many problems will often make it more convenient to begin with a different coordinate system. The three systems to be utilized in this text are rectangular coordinates, circular cylindrical coordinates, and spherical coordinates. These three will be defined briefly here.

The intersection of two surfaces is a line; the intersection of three surfaces is a point; thus the coordinates of a point may be given by stating three parameters, each of which defines a coordinate surface.

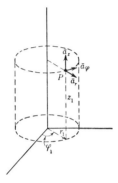

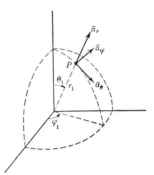

Fig. 2·37a   System of circular cylindrical coordinates.

Fig. 2·37b   System of spherical coordinates.

In rectangular coordinates, the three planes $x = x_1$, $y = y_1$, $z = z_1$ intersect at a point which is designated by the coordinates x_1, y_1, z_1. The elements of length in the three coordinate directions are dx, dy, and dz, the elements of area are $dx\,dy$, $dy\,dz$, and $dz\,dx$, and the element of volume is $dx\,dy\,dz$.

In the circular cylindrical coordinate system, the coordinate surfaces are (a) a set of circular cylinders (r = constant), (b) a set of planes all passing through the axis (ϕ = constant), (c) a set of planes normal to the axis (z = constant). Coordinates of a particular point may then be given as r_1, ϕ_1, z_1 (Fig. 2·37a). The r, ϕ, and z coordinates are known respectively as the radius, the azimuthal angle, and the distance along the axis. Elements of length are dr, $r\,d\phi$, dz, and the element of volume is $r\,dr\,d\phi\,dz$. The system shown is a right-hand system in the order of writing r, ϕ, z.

In spherical coordinates the surfaces are (a) a set of spheres (radius r from the origin = constant), (b) a set of cones about the axis (θ = constant), (c) a set of planes passing through the polar axis (ϕ = constant). The intersection of sphere $r = r_1$, cone $\theta = \theta_1$, and plane

$\phi = \phi_1$ gives a point whose coordinates are said to be r_1, θ_1, ϕ_1 (Fig. 2·37b). r is the radius, θ the polar angle or co-latitude, and ϕ is the azimuth angle or longitude. Elements of distance are dr, $r\,d\theta$, and $r \sin \theta\,d\phi$, elements of area are $r\,dr\,d\theta$, $r^2 \sin \theta\,d\theta\,d\phi$, and $r \sin \theta\,d\phi\,dr$, and the element of volume is $r^2 \sin \theta\,dr\,d\theta\,d\phi$.

In forming the various operations such as divergence and curl in the curvilinear coordinate systems, the fundamental definitions are utilized, but one must recognize that the elements of area or length may

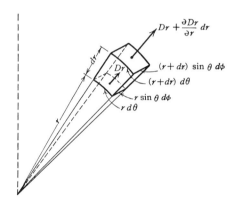

Fig. 2·37c Element of volume in spherical coordinates.

vary as one changes a coordinate as well as the value of the vector components. As an example, let us find the expression for divergence of $\bar{D}$ in the spherical coordinate system. Consider the radial direction first. Both the radial component D_r and the element of area $r^2\,d\theta \sin \theta\,d\phi$ change as one moves from r to $r + dr$ (Fig. 2·37c). Thus the net flux flow out the top over that in at the bottom is

$$d\psi_r = (r + dr)^2 \sin \theta\,d\theta\,d\phi \left(D_r + \frac{\partial D_r}{\partial r}\,dr \right) - r^2 \sin \theta\,d\theta\,d\phi\,D_r$$

To first order differentials, this leaves

$$d\psi_r = r^2 \sin \theta\,d\theta\,d\phi\,\frac{\partial D_r}{\partial r}\,dr + 2r\,dr \sin \theta\,d\theta\,d\phi\,D_r$$

$$= \sin \theta\,dr\,d\theta\,d\phi\,\frac{\partial}{\partial r}\,(r^2 D_r)$$

Note that the same result may be obtained more directly by first forming the product of flux density by area and then taking the rate of change of this product with r:

$$d\psi_r = dr \frac{\partial}{\partial r} (D_r \, r^2 \sin \theta \, d\theta \, d\phi) = \sin \theta \, dr \, d\theta \, d\phi \frac{\partial}{\partial r} (r^2 \, D_r)$$

Similarly for the θ and ϕ directions:

$$d\psi_\theta = d\theta \frac{\partial}{\partial \theta} (D_\theta \, r \sin \theta \, d\phi \, dr) = r \, dr \, d\theta \, d\phi \frac{\partial}{\partial \theta} (\sin \theta \, D_\theta)$$

$$d\psi_\phi = d\phi \frac{\partial}{\partial \phi} (D_\phi \, r \, d\theta \, dr) = r \, dr \, d\theta \, d\phi \frac{\partial}{\partial \phi} (D_\phi)$$

The divergence is then the total $d\psi$ divided by the element of volume

$$\nabla \cdot \bar{D} = \frac{d\psi_r + d\psi_\theta + d\psi_\phi}{r^2 \sin \theta \, dr \, d\theta \, d\phi}$$

$$\nabla \cdot \bar{D} = \frac{1}{r^2} \frac{\partial}{\partial r} (r^2 \, D_r) + \frac{1}{r \sin \theta} \frac{\partial}{\partial \theta} (\sin \theta \, D_\theta) + \frac{1}{r \sin \theta} \frac{\partial D_\phi}{\partial \phi} \qquad (1)$$

Corresponding forms for the other operations in this and other coordinate systems will be given in the last of the chapter.

PROBLEMS

2·37a   Derive the expression for divergence in the circular cylindrical coordinate system.

2·37b   Derive the expression for curl in the spherical coordinate system.

2·38   GENERAL CURVILINEAR COORDINATES

Each of the three systems of the last article, and many others utilized in mathematical physics, are orthogonal coordinate systems in that the lines of intersection of the coordinate surfaces are at right angles to one another at any given point.   It is possible to develop general expressions for divergence, curl, and other vector operations for such systems which make it unnecessary to begin at the beginning each time a new system is met.

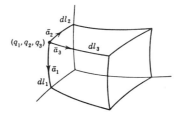

Fig. 2·38a   Element in arbitrary orthogonal curvilinear coordinates.

Suppose that a point in space is thus defined in any orthogonal system by the coordinate surfaces q_1, q_2, q_3. These then intersect at right angles and a set of three unit vectors, $\bar{a}_1$, $\bar{a}_2$, $\bar{a}_3$, may be placed at this point.   These should point in the direction of increasing coordinates.   (See Fig. 2·38a.)   The three coordinates need not necessarily express directly a distance (consider, for example, the angles of spherical coordinates) so that the differential elements of distance must be expressed:

$$dl_1 = h_1 \, dq_1 \qquad dl_2 = h_2 \, dq_2, \qquad dl_3 = h_3 \, dq_3 \qquad (1)$$

where h_1, h_2, h_3 in the most general case may each be functions of all three coordinates, q_1, q_2, q_3.

Scalar and Vector Products. A reference to the fundamental definitions of the two vector multiplications will show that these do not change in form in orthogonal curvilinear coordinates. Thus, for scalar or dot product,

$$\bar{A} \cdot \bar{B} = A_1 B_1 + A_2 B_2 + A_3 B_3 \qquad (2)$$

and, for the vector or cross product,

$$\bar{A} \times \bar{B} = \begin{vmatrix} \bar{a}_1 & \bar{a}_2 & \bar{a}_3 \\ A_1 & A_2 & A_3 \\ B_1 & B_2 & B_3 \end{vmatrix} \qquad (3)$$

When one of these vectors is replaced by the operator ∇, the above expressions do not hold, as will be shown below.

Gradient. According to previous definitions, the gradient of any scalar Φ will be a vector whose component in any direction is given by the change of Φ for a change in distance along that direction. Thus

$$\nabla \Phi = \bar{a}_1 \frac{\partial \Phi}{h_1 \, \partial q_1} + \bar{a}_2 \frac{\partial \Phi}{h_2 \, \partial q_2} + \bar{a}_3 \frac{\partial \Phi}{h_3 \, \partial q_3} \qquad (4)$$

Divergence. In forming the divergence, it is necessary to account for the variations in surface elements as well as the vector components when one changes a coordinate, as was noted in the last article. If the product of surface element by the appropriate component is first formed and then differentiated, both of these changes are taken into account:

$$\nabla \cdot \bar{D} = \frac{1}{h_1 h_2 h_3 \, dq_1 \, dq_2 \, dq_3} \left[dq_1 \frac{\partial}{\partial q_1} (D_1 h_2 h_3 \, dq_2 \, dq_3) \right.$$

$$\left. + \, dq_2 \frac{\partial}{\partial q_2} (D_2 h_1 h_3 \, dq_1 \, dq_3) + dq_3 \frac{\partial}{\partial q_3} (D_3 h_2 h_1 \, dq_2 \, dq_1) \right]$$

$$\nabla \cdot \bar{D} = \frac{1}{h_1 h_2 h_3} \left[\frac{\partial}{\partial q_1} (h_2 h_3 \, D_1) + \frac{\partial}{\partial q_2} (h_1 h_3 \, D_2) + \frac{\partial}{\partial q_3} (h_2 h_1 \, D_3) \right] \qquad (5)$$

Note that for the spherical coordinate system $dl_1 = dr$, $dl_2 = r \, d\theta$, and $dl_3 = r \sin \theta \, d\phi$, so that $h_1 = 1$, $h_2 = r$, and $h_3 = r \sin \theta$. A substitution of these in (5) leads directly to Eq. 2·37(1).

Curl. In forming the curl, it is necessary to account for the variations in length elements with changes in coordinates as one integrates about an elemental path. This may again be done by forming the product of length element and proper vector component and then differentiating. The result may be written

$$\nabla \times \bar{H} = \begin{vmatrix} \dfrac{\bar{a}_1}{h_2 h_3} & \dfrac{\bar{a}_2}{h_3 h_1} & \dfrac{\bar{a}_3}{h_1 h_2} \\[2ex] \dfrac{\partial}{\partial q_1} & \dfrac{\partial}{\partial q_2} & \dfrac{\partial}{\partial q_3} \\[2ex] h_1 H_1 & h_2 H_2 & h_3 H_3 \end{vmatrix} \qquad (6)$$

Laplacian. The Laplacian of a scalar, which is defined as the divergence of the gradient of that scalar, may be found by combining (4) and (5):

$$\nabla^2 \Phi = \nabla \cdot \nabla \Phi$$

$$= \frac{1}{h_1 h_2 h_3} \left[\frac{\partial}{\partial q_1} \left(\frac{h_2 h_3}{h_1} \frac{\partial \Phi}{\partial q_1} \right) + \frac{\partial}{\partial q_2} \left(\frac{h_3 h_1}{h_2} \frac{\partial \Phi}{\partial q_2} \right) + \frac{\partial}{\partial q_3} \left(\frac{h_1 h_2}{h_3} \frac{\partial \Phi}{\partial q_3} \right) \right]$$

$$(7)$$

Laplacian of Vectors. For the Laplacian of a vector in a system of coordinates other than rectangular, it is convenient to use the vector identity, Eq. 2·34(3):

$$\nabla^2 \bar{F} = \nabla (\nabla \cdot \bar{F}) - \nabla \times \nabla \times \bar{F} \qquad (8)$$

Each of the operations on the right has been defined above.

Differentiation of Vectors. The derivative of a vector is sometimes required as in Newton's law for the motion of particles,

$$\bar{F} = m \frac{d\bar{v}}{dt} = m \frac{d}{dt} (\bar{a}_1 \dot{v}_1 + \bar{a}_2 v_2 + \bar{a}_3 v_3) \qquad (9)$$

If this is expanded, we have

$$\frac{\bar{F}}{m} = \bar{a}_1 \frac{dv_1}{dt} + \bar{a}_2 \frac{dv_2}{dt} + \bar{a}_3 \frac{dv_3}{dt} + v_1 \frac{d\bar{a}_1}{dt} + v_2 \frac{d\bar{a}_2}{dt} + v_3 \frac{d\bar{a}_3}{dt}$$

The last three terms involve changes in the unit vectors, which by definition cannot change magnitude, but may change in direction as one moves along the coordinate system. Consider for example the fourth term:

$$v_1 \frac{d\bar{a}_1}{dt} = v_1 \left[\frac{\partial \bar{a}_1}{\partial q_1} \frac{dq_1}{dt} + \frac{\partial \bar{a}_1}{\partial q_2} \frac{dq_2}{dt} + \frac{\partial \bar{a}_1}{\partial q_3} \frac{dq_3}{dt} \right]$$

Partials of the form $\partial \bar{a}_1/\partial q_1$, etc., may not be zero. As an example, consider the term $\partial \bar{a}_\theta/\partial \theta$ in spherical coordinates. From Fig. 2·38b

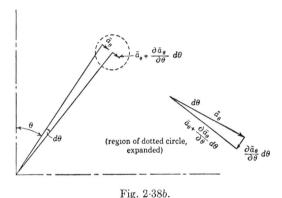

Fig. 2·38b.

the vector $d\theta \, \partial \bar{a}_\theta/\partial \theta$ is seen to have magnitude $d\theta$ and has direction given by $-\bar{a}_r$. Thus $\partial \bar{a}_\theta/\partial \theta = -\bar{a}_r$. Other partials of unit vectors in this and the cylindrical coordinate system are listed in the next article.

PROBLEMS

2·38a   Find $\partial \bar{a}_\phi/\partial \phi$ in the spherical coordinate system, drawing a sketch to show its components.

2·38b   Utilize the partials of unit vectors from the next article to write Newton's law (9) in terms of its components for cylindrical coordinates.

2·38c   Repeat Prob. b for spherical coordinates.

2·39   SUMMARY OF USEFUL VECTOR RELATIONS

From the general equations for all orthogonal systems, the forms of the vector operations in these three most common systems are found to be as follows.

Rectangular Coordinates

$$q_1 = x \qquad q_2 = y \qquad q_3 = z$$

$$h_1 = 1 \qquad h_2 = 1 \qquad h_3 = 1$$

$$\nabla \Phi = \bar{a}_x \frac{\partial \Phi}{\partial x} + \bar{a}_y \frac{\partial \Phi}{\partial y} + \bar{a}_z \frac{\partial \Phi}{\partial z}$$

$$\nabla \cdot \bar{D} = \frac{\partial D_x}{\partial x} + \frac{\partial D_y}{\partial y} + \frac{\partial D_z}{\partial z}$$

$$\nabla \times \bar{H} = \bar{a}_x \left(\frac{\partial H_z}{\partial y} - \frac{\partial H_y}{\partial z} \right) + \bar{a}_y \left(\frac{\partial H_x}{\partial z} - \frac{\partial H_z}{\partial x} \right) + \bar{a}_z \left(\frac{\partial H_y}{\partial x} - \frac{\partial H_x}{\partial y} \right)$$

$$\nabla^2 \Phi = \frac{\partial^2 \Phi}{\partial x^2} + \frac{\partial^2 \Phi}{\partial y^2} + \frac{\partial^2 \Phi}{\partial z^2}$$

All partials of unit vectors $\left(\dfrac{\partial \bar{a}_x}{\partial x}, \dfrac{\partial \bar{a}_x}{\partial y}, \text{ etc.} \right)$ are zero.

Cylindrical Coordinates

$$q_1 = r \qquad q_2 = \phi \qquad q_3 = z$$
$$h_1 = 1 \qquad h_2 = r \qquad h_3 = 1$$

$$\nabla \Phi = \bar{a}_r \frac{\partial \Phi}{\partial r} + \bar{a}_\phi \frac{1}{r} \frac{\partial \Phi}{\partial \phi} + \bar{a}_z \frac{\partial \Phi}{\partial z}$$

$$\nabla \cdot \bar{D} = \frac{1}{r} \frac{\partial}{\partial r} (r\,D_r) + \frac{1}{r} \frac{\partial D_\phi}{\partial \phi} + \frac{\partial D_z}{\partial z}$$

$$\nabla \times \bar{H} = \bar{a}_r \left[\frac{1}{r} \frac{\partial H_z}{\partial \phi} - \frac{\partial H_\phi}{\partial z} \right] + \bar{a}_\phi \left[\frac{\partial H_r}{\partial z} - \frac{\partial H_z}{\partial r} \right]$$

$$+ \bar{a}_z \left[\frac{1}{r} \frac{\partial (rH_\phi)}{\partial r} - \frac{1}{r} \frac{\partial H_r}{\partial \phi} \right]$$

$$\nabla^2 \Phi = \frac{1}{r} \frac{\partial}{\partial r} \left(r \frac{\partial \Phi}{\partial r} \right) + \frac{1}{r^2} \frac{\partial^2 \Phi}{\partial \phi^2} + \frac{\partial^2 \Phi}{\partial z^2}$$

All partials of unit vectors are zero except

$$\frac{\partial \bar{a}_r}{\partial \phi} = \bar{a}_\phi \qquad \frac{\partial \bar{a}_\phi}{\partial \phi} = -\bar{a}_r$$

Spherical Coordinates

$$\nabla \Phi = \bar{a}_r \frac{\partial \Phi}{\partial r} + \bar{a}_\theta \frac{1}{r} \frac{\partial \Phi}{\partial \theta} + \frac{\bar{a}_\phi}{r \sin \theta} \frac{\partial \Phi}{\partial \phi}$$

$$\nabla \cdot \bar{D} = \frac{1}{r^2} \frac{\partial}{\partial r} (r^2 D_r) + \frac{1}{r \sin \theta} \frac{\partial}{\partial \theta} (\sin \theta D_\theta) + \frac{1}{r \sin \theta} \frac{\partial D_\phi}{\partial \phi}$$

$$\nabla \times \bar{H} = \frac{\bar{a}_r}{r \sin \theta} \left[\frac{\partial}{\partial \theta} (H_\phi \sin \theta) - \frac{\partial H_\theta}{\partial \phi} \right]$$

$$+ \frac{\bar{a}_\theta}{r} \left[\frac{1}{\sin \theta} \frac{\partial H_r}{\partial \phi} - \frac{\partial}{\partial r} (rH_\phi) \right] + \frac{\bar{a}_\phi}{r} \left[\frac{\partial}{\partial r} (rH_\theta) - \frac{\partial H_r}{\partial \theta} \right]$$

$$\nabla^2 \Phi = \frac{1}{r^2} \frac{\partial}{\partial r} \left(r^2 \frac{\partial \Phi}{\partial r} \right) + \frac{1}{r^2 \sin \theta} \frac{\partial}{\partial \theta} \left(\sin \theta \frac{\partial \Phi}{\partial \theta} \right) + \frac{1}{r^2 \sin^2 \theta} \frac{\partial^2 \Phi}{\partial \phi^2}$$

All partials of unit vectors are zero except

$$\frac{\partial \bar{a}_r}{\partial \theta} = \bar{a}_\theta \qquad \frac{\partial \bar{a}_\theta}{\partial \theta} = -\bar{a}_r$$

$$\frac{\partial \bar{a}_r}{\partial \phi} = \bar{a}_\phi \sin \theta \qquad \frac{\partial \bar{a}_\theta}{\partial \phi} = \bar{a}_\phi \cos \theta \qquad \frac{\partial \bar{a}_\phi}{\partial \phi} = -(\bar{a}_r \sin \theta + \bar{a}_\theta \cos \theta)$$

Vector Identities. Most of the following vector identities have appeared in previous discussions. They will be useful throughout the book. Φ and ψ represent any scalar quantities, $\bar{A}$ and $\bar{B}$ any vector quantities.

$$\nabla(\Phi + \psi) = \nabla \Phi + \nabla \psi$$

$$\nabla \cdot (\bar{A} + \bar{B}) = \nabla \cdot \bar{A} + \nabla \cdot \bar{B}$$

$$\nabla \times (\bar{A} + \bar{B}) = \nabla \times \bar{A} + \nabla \times \bar{B}$$

$$\nabla(\Phi \psi) = \Phi \nabla \psi + \psi \nabla \Phi$$

$$\nabla \cdot (\psi \bar{A}) = \bar{A} \cdot \nabla \psi + \psi \nabla \cdot \bar{A}$$

$$\nabla \cdot (\bar{A} \times \bar{B}) = \bar{B} \cdot \nabla \times \bar{A} - \bar{A} \cdot \nabla \times \bar{B}$$

$$\nabla \times (\Phi \bar{A}) = \nabla \Phi \times \bar{A} + \Phi \nabla \times \bar{A}$$

$$\nabla \times (\bar{A} \times \bar{B}) = \bar{A} \nabla \cdot \bar{B} - \bar{B} \nabla \cdot \bar{A} + (\bar{B} \cdot \nabla)\bar{A} - (\bar{A} \cdot \nabla)\bar{B}$$

$$\nabla \cdot \nabla \Phi = \nabla^2 \Phi$$

$$\nabla \cdot \nabla \times \bar{A} = 0$$

$$\nabla \times \nabla \Phi = 0$$

$$\nabla \times \nabla \times \bar{A} = \nabla(\nabla \cdot \bar{A}) - \nabla^2 \bar{A}$$

$$\bar{A} \times (\bar{B} \times \bar{C}) = \bar{B}(\bar{A} \cdot \bar{C}) - \bar{C}(\bar{A} \cdot \bar{B})$$

3 SOLUTIONS TO
STATIC FIELD PROBLEMS

Basic Considerations in Solving Field Problems by Differential Equations

3·01 INTRODUCTION

Chapter 2 presented the laws of electricity and magnetism for systems with no time variations, and the concepts of such static systems. It was noted at the beginning of that chapter that it is often necessary to solve problems involving the laws of static systems, not alone for cases involving d-c potentials and direct currents but also for the cases to be discussed later when the results of static solutions may be applied directly to the high-frequency problems of more interest to radio engineers.

If the problem is the solution of a static system, the desired result may be the actual distribution of fields or potentials, as for instance when the maximum gradient is desired for purposes of calculating breakdown voltage between a given set of electrodes. If the static solution is to be used in studying motion of electrons, it will be desired to find the field strength at a given point in space so that forces exerted on the electrons may be calculated at that point. If it is desired to use static solutions for the calculation of inductances and capacitances, or the impedance of a transmission line, it is often necessary to find the field distribution around the desired configuration as a first step. Thus the calculation of the field or potential distribution in the vicinity of an electrode system, a transmission line, or a circuit element is usually the first step in the analysis of each system. This will be the major goal of the present chapter.

The distribution of fields may be desired in regions containing charges, in regions containing currents, or in regions free from both charges and currents. If charges are present in free space, they cannot be in equilibrium, but must be in motion; consequently this part of the problem would require a study of the motion of charges in fields.   The solution for a current-carrying region is of greatest interest when it is desired to calculate the impedance of a circuit element for alternating current.   This aspect of the problem will be reserved until we may include the effect of frequency on the distribution of current through the conductors.   There remain the cases involving distributions in charge-free and current-free regions.   All field distributions may then be obtained by a solution of the one differential equation, Laplace's equation.

Laplace's equation has universal application throughout applied physics, and the mathematics of its solution has received a great amount of attention.   Consequently there are available many special methods for its solution.   Despite the importance of this problem to radio engineers, it would be impossible to attempt completeness here in considering these methods.   We shall study here solutions applicable to certain simple and very useful geometrical configurations, stressing the physical pictures which follow from the above results, and those methods of solution which will best provide background for similar types of solutions in wave problems to follow.

3·02   DISTRIBUTION PROBLEMS GOVERNED BY LAPLACE'S EQUATION

In the previous chapter, Laplace's equation appeared first to relate the derivatives of the electrostatic scalar potential Φ at any point in charge-free space:

$$\nabla^2\Phi = 0 \tag{1}$$

A solution to this equation which satisfies the boundary conditions of the specified electrode configurations and applied potentials will be an equation giving the potential as a function of the space coordinates.

In electrostatics, the potential is not the only quantity which satisfies Laplace's equation.   Certain components of the electric field vector $\bar{E}$ also are distributed in space in accordance with this relation.   This is easily shown by recalling a few basic relations from the previous chapter.   The work integral for electric fields led to the expression

$$\nabla \times \bar{E} = 0$$

If the curl of this equation is taken,

$$\nabla \times \nabla \times \bar{E} = 0$$

or, by a vector equivalence (See Art. 2·39),

$$\nabla(\nabla \cdot \bar{E}) - \nabla^2\bar{E} = 0$$

For a charge-free, homogeneous dielectric, Eq. 2·13(8) becomes

$$\nabla \cdot \bar{E} = 0$$

so that

$$\nabla^2 \bar{E} = 0 \tag{2}$$

The last expression is a vector equation which in general may not be simple in form. (See Art. 2·38.) However, in rectangular coordinates,

$$\nabla^2 \bar{E} = \bar{a}_x \nabla^2 E_x + \bar{a}_y \nabla^2 E_y + \bar{a}_z \nabla^2 E_z \tag{3}$$

so that

$$\nabla^2 E_x = 0 \qquad \nabla^2 E_y = 0 \qquad \nabla^2 E_z = 0 \tag{4}$$

Thus, for a charge-free region, each of the three components of electric field intensity in rectangular coordinates satisfies Laplace's equation. Expansion of $\nabla^2 \bar{E}$ in cylindrical coordinates shows that the axial component of $\bar{E}$ also satisfies Laplace's equation. That is, in cylindrical coordinates

$$\nabla^2 E_z = 0 \tag{5}$$

(but this is not true of E_r and E_ϕ). It may often be more convenient to use these components of field directly in Laplace's equation than to use the potential, as will be illustrated later by example.

Similar arguments show that the magnetic field $\bar{H}$ or the magnetic vector potential $\bar{A}$ or a possible magnetic scalar potential Φ_m (see Prob. 2·32d) satisfies Laplace's equation for a current-free region, and the d-c current density $\bar{\imath}$ satisfies it in a homogeneous conducting region. All this is summarized in Table 3·02.

TABLE 3·02

APPLICATION OF LAPLACE'S EQUATION

Condition	Quantity	Rectangular Coordinates	Cylindrical Coordinates	Spherical Coordinates
Charge-free region (static case)	Electrostatic scalar potential	Φ	Φ	Φ
	Electric field intensity	E_x, E_y, E_z	E_z	
Current-free region (static case)	Vector magnetic potential	A_x, A_y, A_z	A_z	
	Magnetic field intensity	H_x, H_y, H_z	H_z	
	Magnetic scalar potential	Φ_m	Φ_m	Φ_m
Static currents	Current density	i_x, i_y, i_z	i_z	

PROBLEMS

3·02a Find the form of differential equation satisfied by E_r in cylindrical coordinates for a charge-free, homogeneous dielectric region. Repeat for E_ϕ.

3·02b   Derive Laplace's equation for $\bar{H}$, $\bar{A}$ and Φ_m in a current-free region, and for d-c current density $\bar{\imath}$ in a homogeneous conductor.

3·03   UNIQUENESS OF A SOLUTION

Many possible means of obtaining solutions to Laplace's equation will be presented in following sections.   It is important to realize that, when a solution to the equation within a region is obtained, it is the only possible solution if it satisfies the boundary conditions about that region.   To show that this is so, imagine that there are on the contrary two such possible solutions, Φ_1 and Φ_2.   Since they must both reduce to the given potential along the boundary,

$$\Phi_1 - \Phi_2 = 0 \tag{1}$$

along the boundary surface.   Since they are both solutions to Laplace's equation,

$$\nabla^2\Phi_1 = 0 \qquad \text{and} \qquad \nabla^2\Phi_2 = 0$$

or

$$\nabla^2(\Phi_1 - \Phi_2) = 0 \tag{2}$$

throughout the entire region.

In the divergence theorem, Eq. 2·14(3), $\bar{F}$ may be any continuous vector quantity.   In particular, let it be the quantity

$$(\Phi_1 - \Phi_2)\nabla(\Phi_1 - \Phi_2)$$

Then

$$\int_V \nabla \cdot [(\Phi_1 - \Phi_2)\nabla(\Phi_1 - \Phi_2)] \, dV = \int_S [(\Phi_1 - \Phi_2)\nabla(\Phi_1 - \Phi_2)] \cdot \overline{dS}$$

From the vector identity (Art. 2·39)

$$\text{div } (\psi\bar{A}) = \psi \text{ div } \bar{A} + \bar{A} \cdot \text{grad } \psi$$

the equation may be expanded to

$$\int_V (\Phi_1 - \Phi_2)\nabla^2(\Phi_1 - \Phi_2) \, dV + \int_V [\nabla(\Phi_1 - \Phi_2)]^2 \, dV$$
$$= \int_S (\Phi_1 - \Phi_2)\nabla(\Phi_1 - \Phi_2) \cdot \overline{dS}$$

The first integral must be zero by (2); the last integral must be zero, since (1) holds over the boundary surface.   There remains

$$\int_V [\nabla(\Phi_1 - \Phi_2)]^2 \, dV = 0 \tag{3}$$

The gradient of a scalar is a real quantity.   Thus its square can only be positive or zero.   If its integral is to be zero, it can only be zero:

$$\nabla(\Phi_1 - \Phi_2) = 0 \tag{4}$$

or

$$(\Phi_1 - \Phi_2) = \text{constant} \tag{5}$$

This constant must apply even to the boundary, where we know that (1) is true. The constant is then zero, and $\Phi_1 - \Phi_2$ is everywhere zero, which means that Φ_1 and Φ_2 are identical potential distributions. Hence the proof of uniqueness: Laplace's equation can have only one solution which satisfies the boundary conditions of the given region. If by any sort of conniving we find a solution to a field problem that fits all boundary conditions and satisfies Laplace's equation, we may be sure it is the only one.

PROBLEM

3·03   Prove that, if charge density ρ is given throughout a volume, any solution of Poisson's equation 2·22(3), must be the only possible solution provided that it satisfies the boundary conditions around the region.

3·04   SIMPLE EXAMPLE: FIELD BETWEEN COAXIAL CYLINDERS WITH TWO DIELECTRICS

As the first step in the study of problems in which Laplace's equation is used to obtain field and potential distributions, we will take an example with simple boundaries. The prob-
lem is one of finding the potential distribution between two coaxial conducting cylinders of radii a and c (Fig. 3·04), with a dielectric of constant ϵ_1 filling the region between a and b, and a second dielectric of constant ϵ_2 filling the region between b and c. The inner conductor is at potential zero, and the outer at potential V_0. Because of the symmetry of the problem, the solution could be obtained readily by using Gauss's law as in the example of Art. 2·09, but the primary purpose here

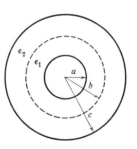

Fig. 3·04   Coaxial cylinders with two dielectrics.

is to demonstrate several processes in the solution by means of differential equations.

The geometrical form suggests that the Laplacian, $\nabla^2\Phi$, be expressed in cylindrical coordinates (Art. 2·39), giving for Laplace's equation

$$\nabla^2\Phi = \frac{1}{r}\frac{\partial}{\partial r}\left(r\frac{\partial\Phi}{\partial r}\right) + \frac{1}{r^2}\frac{\partial^2\Phi}{\partial\phi^2} + \frac{\partial^2\Phi}{\partial z^2} = 0 \qquad (1)$$

It will be assumed that there is no variation in the axial (z) direction, and the cylindrical symmetry eliminates variations with angle ϕ. Equation (1) then reduces to

$$\frac{1}{r}\frac{d}{dr}\left(r\frac{d\Phi}{dr}\right) = 0 \qquad (2)$$

Note that, in the above, the derivative is written as a total derivative, since there is now only one variable remaining in the problem.   Equation (2) may be integrated directly:

$$r \frac{d\Phi}{dr} = C_1 \qquad (3)$$

Integrating again,

$$\Phi_1 = C_1 \ln r + C_2 \qquad (4)$$

This has been labeled Φ_1 because we will consider that the result of (4) is applicable to the first dielectric region $(a < r < b)$.   The same differential equation with the same symmetry applies to the second dielectric region, so the same form of solution applies there also, but the arbitrary constants may be different.   So, for the potential in region 2 $(b < r < c)$, let us write

$$\Phi_2 = C_3 \ln r + C_4 \qquad (5)$$

The boundary conditions at the two conductors are:

(a) $\qquad\qquad\qquad \Phi_1 = 0 \qquad$ at $\quad r = a$

(b) $\qquad\qquad\qquad \Phi_2 = V_0 \qquad$ at $\quad r = c$

In addition, there are continuity conditions at the boundary between the two dielectric media.   The potential and the normal component of electric flux density must be continuous across this charge-free boundary (Art. 2·20):

(c) $\qquad \Phi_1 = \Phi_2 \qquad$ at $\quad r = b$

(d) $\qquad D_{r_1} = D_{r_2} \qquad$ at $\quad r = b$, $\qquad$ or $\quad \epsilon_1 \frac{d\Phi_1}{dr} = \epsilon_2 \frac{d\Phi_2}{dr} \quad$ there

The application of condition (a) to (4) yields

$$C_2 = -C_1 \ln a \qquad (6)$$

The application of (b) to (5) yields

$$C_4 = V_0 - C_3 \ln c \qquad (7)$$

Condition (c), applied to (4) and (5), gives

$$C_1 \ln b + C_2 = C_3 \ln b + C_4 \qquad (8)$$

And condition (d), applied to (4) and (5), gives

$$\epsilon_1 C_1 = \epsilon_2 C_3 \qquad (9)$$

Any one of the constants, as C_1, may be obtained by eliminating between the four equations, (6) to (9):

$$C_1 = \frac{V_0}{\ln\left(\dfrac{b}{a}\right) - \dfrac{\epsilon_1}{\epsilon_2}\ln\left(\dfrac{b}{c}\right)} \tag{10}$$

The remaining constants, C_2, C_3, and C_4, may be obtained from (6), (9), and (7), respectively. The results are substituted in (4) and (5) to give the potential distribution in the two dielectric regions:

$$\Phi_1 = \frac{V_0 \ln\left(\dfrac{r}{a}\right)}{\ln\left(\dfrac{b}{a}\right) + \dfrac{\epsilon_1}{\epsilon_2}\ln\left(\dfrac{c}{b}\right)} \qquad a < r < b \tag{11}$$

$$\Phi_2 = V_0\left[1 - \frac{\dfrac{\epsilon_1}{\epsilon_2}\ln\left(\dfrac{c}{r}\right)}{\ln\left(\dfrac{b}{a}\right) + \dfrac{\epsilon_1}{\epsilon_2}\ln\left(\dfrac{c}{b}\right)}\right] \qquad b < r < c \tag{12}$$

It can be checked that the above distributions do satisfy Laplace's equation and the boundary and continuity conditions of the problem. Only in such simple problems as this will it be possible to obtain solutions of the differential equation by direct integration, but the method of applying boundary and continuity conditions to the solutions, however obtained, is well demonstrated by the example.

PROBLEMS

3·04a Obtain by means of Laplace's equation the potential distribution between two concentric spherical conductors separated by a single dielectric. The inner conductor of radius a is at potential V_0, and the outer conductor of radius b is at potential zero.

3·04b Obtain by means of Laplace's equation the potential distribution between two concentric spherical conductors with two dielectrics filling the region. The inner conductor of radius a is at potential zero, and the outer conductor of radius c is at potential V_0. Dielectric of constant ϵ_1 extends from a to b, and one of constant ϵ_2 extends from b to c.

3·04c Two coaxial cylindrical conductors of radii a and b are at potentials zero and V_0, respectively. There are two dielectrics between the conductors, but this time the plane through the axis is the dividing surface. That is, dielectric ϵ_1 extends from $\phi = 0$ to $\phi = \pi$, and ϵ_2 extends from $\phi = \pi$ to $\phi = 2\pi$. Obtain the potential distribution from Laplace's equation.

3·04d Obtain the electrostatic capacitances for the two conductor systems described in the example of Art. 3·04, and in Probs. a, b, and c.

Graphical Field Mapping

3·05 PRINCIPLES OF GRAPHICAL FIELD MAPPING

By a two-dimensional problem, we mean here one in which the fields do not vary in one linear direction, so that the field distribution need be given in only one cross-sectional plane since it is the same in all cross-sectional planes. We wish to describe first a graphical method for obtaining the potential and field distribution for such two-dimensional problems. It may seem that such a discussion is out of place now that we have set down the principles for the mathematical solution of Laplace's equation, but, since the method offers one of the best

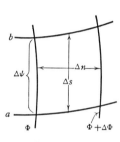

Fig. 3·05a

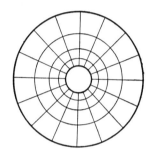

Fig. 3·05b   Map of fields between co-axial conducting cylinders.

aids for visualizing the distribution problem, the physical pictures which it gives will be invaluable as we go on to the next subject, the method of conformal transformations. This graphical method is also a very useful engineering tool, since the configurations of electrodes in vacuum tubes, electron guns, transmission lines, and other practical problems are often not simple mathematical surfaces, so that purely mathematical solutions of the problem may be impractical.

In the method, the known potential difference between electrodes of the boundary is divided into a number of smaller potential divisions, and the equipotential lines (traces of the equipotential surfaces in the cross-sectional plane) are sketched by guess throughout the plot. The electric field lines are also sketched by guess, and these guesses are improved by means of certain properties of the field already studied in Chapter 2. As it was shown there that equipotentials and electric field lines intersect at right angles, a correct field map must show this property. Moreover, if the difference of potential between adjacent equipotentials, and the amount of electric flux between adjacent field lines, are made to be constant throughout the plot, the side ratios for all the little "curvilinear rectangles" formed by the intersection of the equipotentials and the orthogonal field lines must be the same throughout the plot, as will be shown in the following. For convenience in estimating by eye how well this property is satisfied, the side ratio is usually chosen as unity, so that the plot is divided into small "curvilinear squares." This property is demonstrated by the simple plot of the field between coaxial cylinders (Fig. 3·05b). In this, the field lines are radial and the equipotentials are circles with the spacing between adjacent equipotentials proportional to radius.

To demonstrate the side ratio property, consider one of the curvilinear rectangles from a general plot, as in Fig. 3·05a. If Δn is the distance between two adjacent equipotentials, and Δs the distance between two adjacent field lines, the magnitude of electric field, assuming a small square, is approximately $\Delta\Phi/\Delta n$. The electric flux flowing along a flux tube bounded by the two adjacent field lines, for a unit length, is then

$$\Delta\psi = \epsilon\left| E \right| \Delta s = \frac{\epsilon\Delta\Phi\,\Delta s}{\Delta n}$$

or
$$\frac{\Delta s}{\Delta n} = \frac{\Delta\psi}{\epsilon\,\Delta\Phi} \tag{1}$$

So, if the flux per tube $\Delta\psi$, the potential difference per division $\Delta\Phi$, and the dielectric constant ϵ are constant throughout the plot, the side ratio $\Delta s/\Delta n$ must also be constant throughout the plot as stated above.

3·06 THE TECHNIQUE OF GRAPHICAL FIELD MAPPING

In applying the principles of the last article to the sketching of fields, each person will soon develop his own rules of procedure. In beginning the process, some schedule such as the following will be helpful.

(1) Plan on making a number of rough sketches, taking only a minute or so apiece, before starting any plot to be made with care.

(2) Divide the known potential difference between electrodes into an equal number of divisions, say four or eight to begin with.

(3) Begin the sketch of equipotentials in the region where the field is known best, as for example in some region where it approaches a uniform field. Extend the equipotentials according to your best guess throughout the plot. Note that they should tend to hug acute

angles of the conducting boundary, and be spread out in the vicinity of obtuse angles of the boundary.

(4) Draw in the orthogonal set of field lines. As these are started, they should form curvilinear squares, but, as they are extended, the condition of orthogonality should be kept paramount, even though this will result in some rectangles with ratios other than unity.

(5) Look at the regions with poor side ratios, and try to see what was wrong with the first guess of equipotentials. Correct them and repeat the procedure until reasonable curvilinear squares exist throughout the plot.

(6) In regions of low field intensity, there will be large figures, often of five or six sides. In order to judge the correctness of the plot in

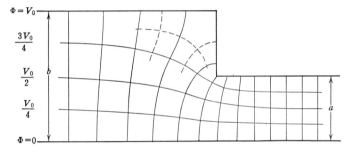

Fig. 3·06a   Map of fields between a plane and stepped conductor.

this region, these large units should be subdivided. The subdivisions should be started back a way, and, each time a flux tube is divided in half, the potential divisions in this region must be divided by the same factor.

There is little more that can be said in words except that the technique can be learned only by the study of some given plots, and by trying the technique on some examples. Some plots are given in Figs. 3·06a and 3·06b. Figure 3·06a shows the field between a plane conductor at potential zero, and a stepped plane at potential V_0, with a step ratio of $\frac{1}{2}$. Figure 3·06b shows a plot that was made to show the field about a particular two-conductor transmission line whose conductors were so shaped as to make difficult an exact mathematical solution. Many of the calculated maps from the method of conformal transformations to follow, especially those for the regions near conducting corners, will also help in forming the physical pictures necessary for this method.

The technique can be extended to some more complicated situations, but it should be pointed out that it becomes enormously more difficult

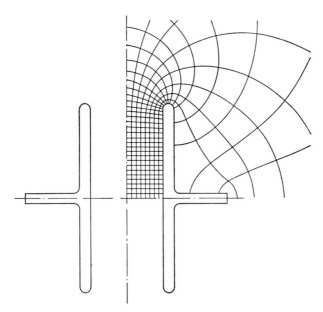

Fig. 3·06b   Map of fields between transmission line conductors of special shape.

to apply for some of these, and that it is impractical except for very important problems.   Some of these extensions are:

(1) to a region with more than one dielectric;

(2) to the magnetic fields within a current-carrying region;

(3) to axially symmetric regions having variations in r and z.   Some of these techniques are discussed in the references.[1]

PROBLEMS

3·06a   Map fields between an infinite plane conductor at potential zero and a second stepped conductor at potential V_0, as in Fig. 3·06a, but for step ratios a/b of $\frac{1}{4}$ and $\frac{3}{4}$.

3·06b   Map fields between an infinite flat plane and a cylindrical conductor parallel to the plane.   The conductor has diameter d, and its axis is at height h above the plane.   Take $d/h = 1, \frac{1}{4}$.

3·06c   The outer conductor of a two-conductor transmission line is a rectangular tube of sides $3a$ and $5a$.   The inner conductor is a circular cylinder of radius a, with axis coincident with the central axis of the rectangular cylinder.   Sketch equipotentials and field lines for the region between conductors, assuming a potential difference V_0 between conductors.

[1] H. Poritsky, "Graphical Field Mapping Methods in Engineering," *Trans. A.I.E.E.*, **57**, 727–732 (1938).   See also S. S. Attwood, *Electric and Magnetic Fields*, Wiley, 3rd ed., 1949; and L. V. Bewley, *Two-Dimensional Fields in Electrical Engineering*, Macmillan, 1948.

3·06d   Two infinite parallel conducting planes defined by $y = a$ and $y = -a$ are at potential zero.   A semi-infinite conducting plane lying halfway between ($y = 0$) and extending from $x = 0$ to $x = \infty$ is at potential V_0.   Sketch a graphical field map for the region between conductors.

3·07   INFORMATION OBTAINED FROM FIELD MAPS

Field maps are made to give not only a general idea of the field distribution for a given problem, but also more specific quantitative information.   For example, the magnitude of electric field may be desired in a problem in which dielectric breakdown is in question.   For a problem in which the motion of an electron through a field is to be computed, both magnitude and direction of field at each point of the path are required.   The direction of the field is given by the direction of the electric field lines at each point, by definition.   The magnitude is approximately the value $\Delta\Phi/\Delta n$, where $\Delta\Phi$ is the difference of potential per division, and Δn the distance between equipotentials.

The electrostatic capacitance per unit length can also be computed readily from a field plot.   By Gauss's law, the charge induced on a conductor is equal to the flux ending there.   This is the number of flux tubes N_f multiplied by the flux per tube.   The potential difference between conductors is the number of potential divisions N_p multiplied by the potential difference per division.   So, for a two-conductor system, the capacitance per unit length is

$$C = \frac{Q}{\Phi_2 - \Phi_1} = \frac{N_f\,\Delta\psi}{N_p\,\Delta\Phi}$$

The ratio $\Delta\psi/\Delta\Phi$ can be obtained from Eq. 3·05(1):

$$C = \frac{N_f}{N_p}\left(\frac{\epsilon\,\Delta s}{\Delta n}\right) \tag{1}$$

And, for a small squares plot with $\Delta s/\Delta n$ equal to unity,

$$C = \epsilon\frac{N_f}{N_p} \text{ farads/meter} \tag{2}$$

For example, in the transmission line plot of Fig. 3·06b, there are 16 potential divisions and 66 flux tubes, so the capacitance, assuming air dielectric, is

$$C = \frac{10^{-9}}{36\pi} \times \frac{66}{16} = 36.5 \times 10^{-12} \text{ farads/meter} \tag{3}$$

PROBLEMS

3·07a   Assume that Fig. 3·06a is full scale, and that V_0 is 1000 volts.   Find the approximate direction of the minimum and maximum electric field strengths in the figure.   Plot a curve of electric field magnitude along the bottom plane as a function of distance along this plane, and a curve showing surface charge density induced on this plane as a function of distance.

3·07b   Calculate the capacitance per unit length from your plots for Probs. 3·06b and 3·06c.

Method of Conformal Transformations

3·08   INTRODUCTION TO COMPLEX FUNCTION THEORY

A very general mathematical attack for the two-dimensional field distribution problem utilizes the theory of functions of a complex

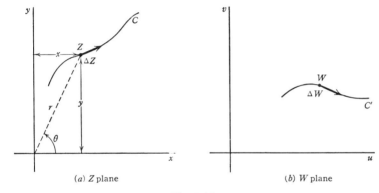

(a) Z plane   (b) W plane

Fig. 3·08.

variable.   The method is in principle the most general for two-dimensional problems, and the work can be carried out to yield actual solutions for a wide variety of practical problems.   For these reasons, the general method with some examples will be presented in this and the following articles.

In the theory of complex variables, the complex notation introduced in Chapter 1 is retained, the imaginary number $\sqrt{-1}$ being denoted by j.   Thus any pure imaginary $\sqrt{-b^2}$ may be written as jb, where b is a pure real.   The sum of a pure real and a pure imaginary, as $a + jb$, is called a complex number.   The variable $Z = x + jy$, where both x and y are real variables, is known as a *complex* variable.   Since Z is defined by a pair of quantities x and y, it is convenient to associate any given value of Z with a point in the x-y plane (Fig. 3·08a), and to call this plane the complex Z plane. Of course the coordinates may also be expressed in the polar form in terms of r and θ:

$$r = \sqrt{x^2 + y^2} \qquad \theta = \tan^{-1}\left(\frac{y}{x}\right)$$

Then
$$Z = x + jy = r\,(\cos\theta + j\sin\theta)$$

The combination in the parentheses is recognized [Eq. 1·05(3)] as $e^{j\theta}$. So the polar form of a complex number, showing the magnitude and phase angle, is most conveniently written

$$Z = re^{j\theta} \tag{1}$$

Suppose that there is now a different complex variable W, where

$$W = u + jv = \rho e^{j\phi}$$

such that W is some function of Z. This means that, for each assigned value of Z, there is a rule specifying a corresponding value of W. The functional relationship is written

$$W = f(Z) \tag{2}$$

If Z is made to vary continuously, the corresponding point in the complex Z plane moves about, tracing out some curve C. The values of W vary correspondingly, tracing out a curve C'. To avoid confusion, the values of W are usually shown on a separate sketch, called the complex W plane (Fig. 3·08b).

Next consider a small change in Z, ΔZ, and the corresponding change in W, ΔW. The derivative of the function will be defined as the usual limit of the ratio $\Delta W/\Delta Z$ as the element ΔZ becomes infinitesimal:

$$\frac{dW}{dZ} = \lim_{\Delta Z \to 0} \frac{\Delta W}{\Delta Z} = \lim_{\Delta Z \to 0} \frac{f(Z + \Delta Z) - f(Z)}{\Delta Z} \tag{3}$$

A complex function is said to be analytic or regular whenever the above defined derivative exists and is unique. The derivative may fail to exist at certain isolated (singular) points where it may be infinite or undetermined, somewhat as in real function theory. But it would appear that there is another ambiguity in respect to complex variables, since ΔZ may be taken in any arbitrary direction in the Z plane from the original point. It would be expected that ΔW would correspondingly lie in different directions, and it is not obvious that the limit of the ratio $\Delta W/\Delta Z$ would turn out to be independent of this direction or phase of ΔZ. The definition requires that this independence be satisfied for analytic functions, since (3) is required to give a unique result for the point of interest.

If this independence of direction is to result, a necessary condition at least is that we obtain the same result if Z is changed in the x direction alone, or in the y direction alone.   For $\Delta Z = \Delta x$,

$$\frac{dW}{dZ} = \frac{\partial W}{\partial x} = \frac{\partial}{\partial x}(u + jv) = \frac{\partial u}{\partial x} + j\frac{\partial v}{\partial x} \tag{4}$$

For a change in the y direction, $\Delta Z = j\,\Delta y$,

$$\frac{dW}{dZ} = \frac{\partial W}{\partial(jy)} = \frac{1}{j}\frac{\partial}{\partial y}(u + jv) = \frac{\partial v}{\partial y} - j\frac{\partial u}{\partial y} \tag{5}$$

Two complex quantities are equal if and only if their real and imaginary parts are separately equal.   Hence (4) and (5) yield the same result if

$$\frac{\partial u}{\partial x} = \frac{\partial v}{\partial y} \tag{6}$$

$$\frac{\partial v}{\partial x} = -\frac{\partial u}{\partial y} \tag{7}$$

The above conditions, known as the Cauchy-Riemann equations, are then necessary conditions for dW/dZ to be unique at a point, and the function $f(Z)$ analytic there.   It can be shown that, if they are satisfied, the same result for dW/dZ is obtained for any arbitrary direction of the change ΔZ, so they are also sufficient conditions.

As an example, from the function

$$W = Z^2 \tag{8}$$

$$u + jv = (x + jy)^2 = (x^2 - y^2) + j2xy$$

$$u = x^2 - y^2$$

$$v = 2xy$$

A check of the Cauchy-Riemann equations yields

$$\frac{\partial u}{\partial x} = \frac{\partial v}{\partial y} = 2x$$

$$\frac{\partial u}{\partial y} = -\frac{\partial v}{\partial x} = -2y$$

So they are satisfied everywhere in the finite Z plane, and the function is analytic everywhere there.

Actually, it is not necessary to apply the check when the functional relation is expressed explicitly between Z and W in terms of functions which possess a power series expansion about the origin, as e^Z, sin Z, etc. The reason is that each term in the series, $C_n Z^n$, can be shown to satisfy the Cauchy-Riemann conditions, and consequently a series of such terms also satisfies them.

PROBLEMS

3·08a Check by the Cauchy-Riemann equations the analyticity of the general power term $W = C_n Z^n$, and a series of such terms,

$$W = \sum_{n=1}^{\infty} C_n Z^n$$

3·08b Check the following functions by the Cauchy-Riemann equations to determine if they are analytic:

$$W = \sin Z$$

$$W = e^Z$$

$$W = Z^* = x - jy$$

$$W = ZZ^*$$

3·08c Check the analyticity of the following, noting isolated points where the derivatives may not remain finite:

$$W = \ln Z$$

$$W = \tan Z$$

3·08d Take the change ΔZ in any general direction $\Delta x + j\Delta y$. Show that, if the Cauchy-Riemann conditions are satisfied, Eq. (3) yields the same result for the derivative as when the change is in the x direction or the y direction alone.

3·09 PROPERTIES OF ANALYTIC FUNCTIONS OF COMPLEX VARIABLES

If Eq. 3·08(6) is differentiated with respect to x, Eq. 3·08(7) differentiated with respect to y, and the resulting equations added, there results

$$\frac{\partial^2 u}{\partial x^2} + \frac{\partial^2 u}{\partial y^2} = 0 \tag{1}$$

Similarly, if the order of differentiation is reversed, there results

$$\frac{\partial^2 v}{\partial x^2} + \frac{\partial^2 v}{\partial y^2} = 0 \tag{2}$$

These are recognized as the Laplace equations in two dimensions. Thus both the real and the imaginary parts of an analytic function of a complex variable satisfy Laplace's equation, and would thus be suitable for use as the potential functions for two-dimensional electrostatic problems. The manner in which these are used in specific problems, and the limitations on this usefulness, will be demonstrated by examples in following articles.

For a problem in which one of the two parts, u or v, is chosen as the potential function, the other becomes proportional to the flux function. To show this, let us suppose that u is the potential function in volts for a particular problem. The electric field, obtained as the negative gradient of u, yields

$$E_x = - \frac{\partial u}{\partial x} \qquad E_y = - \frac{\partial u}{\partial y} \tag{3}$$

By the equation for the total differential, the change in v corresponding to changes in the x and y coordinates of dx and dy is

$$dv = \frac{\partial v}{\partial x} dx + \frac{\partial v}{\partial y} dy$$

But, from Cauchy-Riemann conditions, Eqs. 3·08(6) and 3·08(7),

$$-dv = \frac{\partial u}{\partial y} dx - \frac{\partial u}{\partial x} dy = -E_y\, dx + E_x\, dy$$

or
$$-\epsilon\, dv = -D_y\, dx + D_x\, dy \tag{4}$$

By inspection of Fig. 3·09a, this is recognized to be just the electric flux $d\psi$ between the curves v and $v + dv$, with the positive direction as shown by the arrow. Then

$$-d\psi = \epsilon\, dv \tag{5}$$

And, except for a constant which can be set equal to zero by choosing the reference for flux at $v = 0$,

$$-\psi = \epsilon v \text{ coulombs/meter} \tag{6}$$

Similarly, if v is chosen as the potential function in volts for some problem, ϵu is the flux function in coulombs per meter, with proper choice of the direction for positive flux.

A somewhat different point of view toward the above follows if we refer to the Z and W planes introduced in the preceding article. Since the functional relationship fixes a value of W corresponding to a given value of Z, for a given function

$$W = f(Z)$$

any point (x,y) in the Z plane yields some point (u,v) in the W plane.

As this point moves along some curve $x = F(y)$ in the Z plane, the corresponding point in the W plane traces out a curve $u = F_1(v)$. If it should move throughout a region in the Z plane, the corresponding W point would move throughout some region in the W plane. Thus, in general, a point in the Z plane transforms to a point in the W plane, a curve transforms to a curve, and a region to a region, and the function which accomplishes this is frequently spoken of as a particular *transformation* between the Z and W planes.

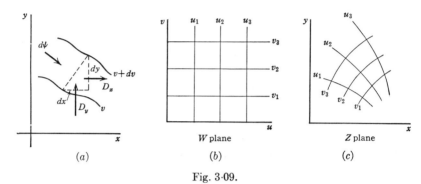

Fig. 3·09.

When the function $f(Z)$ is analytic, as we have seen, the derivative dW/dZ at a point is independent of the direction of the change dZ from the point. The derivative may be written in terms of magnitude and phase:

$$\frac{dW}{dZ} = Me^{j\alpha} \tag{7}$$

or
$$dW = Me^{j\alpha}\,dZ \tag{8}$$

By the rule for the product of complex quantities, the magnitude of dW is M times the magnitude of dZ, and the angle of dW is α plus the angle of dZ. So the entire infinitesimal region in the vicinity of the point W is similar to the infinitesimal region in the vicinity of the point Z. It is magnified by a scale factor M and rotated by an angle α. It is then evident that, if two curves intersect at a given angle in the Z plane, their transformed curves in the W plane intersect at the same angle, since both are rotated through the angle α. A transformation with these properties is called a conformal transformation.

In particular, the lines $u =$ constant and the lines $v =$ constant in the W plane intersect at right angles, so their transformed curves in the Z plane must also be orthogonal (Fig. 3·09b). We already know that this should be so, since the constant v lines have been shown to represent flux lines when the constant u lines are equipotentials, and vice versa. From this point of view, the conformal transformation may be thought of as one which takes a uniform field in the W plane (represented by the equispaced constant u and constant v lines) and transforms it so that it fits within the boundaries of some electrode structure in the Z plane, always keeping the required properties of an electrostatic field.

3·10   THE POWER FUNCTION; FIELD NEAR A CONDUCTING CORNER

As a first example, consider W expressed as Z raised to some power:

$$W = Z^p \tag{1}$$

It is convenient to use the polar form for Z [Eq. 3·08(1)]:

$$W = (re^{j\theta})^p = r^p e^{jp\theta}$$

or

$$u = r^p \cos p\theta \tag{2}$$

$$v = r^p \sin p\theta \tag{3}$$

If v is chosen as the potential function, the form of one curve of constant v (equipotential) is evident by inspection, for v is zero at $\theta = 0$, and also at $\theta = \pi/p$. Thus, if two semi-infinite conducting planes at potential zero intersect at angle α, where

$$p = \frac{\pi}{\alpha} \tag{4}$$

they coincide with this equipotential, and boundary conditions are satisfied. The form of the curves of constant u and of constant v within the angle then give the field configuration near a conducting corner, the sources presumably being far enough away so as not to disturb the field.

The equipotentials in the vicinity of the corner can be plotted by choosing given values of v, and plotting the polar equation of r versus θ from (3) with p given by (4). Similarly, the flux or field lines can be plotted by selecting several values of u and plotting the curves from (2). The form of the field, plotted in this manner, for corners with $\alpha = \pi/4$, $\pi/2$, and $3\pi/2$ are shown in Figs. 3·10a, b, and c, respectively. These plots are of considerable help in judging the correct form of the field in a graphical field map having one or more conducting boundaries.

This is one of the few examples in which the proper form of function to use for the problem might conceivably be arrived at if the boundaries were given as the starting point.   For, if Z is raised to the power π/α, all angles are multiplied by this factor, and the conducting boundary is spread out to a straight line, $v = 0$ in the W plane.   Thus v satisfies Laplace's equation in x and y (Art. 3·09) and the condition of potential

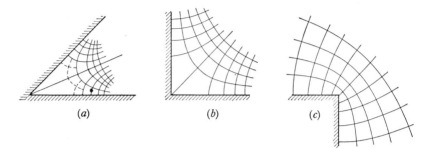

$$(a) \qquad\qquad (b) \qquad\qquad (c)$$

Fig. 3·10   Field near conducting corners of 45°, 90°, 270°.

on the boundary, so is the unique solution for potential inside by Art. 3·03.

PROBLEM

3·10   Plot a few equipotentials and flux lines in the vicinity of conducting corners of angles $\alpha = \pi/3$ and $3\pi/4$.

3·11   THE LOGARITHMIC TRANSFORMATION

Consider next the logarithmic function,

$$W = C_1 \ln Z + C_2 \tag{1}$$

The logarithm of a complex number is readily found if the number is written in the polar form:

$$\ln Z = \ln (re^{j\theta}) = \ln r + j\theta \tag{2}$$

So $W = C_1(\ln r + j\theta) + C_2$

Take the constants C_1 and C_2 as real.   Then

$$u = C_1 \ln r + C_2 \tag{3}$$

$$v = C_1\theta \tag{4}$$

If u is to be chosen as the potential function, we recognize the logarithmic potential forms found previously for potential about a line charge, a charged cylinder, or between coaxial cylinders.   The flux function, $\psi = \epsilon v$, is then proportional to angle θ, as it should be for a problem with radial electric field lines.

To evaluate the constants for a particular problem, take a coaxial line with an inner conductor or radius a at potential zero, and an outer conductor of radius b at potential V_0. Substituting in (3),

$$0 = C_1 \ln a + C_2$$

$$V_0 = C_1 \ln b + C_2$$

Solving,

$$C_1 = \frac{V_0}{\ln (b/a)} \qquad C_2 = -\frac{V_0 \ln a}{\ln (b/a)}$$

So that (1) can be written

$$W = V_0 \left[\frac{\ln (Z/a)}{\ln (b/a)} \right] \tag{5}$$

or

$$\Phi = u = V_0 \left[\frac{\ln (r/a)}{\ln (b/a)} \right] \text{ volts} \tag{6}$$

$$\psi = \epsilon v = \frac{\epsilon V_0 \theta}{\ln (b/a)} \text{ coulombs/meter} \tag{7}$$

In the above, the reference for the flux function came out automatically at $\theta = 0$. If it is desired to use some other reference, the constant C_2 is taken as complex, and its imaginary part serves to fix the reference $\psi = 0$.

PROBLEMS

3·11a   Evaluate the constants C_1 and C_2 in the logarithmic transformation so that u represents the potential function in volts about a line charge of strength q coulombs/meter.   Take potential zero at $r = a$.

3·11b   Show that, if v is taken as the potential function in the logarithmic transformation, it is applicable to the region between two semi-infinite conducting planes intersecting at an angle α, but separated by an infinitesimal gap at the origin so that the plane at $\theta = 0$ may be placed at potential zero, and the plane at $\theta = \alpha$ at potential V_0.   Evaluate the constants C_1 and C_2, taking the reference for zero flux at $r = a$.   Write the flux function in coulombs per meter.

3·11c   In the example of Prob. 3·11b, take the gradient of potential v to give the electric field.   From this, find the electric flux density vector.   Integrate this from radius a to r to give the total flux function, and compare with the result of the above problem.

3·12   THE INVERSE COSINE TRANSFORMATION

Consider the function

$$W = \cos^{-1} Z \tag{1}$$

or $x + jy = \cos(u + jv) = \cos u \cosh v - j \sin u \sinh v$

$x = \cos u \cosh v$

$y = -\sin u \sinh v$

It then follows that

$$\frac{x^2}{\cosh^2 v} + \frac{y^2}{\sinh^2 v} = 1 \tag{2}$$

$$\frac{x^2}{\cos^2 u} - \frac{y^2}{\sin^2 u} = 1 \tag{3}$$

Equation (2) for constant v represents a set of confocal ellipses with foci at ± 1, and (3) for constant u represents a set of confocal hyperbolas orthogonal to the ellipses. These are plotted in Fig. 3·12a. With a proper choice of the region, and the function (either u or v) to serve as the potential function, the above transformation could be made to give the solution to the following problems:

1. Field around a charged elliptic cylinder, including the limiting case of a flat strip.

2. Field between two confocal elliptic cylinders, or between an elliptic cylinder and a flat strip conductor extending between the foci.

3. Field between two confocal hyperbolic cylinders, or between a hyperbolic cylinder and a plane conductor extending from the focus to infinity.

4. Field between two semi-infinite conducting plates, coplanar and with a gap separating them. (This is a limiting case of 3.)

5. Field between an infinite conducting plane and a perpendicular semi-infinite plane separated from it by a gap.

To demonstrate how the result is obtained for a particular one of these, consider example 5, illustrated by Fig. 3·12b. The infinite plane is taken at potential zero, and the perpendicular semi-infinite plane at potential V_0. In using the results of the above general transformation, we must now put in scale factors. To avoid confusion with the preceding, let us denote the variables for this specific problem by primes:

$$W' = C_1 \cos^{-1} kZ' + C_2 \tag{4}$$

The constant C_1 is put in to fix the proper scale of potential, the constant k to fix the scale of size, and the additive constant C_2 to fix the reference for the potential. By comparing with (1),

$$Z = kZ'$$

$$W' = C_1 W + C_2$$

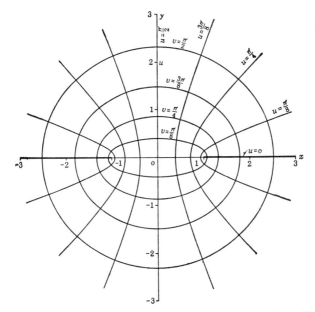

Fig. 3·12a   Plot of the transformation $u + jv = \cos^{-1}(x + jy)$.

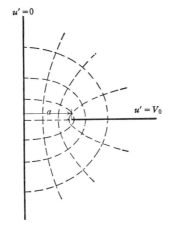

Fig. 3·12b   Field between perpendicular planes with a finite gap.

The constants C_1 and C_2 may be taken as real for this problem. Then

$$u' = C_1 u + C_2 \tag{5}$$

By comparing Figs. 3·12a and b, we want Z' to be a when Z is unity, so $k = 1/a$. Also, when $u = 0$, we want $u' = V_0$; and, when $u = \pi/2$, $u' = 0$. Substitution of these values in (5) yields

$$C_1 = -\frac{2V_0}{\pi} \qquad C_2 = V_0$$

So the transformation with proper scale factors for this problem is

$$W' = u' + jv' = V_0 \left[1 - \frac{2}{\pi} \cos^{-1}\left(\frac{Z'}{a}\right) \right] \tag{6}$$

u' is the potential function in volts, and $\epsilon v'$ is the flux function in coulombs per meter. A few of the equipotential and flux lines with these scale factors applied are shown on Fig. 3·12b.

PROBLEMS

3·12a Find the form of the curves of constant u and constant v for the functions $\sin^{-1} Z$, $\cosh^{-1} Z$, and $\sinh^{-1} Z$. Do these permit one to solve problems in addition to those from the function $\cos^{-1} Z$ of this article?

3·12b Apply the results of the $\cos^{-1}$ transformation to example 4 of Art. 3·12. Take the right-hand semi-infinite plane extending from $x = a$ to $x = \infty$ at potential V_0. Take the left-hand semi-infinite plane extending from $x = -a$ to $x = -\infty$ at potential zero. Evaluate the scale factors and additive constant.

3·12c Apply the results of the transformation to example 2 of Art. 3·12. Take the elliptic cylindrical conductor of semi-major axis a and semi-minor axis b at potential V_0. The inner conductor is a strip conductor extending between the foci, $x = \pm c$, where

$$c = \sqrt{a^2 - b^2}$$

Evaluate all required scale factors and constants. Find the total charge per unit length induced upon the outer cylinder, and the electrostatic capacitance of this two-conductor system.

3·13   PARALLEL CONDUCTING CYLINDERS

Consider next the function

$$W = C \ln \left(\frac{Z - a}{Z + a}\right) \tag{1}$$

This may be written in the form

$$W = C[\ln (Z - a) - \ln (Z + a)]$$

By comparing with the logarithmic transformation of Art. 3·11 which, among other things, could represent the field about a single line charge, it follows that the above can represent the field about two line charges, one at $Z = a$, and the other of equal strength but opposite sign at $Z = -a$. However, it is more interesting to show that this form can also yield the field about parallel cylinders of any radius.

Taking C as real,

$$u = \frac{C}{2} \ln \left[\frac{(x - a)^2 + y^2}{(x + a)^2 + y^2} \right] \tag{2}$$

$$v = C \left[\tan^{-1} \frac{y}{(x - a)} - \tan^{-1} \frac{y}{(x + a)} \right] \tag{3}$$

Thus lines of constant u can be obtained from (2) by setting the argument of the logarithm equal to a constant:

$$\frac{(x - a)^2 + y^2}{(x + a)^2 + y^2} = K$$

As this may be put in the form

$$\left[x - \frac{a(1 + K)}{1 - K} \right]^2 + y^2 = \frac{4a^2 K}{(1 - K)^2} \tag{4}$$

the curves of constant u are circles with centers at

$$x = \frac{a(1 + K)}{1 - K}$$

and radii $(2a \sqrt{K})/(1 - K)$. If u is taken as the potential function, any one of the circles of constant u may be replaced by an equipotential

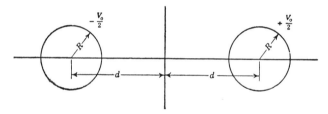

Fig. 3·13   Two parallel conducting cylinders.

conducting cylinder. Thus, if R is the radius of such a conductor with center at $x = d$ (Fig. 3·13), the values of a and the particular value of K (denoted K_0) may be obtained by setting

$$\frac{a(1 + K_0)}{1 - K_0} = d \qquad \frac{2a \sqrt{K_0}}{1 - K_0} = R$$

Solving,

$$a = \sqrt{d^2 - R^2} \tag{5}$$

$$\sqrt{K_0} = \frac{d}{R} + \sqrt{\frac{d^2}{R^2} - 1} \tag{6}$$

The constant C in the transformation depends upon the potential of the conducting cylinder. Let this be $V_0/2$. Then, by the definition of K,

$$\frac{V_0}{2} = C \ln \sqrt{K_0} = C \ln \left[\frac{d}{R} + \sqrt{\frac{d^2}{R^2} - 1} \right]$$

or
$$C = \frac{V_0}{2 \ln \left[\dfrac{d}{R} + \sqrt{\dfrac{d^2}{R^2} - 1} \right]} = \frac{V_0}{2 \cosh^{-1}\left(\dfrac{d}{R}\right)} \tag{7}$$

Substituting in (2), the potential at any point (x,y) is

$$\Phi = u = \frac{V_0}{4 \cosh^{-1}\left(\dfrac{d}{R}\right)} \ln \left[\frac{(x-a)^2 + y^2}{(x+a)^2 + y^2} \right] \tag{8}$$

And the flux function, ϵv, is

$$\psi = \epsilon v = \frac{\epsilon V_0}{2 \cosh^{-1}\left(\dfrac{d}{R}\right)} \left[\tan^{-1}\frac{y}{(x-a)} - \tan^{-1}\frac{y}{(x+a)} \right] \tag{9}$$

Although we have not put in the left-hand conducting cylinder explicitly, the odd symmetry of the potential from (8) will cause this boundary condition to be satisfied also if the left-hand cylinder of radius R with center at $x = -d$ is at potential $-V_0/2$.

If we wish to use the result to obtain the capacitance per unit length of a parallel wire line, we obtain the charge on the right-hand conductor from Gauss's law by finding the total flux ending on it. In passing once around the conductor, the first term of (9) changes by 2π, and the second by zero. So

$$q = 2\pi \frac{\epsilon V_0}{2 \cosh^{-1}\left(\dfrac{d}{R}\right)} \text{ coulombs/meter}$$

or
$$C = \frac{q}{V_0} = \frac{\pi \epsilon}{\cosh^{-1}\left(\dfrac{d}{R}\right)} \text{ farads/meter} \tag{10}$$

PROBLEMS

3·13a Modify the above to apply to the problem of parallel cylinders of unequal radius. Take the left-hand cylinder of radius R_1 with center at $x = -d_1$, the right-hand cylinder of radius R_2 with center at $x = d_2$, and a total difference of potential V_0 between cylinders. Find the electrostatic capacitance per unit length in terms of R_1, R_2, and $(d_1 + d_2)$.

3·13b Show that the lines of constant v in the transformation of Art. 3·13 do represent a family of circles.

3·13c The important bilinear transformation is of the form

$$Z = \frac{aZ' + b}{cZ' + d}$$

Take a, b, c, and d as real constants, and show that any circle in the Z' plane is transformed to a circle in the Z plane by this transformation. (Straight lines are considered circles of infinite radius.)

3·13d Consider the special case of Prob. c with $a = R$, $b = -R$, $c = 1$, and $d = 1$. Show that the imaginary axis of the Z' plane transforms to a circle of radius R, center at the origin, in the Z plane. Show that a line charge at $x' = d$ and its image at $x' = -d$ in the Z' plane transform to points in the Z plane at radii r_1 and r_2 with

$$r_1 r_2 = R^2$$

Compare with the result for imaging line charges in a cylinder (Art. 2·21).

3·14   THE SCHWARZ TRANSFORMATION FOR GENERAL POLYGONS

In all the preceding examples, specific functions have been set down, and the electrostatic problems solvable by these deduced from a study of their properties. In a practical problem, the reverse procedure is usually required, for the specific equipotential conducting boundaries will be given and it will be desired to find the complex function useful in solving the problem. For some of the preceding examples, it is true that the function might have been arrived at if one were given the problem first, and used a good physical picture combined with a bit of ingenuity. However, the greatest limitation on this method of conformal transformations is that, for general shaped boundaries, there is no straightforward procedure by which one can always arrive at the desired transformation if the two-dimensional physical problem is given. There is such a procedure, however, when the boundaries consist of straight line sides with angle intersections. We wish to describe it briefly.

Suppose that a polygon is given in the Z plane (Fig. 3·14a) with vertices at P_1, P_2, $\cdots$, P_n and with corresponding interior angles α_1, α_2, $\cdots$, α_n. Suppose that it is desired to transform this boundary into the straight line $y' = 0$ in some other Z' plane, with P_1 going into the point $Z' = x_1'$, P_2 into x_2', etc. The Schwarz transformation states that the proper function may be found by integrating the derivative:

$$\frac{dZ}{dZ'} = K(Z' - x_1')^{(\alpha_1/\pi)-1}(Z' - x_2')^{(\alpha_2/\pi)-1} \cdots (Z' - x_n')^{(\alpha_n/\pi)-1}$$

$$(1)$$

We do not wish to attempt to prove this, but each factor in the above may be thought of as straightening out the boundary at one of the vertices, as the transformation of Art. 3·10 did for the single corner. That is, if dZ' is changed always in the same direction along the line $y' = 0$, dZ remains of the same direction (phase) except when we pass through a point corresponding to one of the vertices, say x_m'. Here the factor $(Z' - x_m')$ changes phase by a factor π, and the factor

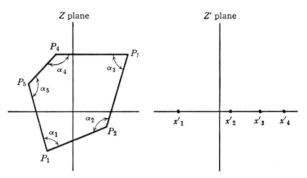

Fig. 3·14a.

$(Z' - x_m')^{(\alpha_m/\pi)-1}$ changes phase by a factor $\alpha_m - \pi$, so the direction of dZ is changed by $\alpha_m - \pi$, and passes along the next side of the polygon.

Although we have spoken of the figure to be transformed as a polygon, in the practical application of the method, one or more of the vertices are often at infinity, and part of the boundary may be at a different potential from the remaining part. Then the line $y' = 0$ in the Z' plane consists of two parts at different potentials. If this latter electrostatic problem is solved, it may be considered a transformation from the Z to the W plane, and thus the transformation from the Z to the W plane is given with the Z' plane only as an intermediate step. Another sort of problem in which the method is useful is that in which a thin charged wire lies on the interior of a conducting polygon, parallel to the elements of the polygon. By the Schwarz transformation, the polygon boundary is transformed to the line $y' = 0$, and the wire will then correspond to some point in the upper half of the Z' plane. This electrostatic problem can be solved by the method of images, and so the original problem can be solved in this case also.

To clarify some of these general statements, let us consider one of the most simple standard examples for the Schwarz transformation. This is the problem of the edge effect for a parallel plate condenser, and is one of the first type described in the preceding paragraph.   The problem is idealized by taking the infinite plane $y = 0$ at potential V_0, and a zero-potential parallel semi-infinite plane extending from $x = 0$, $y = h$ to $x = \infty$, $y = h$ (Fig. 3·14b).   In this example, the vertices (two of which are at infinity) have angles $\alpha_1 = 0$, $\alpha_2 = 2\pi$, $\alpha_3 = \pi$.   We choose to transform the first vertex to the origin of the Z' plane, with the gap separating the two conductors becoming an infinitesimal gap at the origin.   The second vertex is transformed to

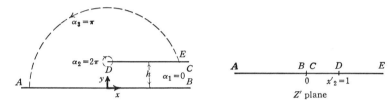

Fig. 3·14b.

$x_2' = 1$, and the third vertex to $x_3' = \infty$.   The factor of Eq. (1) corresponding to a vertex transformed to infinity in the Z' plane is not included in the equation (Prob. 3·14a).   Then

$$\frac{dZ}{dZ'} = K(Z' - 0)^{(0/\pi)-1}(Z' - 1)^{(2\pi/\pi)-1} = K\,\frac{(Z' - 1)}{Z'} \tag{2}$$

or
$$Z = K \int \left(1 - \frac{1}{Z'}\right) dZ' = K(Z' - \ln Z') + C \tag{3}$$

To evaluate the constants K and C, note first that $Z = 0 + jh$ when $Z' = 1$.

$$jh = K + C$$

$$Z = K[Z' - 1 - \ln Z'] + jh \tag{4}$$

A second, less direct, condition may be imposed by integrating between B and C, approaching infinity in the Z plane and zero in the Z' plane:

$$\int_B^C dZ = \int_B^C \frac{dZ}{dZ'}\,dZ' \tag{5}$$

But, from (2) for $Z' \to 0$,

$$\frac{dZ}{dZ'} \to -\frac{K}{Z'}$$

If the right side of (5) is integrated about a circle of radius r',

$$dZ' = d(r'e^{j\theta'}) = jr'e^{j\theta'} \, d\theta' = jZ' \, d\theta'$$

Then

$$\int_{\infty+j0}^{\infty+jh} dZ = \int_{\pi}^{0} \left(-\frac{K}{Z'} \right) jZ' \, d\theta'$$

or

$$jh = jK\pi$$

$$K = \frac{h}{\pi}$$

And the transformation is

$$Z = \frac{h}{\pi}[Z' - 1 - \ln Z' + j\pi] \tag{6}$$

It can be shown (compare with Prob. 3·11b) that the transformed problem in the Z' plane, which consists of the left half plane at potential

TABLE 3·14

$Z = x + jy$; $W = u + jv$, WHERE $u =$ FLUX FUNCTION, $v =$ POTENTIAL

	$Z = \frac{b}{\pi}\left\{ \cosh^{-1}\left[\dfrac{\alpha^2 + 1 - 2\alpha^2 e^{kW}}{1 - \alpha^2}\right] - \alpha \cosh^{-1}\left[\dfrac{2e^{-kW} - (\alpha^2 + 1)}{1 - \alpha^2}\right] \right\}$ $\alpha = \dfrac{a}{b}$ $\qquad k = \dfrac{\pi}{V_0}$
	$Z = \dfrac{b}{\pi}\left[\ln\left(\dfrac{1 + S}{1 - S}\right) - 2\alpha \tan^{-1}\left(\dfrac{S}{\alpha}\right) \right]$ $\alpha = \dfrac{a}{b}$ $\qquad S = \sqrt{\dfrac{e^{kW} + \alpha}{e^{kW} - 1}}$

V_0 and the right half at potential zero, may be solved by the function

$$W = u + jv = \frac{V_0}{\pi} \ln Z'$$

or

$$Z' = e^{\pi W/V_0}$$

In the above, v represents the potential function, and the reference for zero flux is taken at the point D $(r' = 1)$. Substituting in (6),

$$Z = \frac{h}{\pi}\left[e^{\pi W/V_0} - 1 - \frac{\pi W}{V_0} + j\pi \right] \tag{7}$$

Equation (7) is the solution to the problem in that it gives the potential and flux functions as implicit functions of the coordinates x and y. Results for some other important problems which have been solved by the Schwarz technique are given in Table 3·14.

PROBLEMS

3·14a Explain why a factor in the Schwarz transformation is left out when it corresponds to a point transformed to infinity in the Z' plane, as for the third vertex in the above example.

3·14b In the example of the above article, separate Z into real and imaginary parts. Show that the boundary condition for potential is satisfied along the two conductors. Obtain the asymptotic equations for large positive u and for large negative u, and interpret the results in terms of the type of field approached in these limits.

3·14c Work the example of Prob. 3·12b by the Schwarz technique and show that the same result is obtained. This is the problem of two coplanar semi-infinite plane conductors separated by a gap $2a$, with the right-hand conductor at potential zero, and the left-hand conductor at potential V_0.

3·14d For the first example of Table 3·14, find the electrostatic capacitance in excess of that which would be obtained if a uniform field existed in both of the parallel-plane regions.

The Separation of Variables Technique and Product Solutions in Rectangular, Cylindrical, and Spherical Coordinates

3·15 THE PRODUCT SOLUTION METHOD

In spite of the great generality in principle of the transformation method for solving two-dimensional Laplace equation problems, we have seen that there are practical difficulties in using it to yield the solution for all two-dimensional problems. Moreover, there is no direct extension of the method to three-dimensional problems. We wish now to describe one of the standard methods for the solution of partial differential equations in any number of variables. In this method, the solution is expressed as a product of functions, each of which contains only one of the variables of the coordinate system used. For example, in a cylindrical coordinate system, the solution for potential may be expressed as a product of three functions, one in terms of radius r, one in terms of azimuthal angle ϕ, and one in terms of the axial distance z. Substitution in the partial differential equation allows one to separate it into ordinary differential equations in each of the variables, and these may be solved separately. The technique is known as the method of *product solutions* or of *separation of variables*.

It may seem that elimination at the outset of all solutions not of the product form represents a severe limitation, but it is not so severe, since a series of such solutions may be used when one alone will not permit a matching of boundary conditions. This is permissible since the sum of separate solutions to a linear differential equation is also a solution of the equation. The amounts of the individual solutions to be added are determined by the boundary conditions in a manner somewhat analogous to that used to determine the amounts of the individual harmonics to add up to a complex wave shape in a Fourier analysis. (See Arts. 1·13 and 1·28.)

In the following articles, we shall apply the product solutions technique to Laplace's equation in rectangular, cylindrical, and spherical coordinates. Since a solution of Laplace's equation continuous through the second derivative is called a *harmonic* function, the corresponding product solutions for the above cases are often called *rectangular harmonics*, *cylindrical harmonics*, and *spherical harmonics*. Various series of these will be combined to fit, exactly or approximately, the boundary conditions for many shapes of electrodes. In addition to the importance of the method for these specific problems, it is of greatest importance to us since the same technique (and some of the same functions) will be used to obtain solutions of the wave equation for various time-varying problems in later chapters.

3·16   RECTANGULAR HARMONICS

As the simplest example of the method of separation of variables, let us first consider two-dimensional problems in the rectangular coordinates x and y, as we have in the transformation method of the past section. Laplace's equation in these coordinates is

$$\frac{\partial^2 \Phi}{\partial x^2} + \frac{\partial^2 \Phi}{\partial y^2} = 0 \tag{1}$$

We wish to study product solutions of the form

$$\Phi = XY \tag{2}$$

where X denotes a function of x alone, and Y a function of y alone. Substituting in (1),

$$X''Y + XY'' = 0$$

Here X'' denotes the second total derivative of X with respect to x, and Y'' similarly denotes d^2Y/dy^2. To separate variables in this example, divide by XY:

$$\frac{X''}{X} = -\frac{Y''}{Y} \tag{3}$$

Next follows the key argument for this method. Equation (3) is to apply for all values of the variables x and y. Since the right side does not contain x and so cannot vary with x, the left side cannot vary with x either. A function of x which does not vary with x is a constant. Similarly, the left side does not vary with y, so the right side cannot, and therefore must also be equal to a constant—the same constant. Let this constant be denoted α^2. Then

$$\frac{X''}{X} = \alpha^2 \tag{4}$$

$$\frac{Y''}{Y} = -\alpha^2 \tag{5}$$

Equation (4) is recognized (Art. 1·05) as the standard form having solutions in exponentials or hyperbolic functions. Let us write them here in the hyperbolic form:

$$X = A \cosh \alpha x + B \sinh \alpha x \tag{6}$$

Equation (5) is recognized (Art. 1·04) as the form having solutions in sinusoids:

$$Y = C \cos \alpha y + D \sin \alpha y \tag{7}$$

So, substituting (6) and (7) in (2),

$$\Phi = [A \cosh \alpha x + B \sinh \alpha x][C \cos \alpha y + D \sin \alpha y] \tag{8}$$

The separation constant in the above could have been taken negative as well as positive. Let it be $-\beta^2$ in place of α^2. Then

$$\frac{X''}{X} = -\beta^2$$

$$\frac{Y''}{Y} = \beta^2$$

and the solution for the x equation is in sinusoids, the solution for the y equation in hyperbolics or exponentials:

$$\Phi = [A' \cos \beta x + B' \sin \beta x][C' \cosh \beta y + D' \sinh \beta y] \tag{9}$$

The form (8) actually includes the form (9) if α is allowed to take on imaginary values, $\alpha = j\beta$.

For the three-dimensional case in rectangular coordinates, the procedure is simply extended. Laplace's equation is

$$\frac{\partial^2 \Phi}{\partial x^2} + \frac{\partial^2 \Phi}{\partial y^2} + \frac{\partial^2 \Phi}{\partial z^2} = 0 \tag{10}$$

Consider solutions of the form

$$\Phi = XYZ$$

where X is a function of x alone, Y of y alone, and Z of z alone.   Substituting in (10),

$$X''YZ + XY''Z + XYZ'' = 0$$

or
$$\frac{X''}{X} + \frac{Y''}{Y} = -\frac{Z''}{Z} \qquad (11)$$

The left side does not vary with z, and so the right side cannot, so must be a constant.   Denote this by γ^2:

$$\frac{Z''}{Z} = -\gamma^2$$

and
$$Z = E \cos \gamma z + F \sin \gamma z \qquad (12)$$

Substituting in (11) and repeating the argument for x and y,

$$\frac{X''}{X} = -\frac{Y''}{Y} + \gamma^2 = \alpha^2$$

$$X = A \cosh \alpha x + B \sinh \alpha x \qquad (13)$$

and finally for y,

$$\frac{Y''}{Y} = \gamma^2 - \alpha^2 = \beta^2$$

$$Y = C \cosh \beta y + D \sinh \beta y \qquad (14)$$

Combining (12), (13), and (14),

$$\Phi = [A \cosh \alpha x + B \sinh \alpha x][C \cosh \beta y + D \sinh \beta y]$$
$$[E \cos \gamma z + F \sin \gamma z] \qquad (15)$$

where
$$\alpha^2 + \beta^2 = \gamma^2$$

Other forms for the three-dimensional case can be obtained by assigning imaginary values to any or all of the constants α, β, γ in the above.

PROBLEMS

3·16a   Check by differentiation to show that (15) does satisfy (10).

3·16b   Find the basic forms [in the sense that (9) is a different form from (8)] of (15) obtained by allowing α, β, γ, and various combinations to become imaginary.

3·16c   The so-called circular harmonics are the product solutions to Laplace's equation in the two circular cylindrical coordinates r and ϕ. Apply the basic separation of variables technique to Laplace's equation in these coordinates to yield two ordinary differential equations. Show that the r and ϕ equations are satisfied respectively by the functions R and F_ϕ where

$$R = C_1 r^n + C_2 r^{-n}$$

$$F_\phi = C_3 \cos n\phi + C_4 \sin n\phi$$

3·17   FIELD DESCRIBED BY A SINGLE RECTANGULAR HARMONIC

Let us see what boundaries would be required in order to have some one of the forms of Art. 3·16 as a solution. Take the special case of Eq. 3·16(8) with $A = 0$, $C = 0$. The product of remaining constants, BD, may be denoted as a single constant C_1:

$$\Phi = C_1 \sinh \alpha x \sin \alpha y \tag{1}$$

It is evident from (1) that potential is zero at $x = 0$ for all y. Hence one boundary can be a zero-potential conducting plane at $x = 0$. Similarly, potential is zero along the plane $y = 0$, and also at other parallel planes defined by $\alpha y = n\pi$. Let us confine attention to the region $0 < \alpha y < \pi$ and $0 < x < \infty$. The intersecting zero-potential planes of interest then form a rectangular conducting trough. Let its depth in the y direction be b. Then $\alpha b = \pi$ or

$$\alpha = \frac{\pi}{b} \tag{2}$$

If there is to be a finite field in the region, there must be some electrode at a potential other than zero. Without knowing its shape for the moment, let us take the value of x at which it crosses the midplane $y = b/2$ as $x = a$, and the potential of the electrode as V_0. Then, from (1),

$$V_0 = C_1 \sinh \frac{\pi a}{b} \sin \frac{\pi}{2} = C_1 \sinh \frac{\pi a}{b}$$

or, substituting in (1),

$$\Phi = \frac{V_0 \sinh (\pi x/b)}{\sinh (\pi a/b)} \sin (\pi y/b) \tag{3}$$

The potential at any point x,y may be computed from (3). In particular, the form that the electrode at potential V_0 must take, can be found from (3) by setting $\Phi = V_0$, yielding

$$\sinh \frac{\pi x}{b} = \frac{\sinh (\pi a/b)}{\sin (\pi y/b)} \tag{4}$$

Equation (4) can be plotted to show the form of the electrode. This is done for a value $a/b = \frac{1}{2}$ in Fig. 3·17. Actually, the electrodes should extend to infinity, but if they are extended a large but finite distance, the solution studied here will represent the potential very well everywhere except near edges.

PROBLEMS

3·17a Plot the form of equipotentials for $\Phi = \frac{1}{4}V_0$, $\frac{1}{2}V_0$, and $\frac{3}{4}V_0$ for Fig. 3·17.

3·17b Describe the electrode structure for which the single rectangular harmonic $C_1 \cosh \alpha x \sin \alpha y$ is a solution for potential. Take electrodes at potential V_0 passing through $|x| = a$ when $y = a/2$.

3·17c Describe the electrode structure and exciting potentials for which the single circular harmonic (Prob. 3·16c) $Cr^2 \cos 2\phi$ is a solution.

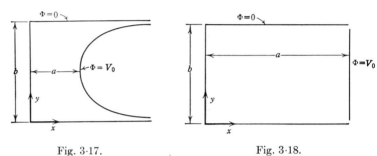

Fig. 3·17.   Fig. 3·18.

3·18   FIELD DESCRIBED BY A SERIES OF RECTANGULAR HARMONICS

As an example of a problem which cannot be solved by using a single one of the solutions of Art. 3·16, but can be by means of a series of these solutions, consider the two-dimensional region of Fig. 3·18 bounded by a zero-potential plane at $x = 0$, a zero-potential plane at $y = 0$, a parallel zero-potential plane at $y = b$, and a plane conducting lid of potential V_0 at $x = a$. In the ideal problem, the lid is separated from the remainder of the rectangular box by infinitesimal gaps. In a practical problem, it would only be expected that these gaps should be small compared with the rest of the box.   •

In selecting the proper forms from Art. 3·16, we will choose the form having sinusoidal solutions in y, since potential is zero at $y = 0$ and also at $y = b$, and sinusoids have repeated zeros. So the form of Eq. 3·16(8) is suitable. Moreover, $\Phi = 0$ at $x = 0$ for all y of interest, so the function of x must go to zero at $x = 0$, showing that $A = 0$. Similarly, since $\Phi = 0$ at $y = 0$ for all x of interest, $C = 0$. Φ is again zero at $y = b$, so $\alpha b = n\pi$, or

$$\alpha = \frac{n\pi}{b}$$

Denoting the product of the remaining constants BD as C_n,

$$\Phi = C_n \sinh \frac{n\pi x}{b} \sin \frac{n\pi y}{b}$$

This form satisfies Laplace's equation and the boundary conditions at $x = 0$, at $y = 0$, and at $y = b$, but a single term of this form cannot satisfy the boundary condition along the plane lid at $x = a$, as a study like that of the preceding article would show.   But a series of such solutions also satisfies Laplace's equation and the boundary conditions at $x = 0$, at $y = 0$, and at $y = b$:

$$\Phi = \sum_{n=1}^{\infty} C_n \sinh \frac{n\pi x}{b} \sin \frac{n\pi y}{b} \tag{1}$$

In order for the sum (1) to give the required constant potential V_0 along the plane $x = a$ over the interval $0 < y < b$, we require

$$V_0 = \sum_{n=1}^{\infty} C_n \sinh \frac{n\pi a}{b} \sin \frac{n\pi y}{b} \qquad 0 < y < b \tag{2}$$

But this is recognized as a Fourier expansion in sines of the constant function V_0 over the interval $0 < y < b$.   This expansion was carried out in Art. 1·15 to yield

$$f(y) = V_0 = \sum_{n=1}^{\infty} a_n \sin \frac{n\pi y}{b} \tag{3}$$

$$a_n = \begin{cases} \dfrac{4V_0}{n\pi}, & n \text{ odd} \\[2mm] 0, & n \text{ even} \end{cases} \tag{4}$$

Comparing (3) with (2) shows that

$$C_n \sinh \frac{n\pi a}{b} = a_n \tag{5}$$

Substitution of the results of (5) and (4) in (1) gives

$$\Phi = \sum_{n \text{ odd}} \frac{4V_0}{n\pi} \frac{\sinh (n\pi x/b)}{\sinh (n\pi a/b)} \sin \frac{n\pi y}{b} \tag{6}$$

This series is rapidly convergent except for values of x approaching a, so it can be used for reasonably convenient calculation of potential at any interior point x,y.

PROBLEMS

3·18a   Obtain a series solution for the two-dimensional box problem in which sides at $y = 0$ and $y = b$ are at potential zero, and end planes at $x = a$ and $x = -a$ are at potential V_0.   *Hint:* Utilize the symmetry of the problem in the evaluation of constants.

3·18b   In a two-dimensional problem, parallel planes at $y = 0$ and $y = b$ extend from $x = 0$ to $x = \infty$, and are at zero potential.   The one end plane at $x = 0$ is at potential V_0.   Obtain a series solution.   *Hint:* Use the exponential form for the solution in x, and consider the condition at infinity.

3·18c   Using the circular harmonics of Prob. 3·16c, form a series for solution of potential inside a long thin split cylinder of radius a whose lower half ($-\pi < \phi < 0$) is at potential $-V_0$, and whose upper half ($0 < \phi < \pi$) is at potential V_0.   Similarly, write a series solution valid for $r > a$.

3·19   CYLINDRICAL HARMONICS

A large class of problems of major interest is that in which field distribution is desired throughout a region having cylindrical symmetry about an axis, such as the familiar electrostatic electron lenses found in many cathode-ray tubes, or in certain coaxial transmission line problems for which static solutions are useful.

The cylindrical shapes indicate the use of cylindrical coordinates. We shall first consider the symmetrical case in which there are no variations with ϕ.   Thus Laplace's equation becomes (Art. 2·39)

$$\frac{\partial^2 \Phi}{\partial r^2} + \frac{1}{r}\frac{\partial \Phi}{\partial r} + \frac{\partial^2 \Phi}{\partial z^2} = 0 \tag{1}$$

To solve this equation let us try to find solutions of the product form. That is, try

$$\Phi = RZ \tag{2}$$

where R is a function of r alone, Z of z alone.   Substitute in the differential equation (1)

$$R''Z + \frac{1}{r}R'Z + RZ'' = 0$$

R'' denotes d^2R/dr^2, Z'' denotes d^2Z/dz^2, etc.   Separate variables by dividing by RZ:

$$\frac{Z''}{Z} = -\left[\frac{R''}{R} + \frac{1}{r}\frac{R'}{R}\right]$$

By the standard argument for the method of separation of variables, the left side, which is a function of z alone, and the right side, which is a function of r alone, must be equal to each other for all values of the variables r and z. Both sides must then be equal to a constant. Let this constant be T^2. Two ordinary differential equations then result as follows:

$$\frac{1}{R}\frac{d^2R}{dr^2} + \frac{1}{rR}\frac{dR}{dr} = -T^2 \tag{3}$$

$$\frac{1}{Z}\frac{d^2Z}{dz^2} = T^2 \tag{4}$$

The second equation is the familiar differential equation of simple harmonic motion studied in Chapter 1. The solution is then in sinusoids if T^2 is negative, in hyperbolic functions (or exponentials) if T^2 is positive.

(a) First consider T^2 positive so that the solution to (4) is in terms of hyperbolic functions. Equation (3) is then

$$\frac{d^2R}{dr^2} + \frac{1}{r}\frac{dR}{dr} + T^2R = 0 \tag{5}$$

In Chapter 1, the familiar equation resulting in sinusoids [as (4) above] was solved by assuming a solution in the form of a power series. Substitution in the differential equation told the form this series must have to be truly a solution of the equation. Similarly, to solve (5), the function R may also be assumed to be some series of powers of r:

$$R = a_0 + a_1r + a_2r^2 + a_3r^3 + \cdots$$

or

$$R = \sum_{p=0}^{\infty} a_p r^p \tag{6}$$

Substitution of this function in (5) shows that it is a solution if the constants are as follows:

$$a_p = a_{2m} = C_1(-1)^m \frac{(T/2)^{2m}}{(m!)^2}$$

(C_1 is any arbitrary constant.) That is,

$$R = C_1 \sum_{m=0}^{\infty} \frac{(-1)^m(Tr/2)^{2m}}{(m!)^2} = C_1\left[1 - \left(\frac{Tr}{2}\right)^2 + \frac{(Tr/2)^4}{(2!)^2} - \cdots\right] \tag{7}$$

is a solution to the differential equation (5).

The series is not recognized as the series for a simple function, as were the series for sines and cosines in Chapter 1, but it is easy to check and find that it is convergent, so that values may be calculated for any argument (Tr).   Such calculations have been made over a wide range of values for the argument, the results tabulated, and the function defined by the series denoted by $J_0(Tr)$ and called a Bessel function (of first kind, zero order; the reason for such specific designation will be apparent later).   Thus defined,

$$J_0(v) \equiv 1 - \left(\frac{v}{2}\right)^2 + \frac{(v/2)^4}{(2!)^2} - \cdots \equiv \sum_{m=0}^{\infty} \frac{(-1)^m (v/2)^{2m}}{(m!)^2} \qquad (8)$$

The particular solution (7) may then be written simply as

$$R = C_1 J_0(Tr)$$

The differential equation (5) is of the second order and so must have a second solution with a second arbitrary constant.   (The sine and cosine constitute the two solutions for the simple harmonic motion equation.)   This solution cannot be obtained by the power series method outlined above, since a general study of differential equations would show that at least one of the two independent solutions of (5) must have a singularity at $r = 0$.   There are several methods for obtaining this second solution, all too detailed to be included here, and several different forms for the solution.   One form for the second solution (any of which may be called Bessel functions of second kind, order zero) easily found in tables is

$$N_0(v) = \frac{2}{\pi} \ln\left(\frac{\gamma v}{2}\right) J_0(v)$$

$$- \frac{2}{\pi} \sum_{m=1}^{\infty} \frac{(-1)^m (v/2)^{2m}}{(m!)^2} \left[1 + \frac{1}{2} + \frac{1}{3} + \cdots \frac{1}{m}\right] \qquad (9)$$

The constant $\ln \gamma = 0.5772 \cdots$ is Euler's constant.   In general, then,

$$R = C_1 J_0(Tr) + C_2 N_0(Tr) \qquad (10)$$

is the solution to (5), with

$$Z = C_3 \sinh (Tz) + C_4 \cosh (Tz) \qquad (11)$$

as the corresponding form for the solution to (4).   It should be noted from (9) that $N_0(Tr)$, the second solution to R, becomes infinite at $r = 0$, so it cannot be present in any problem for which $r = 0$ is included in the region over which the solution applies.

(b) If T^2 is negative, let $T^2 = -\tau^2$ or $T = j\tau$, where τ is real, and (5) may be written

$$\frac{d^2R}{dr^2} + \frac{1}{r}\frac{dR}{dr} - \tau^2R = 0 \tag{12}$$

The series (7) is still a solution, and T in (7) may be replaced by $j\tau$. Since all powers of the series are even, imaginaries disappear, and a new series is obtained which is real and also convergent. That is,

$$J_0(jv) = 1 + \left(\frac{v}{2}\right)^2 + \frac{(v/2)^4}{(2!)^2} + \frac{(v/2)^6}{(3!)^2} + \cdots \tag{13}$$

Values of $J_0(jv)$ may be calculated for various values of v from such a series; these are also tabulated in the references. The defined function is denoted $I_0(v)$ in many of the references. Thus a solution to (12) is

$$R = C_1'J_0(j\tau r) \equiv C_1'I_0(\tau r) \tag{14}$$

There must also be a second solution in this case, and, since it is usually not taken simply as $N_0(j\tau r)$, the choice of this will be discussed in a later article (3·23). One of the forms for the second solution in this case is denoted $K_0(\tau r)$, so that the general solution to (12) may be written

$$R = C_1'I_0(\tau r) + C_2'K_0(\tau r) \tag{15}$$

The second solution K_0 becomes infinite at $r = 0$ just as does N_0, and so will not be required in the simple examples immediately following which include the axis $r = 0$ in the range over which the solution is to apply. The solution to the z equation (4) when $T^2 = -\tau^2$ is

$$Z = C_3' \sin \tau z + C_4' \cos \tau z \tag{16}$$

Summarizing, either of the following forms satisfies Laplace's equation in the two cylindrical coordinates r and z:

$$\Phi = [C_1J_0(Tr) + C_2N_0(Tr)][C_3 \sinh Tz + C_4 \cosh Tz] \tag{17}$$

$$\Phi = [C_1'I_0(\tau r) + C_2'K_0(\tau r)][C_3' \sin \tau z + C_4' \cos \tau z] \tag{18}$$

As was the case with the rectangular harmonics, the two forms are not really different since (17) includes (18) if T is allowed to become imaginary, but the two separate ways of writing the solution are useful, as will be demonstrated in following examples.

PROBLEM

3·19 Demonstrate that the series (7) does satisfy the differential equation (5).

3·20 FIELDS DESCRIBED BY CYLINDRICAL HARMONICS

Let us write a particular one of the cylindrical harmonics of the preceding article as follows:

$$\Phi = CI_0(\tau r)\sin\tau z = V_0\frac{I_0(\pi r/l)\sin(\pi z/l)}{I_0(\pi r_0/l)} \tag{1}$$

Boundaries appropriate to this solution are found as in Art. 3·17 for the rectangular harmonic, and are sketched in Fig. 3·20a for $r_0/l = \frac{1}{8}$.

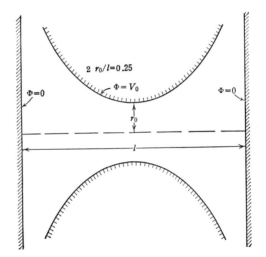

Fig. 3·20a.

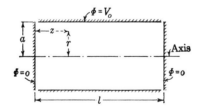

Fig. 3·20b The cylindrical region with given potentials.

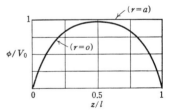

Fig. 3·20c The potential plots at the boundary and along the axis.

For more general problems, a series of the cylindrical harmonics may be required. Consider a region bounded by a circular cylinder at potential V_0 and two planes perpendicular to the axis at zero potential (Fig. 3·20b); cylindrical symmetry exists and product solutions must be obtainable from Art. 3·19. The necessary gaps between electrodes are assumed negligibly small compared to all other dimensions.

Potential must be zero at $z = 0$ and $z = l$ for all values of r; this helps us to select the proper form of the product solution as follows:

1. Sinusoidal solutions for z are desired rather than hyperbolic, since the latter do not have repeated zeros and such a characteristic of the solution is necessary. The form of Eq. 3·19(18) is then utilized.

2. Coefficient of the cosine term must be zero since Φ is to be zero at $z = 0$.

3. Periodicity, τ, is given by $m\pi/l$, where m may be any integer from zero to infinity, if Φ is to be zero at $z = l$.

4. The second solution, K_0, is not present since potential must remain finite on the axis.

Thus all solutions to Laplace's equation of the product form which satisfy the symmetry of the problem and the boundary conditions so far imposed must be of the form

$$\Phi_m = A_m I_0 \left(\frac{m\pi r}{l} \right) \sin \left(\frac{m\pi z}{l} \right)$$

and a series of these harmonics, having amplitudes A_m yet to be determined, will give the potential distribution Φ desired:

$$\Phi = \sum_{m=0}^{\infty} A_m I_0 \left(\frac{m\pi r}{l} \right) \sin \left(\frac{m\pi z}{l} \right) \tag{2}$$

An additional boundary condition remains that, at $r = a$, Φ is zero at $z = 0$ and $z = l$, but equal to V_0 for all other values of z. A plot of this distribution of Φ against z at $r = a$ (Fig. 3·20c) results in a square wave shape such as was expanded in a Fourier series in Chapter 1. From Eq. 1·15(6), this function is representable over the range $0 < z < l$ by the series

$$\Phi \Big|_{r=a} = \frac{4V_0}{\pi} \sum_{m \text{ odd}} \frac{1}{m} \sin \frac{m\pi z}{l}$$

But (2) gives $\Phi \big|_{r=a}$ as

$$\Phi \Big|_{r=a} = \sum_{m=1}^{\infty} A_m I_0 \left(\frac{m\pi a}{l} \right) \sin \left(\frac{m\pi z}{l} \right)$$

Since these values of $\Phi \big|_{r=a}$ must be equal to each other for all values of z, they must be equal term by term. That is, corresponding coefficients of $\sin (m\pi z/l)$ may be equated:

$$A_m I_0 \left(\frac{m\pi a}{l}\right) = \begin{cases} \dfrac{4V_0,}{m\pi} & m \text{ odd} \\ 0, & m \text{ even} \end{cases}$$

Thus every coefficient is determined and the potential at any point in the region is given by substituting these determined coefficients in the series (2):

$$\Phi = \sum_{m \text{ odd}} \frac{4V_0}{m\pi} \frac{I_0(m\pi r/l)}{I_0(m\pi a/l)} \sin (m\pi z/l) \tag{3}$$

A plot of potential distribution along the axis, Φ/V_0 versus z at $r = 0$, is given in Fig. 3·20c for a case with $a/l = 0.25$.

PROBLEMS

3·20a Find the series for potential inside the cylindrical region with end plates $z = 0$ and $z = l$ at potential zero, and the cylinder of radius a in two parts. From $z = 0$ to $z = l/2$, it is at potential V_0; from $z = l/2$ to $z = l$, it is at potential $-V_0$.

3·20b The problem is as in Prob. 3·20a except that the cylinder is divided in three parts with potential zero from $z = 0$ to $z = b$ and also from $z = l - b$ to $z = l$. Potential is V_0 from $z = b$ to $z = l - b$.

3·20c Write the general formula for obtaining potential inside a cylindrical region of radius a, with two zero-potential end plates at $z = 0$ and $z = l$, provided potential is given as $\Phi = f(z)$ at $r = a$.

3·21 BESSEL FUNCTIONS OF ZERO ORDER: REAL ARGUMENTS

In the solution of Laplace's equation in cylindrical coordinates, a differential equation appeared of the form

$$\frac{d^2R}{dr^2} + \frac{1}{r}\frac{dR}{dr} + T^2R = 0 \tag{1}$$

This equation, known as Bessel's equation, is common throughout applied physics, and in particular arises in many field problems involving cylindrical and spherical configurations. Since a large number of the structures of radio engineering, for example, vacuum tube electrodes, circular wave guides, and ordinary round wires, have such forms, the equation and its solutions will occur frequently throughout the book. Although we have already made use of its solutions in the preceding examples, we shall now devote some time to a special study of the properties of its solutions. These solutions to Bessel's equation are called Bessel functions.

Equation (1) is quite similar to the equation of simple harmonic motion. This familiar differential equation,

$$\frac{d^2Z}{dz^2} + K^2Z = 0 \tag{2}$$

was studied in Chapter 1 and found to have solutions in sines and cosines:

$$Z = A \cos Kz + B \sin Kz \tag{3}$$

One solution to the Bessel equation, (1), was obtained in Art. 3·19 by a method also used for solving the simple harmonic motion equation—the method of assuming a power series and determining coefficients so that the differential equation is satisfied. The two inde-

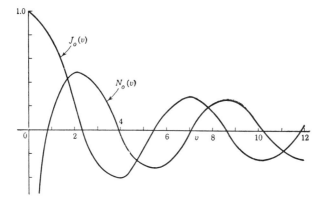

Fig. 3·21   Plot of zero order Bessel functions $J_0(v)$ and $N_0(v)$.

pendent solutions defined by Eqs. 3·19(8) and 3·19(9) were denoted by $J_0(Tr)$ and $N_0(Tr)$, so that a complete solution to (1) is written

$$R = CJ_0(Tr) + DN_0(Tr) \tag{4}$$

Since the differential equations (1) and (2) are similar, it may be expected that the above solutions are similar to sinusoids, but revised somewhat by the presence of the term $1/r(dR/dr)$. This is true, for a plot of the two solutions $J_0(v)$ and $N_0(v)$ as functions of v (Fig. 3·21) shows that both are reminiscent of damped sinusoids. $J_0(v)$ is unity at $v = 0$ and then alternates in sign, actually approaching a modified sinusoidal form as v becomes very large:

$$J_0(v) \underset{v \to \infty}{\longrightarrow} \sqrt{\frac{2}{\pi v}} \cos\left(v - \frac{\pi}{4}\right) \tag{5}$$

$N_0(v)$ is infinite at $v = 0$, but eventually alternates in sign, and for large arguments approaches

$$N_0(v) \underset{v \to \infty}{\longrightarrow} \sqrt{\frac{2}{\pi v}} \sin\left(v - \frac{\pi}{4}\right) \tag{6}$$

Both the functions $J_0(v)$ and $N_0(v)$, called Bessel functions of zero order, first and second kinds respectively, are tabulated extensively in references. Some care should be observed in using these references, for there is a wide variation in notation for the second solution, and not all the functions used are equivalent, since they differ in the values of arbitrary constants selected for the series. The $N_0(v)$ is chosen here because it is the form most common in current mathematical physics, and also the form most commonly tabulated. It is equivalent to the $Y_0(v)$ used by Watson and by McLachlan, and to the $\bar{Y}_0(v)$, but not the $Y_0(v)$, of Gray, Matthews, and MacRobert. Of course, it is quite proper to use any one of the second solutions throughout a given problem, since all the differences will be absorbed in the arbitrary constants of the problem, and the same final numerical result will always be obtained; but it is necessary to be consistent in the use of only one of these throughout any given analysis.

3·22   LINEAR COMBINATIONS OF J_0 AND N_0: THE HANKEL FUNCTIONS

It was found in Chapter 1 that it is sometimes convenient to express the solution to the simple harmonic motion equation in terms of complex exponentials, which are linear combinations of sines and cosines. Thus it is proper to write the solution to 3·21(2) as

$$Z = A_1 e^{jkz} + B_1 e^{-jkz} \tag{1}$$

since

$$e^{jkz} = \cos kz + j \sin kz \tag{2}$$

and

$$e^{-jkz} = \cos kz - j \sin kz$$

This form is of particular value in the study of traveling waves if $e^{j\omega t}$ is to be used to represent sinusoidal time variations, for then

$$Z e^{j\omega t} = e^{j\omega t}(A_1 e^{jkz} + B_1 e^{-jkz})$$
$$= A_1 e^{j(\omega t + kz)} + B_1 e^{j(\omega t - kz)}$$

The first of these terms represents a wave traveling in the negative z direction; the second represents a wave traveling in the positive z direction.

Similarly, for the study of wave propagation in cylindrical coordinates, it is convenient to form linear combinations of the Bessel functions $J_0(Tr)$ and $N_0(Tr)$:

$$H_0^{(1)}(Tr) = J_0(Tr) + jN_0(Tr) \tag{3}$$

$$H_0^{(2)}(Tr) = J_0(Tr) - jN_0(Tr) \tag{4}$$

The meaning of these combinations is similar to that of the exponentials. This is shown by substituting the expressions for J_0 and N_0 at large arguments [Eqs. 3·21(5) and 3·21(6)] in (3) and (4):

$$H_0^{(1)}(v) \underset{v \to \infty}{\longrightarrow} \sqrt{\frac{2}{\pi v}} \left[\cos\left(v - \frac{\pi}{4}\right) + j \sin\left(v - \frac{\pi}{4}\right) \right] = \sqrt{\frac{2}{\pi v}} \, e^{j[v-(\pi/4)]}$$
$$\tag{5}$$

$$H_0^{(2)}(v) \underset{v \to \infty}{\longrightarrow} \sqrt{\frac{2}{\pi v}} \left[\cos\left(v - \frac{\pi}{4}\right) - j \sin\left(v - \frac{\pi}{4}\right) \right] = \sqrt{\frac{2}{\pi v}} \, e^{-j[v-(\pi/4)]}$$
$$\tag{6}$$

The solution to Eq. 3·21(1) may be written in terms of the linear combinations defined above:

$$R = C_1 H_0^{(1)}(Tr) + D_1 H_0^{(2)}(Tr) \tag{7}$$

If this solution is associated with a time function $e^{j\omega t}$,

$$e^{j\omega t} R = e^{j\omega t}[C_1 H_0^{(1)}(Tr) + D_1 H_0^{(2)}(Tr)]$$

For large values of Tr,

$$e^{j\omega t} R \to \sqrt{\frac{2}{\pi Tr}} \left[C_1 e^{-j(\pi/4)} e^{j(\omega t + Tr)} + D_1 e^{j(\pi/4)} e^{j(\omega t - Tr)} \right]$$

so that the first term represents a wave traveling radially inward and the second term represents a wave traveling radially outward. This interpretation of the functions $H_0^{(1)}$ and $H_0^{(2)}$ will be particularly useful in later chapters concerned with wave solutions.

The functions $H_0^{(1)}(v)$ and $H_0^{(2)}(v)$ are called Hankel functions of the first and second kinds, respectively. However, it should be emphasized that these are not new functions, but merely linear combinations of $J_0(v)$ and $N_0(v)$ and so are also solutions of Bessel's equation. Other complete solutions to the Bessel equation might be written

$$R = C_3 J_0(Tr) + D_3 H_0^{(1)}(Tr)$$
$$R = C_4 N_0(Tr) + D_4 H_0^{(2)}(Tr), \quad \text{etc.}$$
$$\tag{8}$$

3·23   BESSEL FUNCTIONS OF ZERO ORDER: IMAGINARY ARGUMENTS

If the constant K of the simple harmonic motion equation is imaginary, $K = jk$ or $K^2 = -k^2$ where k is real, the solution, in terms of exponentials, is

$$Z = A_2 e^{kz} + B_2 e^{-kz}$$

Similarly, the constant T of Bessel's equation is often imaginary: $T = j\tau$ or $T^2 = -\tau^2$ where τ is real. The first solution for this case has been studied in Art. 3·19. The series representing $J_0(j\tau r)$ is real and convergent [see Eq. 3·19(13)] and, as noted in that article, is often denoted $I_0(\tau r)$, or

$$I_0(v) \equiv J_0(jv)$$

Similarly, for a second solution, $N_0(j\tau r)$ could be used, but this is complex and so not convenient to tabulate. One of the linear combinations of J_0 and N_0 studied in Art. 3·22, $H_0^{(1)}$, yields a purely imaginary result for imaginary arguments, and also goes to zero at infinity, so that it is useful as a solution in regions extending to infinity. That is, from Eq. 3·22(5) for $v = jv'$, and large v',

$$H_0^{(1)}(jv') \rightarrow \sqrt{\frac{2}{\pi v'}} \frac{1}{\sqrt{j}} e^{-j(\pi/4)} e^{-v'} = -j\sqrt{\frac{2}{\pi v'}} e^{-v'}$$

This does go to zero at $v' = \infty$. Thus a complete solution to the equation

$$\frac{d^2 R}{dr^2} + \frac{1}{r}\frac{dR}{dr} - \tau^2 R = 0 \tag{1}$$

may always be written

$$R = C_2 J_0(j\tau r) + D_2 H_0^{(1)}(j\tau r) \tag{2}$$

$H_0^{(1)}(jv')$ is always a purely imaginary number (if v' is real), so $jH_0^{(1)}(jv')$ is real. $J_0(jv')$ and $jH_0^{(1)}(jv')$ are tabulated in some of the references as functions of v', and curves of these functions are given in Fig. 3·23. As may be expected, the former is reminiscent of the hyperbolic cosine, the latter of a negative exponential.

The second solution introduced above is related to the second solution, K_0, mentioned in Art. 3·19 by the following:

$$K_0(v') = j\frac{\pi}{2} H_0^{(1)}(jv') \tag{3}$$

K_0 is used, in, among other places, Watson, McLachlan, and Gray, Matthews, and MacRobert. I_0 and K_0 are known as modified Bessel

functions of zero order, first and second kinds, respectively. An
alternative complete solution to (1) may then be written as in Art. 3·19,

$$R = C_2'I_0(\tau r) + D_2'K_0(\tau r) \tag{4}$$

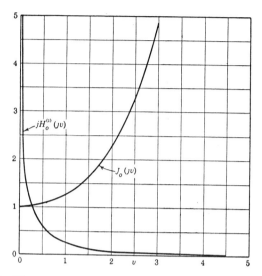

Fig. 3·23   Plot of zero order Bessel functions of imaginary arguments.

3·24   BESSEL FUNCTIONS OF HIGHER ORDER

The simple Bessel equation, 3·21(1), was derived by assuming that a
product solution would satisfy Laplace's equation, first eliminating any
variations with angle ϕ. For certain problems, as, for example, the
solution for field between the two halves of a longitudinally split cylinder, it may be necessary to retain the ϕ variations in the equation.
The solution may be assumed in product form again, RZF_ϕ, where R
is a function of r alone, Z of z alone, and F_ϕ of ϕ alone. Z has solutions
in exponentials or sinusoids as before, and F_ϕ may also be satisfied
by sinusoids:

$$Z = Ce^{Tz} + De^{-Tz} \tag{1}$$

$$F_\phi = E \cos \nu\phi + F \sin \nu\phi \tag{2}$$

The differential equation for R is then slightly different from the zero
order Bessel equation obtained previously:

$$\frac{d^2R}{dr^2} + \frac{1}{r}\frac{dR}{dr} + \left(T^2 - \frac{\nu^2}{r^2}\right)R = 0 \tag{3}$$

It is apparent at once that Eq. 3·21(1) is a special case of this more general equation, i.e., $\nu = 0$. A series solution to the general equation carried through as in Art. 3·19 shows that the function defined by the series

$$J_\nu(Tr) = \sum_{m=0}^{\infty} \frac{(-1)^m (Tr/2)^{\nu+2m}}{m! \Gamma(\nu + m + 1)} \tag{4}$$

is a solution to the equation.

$\Gamma(\nu + m + 1)$ is the gamma function of $(\nu + m + 1)$ and, for ν integral, is equivalent to the factorial of $(\nu + m)$; for ν non-integral, values of this gamma function are tabulated. If ν is an integer n,

$$J_n(Tr) = \sum_{m=0}^{\infty} \frac{(-1)^m (Tr/2)^{n+2m}}{m!(n + m)!} \tag{5}$$

Similarly, a second independent solution† to the equation is

$$N_\nu(Tr) = \frac{\cos \nu\pi J_\nu(Tr) - J_{-\nu}(Tr)}{\sin \nu\pi} \tag{6}$$

So that a complete solution to (3) may be written

$$R = A J_\nu(Tr) + B N_\nu(Tr) \tag{7}$$

The constant ν is known as the order of the equation. J_ν is then called a Bessel function of first kind, order ν; N_ν is a Bessel function of second kind, order ν. Of most interest for this chapter are cases in which $\nu = n$, an integer.

The solution to (3) may also be written in terms of linear combinations of J_ν and N_ν:

$$R = A_1 H_\nu^{(1)}(Tr) + B_1 H_\nu^{(2)}(Tr) \tag{8}$$

where $\qquad H_\nu^{(1)}(Tr) = J_\nu(Tr) + jN_\nu(Tr) \tag{9}$

and $\qquad H_\nu^{(2)}(Tr) = J_\nu(Tr) - jN_\nu(Tr) \tag{10}$

$H_\nu^{(1)}$ and $H_\nu^{(2)}$ are called Hankel functions of order ν, first and second kinds, respectively.

If T is imaginary, $T = j\tau$, (3) becomes

$$\frac{d^2R}{dr^2} + \frac{1}{r}\frac{dR}{dr} - \left(\tau^2 + \frac{\nu^2}{r^2}\right)R = 0 \tag{11}$$

---

† If ν is non-integral, $J_{-\nu}$ is not linearly related to J_ν, and it is then proper to use either $J_{-\nu}$ or N_ν as the second solution; for ν integral, N_ν must be used. Equation (6) is indeterminate for ν integral but is subject to evaluation by usual methods.

If $T = j\tau$ is substituted in the series definitions for $J_\nu(Tr)$ and $H_\nu^{(1)}(Tr)$, the resulting quantities are found to be either pure reals or pure imaginaries if ν is an integer, n. Specifically, the quantities $[j^{-n}J_n(jv)]$ and $[j^{n+1}H_n^{(1)}(jv)]$ are always pure real numbers and are tabulated as functions of v in the references. A complete solution to (11) may be written

$$R = A_2 J_\nu(j\tau r) + B_2 H_\nu^{(1)}(j\tau r) \tag{12}$$

Again it is quite common practice to denote the above solutions as follows:

$$I_n(v) = j^{-n} J_n(jv) \tag{13}$$

$$K_n(v) = \frac{\pi}{2} j^{n+1} H_n^{(1)}(jv) \tag{14}$$

The solution to (11) may then also be written

$$R = A_3 I_\nu(\tau r) + B_3 K_\nu(\tau r) \tag{15}$$

However, note that I and K as defined by (13) and (14) require different recurrence formulas from the ordinary Bessel functions. These formulas will be given in following articles.

3·25 VALUES FOR BESSEL FUNCTIONS OF LARGE ARGUMENTS

As the arguments of the Bessel functions become very large, all these functions approach more and more closely sinusoidal or exponential forms, as in the zero order functions of Arts. 3·21–3·23. These forms are called the asymptotic expressions for the Bessel functions. They are as follows:

$$J_\nu(v) \underset{v \to \infty}{\longrightarrow} \sqrt{\frac{2}{\pi v}} \cos\left(v - \frac{\pi}{4} - \frac{\nu\pi}{2}\right) \tag{1}$$

$$N_\nu(v) \underset{v \to \infty}{\longrightarrow} \sqrt{\frac{2}{\pi v}} \sin\left(v - \frac{\pi}{4} - \frac{\nu\pi}{2}\right) \tag{2}$$

$$H_\nu^{(1)}(v) \underset{v \to \infty}{\longrightarrow} \sqrt{\frac{2}{\pi v}} e^{j[v-(\pi/4)-(\nu\pi/2)]} \tag{3}$$

$$H_\nu^{(2)}(v) \underset{v \to \infty}{\longrightarrow} \sqrt{\frac{2}{\pi v}} e^{-j[v-(\pi/4)-(\nu\pi/2)]} \tag{4}$$

$$j^{-\nu}J_\nu(jv) = I_\nu(v) \underset{v \to \infty}{\longrightarrow} \sqrt{\frac{1}{2\pi v}} e^v \tag{5}$$

$$j^{\nu+1}H_\nu^{(1)}(jv) = \frac{2}{\pi} K_\nu(v) \underset{v \to \infty}{\longrightarrow} \sqrt{\frac{2}{\pi v}} e^{-v} \tag{6}$$

3·26 DIFFERENTIATION OF BESSEL FUNCTIONS

If it is desired to obtain the derivative of the Bessel function $J_0(v)$, the series definition 3·19(8) may be differentiated term by term:

$$\frac{d}{dv}[J_0(v)] = -\left[\frac{v}{2} - \frac{(v/2)^3}{1 \cdot 2!} + \frac{(v/2)^5}{2! \, 3!} - \frac{(v/2)^7}{3! \, 4!} \mid \cdots \right]$$

Comparison with the definition for $J_n(v)$, Eq. 3·24(5), shows that the result is exactly $-J_1(v)$. That is,

$$\frac{d}{dv}[J_0(v)] = -J_1(v)$$

Similarly, it may be shown from the differential equation that the following derivative expressions are true for any of the Bessel functions $J_\nu(v)$, $N_\nu(v)$, $H_\nu^{(1)}(v)$, or $H_\nu^{(2)}(v)$. Let $R_\nu(v)$ denote any one of these, and R_ν' denote $(d/dv)[R_\nu(v)]$.

$$R_0'(v) = -R_1(v) \tag{1}$$

$$R_1'(v) = R_0(v) - \frac{1}{v}R_1(v) \tag{2}$$

$$vR_\nu'(v) = \nu R_\nu(v) - vR_{\nu+1}(v) \tag{3}$$

$$vR_\nu'(v) = -\nu R_\nu(v) + vR_{\nu-1}(v) \tag{4}$$

$$\frac{d}{dv}[v^{-\nu}R_\nu(v)] = -v^{-\nu}R_{\nu+1}(v) \tag{5}$$

$$\frac{d}{dv}[v^\nu R_\nu(v)] = v^\nu R_{\nu-1}(v) \tag{6}$$

Note that

$$R_\nu'(Tr) = \frac{d}{d(Tr)}[R_\nu(Tr)] = \frac{1}{T}\frac{d}{dr}[R_\nu(Tr)] \tag{7}$$

For the I and K functions different forms for the above differentials must be used. They may be obtained from the above by substituting Eqs. 3·24(13) and 3·24(14) in the preceding expressions. Some of these are

$$vI_\nu'(v) = \nu I_\nu(v) + vI_{\nu+1}(v)$$
$$vI_\nu'(v) = -\nu I_\nu(v) + vI_{\nu-1}(v) \tag{8}$$

$$vK_\nu'(v) = \nu K_\nu(v) - vK_{\nu+1}(v)$$
$$vK_\nu'(v) = -\nu K_\nu(v) - vK_{\nu-1}(v) \tag{9}$$

3·27   RECURRENCE FORMULAS FOR BESSEL FUNCTIONS

By recurrence formulas, it is possible to obtain the value for Bessel functions of any order, when the values of functions for any two other orders, differing from the first by integers, are known. For example, subtract Eq. 3·26(4) from Eq. 3·26(3). The result may be written

$$\frac{2\nu}{v} R_\nu(v) = R_{\nu+1}(v) + R_{\nu-1}(v) \tag{1}$$

By this equation, if any two of $R_{\nu-1}$, R_ν, and $R_{\nu+1}$ are known, the third may be found. For instance, if $J_0(v)$ and $J_1(v)$ are known, the equation may be used to find $J_2(v)$; repeating the process with $J_1(v)$ and $J_2(v)$, $J_3(v)$ may be determined and so on to any order desired. As before, R_ν may denote J_ν, N_ν, $H_\nu^{(1)}$, $H_\nu^{(2)}$, but not I_ν or K_ν. For these, the recurrence formulas are

$$\frac{2\nu}{v} I_\nu(v) = I_{\nu-1}(v) - I_{\nu+1}(v) \tag{2}$$

$$\frac{2\nu}{v} K_\nu(v) = K_{\nu+1}(v) - K_{\nu-1}(v) \tag{3}$$

3·28   INTEGRALS OF BESSEL FUNCTIONS

Equation 3·26(1) may be integrated directly:

$$\int R_1(v)\, dv = -R_0(v) \tag{1}$$

Others of the integrals that will be useful in solving later problems are given below. R_ν denotes J_ν, N_ν, $H_\nu^{(1)}$, or $H_\nu^{(2)}$:

$$\int v^{-\nu} R_{\nu+1}(v)\, dv = -v^{-\nu} R_\nu(v) \tag{2}$$

$$\int v^\nu R_{\nu-1}(v)\, dv = v^\nu R_\nu(v) \tag{3}$$

$$\int v R_\nu(\alpha v) R_\nu(\beta v)\, dv$$

$$= \frac{v}{\alpha^2 - \beta^2} [\beta R_\nu(\alpha v) R_{\nu-1}(\beta v) - \alpha R_{\nu-1}(\alpha v) R_\nu(\beta v)] \qquad \alpha \neq \beta \tag{4}$$

$$\int v R_\nu^2(\alpha v)\, dv = \frac{v^2}{2} [R_\nu^2(\alpha v) - R_{\nu-1}(\alpha v) R_{\nu+1}(\alpha v)]$$

$$= \frac{v^2}{2} \left[R_\nu'^2(\alpha v) + \left(1 - \frac{\nu^2}{\alpha^2 v^2} \right) R_\nu^2(\alpha v) \right] \tag{5}$$

3·29   EXPANSION OF A FUNCTION AS A SERIES OF BESSEL FUNCTIONS

In Chapter 1 a study was made of the familiar method of Fourier series by which a function may be expressed over a given region as a series of sines or cosines. It is possible to evaluate the coefficients in such a case because of the orthogonality property of sinusoids, expressed in Art. 1·13. A study of the integrals, Eqs. 3·28(4) and 3·28(5), shows that there are similar orthogonality expressions for Bessel functions. For example, these integrals may be written for zero order Bessel functions, and, if α and β are taken as p_m/a and p_q/a, where p_m and p_q are the mth and qth roots of $J_0(v) = 0$, that is, $J_0(p_m) = 0$ and $J_0(p_q) = 0$, $p_m \neq p_q$, then Eq. 3·28(4) gives

$$\int_0^a rJ_0\left(\frac{p_m r}{a}\right) J_0\left(\frac{p_q r}{a}\right) dr = 0 \tag{1}$$

So, if a function $f(r)$ may be expressed as an infinite sum of zero order Bessel functions,

$$f(r) = b_1 J_0\left(p_1 \frac{r}{a}\right) + b_2 J_0\left(p_2 \frac{r}{a}\right) + b_3 J_0\left(p_3 \frac{r}{a}\right) + \cdots$$

or
$$f(r) = \sum_{m=1}^{\infty} b_m J_0\left(\frac{p_m r}{a}\right) \tag{2}$$

The coefficients b_m may be evaluated in a manner similar to that used for Fourier coefficients by multiplying each term of (2) by $rJ_0(p_m r/a)$ and integrating from 0 to a. Then by (1) all terms on the right disappear except the mth term:

$$\int_0^a rf(r)J_0\left(\frac{p_m r}{a}\right) dr = \int_0^a b_m r\left[J_0\left(\frac{p_m r}{a}\right)\right]^2 dr$$

From Eq. 3·28(5),

$$\int_0^a rJ_0^2\left(\frac{p_m r}{a}\right) dr = \frac{a^2}{2} J_1^2(p_m) \tag{3}$$

So
$$\int_0^a rf(r)J_0\left(\frac{p_m r}{a}\right) dr = \frac{b_m a^2}{2} J_1^2(p_m)$$

or
$$b_m = \frac{2}{a^2 J_1^2(p_m)} \int_0^a rf(r)J_0\left(\frac{p_m r}{a}\right) dr \tag{4}$$

Thus a formula for the coefficients of the series (2) is derived. A mathematical study of the subject would be concerned with showing that the series thus formally derived actually does converge to the desired function over the range of interest. Such a discussion is outside the range of this text, but the results of such studies show that completeness and convergence requirements are met, so that such a series may be used to represent any piecewise continuous function over the range $0 < r < a$.

PROBLEMS

3·29a Write a function $f(r)$ in terms of nth order Bessel functions over the range 0 to a and determine the coefficients.

3·29b Determine coefficients for a function $f(r)$ expressed over the range 0 to a as a series of zero order Bessel functions as follows:

$$f(r) = \sum_{m=1}^{\infty} c_m J_0\left(\frac{p_m' r}{a}\right)$$

where p_m' denotes the mth root of $J_0'(v) = 0$ [i.e., $J_1(v) = 0$].

3·30 CYLINDRICAL HARMONIC SERIES FOR RADIAL MATCHING

If it is desired to find potential distribution in the interior of a region bounded by a circular cylinder and its base at potential zero, and a plane perpendicular to the axis at potential V_0 (Fig. 3·30a), the use of series is similar to that of the example in Art. 3·20, although now a series of Bessel functions is required. The gaps are again assumed negligibly small compared with all other dimensions. In selecting the proper form for the solution from Art. 3·19, the boundary condition that $\Phi = 0$ at $r = a$ for all values of z indicates that the R function must become zero at $r = a$. Thus we select the J_0 functions since the I_0's do not ever become zero. (The corresponding second solution, N_0, does not appear since potential must remain finite on the axis.) The value of T in Eq. 3·19(17) is determined from the condition that $\Phi = 0$ at $r = a$ for all values of z. Thus, if p_m is the mth root of $J_0(v) = 0$, T must be p_m/a. The corresponding solution for Z is in hyperbolic functions, Eq. 3·19(17), but the coefficient of the hyperbolic cosine term must be zero since Φ is zero at $z = 0$ for all values of r. Thus a sum of all cylindrical harmonics with arbitrary amplitudes which satisfy the symmetry of the problem and the boundary conditions so far imposed may be written

$$\Phi = \sum_{m=1}^{\infty} B_m J_0\left(\frac{p_m r}{a}\right) \sinh\left(\frac{p_m z}{a}\right) \tag{1}$$

The remaining condition is that, at $z = l$, $\Phi = 0$ at $r = a$, and $\Phi = V_0$ for all other r's. To use this condition it seems advisable

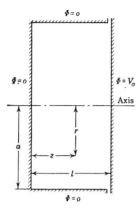

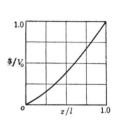

Fig. 3·30a   Cylindrical region ($l/a = 1$).   Fig. 3·30b   Plot of potential vs. z at
$r = 0$ ($l/a = 1$).

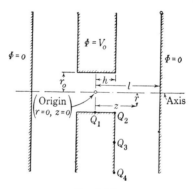

Fig. 3·30c.

to expand such a function over this plane in terms of Bessel functions as in Eq. 3·29(2). For the coefficients, Eq. 3·29(4) is used with $f(r) = 0$ at $r = a$ and $f(r) = V_0$ for $0 < r < a$. Then

$$b_m = \frac{2}{a^2 J_1{}^2(p_m)} \int_0^a r V_0 J_0 \left(\frac{p_m r}{a} \right) dr = \frac{2V_0}{p_m J_1(p_m)}$$

The above integral was evaluated by Eq. 3·28(3). So

$$f(r) = \Phi\big|_{z=l} = \sum_{m=1}^{\infty} \frac{2V_0}{p_m J_1(p_m)} J_0 \left(\frac{p_m r}{a} \right) \tag{2}$$

But (1) at $z = l$ is

$$\Phi\big|_{z=l} = \sum_{m=1}^{\infty} B_m \sinh \left(\frac{p_m l}{a} \right) J_0 \left(\frac{p_m r}{a} \right) \tag{3}$$

Equations (2) and (3) must be equivalent for all values of r. Consequently, coefficients of corresponding terms of $J_0(p_m r/a)$ must be equal. The constant B_m is now completely determined, and the potential at any point inside the region is

$$\Phi = \sum_{m=1}^{\infty} \frac{2V_0}{p_m J_1(p_m) \sinh (p_m l/a)} \sinh \left(\frac{p_m z}{a}\right) J_0 \left(\frac{p_m r}{a}\right) \qquad (4)$$

Potential distribution along the axis is plotted in Fig. 3·30b for a case with $a/l = 1$.

PROBLEMS

3·30a Suppose that the end plate at $z = l$ of Fig. 3·30a is divided into insulated rings and connected to sources in such a way that the potential approximates a single J_0 function of radius. That is,

$$\Phi(r,l) = C J_0 \left(\frac{p_1 r}{a}\right)$$

Write the solution for $\Phi(r,z)$ at any point inside the cylindrical region.

3·30b Write the general formula for obtaining potential inside a cylinder of radius a which, with its plane base at $z = 0$, is at potential zero, provided that the potential is given across some plane surface at $z = l$, as

$$\Phi(r,l) = f(r)$$

3·30c For the axially symmetric region sketched in Fig. 3·30c, write a series solution of the appropriate form with unknown coefficients $a_1, a_2, \cdots a_n$. For a particular case with $r_0/l = h/l = 0.3$, assume that a sufficiently good approximation may be had by retaining only four of the terms of the series. Evaluate the four coefficients of these terms by putting on the known potential V_0 at four points of the central electrode. Take these points, Q_1, Q_2, Q_3, Q_4 with (r,z) coordinates respectively $(0,r_0)$, (h,r_0), $(h,2r_0)$, and $(h,3r_0)$. Calculate the potential at a few points on the axis from the resulting series, and plot Φ/V_0 as a function of z/l.

3·31   SPHERICAL HARMONICS

Consider next Laplace's equation in spherical coordinates for regions with symmetry about the axis so that variations with azimuthal angle ϕ may be neglected. Laplace's equation in the two remaining spherical coordinates r and θ then becomes (Art. 2·39)

$$\frac{\partial^2 (r\Phi)}{\partial r^2} + \frac{1}{r \sin \theta} \frac{\partial}{\partial \theta} \left(\sin \theta \frac{\partial \Phi}{\partial \theta}\right) = 0 \qquad (1)$$

or
$$r \frac{\partial^2 \Phi}{\partial r^2} + 2 \frac{\partial \Phi}{\partial r} + \frac{1}{r} \frac{\partial^2 \Phi}{\partial \theta^2} + \frac{1}{r \tan \theta} \frac{\partial \Phi}{\partial \theta} = 0 \qquad (2)$$

Assume a product solution,

$$\Phi = R\Theta$$

where R is a function of r alone, Θ of θ alone,

$$rR''\Theta + 2R'\Theta + \frac{1}{r}R\Theta'' + \frac{1}{r\tan\theta}R\Theta' = 0$$

and

$$\frac{r^2R''}{R} + \frac{2rR'}{R} = -\frac{\Theta''}{\Theta} - \frac{\Theta'}{\Theta\tan\theta} \tag{3}$$

Following previous logic, if the two sides of the equations are to be equal to each other for all values of r and θ, both sides can be equal only to a constant. Since the constant may be expressed in any nonrestrictive way, let it be $m(m + 1)$. The two resulting ordinary differential equations are then

$$r^2\frac{d^2R}{dr^2} + 2r\frac{dR}{dr} - m(m + 1)R = 0 \tag{4}$$

$$\frac{d^2\Theta}{d\theta^2} + \frac{1}{\tan\theta}\frac{d\Theta}{d\theta} + m(m + 1)\Theta = 0 \tag{5}$$

The first of these has a solution which is easily verified to be

$$R = C_1r^m + C_2r^{-(m+1)} \tag{6}$$

A solution to Eq. (5) in terms of simple functions is not obvious, so, as with the Bessel equation, a series solution may be assumed. The coefficients of this series must be determined so that the differential equation (5) is satisfied and the resulting series made to define a new function. There is one departure here from an exact analogue with the Bessel functions, for it turns out that a proper selection of the arbitrary constants will make the series for the new function terminate in a finite number of terms if m is an integer. Thus, for any integer m, the polynomial defined by

$$P_m(\cos\theta) \equiv \frac{1}{2^m m!}\left[\frac{d}{d(\cos\theta)}\right]^m (\cos^2\theta - 1)^m \tag{7}$$

is a solution to the differential equation (5). The equation is known as Legendre's equation; the solutions are called Legendre polynomials of order m. Their forms for the first few values of m are tabulated below. It is evident that, since they are polynomials and not infinite series, their values can be calculated exactly if desired, but values of the polynomials are also tabulated in many references.

$$P_0(\cos\theta) = 1$$
$$P_1(\cos\theta) = \cos\theta$$
$$P_2(\cos\theta) = \tfrac{1}{2}(3\cos^2\theta - 1) \tag{8}$$
$$P_3(\cos\theta) = \tfrac{1}{2}(5\cos^3\theta - 3\cos\theta)$$
$$P_4(\cos\theta) = \tfrac{1}{8}(35\cos^4\theta - 30\cos^2\theta + 3)$$
$$P_5(\cos\theta) = \tfrac{1}{8}(63\cos^5\theta - 70\cos^3\theta + 15\cos\theta)$$

It is recognized that $\Theta = C_1 P_m(\cos\theta)$ is only one solution to the second order differential equation (5). There must be a second independent solution, which may be obtained in a similar manner, but it turns out that this solution becomes infinite for $\theta = 0$. Consequently it will never be present for any case in which the axis of spherical coordinates is included in the region over which the solution applies. However, several important situations require their use; when this occurs certain of the references should be consulted.

PROBLEM

3·31 Apply the separation of variables technique to Laplace's equation in the three spherical coordinates r, θ, and ϕ, obtaining the three resulting ordinary differential equations. Write solutions to the r equation and the ϕ equation. (Solutions to the θ equation will be discussed in Chapter 10.)

3·32 EXAMPLE OF USE OF SPHERICAL HARMONICS WHEN POTENTIAL IS SPECIFIED ON A SPHERICAL BOUNDARY

As an example of the application of spherical harmonics when potential is given over a spherical shell, consider the problem sketched in Fig. 3·32 in which the two thin hemispherical shells at different potentials are separated by a gap negligibly small compared with the radius. As the problem is axially symmetric, the solutions discussed in Art. 3·31 are applicable. If the solution is first desired for the region inside the shell, the constant C_2 of Eq. 3·31(6) must be zero, since potential cannot become infinite at $r = 0$. If a solution outside the shell is desired, C_1 must be zero since potential cannot become infinite at $r = \infty$. Only the first type of Legendre solution discussed in Art. 3·31 is required since both regions include the axis. Thus all spherical harmonics which satisfy the symmetry of the problem and the boundary conditions so far imposed may be written

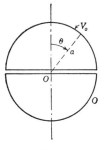

Fig. 3·32 Two hemispheres separated by a gap.

$$\Phi_{\text{inside}} = \sum_{m=0}^{\infty} A_m r^m P_m(\cos \theta) \tag{1}$$

$$\Phi_{\text{outside}} = \sum_{m=0}^{\infty} B_m r^{-(m+1)} P_m(\cos \theta) \tag{2}$$

The additional boundary condition remains that, at $r = a$, $\Phi = V_0$ for $0 < \theta < \pi/2$; $\Phi = 0$ for $\pi/2 < \theta < \pi$ for all values of ϕ. This $f(\theta)$ has been expanded in a Fourier series over the region $0 < \theta < \pi$, but it is desirable to express this square wave in terms of Legendre polynomials directly. An orthogonality relation for these polynomials is quite similar to those for sinusoids and Bessel functions which led to the Fourier series and expansion in Bessel functions respectively.

$$\int_0^\pi P_m(\cos \theta) \, P_n(\cos \theta) \, \sin \theta \, d\theta = 0, \qquad m \neq n \tag{3}$$

$$\int_0^\pi [P_m(\cos \theta)]^2 \, \sin \theta \, d\theta = \frac{2}{2m + 1} \tag{4}$$

It follows that, if a function $f(\theta)$ defined between the limits of 0 to π is written as a series of Legendre polynomials,

$$f(\theta) = \sum_{m=0}^{\infty} \alpha_m P_m(\cos \theta), \qquad 0 < \theta < \pi \tag{5}$$

the coefficients must be given by the formula

$$\alpha_m = \frac{2m + 1}{2} \int_0^\pi f(\theta) \, P_m(\cos \theta) \, \sin \theta \, d\theta \tag{6}$$

For the present problems, $f(\theta)$ is given as a constant V_0 over the range 0 to $\pi/2$, and is zero over the range $\pi/2 < \theta < \pi$. Evaluation of α_m from (6) requires the following integral of Legendre functions:

$$\int_0^{\pi/2} P_m(\cos \theta) \, \sin \theta \, d\theta = \begin{cases} 1, & m = 0 \\ 0, & m \text{ even} \\ (-1)^{\frac{m-1}{2}} \cdot \dfrac{1 \cdot 3 \, \cdots \, (m-2)}{m+1} \cdot \dfrac{1 \cdot 3 \, \cdots \, (m-2)}{2 \cdot 4 \, \cdots \, (m-1)}, & m \text{ odd} \end{cases} \tag{7}$$

The results for α_m, substituted in the series, yield

$$f(\theta) = \Phi(a,\theta)$$

$$= V_0 \left[\frac{1}{2} + \frac{3}{4} P_1(\cos \theta) - \frac{7}{8} \cdot \frac{1}{2} P_3(\cos \theta) + \frac{11}{12} \cdot \frac{1 \cdot 3}{2 \cdot 4} P_5(\cos \theta) + \cdots \right] \tag{8}$$

But (1) gives

$$\Phi_{\text{inside}}\big|_{r=a} = A_0 + A_1 a P_1(\cos\theta) + A_2 a^2 P_2(\cos\theta) + \cdots \quad (9)$$

These two expressions must be identical for all values of θ; consequently, they may be equated term by term and all A_m's evaluated. The potential at any point inside the shell is then given by the series

$$\Phi_{\text{inside}} = V_0\left[\frac{1}{2} + \frac{3}{4}\frac{r}{a}P_1(\cos\theta) - \frac{7}{8}\cdot\frac{1}{2}\frac{r^3}{a^3}P_3(\cos\theta) + \cdots\right] \quad (10)$$

Similarly, the series giving potential at any point outside the shell is found to be

$$\Phi_{\text{outside}} = V_0\left[\frac{a}{2r} + \frac{3}{4}\frac{a^2}{r^2}P_1(\cos\theta) - \frac{7}{8}\cdot\frac{1}{2}\frac{a^4}{r^4}P_3(\cos\theta) + \cdots\right] \quad (11)$$

PROBLEM

3·32   Write the general formula for obtaining potential for $r < a$, and for $r > a$, when potential is given as a general function $f(\theta)$ over a thin spherical shell at $r = a$.

3·33 EXPANSION IN SPHERICAL HARMONICS WHEN FIELD IS GIVEN ALONG AN AXIS

It is often relatively simple to obtain the field or potential along an axis of symmetry by direct application of fundamental laws, yet difficult to obtain it at any point off this axis by the same technique. Once field is found along axis of symmetry, expansions in spherical harmonics give its value at any other point. Thus, if potential, or any component of field which satisfies Laplace's equation, is given for every point along an axis in such a form that it may be expanded in a power series in z, the distance along this axis,

$$\Phi\big|_{\text{axis}} = \sum_{m=0}^{\infty} b_m z^m \qquad 0 < z < a \quad (1)$$

If this axis is taken as the axis of spherical coordinates, $\theta = 0$, the potential off the axis may be written

$$\Phi(r,\theta) = \sum_{m=0}^{\infty} b_m r^m P_m(\cos\theta) \quad (2)$$

This is true since it is a solution of Laplace's equation (Art. 3·31) and does reduce to the given potential (1) for $\theta = 0$ where all $P_m(\cos\theta)$ are unity.

If potential is desired outside of this region, the potential along the axis must be expanded in a power series good for $a < z < \infty$.

$$\Phi\big|_{\theta=0} = \sum_{m=1}^{\infty} c_m z^{-(m+1)} \qquad z > a \tag{3}$$

Then Φ at any point outside is given by comparison with Eq. 3·32(2):

$$\Phi = \sum_{m=0}^{\infty} c_m P_m(\cos\theta) r^{-(m+1)} \qquad r > a \tag{4}$$

For example, the magnetic field H_z was found along the axis of a circular loop of wire carrying current I in Art. 2·26 as

$$H_z = \frac{a^2 I}{2(a^2 + z^2)^{3/2}} = \frac{I}{2a[1 + (z^2/a^2)]^{3/2}} \tag{5}$$

The binomial expansion

$$(1 + u)^{-3/2} = 1 - \tfrac{3}{2}u + \tfrac{15}{8}u^2 - \tfrac{105}{48}u^3 + \cdots$$

is good for $0 < |u| < 1$. Applied to (5),

$$H_z\big|_{\text{axis}} = \frac{I}{2a}\left[1 - \frac{3}{2}\left(\frac{z^2}{a^2}\right) + \frac{15}{8}\left(\frac{z^2}{a^2}\right)^2 - \frac{105}{48}\left(\frac{z^2}{a^2}\right)^3 + \cdots\right]$$

Since H_z, axial component of magnetic field, satisfies Laplace's equation (Art. 3·02), H_z at any point r, θ with $r < a$ is given by

$$H_z(r,\theta) = \frac{I}{2a}\left[1 - \frac{3}{2}\left(\frac{r^2}{a^2}\right)P_2(\cos\theta) + \frac{15}{8}\left(\frac{r^4}{a^4}\right)P_4(\cos\theta) + \cdots\right] \tag{6}$$

PROBLEMS

3·33a For the above example, write the series for H_z at any point r, θ with $r > a$.

3·33b A Helmholtz coil is used to obtain very nearly uniform magnetic field over a region through the use of coils of large radius compared with coil cross sections. Consider two such coaxial coils, each of radius a, one lying in the plane $z = d$, and the other in the plane $z = -d$. Take the current for each coil (considered as a single turn) as I. Obtain the series for H_z applicable to a region containing the origin, writing specific forms for the first three coefficients. Show that, if $a = 2d$, the first non-zero coefficient (other than the constant term) is the coefficient of r^4.

4 MAXWELL'S EQUATIONS
AND HIGH-FREQUENCY
POTENTIAL CONCEPTS

The Laws of Time-Variable Electrical Phenomena

4·01 INTRODUCTION

When the subject material of Chapter 2 was introduced, the objective was stated to be the derivation of a group of equations which would contain a description of fields due to static charges and static currents. It was claimed that in the solution of problems it would be well to have several forms for the statement of fundamental laws so that the most convenient might be chosen for the problem at hand. A number of the techniques involved in this process of selection of equations and their subsequent solution were discussed in Chapters 2 and 3.

In a similar way, an attempt will now be made to present the more complex theory that underlies electric and magnetic effects that vary with time. Of course, some of this theory is only an extension of the static theory. But the additional effects brought in by the varying of charges and currents very frequently complicate the solution of problems. Instead of presenting the different laws in equation form and giving methods of solution in one or two chapters, we shall require the rest of the book for the analysis of time-varying systems. In this chapter, a consistent set of equations describing varying electric and magnetic effects will be obtained. This material will serve as a basis for several subsequent chapters in which the equations will be applied to the field and wave problems of modern radio.

4·02 VOLTAGES INDUCED BY CHANGING MAGNETIC FIELDS

Faraday discovered experimentally that, when the magnetic flux linking a closed circuit is altered, a voltage is induced in that circuit proportional to the rate of change of flux linking the circuit. This law is an experimental law of electricity and magnetism that requires little generalization to be widely useful.   In the consideration of most circuits and electrical machinery it is necessary only to write

$$V = n \frac{d\psi}{dt} \tag{1}$$

where V is the voltage induced in a coil having n turns, and ψ is the flux linking the coil.   The equation may be used directly to find the voltage induced by a generator coil moving in a magnetic field that varies with space, or to calculate the impedance presented by a coil to an alternating voltage.   In ordinary circuit and machine problems, Faraday's law is ordinarily applied to circuits taken along conductors. One important generalization is to an electromotive force about·any closed path in space.   This is indicated by the fact that the resistance of the path does not enter into the law, so that it seems logical that the law could be extended to an infinite resistance path.   Perhaps the most graphic illustration of this fact comes from the betatron,[1] which accelerates charged particles in vacuum by means of an electric field induced by a changing magnetic field, as predicted by Faraday's law.

If the electromotive force about any closed path, whether in space, in dielectrics, along conductors, or any combination of these, is defined as the line integral of electric field about that path,

$$\text{emf} = \oint \bar{E} \cdot \overline{dl}$$

it is equal by Faraday's law to the (negative) time rate of change of magnetic flux flowing through that path.   The magnetic flux may be evaluated by taking the integral of the normal component of magnetic flux density $\bar{B}$ over any surface which has the desired path as a boundary.   Then

$$\oint \bar{E} \cdot \overline{dl} = - \frac{\partial}{\partial t} \int_S \bar{B} \cdot \overline{dS} \tag{2}$$

The negative sign is introduced so that the law is correct when the line integral is taken in the usual positive sense of circulation about the path with respect to the positive direction of flow through the surface. This is obtainable by the usual right-hand rule, and is indicated in Fig. 4·02.   The partial derivative with time is used to distinguish it from variations in space, indicating that the law as written refers to a fixed region in space.

---

[1] D. W. Kerst and R. Serber, "Electronic Orbits in the Induction Accelerator," *Phys. Rev.* **60,** 53 (1941).

To transform to the differential equation form, refer to Stokes's theorem, Art. 2·31.   Applied to (2),

$$\oint \bar{E} \cdot \overline{dl} = \int_S (\nabla \times \bar{E}) \cdot \overline{dS} = -\frac{\partial}{\partial t} \int_S \bar{B} \cdot \overline{dS}$$

If this equation is to be true for any surface, the integrands of the surface integrals must be equal, and we have the differential equation form of Faraday's law:

$$\nabla \times \bar{E} = -\frac{\partial \bar{B}}{\partial t} \tag{3}$$

Since the line integral of electric field about a closed path need not be zero for a time-varying field, work may be done in taking a charge

Fig. 4·02   Right-hand sense relation.

about a closed path in such a field.   The principle of energy conservation is of course not violated, for the energy comes from that in the changing magnetic fields.

PROBLEM

4·02   The betatron makes use of the electric field produced by a time-varying magnetic field in space to accelerate charged particles.   Suppose that the magnetic field of a betatron has an axial component in cylindrical coordinates which is a function of r but not of ϕ:

$$H_z = f(r,t)$$

Find the induced electric field in magnitude and direction at radius r.   Find the specific form for electric field when $f(r,t)$ is given over an interval of time by

$$f(r,t) = Ctr^{-n}$$

4·03   CONTINUITY OF CHARGE

Faraday's law is but one of the fundamental laws for changing fields. Let us assume for the moment that certain of the laws derived for static fields in Chapter 2 can be extended simply to time-varying fields.   We will write the divergence of electric and magnetic fields in exactly the same form as in statics.   For the curl of electric field we will take the result of Faraday's law, Eq. 4·02(3).   For the curl of magnetic field, we will take for the time being the result corresponding to Biot's law, Eq. 2·30(7).

$$\nabla \cdot \bar{D} = \rho \tag{1}$$

$$\nabla \cdot \bar{B} = 0 \tag{2}$$

$$\nabla \times \bar{E} = -\frac{\partial \bar{B}}{\partial t} \tag{3}$$

$$\nabla \times \bar{H} = \bar{\imath} \tag{4}$$

An elimination between the above equations can be made to give an equation relating charge and current. We would expect this to show that, however ρ may vary with space or time, total charge should be conserved. If current flows out of any volume, the amount of charge inside must decrease, and, if current flows in, charge inside increases. Considering a smaller and smaller volume, in the limit the outward flow of current per unit time and per unit volume (which is recognized as the divergence of current density) must give the negative of the time rate of change of charge per unit volume at that point:

$$\nabla \cdot \bar{\imath} = -\frac{\partial \rho}{\partial t} \tag{5}$$

However, if we take the divergence of $\bar{\imath}$ from (4),

$$\nabla \cdot \bar{\imath} = \nabla \cdot (\nabla \times \bar{H}) \equiv 0$$

which does not agree with the continuity argument and equation (5). Maxwell, by reasoning similar to this, recognized that (4), borrowed from statics, was not complete for time-varying fields. He postulated an added term $\partial \bar{D}/\partial t$:

$$\nabla \times \bar{H} = \bar{\imath} + \frac{\partial \bar{D}}{\partial t} \tag{6}$$

Continuity is now satisfied, as may be shown by taking the divergence of (6) and substituting from (1):

$$\nabla \cdot \bar{\imath} = -\frac{\partial}{\partial t} (\nabla \cdot \bar{D}) = -\frac{\partial \rho}{\partial t}$$

4·04 THE CONCEPT OF DISPLACEMENT CURRENT

The term added to form Eq. 4·03(6) contributes to the curl of magnetic field in the same way as an actual conduction current density (motion of charges in conductors), or convection current density (motion of charges in space). Because it arises from the displacement vector $\bar{D}$, it has been named the displacement current term. Thus Eq. 4·03(6) could be written

$$\nabla \times \bar{H} = \bar{\imath}_c + \bar{\imath}_d \tag{1}$$

where $\bar{\imath}_c$ = conduction or convection current density in amperes per square meter; $\bar{\imath}_d$ = displacement current density = $\partial\bar{D}/\partial t$ amperes per square meter.

The displacement current term disappears in the static case, but there is no violation of the continuity equation since, for this special case,

$$\nabla \cdot \bar{\imath} = -\frac{\partial \rho}{\partial t} = 0$$

The displacement current term is not of great importance in many low-frequency problems, because it is much smaller than common current densities in conductors. For example, a field of 10^4 volts per meter would yield a displacement current density of 0.555 ampere per square meter if varying sinusoidally at a frequency of 10^6 cycles per second in air. Of course the term may be of importance even for low frequencies in such places as the region between condenser plates, as will be explained in more detail in the next article. However, it becomes important in more and more situations as the frequency is raised to the range of higher radio frequencies. As will be seen in following chapters, it is this term combined with the Faraday's law term for electric field induced by changing magnetic fields that permits the prediction of the phenomena of wave propagation, resonance, and radiation.

4·05 DISPLACEMENT CURRENT IN A CONDENSER

The displacement current term enables one to explain certain things that would have proved inconsistent had only conduction current been included in the law of Biot and Savart. Consider, for example, the circuit including the a-c generator and the condenser of Fig. 4·05. Suppose that it is required to evaluate the line integral of magnetic field around the loop a-b-c-d-a. The law from statics states that the result obtained should be the current enclosed, that is, the current through any surface of which the loop is a boundary. Then it is true that, if we take as the arbitrary surface through which current is to be evaluated one which cuts the wire A, as S_1, a finite value is obtained for the line integral.   But suppose that the surface selected is one which does not cut the wire, but instead passes between the plates of the condenser, as S_2.   If conduction current alone were included, the computation would have indicated no current passing through this surface and the result would be zero.   The path around which the integral is evaluated is the same in each case, and it would be quite annoying to possess two different results.   It is the displacement current term which appears at this point to preserve the continuity of current between the plates of the condenser, giving the same answer in either case.

To show how this continuity is preserved, consider a parallel-plate condenser of capacity C, spacing d, area of plates A, and applied voltage $V_0 \sin \omega t$.   From circuit theory the charging current

$$I_c = C \frac{dV}{dt} = \omega C V_0 \cos \omega t$$

The field inside the condenser has a magnitude $E = V/d$, so the displacement current density is

$$i_d = \epsilon \frac{\partial E}{\partial t} = \omega \epsilon \frac{V_0}{d} \cos \omega t$$

Total displacement current flowing between the plates is the area of the plate multiplied by the density of displacement current:

$$I_d = A i_d = \omega \left(\frac{\epsilon A}{d} \right) V_0 \cos \omega t$$

The factor in parentheses is recognized as the electrostatic capacitance for the ideal parallel-plate condenser in mks units, so

$$I_d = \omega C V_0 \cos \omega t$$

This value for total displacement current flowing between the condenser plates is then exactly the same as the value of charging current flowing in the leads, calculated by the usual circuit methods above, so the displacement current does act to complete the circuit, and the same result would be obtained by the use of either S_1 or S_2 of Fig. 4·05, as required.

PROBLEMS

4·05a   For a coaxial cylindrical condenser of radii a and b and length l, evaluate the total displacement current flowing across any cylindrical surface of radius r $(a < r < b)$, taking the voltage variation as sinusoidal in time, and the variation of electric field with radius the same as in statics. Show that the result is independent of radius and equal to the charging current for the condenser.

4·05b   Repeat Prob. *a* for the spherical surface of radius *r* lying between the concentric conductors of radii *a* and *b* of a spherical condenser.

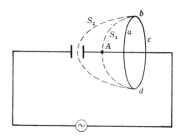

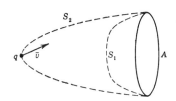

Fig. 4·05   Evaluation of $\oint \bar{H} \cdot \overline{dl}$ for an a-c circuit with a condenser.

Fig. 4·06   Evaluation of $\oint \bar{H} \cdot \overline{dl}$ for charge *q* moving toward loop *A*.

4·06 DISPLACEMENT CURRENT DUE TO A MOVING CHARGE

Inclusion of displacement current is necessary for a valid discussion of another example in which a charge region *q* (Fig. 4·06) moves with velocity $\bar{v}$. If the line integral of magnetic field is to be evaluated about some loop *A* at a given instant, it should be possible to set it equal to the current flow for that instant through any surface of which *A* is a boundary. If the displacement current term were ignored, we could use any one of the infinite number of possible surfaces, as S_1, having no charge passing through it, and obtain the result zero. However, if one of the surfaces is selected, as S_2, through which charge is passing at that instant, there is a contribution from convection current, and a non-zero result. The apparent inconsistency is resolved when one notes that the electric field arising from the moving charge will be varying with time, and thus will actually give rise to a displacement current term through both of the surfaces S_1 and S_2. The sum of displacement and convection currents for the two surfaces is the same at the given instant.

PROBLEM

4·06   Starting from Eq. 4·04(1), prove that for a closed surface

$$\oint_S (\bar{\imath}_c + \bar{\imath}_d) \cdot \overline{dS} = 0$$

From this, show that the sum of convection and displacement currents is the same for both of the surfaces S_1 and S_2 in Fig. 4·06.

4·07   MAXWELL'S EQUATIONS IN DIFFERENTIAL EQUATION FORM

Rewriting the group of equations of Art. 4·03 with the displacement current term added, we have

$$\nabla \cdot \bar{D} = \rho \tag{1}$$

$$\nabla \cdot \bar{B} = 0 \tag{2}$$

$$\nabla \times \bar{E} = -\frac{\partial \bar{B}}{\partial t} \tag{3}$$

$$\nabla \times \bar{H} = \bar{\imath} + \frac{\partial \bar{D}}{\partial t} \tag{4}$$

This set of equations, together with certain auxiliary relations and definitions, is the basic set of equations of classical electricity and magnetism, governing all electromagnetic phenomena in the range of frequencies from zero through the highest-frequency radio waves (and many phenomena at light frequencies), and in the range of sizes above atomic size.   The equations were first written (not in the above notation) by Maxwell in 1863, and are known as *Maxwell's equations*.   The material in the sections preceding this should not be considered a derivation of the laws, for they cannot in any real sense be derived from less fundamental laws.   Their ultimate justification comes, as with all experimental laws, in that they have predicted correctly, and continue to predict, all phenomena in the range over which they were intended to apply.

The set of equations written above is a set of differential equations, relating the time and space rates of change of the various field quantities at a point in space.   The use of these will be demonstrated in many following chapters.   Equivalent large-scale equations will be given in the following article.

The major definitions and auxiliary relations that must be added to complete the information are:

1. *The Force Law.*   This is from one point of view merely the definition of the electric and magnetic fields.   For a charge q moving with velocity $\bar{v}$ through an electric field $\bar{E}$ and a magnetic field of flux density $\bar{B}$, the force is

$$\bar{f} = q[\bar{E} + \bar{v} \times \bar{B}] \text{ newtons} \tag{5}$$

2. *The Definition of Conduction Current (Ohm's Law).*   For a conductor,

$$\bar{\imath} = \sigma \bar{E} \text{ amp/meter}^2 \tag{6}$$

where σ = conductivity in mhos per meter.

3. *The Definition of Convection Current.* For a charge density ρ moving with velocity $\bar{v}_\rho$, the current density is

$$\bar{\imath} = \rho\bar{v}_\rho \text{ amp/meter}^2 \tag{7}$$

4. *Definition of Dielectric Constant.*

$$\epsilon = \epsilon'\epsilon_0 = \frac{\bar{D}}{\bar{E}} \tag{8}$$

where ϵ' = relative dielectric constant (specific inductive capacity); ϵ_0 = dielectric constant of space $\approx (1/36\pi) \times 10^{-9}$ farads per meter.

5. *Definition of Permeability.*

$$\mu = \mu'\mu_0 = \frac{\bar{B}}{\bar{H}} \tag{9}$$

where μ' = relative permeability; μ_0 = permeability of space = $4\pi \times 10^{-7}$ henrys per meter.

In addition, the major quantities appearing in Maxwell's equations have definitions and units as given below.

	Quantity	Units
D	electric flux density vector	coulombs/meter^2
ρ	charge density	coulombs/meter^3
B	magnetic flux density vector	webers/meter^2 = volt sec/meter^2
$\bar{E}$	electric field vector	volts/meter
$\bar{H}$	magnetic field vector	amp/meter
$\bar{\imath}$	conduction or convection current density	amp/meter^2

PROBLEMS

4·07a Check the dimensional consistency of equations (1) through (9) of this article.

4·07b Show that, in a charge-free, current-free dielectric, the two divergence equations, (1) and (2), may be derived from the two curl equations, (3) and (4), so far as time-varying parts of the field are concerned.

4·07c Show that, if the equation for continuity of charge is assumed, the two divergence equations, (1) and (2), may be derived from the curl equations, (3) and (4), so far as a-c components of the field are concerned, for regions with finite ρ and $\bar{\imath}$. This fact has made it quite common to refer to the two curl equations alone as Maxwell's equations.

4·08 MAXWELL'S EQUATIONS IN LARGE-SCALE FORM

It is also convenient to have the information of Maxwell's equations in large-scale form applicable to over-all regions of space, to paths surrounding conductors, etc. This is of course the type of relation that we started with in the discussion of Faraday's law, Art. 4·02, when we derived the differential expression from it.   The large-scale equivalents for Eqs. 4·07(1)–4·07(4) are

$$\oint_S \bar{D} \cdot \overline{dS} = \int_V \rho \, dV \tag{1}$$

$$\oint_S \bar{B} \cdot \overline{dS} = 0 \tag{2}$$

$$\oint \bar{E} \cdot \overline{dl} = -\frac{\partial}{\partial t} \int_S \bar{B} \cdot \overline{dS} \tag{3}$$

$$\oint \bar{H} \cdot \overline{dl} = \int_S \bar{\imath} \cdot \overline{dS} + \frac{\partial}{\partial t} \int_S \bar{D} \cdot \overline{dS} \tag{4}$$

Equations (1) and (2) are obtained by integrating respectively Eqs. 4·07(1) and 4·07(2) over a volume and applying the divergence theorem.   Equations (3) and (4) are obtained by integrating respectively Eqs. 4·07(3) and 4·07(4) over a surface and applying Stokes's theorem.   For example, integrating Eq. 4·07(1),

$$\int_V \nabla \cdot \bar{D} \, dV = \int_V \rho \, dV$$

and applying the divergence theorem,

$$\oint_S \bar{D} \cdot \overline{dS} = \int_V \rho \, dV$$

Equation (1) is seen to be the familiar form of Gauss's law utilized so much in Chapter 2.   Now that we are concerned with fields which are a function of time, the interpretation is that the electric flux flowing out of any closed surface *at a given instant* is equal to the charge enclosed by the surface *at that instant*.

Equation (2) states that the surface integral of magnetic field or total magnetic flux flowing out of a closed surface is zero for all values of time, expressing the fact that magnetic charges have never been found in nature.   Of course the law does not prove that such charges will never be found; if they are, a term on the right similar to the electric charge term in (1) will simply be added, and a corresponding magnetic current term will be added to (3).

Equation (3) is Faraday's law of induction, stating that the line integral of electric field about a closed path (electromotive force) is the negative of the time rate of change of magnetic flux flowing through the path.   The law was discussed in some detail in Art. 4·02.

Equation (4) is the generalized Ampère's law including Maxwell's displacement current term, and it states that the line integral of magnetic field about a closed path (magnetomotive force) is equal to the current (conduction, convection, or displacement) flowing through the path. The physical significance of this complete law has been discussed in Arts. 4·04–4·06.

PROBLEMS

4·08a   A conducting spherical balloon is charged with a constant charge Q, and its radius made to vary sinusoidally in some manner from a minimum value, r_{min}, to a maximum value, r_{max}. It might be supposed that this would produce a spherically symmetric, radially outward propagating electromagnetic wave. Show that this does not happen by finding the electric field at some radius $r > r_{max}$.

4·08b   A condenser formed by two circular parallel plates has an essentially uniform axial electric field produced by a voltage $V_0 \sin \omega t$ across the plates. Utilize the symmetry to find the magnetic field at radius r between the plates. Show that the axial electric field could not be exactly uniform under this time-varying condition.

4·09   MAXWELL'S EQUATIONS FOR THE TIME-PERIODIC CASE

By far the most important time-varying case is that involving steady state a-c fields varying sinusoidally in time. The reasons for this are that the majority of radio engineering applications utilize such fields (at least approximately), and also that transients or time variations of other forms, by the method of Fourier analysis, may be considered a superposition of such steady state sinusoids of different frequency. The advantages of the use of the complex exponential form $(e^{j\omega t})$ described in Chapter 1 for circuit problems are perhaps even more important for the more intricate field problems. Formally, the set of equations 4·07(1)–4·07(4) are easily changed over by replacing $\partial/\partial t$ by $j\omega$:

$$\nabla \cdot \bar{D} = \rho \tag{1}$$

$$\nabla \cdot \bar{B} = 0 \tag{2}$$

$$\nabla \times \bar{E} = -j\omega \bar{B} \tag{3}$$

$$\nabla \times \bar{H} = \bar{\imath} + j\omega \bar{D} \tag{4}$$

And the auxiliary relations, Eqs. 4·07(6)–4·07(9), remain

$$\bar{\imath} = \sigma \bar{E} \quad \text{for conductors} \tag{5}$$

$$\epsilon = \frac{\bar{D}}{\bar{E}} = \epsilon' \epsilon_0 \tag{6}$$

$$\mu = \frac{\bar{B}}{\bar{H}} = \mu' \mu_0 \tag{7}$$

Equations 4·07(5) and 4·07(7) should be used with instantaneous values because of the non-linear terms in the equations.

It must be recognized that the symbols in the equations of this article have a different meaning from the same symbols used in Art. 4·07. There they represented the instantaneous values of the indicated vector and scalar quantities. Here they represent the complex multipliers of $e^{j\omega t}$, giving the in-phase and out-of-phase parts with respect to the chosen reference. It might seem less confusing to use a different notation for the two kinds of quantities, but it is not customary to do this because the difference is always clear from the context, and the two notations required become very unwieldy.

If it is desired to obtain the instantaneous values of a given quantity from the complex value, as in Chapter 1, the $e^{j\omega t}$ is inserted and the real part taken. For example, for the scalar ρ suppose that the complex value of ρ is

$$\rho = \left| \rho \right| e^{j\theta_\rho} \tag{8}$$

where ρ_r and ρ_i are real scalars. The instantaneous value of ρ is then

$$\rho_{\text{inst.}} = \text{Re}\left[(\rho_r + j\rho_i)e^{j\omega t}\right] = \rho_r \cos \omega t - \rho_i \sin \omega t \tag{9}$$

Or, alternatively, if ρ is given in magnitude and phase,

$$\rho = \left| \rho \right| e^{j\theta_\rho} \tag{10}$$

where

$$\left| \rho \right| = \sqrt{\rho_r{}^2 + \rho_i{}^2}$$

$$\theta_\rho = \tan^{-1} \frac{\rho_i}{\rho_r}$$

the instantaneous value is

$$\rho_{\text{inst.}} = \text{Re}\left[\left| \rho \right| e^{j(\omega t+\theta_\rho)}\right] = \left| \rho \right| \cos (\omega t + \theta_\rho) \tag{11}$$

For a vector quantity, such as $\bar{E}$, the complex value may be written

$$\bar{E} = \bar{E}_r + j\bar{E}_i \tag{12}$$

where $\bar{E}_r$ and $\bar{E}_i$ are real vectors. Then

$$\bar{E}_{\text{inst.}} = \text{Re}\left[(\bar{E}_r + j\bar{E}_i)e^{j\omega t}\right] = \bar{E}_r \cos \omega t - \bar{E}_i \sin \omega t \tag{13}$$

Note that $\bar{E}_r$ and $\bar{E}_i$ do not in general have the same direction in space. (This aspect of the subject is discussed more in Art. 7·06 under the heading of polarization.) For the vector quantity, the information cannot in general be given by single values of magnitude and phase angle. Of course the magnitude and phase can be given for each of the three scalar components of the vector $\bar{E}$ to define the complete complex vector.

PROBLEMS

4.09a   Under what conditions can a complex vector quantity $\bar{E}$ be represented by a vector magnitude and phase angle,

$$\bar{E} = \bar{E}_0 e^{j\theta_E}$$

where $\bar{E}_0$ is a real vector and θ_E a real scalar?

4·09b   Consider a case in which the complex field vectors can be represented by single values of magnitude and phase,

$$\bar{E} = \bar{E}_0(x,y,z)e^{j\theta_1(x,y,z)}$$

$$\bar{H} = \bar{H}_0(x,y,z)e^{j\theta_2(x,y,z)}$$

$$\bar{\imath} = \bar{\imath}_0(x,y,z)e^{j\theta_3(x,y,z)}$$

$$\rho = \rho_0(x,y,z)e^{j\theta_4(x,y,z)}$$

Substitute in Maxwell's equations for the complex form, and separate real and imaginary parts to obtain the set of differential equations relating $\bar{E}_0$, $\bar{H}_0$, $\cdots$, θ_4. Check the result by using the corresponding instantaneous expressions,

$$\bar{E}_{\text{inst.}} = \text{Re}[\bar{E}_0 e^{j\theta_1}e^{j\omega t}] = \bar{E}_0(x,y,z) \cos [\omega t + \theta_1(x,y,z)], \text{ etc.}$$

substituting in Maxwell's equations for general time variations, eliminating the time variations, and again getting the set of equations relating E_0, $\cdots$, θ_4.

4·10   OTHER SYSTEMS OF UNITS FOR ELECTROMAGNETIC QUANTITIES

Although the rational mks system of practical units is now uniformly used in the discussion of electromagnetic problems in engineering, the valuable literature still existing in the other systems of units requires some knowledge of these. Conversion factors are given in Table 4·10.

The Gaussian system of units, used most commonly before about 1930, utilized esu units for all electric quantities, and the emu system for all magnetic quantities. A conversion factor c (which turns out to be equal to the velocity of light) is then required in the electromagnetic equations relating the two kinds of quantities. Maxwell's equations in Gaussian units are then as follows:

$$\nabla \cdot \bar{D} = 4\pi\rho \tag{1}$$

$$\nabla \cdot \bar{B} = 0 \tag{2}$$

$$\nabla \times \bar{E} = -\frac{1}{c}\frac{\partial \bar{B}}{\partial t} \tag{3}$$

$$\nabla \times \bar{H} = \frac{4\pi}{c}\left(\bar{\imath} + \frac{\partial \bar{D}}{\partial t}\right) \tag{4}$$

In the above, ρ is charge density in statcoulombs per cubic centimeter, E is electric field in statvolts per centimeter, B is magnetic flux density in gauss, H is magnetic field in oersteds, and i is the current density in statamps per square centimeter.

TABLE 4·10

MULTIPLY	BY	TO OBTAIN
1. Coulombs	$\frac{1}{10}$	abcoulombs
Coulombs	3×10^9	statcoulombs
Coulombs	$\dfrac{3 \times 10^9}{\sqrt{4\pi}} = 8.46 \times 10^8$	hlucoulombs
2. Amperes	$\frac{1}{10}$	abamperes
Amperes	3×10^9	statamperes
Amperes	$\dfrac{3 \times 10^9}{\sqrt{4\pi}} = 8.46 \times 10^8$	hluamperes
3. Volts	10^8	abvolts
Volts	$\frac{1}{300}$	statvolts
Volts	$\dfrac{\sqrt{4\pi}}{300} = 0.0118$	hluvolts
4. Ohms	10^9	abohms
Ohms	$\frac{1}{9} \times 10^{-11}$	statohm
Ohms	$\dfrac{4\pi}{9} \times 10^{-11}$	hluohms
5. Farads	9×10^{11}	statfarads
6. Henrys	10^9	abhenrys
7. Watts (joules/second)	10^7	ergs/second
8. Volts/meter	$\frac{1}{3} \times 10^{-4}$	statvolt/centimeter
9. Webers	10^8	maxwells
10. Webers/meter^2	10^4	gauss

The Heaviside-Lorentz system of rational units is the same as the Gaussian system except that the units of charge, current, and electric field have been modified by a factor of $\sqrt{4\pi}$ to eliminate the factors of 4π from Maxwell's equations. Note that this is a somewhat different way of eliminating the 4π from that employed in the rational mks system. Maxwell's equations in Heaviside-Lorentz units are then

$$\nabla \cdot \bar{D} = \rho \qquad (5)$$

$$\nabla \cdot \bar{B} = 0 \qquad (6)$$

$$\nabla \times \bar{E} = -\frac{1}{c}\frac{\partial \bar{B}}{\partial t} \qquad (7)$$

$$\nabla \times \bar{H} = \frac{1}{c}\left(\bar{\imath} + \frac{\partial \bar{D}}{\partial t}\right) \qquad (8)$$

A rational system of cgs practical units utilizing volts, amperes, coulombs, ohms, and watts for the electromagnetic quantities, as in the mks system, but centimeters, grams, and seconds for the units of length, mass, and time, has also been used to some extent in the engineering literature. The form of the equations appears exactly as in that given for the mks system (Arts. 4·07–4·09), but ρ is in coulombs per cubic centimeter, D in coulombs per square centimeter, E in volts per centimeter, B in webers per square centimeter, H in amperes per centimeter, and i in amperes per square centimeter. The following values of permeability and dielectric constant for space apply:

$$\mu_0 = 4\pi \times 10^{-9} \text{ henrys/cm} \tag{9}$$

$$\epsilon_0 = \frac{1}{36\pi} \times 10^{-11} \text{ farads/cm} \tag{10}$$

In addition, the force equation, Eq. 4·07(5), gives a force in joules per centimeter, so that a factor of 10^7 must be introduced in Newton's laws in studying the motion of charged particles, if mass is to be measured in grams.

$$m\frac{d\bar{v}}{dt} = 10^7\, q(\bar{E} + \bar{v} \times \bar{B}) \tag{11}$$

Boundary Conditions for Time-Varying Systems

4·11 CONTINUITY CONDITIONS FOR TANGENTIAL COMPONENTS OF FIELDS AT A BOUNDARY

In Chapter 2, certain boundary and continuity conditions were stated for static fields. For the remainder of the text we shall be interested in the corresponding boundary and continuity conditions to be applied to the solutions of Maxwell's equations. These conditions may be deduced by referring to Maxwell's equations. Consider first Faraday's law in large-scale form, Eq. 4·08(3), applied to a path formed by moving distance Δl along one side of the boundary between any two materials, and returning on the other side, an infinitesimal distance into the second medium (Fig. 4·11). The line integral of electric field is

$$\oint \bar{E} \cdot d\bar{l} = (E_{t1} - E_{t2})\, \Delta l \tag{1}$$

Since the path is an infinitesimal distance on either side of the boundary, its area is zero, and therefore the contribution from changing magnetic flux is zero so long as rate of change of magnetic flux density is finite. Consequently,

$$(E_{t1} - E_{t2})\, \Delta l = 0 \qquad \text{or} \qquad E_{t1} = E_{t2} \tag{2}$$

Similarly, the generalized Ampère law in large-scale form, Eq. 4·08(4), may be applied to a like path with its two sides on the two sides of the boundary. Again there is zero area enclosed by the path, and, so long as current density and rate of change of electric flux density are finite, the integral is zero, and in like manner to the above

$$H_{t1} = H_{t2} \tag{3}$$

Thus tangential components of electric and magnetic field must be equal on the two sides of any boundary between physically real media. The condition (3) may be modified for an idealized case such as the perfect conductor where the current densities are allowed to become infinite. This case will be discussed separately in Art. 4·13.

Fig. 4·11.

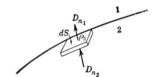

Fig. 4·12 Surface charge ρ_s on a boundary between two media.

4·12 CONTINUITY CONDITIONS FOR NORMAL COMPONENTS OF FIELD AT A BOUNDARY

The integral form of Gauss's law is Eq. 4·08(1). If two very small elements of area ΔS are considered (Fig. 4·12), one on either side of the boundary between any two materials, with a surface charge density ρ_s existing on the boundary, the application of Gauss's law to this elemental volume gives

$$\Delta S(D_{n1} - D_{n2}) = \rho_s \, \Delta S$$

or $$D_{n1} - D_{n2} = \rho_s \tag{1}$$

For a charge-free boundary,

$$D_{n1} = D_{n2} \quad \text{or} \quad \epsilon_1 E_{n1} = \epsilon_2 E_{n2} \tag{2}$$

That is, for a charge-free boundary, normal components of electric flux density are continuous; for a boundary with charges, they are discontinuous by the amount of the surface charge density.

With no magnetic charge term on the right of Eq. 4·08(2), a corresponding development to the above shows that always the magnetic flux density is continuous:

$$B_{n1} = B_{n2} \quad \text{or} \quad \mu_1 H_{n1} = \mu_2 H_{n2} \tag{3}$$

For the time-periodic case, which is of greatest importance to our study, the above conditions on normal components are not independent of those given for the tangential components in Art. 4·11. The reason is that the above are derived from the two divergence equations (or their equivalent in large-scale form), and these may be obtained from the two curl equations in the time-varying case (Probs. 4·07b and c). The conditions on tangential components in Art. 4·11 were derived from the large-scale equivalents of the curl equations. Hence, for the a-c solutions, it is necessary only to apply the continuity conditions on tangential components of electric and magnetic fields at a boundary between two media, and the above conditions on normal components used as a check; or, if the normal components of D turn out to be discontinuous, (1) tells the amount of surface charge that is induced on the boundary.

4·13 BOUNDARY CONDITIONS AT A PERFECT CONDUCTOR

For a general conductor, the conduction current density is given by Ohm's law, Eq. 4·07(6):

$$\bar{\imath} = \sigma\bar{E} \tag{1}$$

No conductor is perfect, but in many practical problems with good conductors it is desirable in some stages of the analysis to neglect the small but finite electric field along the conductor required to produce the current flow through it. This can be done by assuming the conductor perfect ($\sigma = \infty$) for these parts of the analysis. Since the current must remain finite, it follows that electric field in the conductor, and the tangential component of electric field at the surface of the conductor, must be zero by (1). Thus the basic boundary condition for the idealized case of the perfect conductor is that the tangential component of electric field at the surface of the conductor shall be zero:

$$E_t = 0 \quad \text{at conductor surface} \tag{2}$$

It will be shown in the skin effect studies of Chapter 6 that for a perfect conductor all a-c fields must go to zero inside the conductor. Since the normal component of magnetic flux density must always be continuous, it follows that this component must always go to zero at the surface in the time-varying solution:

$$B_n = 0 \quad \text{at conductor surface} \tag{3}$$

However, as pointed out in the last article, the continuity condition on normal $\bar{B}$ is not independent of the condition on tangential $\bar{E}$ in the time-varying case.   Thus, in the a-c solution, (3) follows from (2), but may sometimes be useful as a check, or as an alternative boundary condition.

The normal component of electric flux density is zero inside the perfect conductor, as are all field components, but it is not in general zero just outside the conductor.   By Eq. 4·12(1), the surface charge density induced by this discontinuity in electric flux density is

$$\rho_s = D_n \quad \text{at conductor surface} \tag{4}$$

The tangential component of magnetic field is likewise zero inside the perfect conductor but is not in general zero just outside.   This discontinuity would appear to violate the condition of Eq. 4·11(3), but it will be recalled that a condition for that proof was that current density must remain finite.   For the perfect conductor, the finite current $\bar{J}$ per unit width is assumed to flow as a current sheet of zero thickness, so that current *density* is infinite.   The discontinuity in tangential magnetic field is found by a construction similar to that of Fig. 4·11.   The current enclosed by the path is the current per unit width $\bar{J}$ flowing on the surface of the conductor perpendicular to the direction of the tangential magnetic field at the surface.   Then

$$\oint \bar{H} \cdot \bar{dl} = H_t \, dl = J \, dl$$

or
$$J = H_t \tag{5}$$

The direction and sense relations for (5) are given most conveniently by the vector form of the law below.

To write the relations of (2) to (5) in vector notation, a unit vector $\bar{n}$, normal to the conductor at any given point and pointing from the conductor into the region where fields exist, is defined (Fig. 4·13). Then conditions (2) to (5) become, respectively, (6) to (9) below:

$$\bar{n} \times \bar{E} = 0 \tag{6}$$

$$\bar{n} \cdot \bar{B} = 0 \tag{7}$$

$$\rho_s = \bar{n} \cdot \bar{D} \tag{8}$$

$$\bar{J} = \bar{n} \times \bar{H} \tag{9}$$

For an a-c problem, (6) represents the only required boundary condition at a perfect conductor.   Equation (7) serves as a check or sometimes as an alternative to (6).   Equations (8) and (9) are used to give the charge and current induced on the conductor by the presence of the electromagnetic fields.

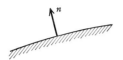

Fig. 4·13.

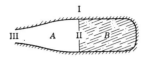

Fig. 4·14　Region containing two dielectrics partially enclosed by a conductor.

4·14　USE OF THE BOUNDARY RELATIONS FOR TIME-VARYING PROBLEMS

The previously discussed boundary relations are of the highest practical importance in the solution of high-frequency problems. They may enter into the problems in a number of ways. For example, the fields may be known on one side of a boundary, and the fields on the other side may be desired. Or the fields at the surface of a perfect conductor may be known, the current and charges on the conductor then being given by the boundary relations. But more important than these two examples is that the boundary relations are tied up basically with the whole technique of finding the distribution of electromagnetic effects by solving Maxwell's equations. In general, the problem is always one of writing down solutions to these equations and selecting or fitting them to the particular problem by making certain that they satisfy the boundary conditions of the space being studied. Hence the boundary relations appear directly or indirectly every time a high-frequency problem is solved.

The way in which these relations enter into the solution of a problem will be clarified by the discussion of a more or less general example. Figure 4·14 shows a space bounded everywhere except at the input surface III by a perfect conductor I, and filled with two dielectrics A and B which are separated by a surface II. It is assumed that electromagnetic fields in the region are excited by impressed fields at the boundary III, with tangential components given. Only the time-varying parts of the fields are of interest.

To obtain the distribution of fields, currents, and charges, various solutions of Maxwell's equations are now considered, and the process of selection of appropriate types and amounts of these solutions is ready to begin. In both regions A and B, we reject first of all those which fail to give zero tangential electric field on the boundary of the perfect conductor I. Of all the possible solutions that satisfy this boundary condition at the perfect conductor, those are retained which have continuity between the tangential electric and magnetic fields between regions A and B along the boundary II (Art. 4·11). Finally, of all the solutions which satisfy the boundary conditions on the perfect conductor and have continuity of tangential field components across the boundary II, one of these, or a sum, is retained to give continuity with the tangential components of the impressed fields at III. Then the charges and currents on the conductor can be found, if desired, by the normal component of $\bar{D}$ at the conductor and the tangential component of $\bar{H}$, respectively.

Potentials Used with Varying Charges and Currents

4·15   A POSSIBLE SET OF POTENTIALS FOR TIME-VARYING FIELDS

The set of differential equations known as Maxwell's equations, with certain auxiliary relations, gives the complete information for obtaining electric and magnetic effects due to currents and charges. It will sometimes be convenient to put the information in a different form by the introduction of new variables. In the study of static fields, it was found that new functions known as potentials helped in the solution of static problems. We might then look for similar potential functions which will help in the solution of more general problems. The potential functions of static fields were given in terms of integral expressions of charges and currents. They could be differentiated in certain specified ways to give the fields. We will then look for more general potential functions as integrals of the time-varying charges and currents, which potentials may be differentiated to give the time-varying fields.

In speculating on the form which the potential function for electric field might take, we could hope to have one of the simple forms found useful in Chapter 2, such as gradient of a scalar or the curl of a vector. However, we are faced with this problem: the electric field for time-varying conditions cannot be derived alone as the gradient of scalar potential since this would require that it have zero curl, and it may actually have a finite curl of value $-\partial\bar{B}/\partial t$; it cannot be derived alone as the curl of a vector potential since this would require that it have zero divergence, and it may have a finite divergence of value ρ/ϵ.

Since the divergence of magnetic field is zero in the general case as it was in the static, it seems that $\bar{B}$ may still be set equal to the curl of some magnetic vector potential, $\bar{A}$. Suppose that the substitution of $\bar{B} = \nabla \times \bar{A}$ is made in Maxwell's equations and an attempt is then made to obtain a value for the potential function of electric fields which vary with time. Equation 4·07(3) can be written

$$\nabla \times \left[\bar{E} + \frac{\partial\bar{A}}{\partial t} \right] = 0 \tag{1}$$

This equation states that the curl of a certain vector quantity is zero. But this is the condition that permits a vector to be derived as the gradient of a scalar, say Φ. That is,

$$\bar{E} + \frac{\partial \bar{A}}{\partial t} = -\nabla\Phi$$

or

$$\bar{E} = -\nabla\Phi - \frac{\partial \bar{A}}{\partial t} \tag{2}$$

The electric field, $\bar{E}$, has consequently been obtained in terms of both a scalar and a vector potential.

To continue the substitutions in Maxwell's equations: in Eq. 4·07(1),

$$-\nabla^2\Phi - \frac{\partial}{\partial t}(\nabla \cdot \bar{A}) = \frac{\rho}{\epsilon} \tag{3}$$

in Eq. 4·07(4)

$$\nabla \times \nabla \times \bar{A} = \mu\bar{\imath} + \mu\epsilon\left[-\nabla\left(\frac{\partial\Phi}{\partial t}\right) - \frac{\partial^2\bar{A}}{\partial t^2}\right]$$

The vector identity (Art. 2·39)

$$\nabla \times \nabla \times \bar{A} = \nabla(\nabla \cdot \bar{A}) - \nabla^2\bar{A}$$

so

$$\nabla(\nabla \cdot \bar{A}) - \nabla^2\bar{A} = \mu\bar{\imath} - \mu\epsilon\nabla\left(\frac{\partial\Phi}{\partial t}\right) - \mu\epsilon\frac{\partial^2\bar{A}}{\partial t^2} \tag{4}$$

The equations (3) and (4) scarcely seem simple. However, it is realized that $\bar{A}$ is not unique until it is further specified. That is, there are any number of vector functions whose curl is the same. It may be shown that it is necessary only to specify the divergence of $\bar{A}$ to make it unique, and this may be done according to convenience. If the divergence of $\bar{A}$ is chosen as

$$\nabla \cdot \bar{A} = -\mu\epsilon\frac{\partial\Phi}{\partial t} \tag{5}$$

(3) and (4) then simplify to

$$\nabla^2\Phi - \mu\epsilon\frac{\partial^2\Phi}{\partial t^2} = -\frac{\rho}{\epsilon} \tag{6}$$

$$\nabla^2\bar{A} - \mu\epsilon\frac{\partial^2\bar{A}}{\partial t^2} = -\mu\bar{\imath} \tag{7}$$

And, repeating from the above,

$$\bar{B} = \nabla \times \bar{A} \qquad (8)$$

$$\bar{E} = -\nabla\Phi - \frac{\partial \bar{A}}{\partial t} \qquad (9)$$

Thus the potentials $\bar{A}$ and Φ, defined in terms of the sources $\bar{\imath}$ and ρ by the differential equations (6) and (7), may be used to derive the electric and magnetic fields by (8) and (9). It is easy to see that they do reduce to the corresponding expressions of statics, for, if time derivatives are allowed to go to zero, the set of equations (6)–(9) becomes

$$\nabla^2\Phi = -\frac{\rho}{\epsilon} \qquad \bar{E} = -\nabla\Phi \qquad (10)$$

$$\nabla^2\bar{A} = -\mu\bar{\imath} \qquad \bar{B} = \nabla \times \bar{A} \qquad (11)$$

which are recognized as the appropriate expressions from Chapter 2.

PROBLEMS

4·15a. A potential function commonly used in electromagnetic theory is the Hertz vector potential $\bar{\Pi}$, so defined that electric and magnetic fields are derived from it as follows, for a homogeneous medium:

$$\bar{H} = \epsilon \frac{\partial}{\partial t} (\nabla \times \bar{\Pi})$$

$$\bar{E} = \nabla(\nabla \cdot \bar{\Pi}) - \mu\epsilon \frac{\partial^2 \bar{\Pi}}{\partial t^2}$$

where

$$\nabla^2\bar{\Pi} - \mu\epsilon \frac{\partial^2 \bar{\Pi}}{\partial t^2} = -\frac{\bar{P}}{\epsilon}$$

and $\bar{P}$, the "polarization vector" associated with sources, is so defined that

$$\bar{\imath} = \frac{\partial \bar{P}}{\partial t} \qquad \rho = -\nabla \cdot \bar{P}$$

Show that $\bar{E}$ and $\bar{H}$ derived in this manner are consistent with Maxwell's equations.

4·15b. Show that $\bar{E}$ and $\bar{H}$ satisfy the following differential equations in a homogeneous medium containing charges and currents:

$$\nabla^2\bar{E} - \mu\epsilon \frac{\partial^2 \bar{E}}{\partial t^2} = \frac{1}{\epsilon}\nabla\rho + \mu \frac{\partial \bar{\imath}}{\partial t}$$

$$\nabla^2\bar{H} - \mu\epsilon \frac{\partial^2 \bar{H}}{\partial t^2} = -\nabla \times \bar{\imath}$$

4·16　THE RETARDED POTENTIALS AS INTEGRALS OVER CHARGES AND CURRENTS

Although the potential functions $\bar{A}$ and Φ for time-varying fields are defined in terms of the currents and charges by the differential equations 4·15(6) and (7), it is also desirable to have expressions giving the potentials as integrals over the charges and currents as in the static case. The following discussion applies to the very important case of a single homogeneous dielectric region extending to infinity.

From Chapter 2, the integrals for the static potentials, which may be considered the solutions of Eqs. 4·15(10) and (11), are

$$\Phi = \int_V \frac{\rho \, dV}{4\pi\epsilon r} \tag{1}$$

$$\bar{A} = \mu \int_V \frac{\bar{\imath} \, dV}{4\pi r} \tag{2}$$

A mathematical development to yield the corresponding integral solutions of the inhomogeneous wave equations, 4·15(6) and (7), is moderately difficult, so only a qualitative discussion is given here. It can be shown that the solutions are

$$\Phi = \int_V \frac{[\rho]_{t-(r/v)} \, dV}{4\pi\epsilon r} \tag{3}$$

$$\bar{A} = \mu \int_V \frac{[\bar{\imath}]_{t-(r/v)} \, dV}{4\pi r} \tag{4}$$

where

$$v = \frac{1}{\sqrt{\mu\epsilon}} \tag{5}$$

(For free space, $v = c \approx 3 \times 10^8$ meters per second.)

In the above, the bracket with subscript $t - (r/v)$ denotes that, for an evaluation of Φ at time t, the value of charge density ρ at time $t - (r/v)$ should be used. That is, for each element of charge $\rho \, dV$, the equation says that the contribution to potential is of the same form as in statics, Eq. (1), except that we must recognize a finite time of propagating the effect from the charge element to the point P at which potential is being computed, distance r away. The effect travels with velocity $v = 1/\sqrt{\mu\epsilon}$, which, as we shall see, is just the velocity of a simple plane wave through the medium as predicted from the corresponding homogeneous wave equations [Eqs. 4·15(6) and (7) with ρ and $\bar{\imath}$ zero].

$$\nabla^2 \Phi - \mu\epsilon \frac{\partial^2 \Phi}{\partial t^2} = 0 \tag{6}$$

$$\nabla^2 \bar{A} - \mu\epsilon \frac{\partial^2 \bar{A}}{\partial t^2} = 0 \tag{7}$$

A special case of the wave equation for one-dimensional flow has already been studied in Chapter 1, revealing the general phenomenon of wave propagation with a given velocity governed by this type of equation. Thus, in computing the total contribution to potential Φ at a point P at a given instant t, we must use the values of charge density from points distance r away at an earlier time, $t - (r/v)$, since for a given element it is that effect which just reaches P at time t. The integral (3) states this. A similar interpretation applied to the computation of $\bar{A}$ from currents in (4). Because of this "retardation" effect, the potentials Φ and $\bar{A}$ are called the *retarded potentials*. Once the phenomenon of wave propagation predicted from Maxwell's equations is known, this is about the simplest revision of the static formulas (1) and (2) that could possibly be expected.

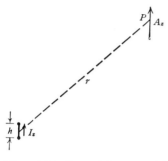

Fig. 4·16 Retarded potential from small current element.

One of the simplest examples illustrating the meaning of this retardation, and one which will be met again in the study of radiating systems, is that of a very short current element carrying an a-c current varying sinusoidally in time between two small spheres on which charges accumulate (Fig. 4·16). For a filamentary current in a small wire, the difference in distance from P to any point of a given cross section of the wire is unimportant, so that two of the integrations of the volume integral may be made by integrating current density over the cross section to yield the total current in the wire. Thus, for any filamentary current,

$$\bar{A} = \mu \int \frac{[\bar{I}]_{t-(r/v)} \, dl}{4\pi r} \tag{8}$$

For the particular case of Fig. 4·16, current is in the z direction only, so, by the above, $\bar{A}$ is also. If h is so small compared with r that it may be taken as infinitesimal, the remaining integration of (8) is performed by multiplying the current by h:

$$A_z = \frac{\mu h}{4\pi r} [I_z]_{t-(r/v)} \tag{9}$$

Finally, if the current in the small element has the form

$$I_z = I_0 \cos \omega t$$

substitution in (9) gives A_z as

$$A_z = \frac{\mu h I_0}{4\pi r} \cos \omega \left(t - \frac{r}{v} \right) \tag{10}$$

From this value of $\bar{A}$ the magnetic field may be derived, and in fact the electric field also, but this part of the problem will be left for the chapter on radiation.

PROBLEMS

4·16a By analogy with the integral solutions for $\bar{A}$ and Φ, write the integral for the Hertz vector $\bar{\bar{\Pi}}$ in terms of the polarization $\bar{P}$. (See Prob. 4·15.)

4·16b Repeat the example of the small current element worked out above (Fig. 4·16), but in complex notation, $I_z = I_0 e^{j\omega t}$, finding the vector potential $\bar{A}$.

4·17 THE RETARDED POTENTIALS FOR THE TIME-PERIODIC CASE

If all electromagnetic quantities of interest are varying sinusoidally in time, in the complex notation with $e^{j\omega t}$ understood, the set of equations 4·15(8) and (9), 4·16(3) and (4), and 4·15(5) becomes

$$\bar{B} = \nabla \times \bar{A} \tag{1}$$

$$\bar{E} = -\nabla\Phi - j\omega\bar{A} \tag{2}$$

$$\Phi = \int_V \frac{\rho e^{-jkr} \, dV}{4\pi\epsilon r} \tag{3}$$

$$\bar{A} = \int_V \frac{\mu\bar{\imath} e^{-jkr} \, dV}{4\pi r} \tag{4}$$

$$\nabla \cdot \bar{A} = -j\omega\mu\epsilon\Phi \tag{5}$$

where $k = \omega/v = \omega\sqrt{\mu\epsilon}$. Note that the retardation in this case is taken care of by the factor e^{-jkr} and amounts to a shift in phase of each contribution to potential according to the distance r from the contributing element to the point P at which potential is to be computed.

It is evident in this case of steady state sinusoids that the relation between $\bar{A}$ and Φ [Eq. (5)] fixes Φ uniquely once $\bar{A}$ is determined. Thus, it is not necessary to compute the scalar potential Φ separately. Both $\bar{E}$ and $\bar{B}$ may be written in terms of $\bar{A}$ alone:

$$\bar{B} = \nabla \times \bar{A} \tag{6}$$

$$\bar{E} = -\frac{j\omega}{k^2} \nabla(\nabla \cdot \bar{A}) - j\omega\bar{A} \tag{7}$$

$$\bar{A} = \mu \int_V \frac{\bar{\imath}e^{-jkr} \, dV}{4\pi r} \tag{8}$$

It is then necessary only to specify the current distribution over the system, to compute the vector potential $\bar{A}$ from it by (8), and then find the electric and magnetic fields by (6) and (7). It may appear that the effects of the charges of the system are being left out, but of course the continuity equation

$$\nabla \cdot \bar{\imath} = -j\omega\rho \tag{9}$$

relates the charges to the currents, and in fact, in this steady state sinusoidal case, fixes ρ uniquely once the distribution of $\bar{\imath}$ is given. So an equivalent but lengthier procedure would be that of computing the charge distribution from the specified current distribution by means of the continuity equation (9), then using the complete set of equations (1) to (4).

PROBLEMS

4·17a Continuing Prob. 4·16b, find the charges that must exist on the ends of the current element to be consistent with continuity. From these, find the retarded potential Φ at point P distance r away, making use of the inequalities $h/r \ll 1$ and $kh \ll 1$. Show that the same result is obtained for Φ by employing Eq. (5) and the result for $\bar{A}$ from Prob. 4·16b.

4·17b For a particular solution (the so-called TM_{111} mode) to be studied inside a rectangular cavity resonator of sides a, b, and d, the fields may be derived from a vector potential which has only a z component,

$$A_z = C \sin \frac{\pi x}{a} \sin \frac{\pi y}{b} \cos \frac{\pi z}{d}$$

Find the corresponding electric and magnetic fields.   (Time variations are as $e^{j\omega t}$.)

4·17c As in Prob. b, but for the so-called TE_{01} mode in a circular cylindrical wave guide where the vector potential has only a ϕ component,

$$A_\phi = CJ_1(k_c r)e^{-j\beta z}$$

find electric and magnetic fields.

4·17d Find the relation between the Hertz potential $\bar{\Pi}$ of Prob. 4·15 and the vector potential $\bar{A}$ when time variations are taken of the form $e^{j\omega t}$.

4·18   COMPARISON OF VOLTAGE AND POTENTIAL DIFFERENCE

The voltage between two points, 1 and 2, may be defined as the negative line integral of electric field taken along a path from 1 to 2:

$$V_{21} = - \int_1^2 \bar{E} \cdot \overline{dl} \tag{1}$$

If we utilize the expression for electric field in terms of the potential functions, Eq. 4·15(9), we have

$$V_{21} = - \int_1^2 \left[-\nabla\Phi - \frac{\partial \bar{A}}{\partial t} \right] \cdot \overline{dl}$$

In evaluating the first term, it is recalled that the component of the gradient of a scalar in any direction gives the rate of change of the scalar with respect to that direction:

$$V_{21} = \int_1^2 \frac{\partial \Phi}{\partial l} \, dl + \frac{\partial}{\partial t} \int_1^2 \bar{A} \cdot \overline{dl}$$

or

$$V_{21} = (\Phi_2 - \Phi_1) + \frac{\partial}{\partial t} \int_1^2 \bar{A} \cdot \overline{dl} \tag{2}$$

For static fields, the last term is zero and the voltage defined by (1) is exactly the difference in the scalar potential function Φ between the two points and so is independent of the path taken between 1 and 2. For time-varying fields we see by (2) that there is a term in addition to the difference in scalar potential, and this term will in general depend on the path taken between 1 and 2. Thus voltage in time-varying systems in general depends upon the path taken between two specified points, and is usually not equal to a difference in scalar potential between these points. There are important cases for which the last term is exactly or approximately zero, and the identification between voltage and potential difference is correct and useful, but the justification must be supplied for each specific case if the fields are time-varying.

A slightly different approach which stresses this same point comes by evaluating the voltage along two paths C and C' between points 1 and 2 (Fig. 4·18). For, if the emf is evaluated about a closed path formed by integrating along C and returning on C', the result is just the difference in the voltages found along the two paths:

$$\oint \bar{E} \cdot \overline{dl} = \int_{1C}^2 \bar{E} \cdot \overline{dl} - \int_{1C'}^2 \bar{E} \cdot \overline{dl} = V_{21}' - V_{21}$$

But by Faraday's law [Eq. 4·02(2)] this is just the negative rate of change of magnetic flux through the surface bounded by these paths:

$$V_{21}' - V_{21} = -\frac{\partial}{\partial t} \int_S \bar{B} \cdot d\overline{S} \tag{3}$$

So we see that the voltages defined along the two paths will be different whenever there is any time-varying magnetic flux enclosed between the two paths. In such cases, voltage cannot be synonymous with potential difference.

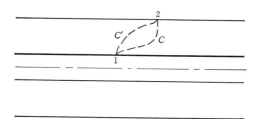

Fig. 4·18.

The example of Fig. 4·18 might be considered a coaxial transmission line for which, as will be shown, there is magnetic field in the circumferential direction only. Hence, for all paths between the two conductors *lying in a given transverse plane*, the same result for voltage will be obtained since there is no changing magnetic flux included between any two of them. The voltage for such paths can then be interpreted as difference in potential between conductors *at a specified cross-sectional plane*. But, if voltage is desired between the two conductors for points 1 and 2 not in the same transverse plane, two paths C and C' will yield different results in general, since the circumferential magnetic field threads between the two paths and will in general yield a finite result for (3). The voltage between such points cannot then be defined until the path is specified, and it is not equal to the difference of potential between points 1 and 2.

4·19 MAXWELL'S EQUATIONS IN SEVERAL COORDINATE SYSTEMS

Rectangular Coordinates.

1. $\dfrac{\partial D_x}{\partial x} + \dfrac{\partial D_y}{\partial y} + \dfrac{\partial D_z}{\partial z} = \rho$

2. $\dfrac{\partial B_x}{\partial x} + \dfrac{\partial B_y}{\partial y} + \dfrac{\partial B_z}{\partial z} = 0$

3. $\dfrac{\partial E_z}{\partial y} - \dfrac{\partial E_y}{\partial z} = -\dfrac{\partial B_x}{\partial t}$

$\dfrac{\partial E_x}{\partial z} - \dfrac{\partial E_z}{\partial x} = -\dfrac{\partial B_y}{\partial t}$

$\dfrac{\partial E_y}{\partial x} - \dfrac{\partial E_x}{\partial y} = -\dfrac{\partial B_z}{\partial t}$

4. $\dfrac{\partial H_z}{\partial y} - \dfrac{\partial H_y}{\partial z} = i_x + \dfrac{\partial D_x}{\partial t}$

$\dfrac{\partial H_x}{\partial z} - \dfrac{\partial H_z}{\partial x} = i_y + \dfrac{\partial D_y}{\partial t}$

$\dfrac{\partial H_y}{\partial x} - \dfrac{\partial H_x}{\partial y} = i_z + \dfrac{\partial D_z}{\partial t}$

Cylindrical Coordinates.

1. $\dfrac{1}{r}\dfrac{\partial}{\partial r}(rD_r) + \dfrac{1}{r}\dfrac{\partial D_\phi}{\partial \phi} + \dfrac{\partial D_z}{\partial z} = \rho$

2. $\dfrac{1}{r}\dfrac{\partial}{\partial r}(rB_r) + \dfrac{1}{r}\dfrac{\partial B_\phi}{\partial \phi} + \dfrac{\partial B_z}{\partial z} = 0$

3. $\dfrac{1}{r}\dfrac{\partial E_z}{\partial \phi} - \dfrac{\partial E_\phi}{\partial z} = -\dfrac{\partial B_r}{\partial t}$

$\dfrac{\partial E_r}{\partial z} - \dfrac{\partial E_z}{\partial r} = -\dfrac{\partial B_\phi}{\partial t}$

$\dfrac{1}{r}\dfrac{\partial}{\partial r}(rE_\phi) - \dfrac{1}{r}\dfrac{\partial E_r}{\partial \phi} = -\dfrac{\partial B_z}{\partial t}$

4. $\dfrac{1}{r}\dfrac{\partial H_z}{\partial \phi} - \dfrac{\partial H_\phi}{\partial z} = i_r + \dfrac{\partial D_r}{\partial t}$

$\dfrac{\partial H_r}{\partial z} - \dfrac{\partial H_z}{\partial r} = i_\phi + \dfrac{\partial D_\phi}{\partial t}$

$\dfrac{1}{r}\dfrac{\partial}{\partial r}(rH_\phi) - \dfrac{1}{r}\dfrac{\partial H_r}{\partial \phi} = i_z + \dfrac{\partial D_z}{\partial t}$

Spherical Coordinates.

1. $\dfrac{1}{r^2}\dfrac{\partial}{\partial r}(r^2 D_r) + \dfrac{1}{r\sin\theta}\dfrac{\partial}{\partial \theta}(D_\theta \sin\theta) + \dfrac{1}{r\sin\theta}\dfrac{\partial D_\phi}{\partial \phi} = \rho$

2. $\dfrac{1}{r^2} \dfrac{\partial}{\partial r} (r^2 B_r) + \dfrac{1}{r \sin \theta} \dfrac{\partial}{\partial \theta} (B_\theta \sin \theta) + \dfrac{1}{r \sin \theta} \dfrac{\partial B_\phi}{\partial \phi} = 0$

3. $\dfrac{1}{r \sin \theta} \left[\dfrac{\partial}{\partial \theta} (E_\phi \sin \theta) - \dfrac{\partial E_\theta}{\partial \phi} \right] = -\dfrac{\partial B_r}{\partial t}$

$\dfrac{1}{r} \left[\dfrac{1}{\sin \theta} \dfrac{\partial E_r}{\partial \phi} - \dfrac{\partial}{\partial r} (r E_\phi) \right] = -\dfrac{\partial B_\theta}{\partial t}$

$\dfrac{1}{r} \left[\dfrac{\partial}{\partial r} (r E_\theta) - \dfrac{\partial E_r}{\partial \theta} \right] = -\dfrac{\partial B_\phi}{\partial t}$

4. $\dfrac{1}{r \sin \theta} \left[\dfrac{\partial}{\partial \theta} (H_\phi \sin \theta) - \dfrac{\partial H_\theta}{\partial \phi} \right] = i_r + \dfrac{\partial D_r}{\partial t}$

$\dfrac{1}{r} \left[\dfrac{1}{\sin \theta} \dfrac{\partial H_r}{\partial \phi} - \dfrac{\partial}{\partial r} (r H_\phi) \right] = i_\theta + \dfrac{\partial D_\theta}{\partial t}$

$\dfrac{1}{r} \left[\dfrac{\partial}{\partial r} (r H_\theta) - \dfrac{\partial H_r}{\partial \theta} \right] = i_\phi + \dfrac{\partial D_\phi}{\partial t}$

Forms for Steady State Sinusoids $(e^{j\omega t})$.

DIFFERENTIAL EQUATION FORM   RETARDED POTENTIAL FORM

$\nabla \cdot \bar{D} = \rho$ $\bar{B} = \nabla \times \bar{A}$

$\nabla \cdot \bar{B} = 0$ $\bar{E} = -j\omega \left[\bar{A} + \dfrac{1}{k^2} \nabla (\nabla \cdot \bar{A}) \right]$

$\nabla \times \bar{E} = -j\omega\mu\bar{H}$ $\bar{A} = \displaystyle\int_V \dfrac{\mu \bar{i}}{4\pi r} e^{-jkr} \, dV$

$\nabla \times \bar{H} = \bar{i} + j\omega\epsilon\bar{E}$ $k = \omega \sqrt{\mu\epsilon}$

5 CIRCUIT CONCEPTS

AND THEIR DERIVATION

FROM THE FIELD EQUATIONS

5·01 INTRODUCTION

From the preceding chapter we have a set of laws (Maxwell's equations) that contains the core of the classical theory of electricity and magnetism. The applications of these to most problems is not difficult, speaking of concepts alone. There are plenty of mathematical difficulties—inability to integrate certain forms or to solve certain differential equations—but the ideas behind everything in modern radio, in so far as they depend on classical electricity and magnetism, should always be clarified by proper reference to Maxwell's equations. Our purpose for the remainder of the book is to study the systems and phenomena important to radio by means of these laws. They will be made to give quantitative design results, exact or approximate, whenever this is possible, but more important, we shall always use them to understand the concepts and physical pictures underlying the phenomena in question.

Of the many types of problems to be studied, many involve circuits, a term that covers a huge percentage of all phenomena with which the radio engineer is concerned and with which he associates many of the important concepts in electromagnetics. In a circuit problem there is often an applied voltage, and there are currents in the conductors of the circuit, charges on condensers in the circuit, ohmic losses, and power losses by radiation. These effects include almost everything that can happen when electric currents, charges, and conductors are let loose. The circuit problem is also one of the commonest problems illustrating the idea of cause and effect relationships. For these reasons, and, most important of all, because the circuit technique is one of the most familiar and useful to engineers, this will be the first problem to be investigated from the starting point of the fundamental laws.

In this chapter only the concepts and the general techniques of circuits are to be studied; quantitative analysis is reserved for the next chapter. From the rigorous starting point of the fundamental laws, it will be found that for circuits which are small compared with wavelength, this exact approach leads directly to the familiar circuit ideas based upon Kirchhoff's laws, and the concepts of lumped inductances and capacitances are sufficient for analysis. For such circuits there would then be little need for going beyond Kirchhoff's laws. Although many of the circuits the average radio engineer encounters may be of this type, two reasons make it necessary to go beyond this stage in the understanding of circuit concepts. First, the increasing use of high frequencies increases the uncertainties in the engineering and development of systems which are thought up, designed, and experimented upon without sufficiently broad tools. For instance, most notions of circuits came out of studies of systems in which the current flows in relatively small cross-section filaments or wires (and in which the matter of distribution of current over this confined path is a secondary effect easily added on separately). But at ultra-high frequencies we would like to be able to use convenient circuit concepts, without going astray, on circuits which have the total current flow distributed over a wider or larger region than the physical confines of the circuit materials themselves. Secondly, when the radiation of electromagnetic energy is considered at any frequency, the radiating system must eventually be understood both as to the mechanism of the release of energy and the feeding of the antenna by the applied electromagnetic forces. The desire to utilize the convenient concepts of applied voltage, impedance, etc., in the latter case leads to a combination field-circuit problem, which, with no background in the electromagnetics of circuit notions, would be unnecessarily difficult even in qualitative thinking.

The Formulation of a Circuit Concept Consistent with Maxwell's Equations

5·02   KIRCHHOFF'S FIRST LAW

In classical circuit theory, Kirchhoff's first law states that the algebraic sum of all currents flowing out of a junction must be zero. Thus, referring to Fig. 5·02,

$$\sum_{n=1}^{N} I_n = 0 \qquad (1)$$

It is evident that the idea behind this law is that of continuity of cur-

·rent, so we should refer to the continuity equation implicit in Maxwell's equations, Eq. 4·03(5), or its large-scale equivalent,

$$\oint_S \bar{\imath} \cdot \overline{dS} = - \frac{\partial}{\partial t} \int_V \rho \, dV \tag{2}$$

If we apply this to a surface S surrounding the junction, the only conduction current flowing out of the surface is that in the wires, so the left side of (2) becomes just the algebraic sum of the currents flowing out in the wires, as in (1). The right side is the negative time rate of change of charge Q, if any, accumulating at the junction. So (2) may be written

$$\sum_{n=1}^{N} I_n = - \frac{dQ}{dt} \tag{3}$$

Comparison of (1) and (3) indicates an apparent difference. However, we know that, in the application of Kirchhoff's first law, we add a new branch, calling it a capacitance current of dQ/dt if there is charge accumulating at the junction, so in the practical application of the law it is entirely consistent with (3). That is, in interpreting (3), the current terms on the left are to be taken only as convection or conduction currents, whereas in (1) displacement or capacitance currents must be included. The explicit statement of the capacitance currents as in (3) makes it more obvious that the law is just a statement of the continuity equation for circuit junctions, but the form (1) is in other respects neater and is more common.

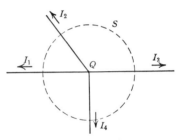

Fig. 5·02   Current flow from a junction.

PROBLEM

5·02 Show that the term on the right of (3) is just the displacement current flow out of the surface S.

5·03   APPLIED FIELD AND RESULTANT CURRENT DENSITY

Perhaps the most important single relation that appears in classical circuit theory is Ohm's law, which relates current flow to voltage drop in a conductor. This law may be generalized so that it applies to an infinitesimal conducting cube and is then written [Eq. 4·07(6)]:

$$\bar{\imath} = \sigma \bar{E} \tag{1}$$

Equation (1) relates the current density at a point in a conductor to the electric field intensity at that point through the constant σ, known as the conductivity of the material. The electric intensity $\bar{E}$ is the total electric intensity at the point, not just a portion. The use of total field is emphasized because partial fields are superposed in the circuit approach. That is, in a circuit to which an external voltage has been applied, the notions of circuit theory have us subtract from this applied voltage the back voltages or voltage drops due to the varying currents of the system and the varying charges of the system, leaving a certain net voltage available for the ohmic drop. To set the background for an approach to circuit ideas from the field equations, such a division will be followed in the electric fields and the notions of voltages will be arrived at by way of the fields.[1]

Thus, $\bar{E}$ may be made up of one part $\bar{E}_0$ applied from another system (the external generator) and another part $\bar{E}'$ arising from charges and currents in the circuit or system considered:

$$\bar{E} = \bar{E}_0 + \bar{E}' \tag{2}$$

Recall that in Maxwell's equations, Art. 4·07, if all charges and currents are included in the equations, the electric intensity $\bar{E}$ appearing in the equations must be total electric intensity. If a system is considered which we have decided to call a circuit, and if this is influenced by another system which is the generator or source of applied voltage or applied field for the circuit, Maxwell's equations might, of course, be applied to the totality of the two systems, including all charges and currents for the circuit and its generator. Such an approach would be unnecessarily complicated if the generating system is, for all practical purposes, independent of the driven circuit. This is the case, for example, if the circuit obtains its applied field from an influencing system which is a distant antenna, a battery, a source of thermal emf, or a well-shielded signal generator. It is then easier to divide total field into two parts. There is the applied field which does not depend upon the charges and currents in the circuit, and there is an induced field which arises directly from these charges and currents. The basic laws applied only to the charges and currents of the circuit give only the amount of the induced field.

Total field, to be used in Ohm's law, is the sum of applied and induced components:

$$\frac{\bar{\imath}}{\sigma} = \bar{E}_0 + \bar{E}' \tag{3}$$

[1] This follows closely the procedure of Carson, *Bell Sys. Tech. J.*, **6**, 1–17 (Jan. 1927).

The component $\bar{E}'$ due to charges and currents in the circuit may be stated conveniently in terms of the potentials (Art. 4·15):

$$\bar{E}' = -\nabla\Phi - \frac{\partial\bar{A}}{\partial t}$$

where Φ is the scalar potential calculated from charges of the system, and $\bar{A}$ is the vector potential calculated from currents of the system as explained in Art. 4·16. Substituting these in (3),

$$\frac{\bar{\imath}}{\sigma} = \bar{E}_0 - \nabla\Phi - \frac{\partial\bar{A}}{\partial t}$$

or $$\bar{E}_0 = \frac{\bar{\imath}}{\sigma} + \nabla\Phi + \frac{\partial\bar{A}}{\partial t} \qquad (4)$$

Equation (4) is the type of cause and effect relationship desired, since an applied field $\bar{E}_0$ results in an ohmic term and terms due to the charges and currents of the system. It is the first step in obtaining a circuit equation that relates voltages to currents and is based upon rigorous field theory. We must now define exactly what is meant by a circuit so that (4), which holds at a point in a conductor, may be extended to some proper integral relation that is true for a loop or circuit.

5·04 APPLIED VOLTAGE AND THE CIRCUIT RELATIONS: KIRCHHOFF'S SECOND LAW

A circuit between points 1 and 2 (Fig. 5·04) will be defined merely as any line path between the two points. If there is to be any advantage in looking at the system as a circuit, this path will almost always lie along a conductor. For any point on the path, the relation between cause and effect may be taken as that derived from Maxwell's equations, Eq. 5·03(4). To obtain a circuit equation it is necessary only to integrate this differential expression along the path chosen as the circuit:

Fig. 5·04.

$$\int_2^1 \bar{E}_0 \cdot \overline{dl} = \int_2^1 \frac{\bar{\imath}}{\sigma} \cdot \overline{dl} + \int_2^1 \frac{\partial\bar{A}}{\partial t} \cdot \overline{dl} + \int_2^1 \nabla\Phi \cdot \overline{dl} \qquad (1)$$

The first term of the equation is defined as the applied voltage of the circuit. (The sense is defined in such a way that the applied voltage is said to be positive at terminal 2 with respect to 1 when it produces a current flow into the circuit from terminal 2 for a pure resistance load.)

$$(V_0)_{21} = \int_2^1 \bar{E}_0 \cdot \overline{dl}$$

The defined applied voltage of a circuit brings us to the first of several concepts which call for careful handling to avoid confusion. First let us look at the easy case of direct current. Suppose it is made to flow in a conducting loop connected across the terminals of a battery. The battery voltage causes the current flow, and it is the only thing causing such a flow, since there is no electric field due to alternating currents, and there is no electric field in the conducting loop due to charges. (The capacitances of the battery plates and the conductor are neglected as being immaterial even if they are not small, since these capacitances, once charged, do not enter into current flow considerations.) Usual circuit theory would say that the battery applies a voltage between the two ends of the loop. Field theory says first that the battery must be applying an electric field in the conductor, otherwise there would be no current flow there. The two theories harmonize when applied voltage between two points is defined as the integral of applied electric field between those points. The circuit equations and concepts do not concern themselves with how the battery caused the voltage; neither do the field equations concern themselves with how it produced the applied field.

Consider next a closed loop of wire, the wire being of infinitesimally small cross-sectional area. Let magnetic flux through this loop be produced by some independent system which causes this flux to increase uniformly with time. The effect of this constant rate of change is to yield an applied d-c voltage, and, by Ohm's law, this yields a certain d-c flow. If the field in the loop is oscillating in time, as in a receiving antenna excited by the field of a distant transmitting antenna, it is again clear that the applied voltage is the integral around the loop of the electric field due to the distant transmitter.

For the applied voltage produced by the battery, we did not know or care exactly how it was produced; it was known only that this voltage was of a certain amount and was independent of the path chosen for its circuit. However, when the applied voltage arises from the field of a distant antenna, the amount of this voltage depends very definitely upon the path of the circuit. It may be different for different sizes, orientations, and positions of the circuit. So, in general, the applied voltage around any loop to which the circuit concept is applied may vary radically in magnitude as different loops are selected, even when voltage is due to the same source.

With the first term of (1) defined as an applied voltage, the equation is of the same general form as Kirchhoff's second law which may be stated:

applied voltage = sum of voltage drops about the circuit   (2)

If the voltage drops about a circuit are defined by the three terms on the right of (1), the equation then becomes identical with Kirchhoff's second law.   However, as we shall see, in the practical application of circuit theory to conventional circuits, the terms normally taken as the voltage drops are only approximately equal to the terms on the right of (1).   The approximations are good at lower frequencies, but may become poor for high frequencies (circuits large compared with wavelength).   For high frequencies it becomes very difficult to attempt to extend the circuit concepts so that the terms become identical with the terms of (1).

For convenience in the following discussions, the terms in (1) will be given the following designations, although the names have real significance only for the low-frequency approximations.

$$\int_2^1 \bar{E}_0 \cdot \overline{dl} = \text{applied voltage (2 taken as + terminal)} \tag{3}$$

$$\int_2^1 \frac{\bar{i}}{\sigma} \cdot \overline{dl} = \text{"internal-impedance" voltage drop} \tag{4}$$

$$\int_2^1 \frac{\partial \bar{A}}{\partial t} \cdot \overline{dl} = \text{"inductive" voltage drop} \tag{5}$$

$$\int_2^1 \nabla \Phi \cdot \overline{dl} = \text{"capacitive" voltage drop} \tag{6}$$

D-C and Low-Frequency Circuit Concepts

5·05   KIRCHHOFF'S SECOND LAW FOR A D-C CIRCUIT

For simplicity, let us consider first the case of a single d-c circuit for the interpretation of Eq. 5·04(1).   For this case the time variations are zero, so the inductive term, Eq. 5·04(5), becomes zero. Moreover, no current will flow in the d-c circuit unless the path is completely closed by conductors, so the circuit may be taken as a closed path.   In this case the capacitive term, Eq. 5·04(6), becomes just the integral of the gradient of a scalar about a closed path and is therefore zero:

$$\oint \nabla \Phi \cdot \overline{dl} \equiv 0$$

In the internal-impedance term, Eq. 5·04(4), it is seen that, since the d-c current is distributed uniformly over the cross section, the current density is

$$i = \frac{I}{A}$$

where A is the cross-sectional area of the conductor, not necessarily constant about the path. So the term becomes

$$\int_2^1 \frac{\bar{\imath}}{\sigma} \cdot \overline{dl} = \int_2^1 \frac{I\, dl}{\sigma A} = I \int_2^1 \frac{dl}{\sigma A}$$

Current I has been taken outside the integral since by continuity the d-c current must be constant about the path. A study of the integral multiplying I reveals that it is just the total d-c resistance of the path,

$$R = \int_2^1 \frac{dl}{\sigma A} \tag{1}$$

so that the term is just IR, and Eq. 5·04(1) assumes the common form

$$V_0 = IR \tag{2}$$

5·06 THE INTERNAL-IMPEDANCE TERM AT LOW FREQUENCIES

By "low frequencies" in the following discussion, we mean only that the circuits under discussion are small compared with wavelength (wavelength = velocity of light/frequency). The approximate forms to be developed may apply for certain circuits up to frequencies of thousands of megacycles per second. The two basic assumptions to be made in this and the two following articles which are a consequence of the above condition are:

1. Current is to be taken the same about the entire path.

2. Retardation is to be neglected in computing the potentials $\bar{A}$ and Φ.

We are concerned in this article with the "internal-impedance" term, Eq. 5·04(4). In the following chapter, in the study of skin effect, we shall see that for a-c effects the current does not distribute itself uniformly over the cross section of the conductor, so the current density cannot be found simply as it was for direct currents in the preceding article. However, if we choose as our circuit for the integration a path lying on the *surface* of the conductor, the term $\bar{\imath}_s/\sigma$ gives the electric field at the surface of the conductor, $\bar{E}_s$. If we define the internal impedance per unit length for the conductor as the ratio of this surface electric field (voltage per unit length) to the total current in the conductor,

$$Z_s' = \frac{E_s}{I} \tag{1}$$

then the term under consideration becomes the product of current and a total internal impedance Z_s:

$$\int_2^1 \frac{\bar{\imath}_s \cdot \overline{dl}}{\sigma} = I \int_2^1 \frac{\bar{E}_s \cdot \overline{dl}}{I} = I \int_2^1 Z_s{}' \, dl = IZ_s \qquad (2)$$

By the above, the total internal impedance is equal to the integral of the internal impedance per unit length over the circuit. The steady state form ($e^{j\omega t}$) has been implicitly assumed in all of the above.

The internal impedance has an imaginary part as well as a real part since the surface field is not in phase with the total current in the conductor for a-c circuits because of the rate of change of magnetic flux within the conductor. The real part gives the a-c resistance of the wire, and the imaginary part gives the internal reactance (that part of the reactance arising from magnetic flux within the wire) for simple geometrical configurations where the magnetic flux can be divided in that manner. The complete internal-impedance term will be treated in considerably detail for several simple shapes of conductor in the part of Chapter 6 concerned with skin effect.

Finally, we should note that the choice of a path for the circuit along the surface of the wire was arbitrary, and could be made in other ways, say along the center of the conductor, or halfway in. The point is that it must be taken in the same place for the treatment of each of the terms of the circuit equation. The choice along the surface is convenient because it does give the separation between "internal inductance" and "external inductance" for many simple shapes.

5·07 THE INDUCTIVE TERM OF LOW FREQUENCIES

Let us next consider the inductive term in the circuit equation, Eq. 5·04(5), for the case of circuits small compared with wavelength. For such circuits, the time necessary to propagate electromagnetic effects over the extent of the circuit is a negligible part of a period of the a-c effects, since by definition a wavelength is the distance over which effects are propagated in a complete period. Retardation effects may then be neglected in computing the potentials in the vicinity of the circuit, as stated in one of the basic assumptions at the beginning of Art. 5·06. The vector potential $\bar{A}$, Eq. 4·16(4), may then be written

$$\bar{A} = \int_V \frac{\mu \bar{\imath} \, dV}{4\pi r} \qquad (1)$$

The current density $\bar{\imath}$ may be written as the product of total current I and some vector function of the cross-sectional coordinates of the conductor, say $\bar{f}(x_1, x_2)$, so that $\bar{A}$ is proportional to the total current I, assumed constant about the circuit:

$$\bar{A} = I \int_V \frac{\mu \bar{j}(x_1, x_2) \, dV}{4\pi r}$$

The integral multiplier of I is a function of the geometrical configuration and the *relative* distribution of current density. Then a coefficient L, a function of the circuit configuration, permeability, and the relative current distribution but not of total current, will be defined as follows:

$$L = \frac{\int_2^1 \bar{A} \cdot \overline{dl}}{I} \tag{2}$$

With this coefficient defined, the term of Eq. 5·04(5) becomes

$$\int_2^1 \frac{\partial \bar{A}}{\partial t} \cdot \overline{dl} = \frac{d}{dt} \int_2^1 \bar{A} \cdot \overline{dl} = \frac{d}{dt}(LI) = L \frac{dI}{dt} \tag{3}$$

The partial derivative has been changed to a total derivative since we are concerned here with stationary circuits. The term under consideration is seen to be of the form of the usual inductance drop of classical circuit theory, with the coefficient L simply the inductance of the circuit. Equation (2) then becomes a definition for inductance, and, although a useful form for many purposes, it is not the most common form. To identify it with more common forms, consider a closed circuit. From Stoke's theorem,

$$\oint \bar{A} \cdot \overline{dl} = \int_S \nabla \times \bar{A} \cdot \overline{dS}$$

But

$$\bar{B} = \nabla \times \bar{A}$$

so

$$L = \frac{\int_S \bar{B} \cdot \overline{dS}}{I} \tag{4}$$

Since $\int_S \bar{B} \cdot \overline{dS}$ is the amount of magnetic flux passing through the circuit, (4) is the exact equivalent of the usual low-frequency definition, which defines inductance as the flux linkage per unit current, $L = \psi/I$, and a complete identification with the classical inductance drop term has been shown for the assumptions of this article.

At this stage some clarification of this term in relation to the internal inductance of the preceding article is in order. Consider the wire circuit sketched in Fig. 5·07a. If the path of integration is taken along the inside surface of the wire, the magnetic flux to be used in computing inductance from (4) may be taken as flux flowing through the interior of the loop, not entering the conductor, for the surface S may be any bounded by the path. In this case, the inductance so calculated would be called "external inductance" since it arises from flux external to the wire.   The remaining inductive term in the internal impedance of Art. 5·06 would then be associated with flux inside the wire and is called the "internal inductance."   For other choices of the path the division between the two terms will be different, and the above names may not apply.   The *sum* of all terms in the circuit equation will, however, be the same for all paths of integration.

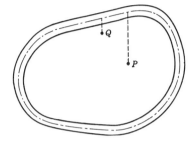

Fig. 5·07a   Arbitrary circuit formed of a conductor of circular cross section.

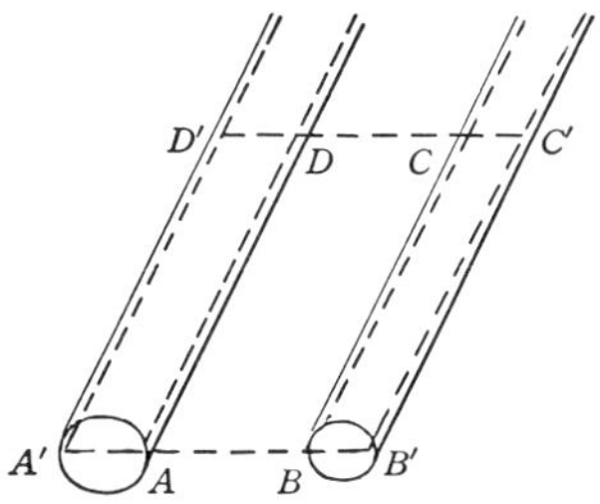

Fig. 5·07b   Parallel-wire conductors.

PROBLEM

5·07   For a parallel-wire transmission line, the current density and surface electric field are greatest on the inside surfaces of the wires and least on the outside surfaces.   If a path of integration is made along the inside surface $ABCD$ of Fig. 5·07b and internal impedance is defined as in Art. 5·06, a different result is obtained from that given by taking the path along the outer surface, as $A'B'C'D'$.   Discuss the choice qualitatively, specifically answering the question: If the two paths are to be equally valid alternatives, how is the difference in the "internal impedance" obtained by the two paths accounted for?

5·08   THE CAPACITIVE TERM AT LOW FREQUENCIES

The circuit of the preceding derivation was continuous.   Let us now break the circuit at some point.   There is then the possibility of the accumulation of charge.   The break we shall specify as rather small compared with other dimensions of the circuit, but plates may be placed at the discontinuity, if desired, to increase the possibility of accumulating charge.   Thus, in spite of the camouflage of careful specification, a lumped capacitance has been inserted in an otherwise completely conducting filamentary path.

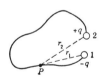

Fig. 5·08   Circuit containing a lumped capacitance.

In Fig. 5·08 is shown the circuit with discontinuity.   It might at first seem that the exact differential relation, 5·04(1), could again be integrated around a closed path, the discontinuity ignored, and the term in $\nabla\Phi$ eliminated as before.   However, if this is done, there is no way of knowing what happens to the term i/σ over the gap, for, although current i is zero in the gap, so also is σ.   This term is thus indeterminate.   That it need not be zero becomes evident when it is recalled that this term is the difference between applied and induced electric fields, and this difference can be made to have any value.   In particular, consider the special case of all gap, that is, just an imaginary line in free space. Here, no matter what the applied field may be, there are no charges and no currents along the path, and so no induced field E' at all.

If a circuit equation is to be written for a discontinuous conducting path, it is then to be obtained by integrating only over the conductor, from 1 to 2, where we know all terms of the equation.   Considering the "capacitive" term, Eq. 5·04(6),

$$\int_2^1 \nabla\Phi \cdot \overline{dl} = \int_2^1 \frac{\partial\Phi}{\partial l} \, dl = \Phi_1 - \Phi_2 \tag{1}$$

Retardation may be neglected for the circuits small compared with wavelength, so the definition for Φ, Eq. 4·16(3), becomes

$$\Phi = \int_V \frac{\rho \, dV}{4\pi\epsilon r} \tag{2}$$

If stray capacitances are negligible so that all significant charge is concentrated at the discontinuity, Q on one plate and $-Q$ on the other, the value of Φ will be proportional to Q, and hence $\Phi_1 - \Phi_2$ will be also.   Let $1/C$ be the constant of proportionality:

$$\Phi_1 - \Phi_2 = \frac{Q}{C} \tag{3}$$

The charge at the discontinuity may be related to the current flowing toward the discontinuity by the continuity equation

$$Q = \int I \, dt$$

so that the term under consideration may be written finally

$$\int_2^1 \nabla\Phi \cdot \overline{dl} = \frac{1}{C} \int I \, dt \tag{4}$$

This is the usual capacitance term in classical circuit theory, and (3) is the definition for electrostatic capacitance used in such circuit calculations.

To summarize, we have found in this and the two preceding sections all the types of terms included in the classical calculation of a single-loop a-c circuit, the skin effect resistance, the internal-inductance term, the external-inductance term, and the capacitance term.   In steady state notation ($e^{j\omega t}$), the Kirchhoff second law then reads

$$V_0 = I\left[(R + j\omega L_i) + j\omega L_e + \frac{1}{j\omega C}\right] \tag{5}$$

where L_i and L_e are internal and external inductances respectively.

5·09   EXTENSION TO MULTI-LOOP CIRCUITS AND DISTRIBUTED CONSTANT CIRCUITS

For simplicity, the case of a single-loop circuit with current constant about the path and no mutual effects was considered in the preceding articles relating classical circuit theory to field theory.   It is now in order to see how some important extensions of classical circuit theory are related to the exact formulation based upon Maxwell's equations.

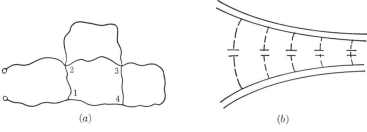

(a)   (b)

Fig. 5·09.

For the case of a multi-loop circuit, as indicated in Fig. 5·09a, the integral may be taken about any closed loop, as 1-2-3-4, but is broken into the four parts or branches, 1-2, 2-3, 3-4, and 4-1.   For any one of these parts, the current is taken as constant, and the internal-impedance terms, external-inductance terms, and capacitance terms for that branch are calculated in terms of the current *in that branch* by the concepts of the preceding sections.   That is, it is most often assumed that the induced fields along a given branch are related only to the current in that particular branch, and not to currents in other parts of the circuit.   When this assumption is not justified, coupling effects from other branches are taken into account by mutual terms of the type to be described in the next article.   The Kirchhoff first law (Art. 5·02) applied at each of the junctions, together with the circuit integration for each of the branches, gives the complete information necessary for solution by classical circuit theory.

For a distributed constant circuit as in Fig. 5·09b, circuit theory proceeds by approximating the distributed constants by a series of lumped constants, reducing this to a multi-loop circuit of the type described above. This approximation may be carried to the limit of infinitesimals, and may become exact for some systems such as certain ideal transmission lines, as will be shown in a following chapter. For more general shapes of circuits, the approximation may become poorer as one goes to higher frequencies. In any event, for such general circuits, it becomes very difficult to decide how the distributed constants should be calculated, and field theory must eventually be resorted to for an opinion.

5·10 MUTUAL COUPLINGS IN LOW-FREQUENCY CIRCUITS

By a mutual inductive coupling we mean that current in one branch of the circuit produces a significant induced field in some other branch. For example, in the two closed filamentary circuits of Fig. 5·10a, the induced electric field at point P_1 in circuit 1 may have one part related to the current I_1 of circuit 1, and another part related to the current I_2 of circuit 2. To compute the latter part, we consider the inductive term, Eq. 5·04(5),

$$\oint_{C_1} \frac{\partial \bar{A}_2}{\partial t} \cdot d\bar{l}_1 = \frac{d}{dt} \oint_{C_1} \bar{A}_2 \cdot d\bar{l}_1 \tag{1}$$

where $\bar{A}_2$ denotes the vector potential associated with the current I_2. For a filamentary current, neglecting retardation, it may be written [see Eq. 4·16(8)]

$$\bar{A}_2 = I_2 \oint_{C_2} \frac{\mu \, d\bar{l}_2}{4\pi r} \tag{2}$$

The current I_2 has been taken as constant about the path. So $\bar{A}_2$ is proportional to I_2 through a constant which is a function of the circuit configuration, and therefore $\oint_{C_1} \bar{A}_2 \cdot d\bar{l}_1$ is also. Define

$$M_{12} = \frac{1}{I_2} \oint_{C_1} \bar{A}_2 \cdot d\bar{l}_1 \tag{3}$$

Then the term expressing the induced voltage in circuit 1 due to the changing current in circuit 2 may be written

$$\oint_{C_1} \frac{\partial \bar{A}_2}{\partial t} \cdot d\bar{l}_1 = \frac{d}{dt} (M_{12} I_2) = M_{12} \frac{dI_2}{dt} \tag{4}$$

This is the usual mutual inductance term of classical circuit theory with (3) constituting the definition of mutual inductance. A more common form for the mutual inductance may be had by applying Stokes's theorem to (3):

$$M_{12} = \frac{1}{I_2} \int_{S_1} (\nabla \times \bar{A}_2) \cdot d\bar{S}_1 = \frac{\int_{S_1} \bar{B}_2 \cdot d\bar{S}_1}{I_2} \tag{5}$$

In this form the mutual inductance is written as the magnetic flux linking circuit 1 from the current of circuit 2, per unit of current in 2. Still another form is obtained if (2) is substituted in (3):

$$M_{12} = \frac{\mu}{4\pi} \oint_{C_1} \oint_{C_2} \frac{d\bar{l}_1 \cdot d\bar{l}_2}{r} \tag{6}$$

This is a classical form for mutual inductance of filamentary circuits and is known as the Neumann form. From the symmetry of this form one can immediately conclude the reciprocal relation,

$$M_{21} = M_{12} \tag{7}$$

That is, the voltage induced in circuit 2 by a unit rate of change of current in circuit 1 is the same as the voltage induced in circuit 1 by a unit rate of change of current in circuit 2.

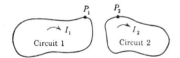

Fig.   5·10a   Two   circuits   coupled through inductive effects.

Fig.   5·10b   Two   circuits   coupled through capacitive effects.

Finally, by a mutual capacitance coupling we mean that the charge of one branch of the circuit produces a significant induced field in some other branch. For example, in the two circuits of Fig. 5·10b, the induced electric field at P_1 from charges may have one part proportional to the charge q_1 of circuit 1, and another part proportional to the charge q_2 of circuit 2. The mutual capacitance term arising from the term, Eq. 5·04(6), and representing the induced voltage in 1 due to charges in 2 might then be written

$$\int_b^a \nabla\Phi_2 \cdot d\bar{l}_1 = \Phi_{2a} - \Phi_{2b} = \frac{q_2}{C_{12}} \tag{8}$$

Actually, the situation is more complicated than this because the charges at the two plates of circuit 1 may not be equal and opposite when influenced by fields from the charges of 2, and vice versa. The more complete discussion will be reserved for the section on self- and mutual capacitances in Chapter 6.

PROBLEM

5·10   Modify the form (3) for mutual inductance so that it applies when the circuits 1 and 2 are not closed (for example, as in Fig. 5·10b). Similarly, modify the Neumann form (6). Can the common form (5) in terms of flux linkages be modified to apply to this case?

High-Frequency or Large-Dimension Circuit Concepts

5·11   EXTENSION OF THE CIRCUIT INDUCTANCE CONCEPT

Of the approximations necessary to obtain the usual low-frequency definition of inductance, the assumptions of infinite velocities of propa-

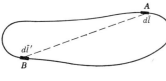

Fig. 5·11.

gation and negligible distributed capacities are most directly related to frequency. At the higher frequencies, the time required to propagate the effect of a change in charge or current over the dimensions of the circuit may be appreciable compared with a period of the changing effects. We shall next consider the circuit at such frequencies, concentrating on the modifications introduced by considering the retardation effects which were neglected in the preceding section.

Consider the circuit of Fig. 5·11. With assumed infinite velocities of propagation, the effect of a change in current in the element $\overline{dl}$ at A would be felt instantaneously at all other points of the circuit (as at the element $\overline{dl}'$ at B), and, for steady state sinusoidal time changes, only induced voltage drops in time quadrature with the current would be obtained at any point of the circuit. However, when finite velocities are considered, the time necessary to propagate the effect of a change in current at A to any other point B may be great enough so that this exact 90° relationship is destroyed. There may then result from the changing magnetic effects a component of induced field in phase with the current as well as an alteration in the magnitude of the 90° out-of-phase component. These corrections might be calculated relatively simply if the current were assumed to be all of the same phase and magnitude around the circuit; but it must be recognized that this need not always be true when retardation is of importance. Retardation enters because the time necessary to propagate an effect of changing current at one point of a circuit to another point through space is appreciable compared with the period of changing current; phase differences between currents at different points about the circuit enter because the time necessary to propagate changing currents about the conductor of the circuit is appreciable compared with a period of changing current. The two effects are closely allied. And, if current, at any one instant in time, varies around the loop, there must be a temporary piling up, or a decreasing, of charge at various points around the loop. Nevertheless, in the following, current will be assumed constant in magnitude and phase about the circuit even though retardation is to be considered. There are actually some circuits large compared with wavelength where the constant current approximation is good, so that these results would be directly applicable. However, the main point of the discussion is to show generally the types of modifications found when retardation effects become important, and to demonstrate the difficulty in extending circuit concepts to high frequencies.

For simplicity, we shall take the circuit as a stationary, closed, filamentary path excited with steady-state a-c effects of the form $e^{j\omega t}$. We shall concentrate in this article on the modification of the inductive term, Eq. 5·04(5),

$$V_i = \oint \frac{\partial \bar{A}}{\partial t} \cdot \overline{dl} = j\omega \oint \bar{A} \cdot \overline{dl} \tag{1}$$

As is explained in Art. 4·17, retardation is accounted for in the time-periodic case by a shift in phase by amount kr, where k is ω/v and v is the velocity of propagation. Specializing Eq. 4·17(8) to filamentary currents, we get

$$\bar{A} = \oint \frac{\mu I e^{-jkr} \overline{dl'}}{4\pi r} \tag{2}$$

Substitution in (1) gives

$$V_i = j\omega\mu I \oint\oint \frac{e^{-jkr}}{4\pi r} \overline{dl'} \cdot \overline{dl} \tag{3}$$

By expanding e^{-jkr} into its real and imaginary parts, $\cos kr + j \sin kr$, we obtain

$$V_i = j\omega\mu I \left[\oint\oint \frac{\cos kr}{4\pi r} \overline{dl'} \cdot \overline{dl} - j \oint\oint \frac{\sin kr}{4\pi r} \overline{dl'} \cdot \overline{dl} \right] \tag{4}$$

The term may then be written

$$V_i = I[R_r + j\omega L] \tag{5}$$

where
$$L = \oint\oint \frac{\mu \cos kr \, \overline{dl'}}{4\pi r} \cdot \overline{dl} \qquad \text{henrys} \tag{6}$$

and
$$R_r = \oint\oint \frac{\mu\omega \sin kr \, \overline{dl}' \cdot \overline{dl}}{4\pi r} \qquad \text{ohms} \qquad (7)$$

Analogy between (5) and the familiar low-frequency circuit equation using complex notation identifies L as inductance, but, from (6), L is seen now to be a function of frequency.† Its connection with low-frequency inductance, which is taken as a constant of geometry independent of frequency, becomes apparent if the cosine term in (6) is written in series form:

$$L = \mu \oint\oint \left(1 - \frac{k^2 r^2}{2!} + \frac{k^4 r^4}{4!} \cdots\right) \frac{\overline{dl}' \cdot \overline{dl}}{4\pi r} \qquad (8)$$

At low frequencies (kr very small compared with unity) all terms but the first are negligible in the series, so that

$$L_{LF} = \oint\oint \frac{\mu \, \overline{dl}' \cdot \overline{dl}}{4\pi r} \qquad (9)$$

By comparison with Eq. 5·10(6), this may be considered as Neumann's form for low-frequency inductance as a function of circuit geometry, and is, of course, independent of frequency.‡ At higher frequencies, other terms of the series appear as correction terms to this low-frequency value of inductance.

5·12 CIRCUIT RADIATION RESISTANCE

Let us investigate the additional term IR_r, which appears in the circuit equation when the frequency is high. This term is in phase with the current, just as is the ohmic term IR, and so represents an actual departure of energy from the source. The ohmic term represents energy transfer from the source to heat in the conductors. The new in-phase term does not represent any such dissipation of electromagnetic energy into heat energy, but it does represent an actual energy which leaves the circuit and can accordingly be labeled radiated electromagnetic energy. In Chapter 12 several ways of looking at this radiation term and of calculating its magnitude will be studied. For the present, we are most interested in the term as a correction term to

---

† This is not to be confused with the change of inductance with frequency due to skin effect phenomena, which is another matter and will be studied in the next chapter.

‡ Actually, Neumann's formula is of practical use only in calculating mutual inductance, since it has in it the assumption of filamentary currents, and this leads to bothersome infinities in evaluation of the self-inductance. All this will be discussed in detail in the next chapter, when the objective will be the computation of circuit impedance.

the circuit equations at high frequencies.   From this point of view, it is convenient to expand Eq. 5·11(7) in its series form, as was done previously for Eq. 5·11(6):

$$R_r = \oint\oint \frac{\mu\omega}{4\pi r}\left(kr - \frac{k^3 r^3}{3!} + \frac{k^5 r^5}{5!} \cdots\right) \overline{dl'} \cdot \overline{dl} \tag{1}$$

But, since $\oint \overline{dl'} = 0$, the first term (which contains no r) disappears entirely and there remains only

$$R_r = \oint\oint \frac{\mu\omega}{4\pi}\left(-\frac{k^3 r^2}{3!} + \frac{k^5 r^4}{5!} \cdots\right) \overline{dl'} \cdot \overline{dl} \tag{2}$$

R_r, because of its similarity to the ohmic term, may be called a *radiation resistance*.

This radiation resistance, representing an in-phase component of the induced voltage due to varying magnetic effects, and the correction to inductance or out-of-phase component of induced voltage found in the previous article were direct consequences of retardation. As pointed out earlier, this form for radiation resistance applies only to circuits in which current is constant about the path, and this is not often the case at high frequencies.   In spite of this incompleteness, the analysis does demonstrate the important effects that may arise when retardation is considered.   An extension of this particular approach toward radiation will be given in Chapter 12 (Art. 12·12).

5·13   EXAMPLE OF USE OF CIRCUIT CONCEPTS IN AN INDUCTIVE CIRCUIT OF LARGE DIMENSIONS

One example in which symmetry makes it possible to realize the assumption of constant current about the loop is that of a circular loop of wire.   Of course, excitation must also be symmetrical, as for example from an electric field induced by a time-varying uniform magnetic field through the loop.   Let the loop have radius a, and neglect the finite size of the wire (Fig. 5·13).   The magnitude of $\overline{dl'}$ is $a\,d\phi$.   From the definition of the scalar product,

$$\overline{dl'} \cdot \overline{dl} = a\,d\phi\,dl\,\cos\phi$$

The distance between the elements $\overline{dl}$ and $\overline{dl'}$ is

$$r = 2a\sin\frac{\phi}{2}$$

Fig.   5·13   Circular   current-carrying loop.

Thus, neglecting all but the first term in the expression for radiation

resistance, Eq. 5·12(2),

$$R_r = -\frac{\omega\mu k^3}{24\pi} \oint\oint r^2 \, \overline{dl'} \cdot \overline{dl} = -\frac{\omega\mu a^3 k^3}{6\pi} \int_0^{2\pi a} dl \int_0^{2\pi} \sin^2 \frac{\phi}{2} \cos\phi \, d\phi$$

$$R_r = \left(-\frac{\omega\mu a^3 k^3}{6\pi}\right)(2\pi a)\left(-\frac{\pi}{2}\right) = \frac{\pi}{6}\sqrt{\frac{\mu}{\epsilon}} (ka)^4 \quad \text{ohms}$$

For free space surrounding the wire, $\sqrt{\mu_0/\epsilon_0} = 120\pi$ ohms, and

$$R_r = 20\pi^2 (ka)^4 \quad \text{ohms} \tag{1}$$

As a numerical example, consider a loop with circumference one quarter of a wavelength ($ka = \frac{1}{4}$).

$$R_r = 20\pi^2(\tfrac{1}{4})^4 = 0.773 \text{ ohms}$$

PROBLEM

5·13 Obtain in terms of (ka) the first correction term to inductance by Eq. 5·11(8) for the above circular loop of wire.

5·14 MODIFICATION OF OTHER CIRCUIT TERMS AT HIGH FREQUENCIES

Not only the inductive term but also other terms of the circuit equation require modification at frequencies high enough so that retardation effects are important. For a qualitative study of the capacitive term under these circumstances consider the circuit of Fig. 5·08. Charges are again considered concentrated at the discontinuity. That is, we are still neglecting any stray capacity effects from distributed charges resting on the surface of the wire. At low frequencies, the electric field at any point, such as point P, from these two lumped charges, is always 90° out of time phase with the current, so that this component represents no average power flow. The energy in the electric field simply oscillates between the source and the surrounding space. If the frequency becomes very high, the length of time necessary to propagate the effect of charges $+q$ and $-q$, at 2 and 1, to P, any other point on the circuit, may destroy the previous 90° phase relationship. It is quite apparent that there may now be a component of the electric field due to charges which is in phase with the current at any point of the circuit because of this retardation, also representing a radiation of energy.

Similarly, the mutual inductance and capacitance terms discussed in Art. 5·10 will be modified by retardation effects, and this modification will not only change the amounts of the mutual inductance or capacitance coefficients, but may also add new radiation terms arising from the component of field associated with currents and charges of circuit 2,·in phase with the current of circuit 1 for points about circuit 1.

5·15   CONSIDERATIONS INVOLVED IN AN EXACT APPROACH TO CIRCUITS OF LARGE DIMENSIONS

At the higher frequencies, stray capacities become of increasing importance, and the assumptions of uniform current distributions and no charges on the surfaces of wires may require revision if useful answers are to be predicted.   The exact circuit equation is always that derived in Art. 5·04:

$$V_{21} = \int_1^2 \frac{\bar{\imath}}{\sigma} \cdot \overline{dl} + \int_1^2 \frac{\partial \bar{A}}{\partial t} \cdot \overline{dl} + \int_1^2 \nabla \Phi \cdot \overline{dl} \tag{1}$$

with
$$\bar{A} = \int_V \frac{\mu[\bar{\imath}]\, dV}{4\pi r} \tag{2}$$

$$\Phi = \int_V \frac{[\rho]\, dV}{4\pi \epsilon r} \tag{3}$$

where the square brackets denote retardation.   Difficulties in applying these equations arise since the current and charge distributions are not known, but are determined by the field distributions which are calculated from the retarded potentials which depend upon current and charge distribution—a vicious circle!   The exact solution of this problem is usually of prohibitive difficulty.   However, it is often possible to assume a reasonable current distribution, calculating from it the retarded potentials and hence the fields; from these the first assumption of current distribution may be corrected, and the process repeated until the desired accuracy is reached.   This is not often done, however, since it is obviously a laborious method, and, as soon as frequencies become so high that these distributed capacities are important, field theory usually offers a superior way of looking at the problem.   So we shall talk more about what might be called circuits of large dimensions later under the various headings of transmission lines, wave guides, resonant cavities, and antennas.

In calculating the radiation of energy by the use of circuit equations, it may be necessary only to consider one step of the above outlined procedure; that is, reasonable current distributions are assumed and radiated energy is calculated from these.   If the concept of radiation resistance is used, it must be defined properly, and used with care, for it is the total energy radiated from the system which has meaning.   If it is desired to express this radiation by multiplying some radiation resistance by the square of a current, it must be remembered that current may no longer be the same at all points around the circuit. Thus the value of radiation resistance for a given system will depend upon the particular current which is selected for this purpose.

5·16 SELF-ENCLOSING A CIRCUIT TO PREVENT RADIATION

When retardation is·neglected in the analysis of a circuit, the result will inevitably contain no possibility for radiation of energy. When retardation is included, the possibility exists that the answer may disclose loss of energy by electromagnetic field leakage (or radiation) into the surrounding space. This does not mean that retardation of itself, no matter how great, always leads to radiation.

The emphasis should rather be on the fact that retardation means that the electric fields arising from any current element will, in the surrounding space, not be 90° out of phase with that current element. There is accordingly a possibility always that the total induced electric field at any point in the circuit may have a component in phase with the current at that point. This possibility changes to actuality in many of the most common types of wire circuits. Useful and well-nigh universal though they may be at low frequencies, it is apparent that this loss characteristic, radiation, that rises rapidly with frequency, will limit their application. For antennas, devices that are chosen because they do indeed "leak" electromagnetic energy to the surrounding space, these circuits are candidates. For narrow-band filters, resonant circuit impedances, and a host of other conventional circuit applications, it is much preferred to have a non-radiating circuit.

Now there are ways to minimize radiation, even to make it zero for all practical purposes. We mention two of them here, not to complete the discussion of circuits (because to appreciate these new things fully will require techniques of electromagnetic waves that will be discussed in following chapters) but rather to make it evident that the story on circuits is not complete in this chapter, although its purpose was to examine circuit concepts. One way to prevent radiation is to enclose completely the circuit and source by a very good conductor. Such a shield, as we shall see in detail later, will stop the electromagnetic energy leaving the circuit, reflect it, and cause additional electric field in the circuit that will buck out that undesired induced electric field component in phase with the current at each point of the circuit. Practically, the conductivity of the shield cannot be infinite, and so some small amount of energy will get through, and the reflected electric field will fall short of exactly neutralizing the in-phase component of induced electric field. We cannot discuss this problem completely until we have learned more about handling the electromagnetic energy as a wave phenomenon.

Another way to build a circuit so as to minimize radiation is exemplified in Fig. 5·16. Here we deal with cavities, such that for any cross section which includes the axis of symmetry we have a circuit of the parallel resonant L–C type, consisting of the condenser plates A and B closed by the one turn inductance which encloses itself and the condenser. Because of the fact (which emerges easily from electro-magnetic wave studies) that all electromagnetic effects, practically speaking, fail to penetrate metals at very high frequencies, the leakage by radiation from such a circuit will be negligible. This means that current

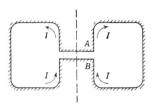

Fig. 5·16 A self-enclosed circuit.

distribution is not uniform but rather such that all net induced electric field at every point in the conductor is essentially 90° out of phase with the current at that point even at very high frequencies when retardation must be and is included. Such a circuit is best analyzed as a resonant cavity by the use of electromagnetic wave pictures and equations, so we shall leave the discussion at this point. We add only that certain concepts which can properly be called "circuit concepts" will be helpful in studying these resonant cavities, and the fundamental concepts discussed in this chapter should not be forgotten when we pass over to the wave method.

6 SKIN EFFECT
AND CIRCUIT IMPEDANCE
ELEMENTS

6·01 INTRODUCTION

The discussion of the previous chapter justified circuit concepts, like inductive and capacitive reactances, as they are universally used and understood in conventional circuit analysis. To be sure, it was found that the well-known definitions of all these quantities involve approximations; but, on the whole, for circuits physically small compared with wavelength, rigorous approach by Maxwell's equations shows that the ordinary methods of circuit analysis stem from correct formulations and are accurate. Even at higher frequencies, where the approximations become poorer, these circuit concepts are still practical for part if not all of the problem, although correction terms may have to be used.

Chapter 5 also discussed the various factors which enter into a rigorous analysis of all the effects which may take place in the neighborhood of a simple loop of conductor. We shall be satisfied in the present chapter to make simplifying assumptions, particularly those approximations which permit us to think in terms of an applied voltage around a circuit being taken up in impedance drops: ohmic resistance, inductive reactance, and capacitive reactance. There is a tremendous range of practical problems for which these assumptions are justified, and, when the approximate quantities called resistance, capacitance, and inductance have been computed, the electromagnetics of these circuits may be said to have been completely worked out. The obtaining of these impedance elements will occupy us throughout this chapter.

Of course, a huge store of knowledge exists on the handling of circuit problems once all the equations are set up and the circuit parameters computed. This special subject of circuit analysis and synthesis is not,

however, within the scope of interest of this text, and the reader is left
to consult the numerous sources dealing primarily with such material.

Skin Effect and the Internal Impedance of a Conductor

6·02   THE IMPORTANCE OF SKIN EFFECT IN IMPEDANCE CALCULATIONS

Many aspects of a phenomenon called *skin effect* will be important
throughout the book.   This chapter will be concerned mainly with
applications to impedance calculations for wires and other conductors,
yet it is important to start with a much broader picture of the subject.
Skin effect is most often introduced through the example of high-

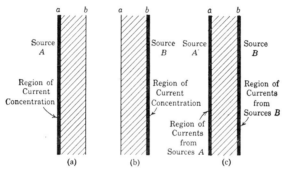

Fig. 6·02*abc*   Current concentration caused by skin effect.

frequency current flow in a solid round conductor, in which it can be
demonstrated that current flow at very high frequencies is essentially
concentrated in a thin layer or skin near the surface.   Students often
leave such first introductions to the subject with the impression that
this is the most important aspect of skin effect and, worse, believe
erroneously that the above phenomenon is caused by some sort of
mutual repulsion between small filamentary current elements in the
wire.   With such a picture, they expect always to find current seeking
the outside of any conducting system, an impression that would be
unfortunate indeed as a preliminary to the study of resonant cavities,
wave guides, shields, etc., in which currents may be concentrated on
the inner, not outer, walls of the conductors.

A broad picture of skin effect shows that it is a phenomenon which
tends to concentrate currents on the surfaces of conductors that are
nearest to the field sources producing them.   Thus in Fig. 6·02*a*, if
there is an exciting source *A* of extremely high frequency near a conducting sheet, current may be essentially concentrated on the side *a* of
the sheet; if there is a source *B*, as in Fig. 6·02*b*, current may be con-

centrated on the side b; if there are both sources, A and B, Fig. 6·02c, there may be currents on the two sides, a due to A and b due to B, for all practical purposes completely independent.   At such frequencies the conducting wall has acted as a complete shield between the sources A and B.   The reservations "essentially" and "for all practical purposes" will be clearer when we next study the equations of skin effect. It will then be seen that penetration of current into the conductor decreases gradually, so that current is not actually concentrated in a small layer at the surface with no current beneath.   In any real conductor, current will not actually decrease to zero no matter how thick the conductor.   This statement should not mask the fact that at the highest radio frequencies current density may decrease to one millionth

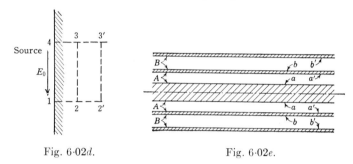

Fig. 6·02d.   Fig. 6·02e.

its surface value in a distance of only a few thousandths of an inch, so that any practical thickness of any conductor becomes the "practically perfect" shield referred to above.

The general reason for skin effect behavior can be visualized in terms of applied and induced voltages.   Imagine a high-frequency source as in Fig. 6·02d, producing an applied electric field E_0 in the neighborhood of the conductor.   This must cause current flow in the conductor, producing a magnetic field at right angles to E_0.   This changing magnetic field produces an induced electric field E' opposite to E_0. If a study is made of the two closed line integrals, 1–2–3–4–1 and 1–2'–3'–4–1, it is found that more magnetic flux is enclosed in the latter, so that induced voltage around this path is the greater, and it may be deduced that the induced field along 2'–3' is greater than that along 2–3.   It follows that there is less net field, $E_0 + E'$, left to produce current flow as one progresses farther into the conductor.

Another physical picture of skin effect phenomena will follow from the wave concepts of Chapter 7.   From such a viewpoint, one can consider the source as a source of waves which impinge upon the conductor.   Some wave energy is, of course, reflected as a result of impedance mismatch at the discontinuities between air and conductor. Those waves which pass into the conductor attenuate at a rate determined by the conductivity of the conductor, just as transmission line waves attenuate in a line with high leakage conductance.

The classical example of current flow in a solid round conductor is now seen to be a special case of this general viewpoint; certainly, if the conductor is solid, the exciting sources must be on the outside, so current will concentrate near the outside. However, if exciting sources are on the inside of a hollow conductor, as they are for the outer conductor of a coaxial line, current will concentrate on the inner wall of that conductor. Finally, we might imagine a double coaxial line, as in Fig. 6.02e, formed of good conductors and operated at very high frequencies. Currents due to the source A are concentrated on the walls a and a'; currents due to B are concentrated on the walls b and b'. For all practical purposes shielding between the two coaxial regions may be considered perfect, and phenomena of the two regions completely independent.

The general concentration of current into thin layers, as found in skin effect phenomena, should have a marked effect on impedances, causing them to change with frequency. If current is concentrated over a smaller part of the cross section of a conductor than at low frequencies, the effective conductor cross section is decreased and resistance should increase. Also, if penetration of fields into the conductor becomes less as frequency increases, there should not be as much magnetic flux inside the conductor and internal inductance should decrease. All these phenomena will be studied quantitatively in articles to follow.

6·03 SPECIALIZATION OF MAXWELL'S EQUATIONS TO GOOD CONDUCTORS

We wish to study the current distribution problem from Maxwell's equations, but there are certain simplifications that can be made when we are concerned with good conductors. Maxwell's equations are given in Art. 4·07. In addition, there is Ohm's law, which may be taken as defining a conductor:

$$\bar{\imath} = \sigma \bar{E} \tag{1}$$

The constant σ is the conductivity of the conductor. Substitution of Ohm's law in Eq. 4·07(4) gives

$$\nabla \times \bar{H} = \sigma \bar{E} + \frac{\partial \bar{D}}{\partial t} \tag{2}$$

We now take the divergence of both sides of (2) and recall that the divergence of the curl of any vector is zero:

$$\nabla \cdot \nabla \times \bar{H} \equiv 0 = \frac{\sigma}{\epsilon} \nabla \cdot \bar{D} + \frac{\partial(\nabla \cdot \bar{D})}{\partial t}$$

Divergence of $\bar{D}$ is equal to charge density ρ by Eq. 4·07(1).   Thus

$$\frac{\sigma}{\epsilon} \rho + \frac{\partial \rho}{\partial t} = 0 \tag{3}$$

Equation (3) is a differential equation in ρ alone.   Its solution,

$$\rho = \rho_0 e^{-\sigma(t/\epsilon)} \tag{4}$$

shows that any charge density which may exist in a conductor obeying Ohm's law must decay exponentially with time, and at an extremely rapid rate since the time constant ϵ/σ is found to be very small for typical conductors.   This means that any charges, if ever placed in the interior of such a conductor, would flow at once to the surface, and in the steady state the free charge term in Gauss's law would be zero.

This fact may be shown in a slightly different way by taking the steady state equivalent of (2) in complex notation,

$$\nabla \times \bar{H} = (\sigma + j\omega\epsilon)\bar{E} \tag{5}$$

If the divergence is taken, it must again be zero:

$$(\sigma + j\omega\epsilon)\nabla \cdot \bar{E} = \nabla \cdot \nabla \times \bar{H} \equiv 0$$

or

$$\nabla \cdot \bar{D} = 0 \tag{6}$$

Some comment on the above result is in order.   We know first that not all currents are of this type, since the space-charge type of current flow found in a vacuum tube comes about from a motion of free charges, so that ρ would not there be zero.   We might expect the current caused by a motion of charges in a conductor to be much the same, but we remember that the simple picture here is one of mobile electrons moving through the bound positive charges, so that on the average the net charge in any volume element is zero, even though some of the charges are moving through the element and producing the current.   However, we need only note here that (6) is a conclusion drawn from Ohm's law and Maxwell's equations.   We shall leave to experts in the modern theory of solids the mechanism which goes on in the conductor making $\bar{\imath}$ proportional to $\bar{E}$.

The equations may be further simplified, since the displacement current will never be appreciable in any reasonably good conductor, even at the highest radio frequencies. Consider again variations which are sinusoidal with time (of the form $e^{j\omega t}$). The terms to be compared in (5) are σ and $\omega\epsilon$. The precise values of ϵ for conductors are not known, yet most indications show that the range of dielectric constants is much the same for conductors as for dielectrics. For platinum, a relatively poor conductor, the term $\omega\epsilon$ becomes equal to σ at about 1.5×10^{15} cps, if the dielectric constant is taken as ten times that of free space. This frequency is in the range of ultraviolet light. Consequently, for all but the poorest conductors (such as earth) the displacement current term is completely negligible compared with conduction current at any radio frequency.

Thus, to summarize, the following specializations are appropriate to Maxwell's equations applied to good conductors, and may in fact be taken as a definition of a good conductor:

1. The free-charge term is zero, $\rho = 0$.

2. Conduction current is given by Ohm's law, $\bar{\imath} = \sigma\bar{E}$.

3. Displacement current is negligible in comparison with conduction current, $\omega\epsilon \ll \sigma$.

PROBLEM

6·03 The conductivity of graphite is about 0.12 mhos/meter. Take its dielectric constant as $5\epsilon_0$, and find the approximate frequency range over which it might be classed as a good conductor.

6·04   EQUATION DETERMINING CURRENT DISTRIBUTION IN A CONDUCTOR

With displacement current taken as negligible for a good conductor, Eq. 6·03(2) becomes

$$\nabla \times \bar{H} = \sigma\bar{E} \tag{1}$$

The curl of both sides may be taken and the left side expanded by a vector identity of Art. 2·39:

$$\nabla \times \nabla \times \bar{H} \equiv \nabla(\nabla \cdot \bar{H}) - \nabla^2\bar{H} = \sigma\nabla \times \bar{E}$$

Values for $\nabla \cdot \bar{H}$ and $\nabla \times \bar{E}$ are obtained from Maxwell's equations, 4·07(2) and 4·07(3), leaving

$$\nabla^2\bar{H} = \sigma\mu\,\frac{\partial\bar{H}}{\partial t} \tag{2}$$

This equation for the variation of $\bar{H}$ in a conductor is in the form of a standard differential equation similar to Laplace's equation, or the

wave equation. The equation is often called the skin effect or distribution equation and may also be derived in terms of $\bar{E}$, taking first
the curl of Eq. 4·07(3) instead of 4·07(4), and expanding as before
to yield

$$\nabla^2 \bar{E} = \sigma\mu \frac{\partial \bar{E}}{\partial t} \tag{3}$$

Since $\bar{\imath} = \sigma\bar{E}$, the same equation may be written in terms of current
density:

$$\nabla^2 \bar{\imath} = \sigma\mu \frac{\partial \bar{\imath}}{\partial t} \tag{4}$$

When all quantities can be regarded as varying as $e^{j\omega t}$, the above
equations may be written

$$\nabla^2 \bar{H} = j\omega\sigma\mu\bar{H} \tag{5}$$

$$\nabla^2 \bar{E} = j\omega\sigma\mu\bar{E} \tag{6}$$

$$\nabla^2 \bar{\imath} = j\omega\sigma\mu\bar{\imath} \tag{7}$$

These equations give the relation between space and time derivatives
of magnetic field, electric field, or current density at any point in a conductor. It remains to solve these differential equations subject to the
boundary conditions imposed by certain physical shapes of interest for
practical conductors.

6·05 CURRENT DISTRIBUTION IN A FLAT OR PLANE CONDUCTOR; DEPTH OF PENETRATION

The simplest case to solve, though possibly not the simplest to
visualize, is that of a plane conductor of infinite depth, and with no
field variations along the width or length dimension. This case is frequently taken as that of a conductor filling the lower half of space
$x < 0$ in a rectangular coordinate system with the y-z plane coinciding
with the conductor surface, and is then spoken of as a "semi-infinite
solid." Actually, quantities are calculated for a finite width and
finite length, so that the infinite dimensions in the y and z directions
are not necessary to the discussion. The analysis of this case is of
the greatest practical importance, though it would not seem to be
because of the infinite depth requirement. It is important to many
conductors of finite extent, and with curved surfaces, because at high
frequencies the depth over which significant current is concentrated
is very small, so that radii of curvature and conductor depth may be
taken as infinite in comparison. Moreover, any field variations along

the length or width dimension due to curvature, edge effects, or variations along a wavelength are ordinarily so small compared with the variations into the conductor that they may be neglected.

For the case of a plane conductor with current flow in the z direction, x normal to the surface, and no variations in the y and z directions

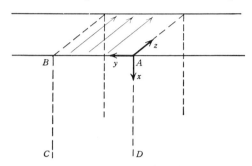

Fig. 6·05a   Plane solid conductor.

(Fig. 6·05a), the current distribution equation, Eq. 6·04(7), becomes simply

$$\frac{d^2 i_z}{dx^2} = j\omega\mu\sigma i_z = \tau^2 i_z \tag{1}$$

where

$$\tau^2 = j\omega\mu\sigma \tag{2}$$

Since $\sqrt{j} = (1 + j)/\sqrt{2}$ (taking the root with positive sign),

$$\tau = (1 + j)\sqrt{\pi f \mu\sigma} = \frac{(1 + j)}{\delta} \tag{3}$$

where

$$\delta = \frac{1}{\sqrt{\pi f \mu\sigma}} \quad \text{meters} \tag{4}$$

A complete solution to (1) is in terms of exponentials:

$$i_z = C_1 e^{-\tau x} + C_2 e^{\tau x} \tag{5}$$

Current density will increase to the impossible value of infinity at $x = \infty$ unless C_2 is zero. C_1 may be written as the current density at the surface if we let $i_z = i_0$ when $x = 0$. Then

$$i_z = i_0 e^{-\tau x} \tag{6}$$

Or, in terms of the quantity δ defined by (3) and (4),

$$i_z = i_0 e^{-x/\delta} e^{-j(x/\delta)} \tag{7}$$

In this form it is apparent that magnitude of current decreases exponentially with penetration into the conductor, and δ has the significance as the depth at which current density has decreased to $1/e$ (about 36.9 per cent) of its value at the surface.   The quantity δ is accordingly called *depth of penetration* or *skin depth*.   The phase of current density is also seen to lag from its surface value by x/δ radians at depth x into the conductor.

It is important to develop a familiarity for values of depth of penetration for different materials at different frequencies, and a study of

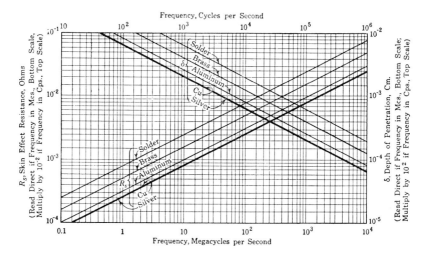

Fig. 6·05b   Skin effect quantities for plane conductors.

the chart, Fig. 6·05b, is helpful for this.   The student should also retain these facts:

1. Depth of penetration is smaller the higher the conductivity, the higher the permeability, and the higher the frequency, since it is inversely proportional to the square root of each of these.

2. Current does not fail to penetrate below the depth δ; this is merely the point at which current densities and fields have decreased to $1/e$ their value at the surface.   Later another important significance of this quantity will appear.

3. The concept as stated here applies strictly only to plane solids. However, it may be extended to conductors of other shapes so long as the value of δ calculated is much smaller than any curvatures of the surfaces.

4. In addition to its special significance for the plane solid, δ as defined by (4) may be considered simply a constant of a given material

at frequency f, and it is useful as a parameter in exact analyses of other geometrical configurations, as will appear.

PROBLEMS

6·05a   Make a polar plot of $|i_z|$ versus the phase of i_z, with x/δ taken as the parameter.

6·05b   Show that δ as defined by (4) does have the dimensions of meters, as indicated.

6·05c   Defining wavelength λ as $v/f = (f\sqrt{\mu\epsilon})^{-1}$, show that, for a good conductor as defined in Art. 6·03, depth of penetration is always a very small quantity compared with wavelength, $\delta \ll \lambda$.

6·06   INTERNAL IMPEDANCE OF A PLANE CONDUCTOR

The internal impedance term, which includes the resistance and internal reactance as discussed in Art. 5·06, may now be found for the plane solid example of the last article.   We shall compute the term for a unit length and unit width.   As defined in Art. 5·06, the internal impedance term per unit length is the quotient of electric field at the surface and total current.   The total current flowing in the plane conductor is found by integrating the current density, Eq. 6·05(7), from the surface to the infinite depth.   For a unit width,

$$J_z = \int_0^\infty i_z \, dx = \int_0^\infty i_0 e^{-(1+j)(x/\delta)} \, dx = \frac{i_0\delta}{(1+j)} \tag{1}$$

The electric field at the surface is given by the current density at the surface,

$$E_{z0} = \frac{i_0}{\sigma} \tag{2}$$

Internal impedance for a unit length and unit width is then

$$Z_s = \frac{E_{z0}}{J_z} = \frac{(1+j)}{\sigma\delta} \tag{3}$$

Define $$Z_s = R_s + j\omega L_i \tag{4}$$

Then $$R_s = \frac{1}{\sigma\delta} = \sqrt{\frac{\pi f \mu}{\sigma}} \tag{5}$$

$$\omega L_i = \frac{1}{\sigma\delta} = R_s \tag{6}$$

The resistance and internal reactance of such a plane conductor are equal at any frequency. The internal impedance Z_s thus has a phase angle of 45°. Equation (5) gives another interpretation of depth of penetration δ, for this equation shows that the skin effect resistance of the semi-infinite plane conductor is exactly the same as the d-c resistance of a plane conductor of depth δ. That is, resistance of this conductor with exponential decrease in current density is exactly the same as though current were uniformly distributed over a depth δ.

R_s, the resistance of the plane conductor for a unit length and unit width, is called the *surface resistivity*. For a finite area of conductor, the resistance is obtained by multiplying R_s by length, and dividing by width since the width elements are essentially in parallel. Thus the dimension of R_s is ohms or, as it is sometimes called, *ohms per square*. Like the depth of penetration δ, R_s as defined by (5) may also be a useful parameter in the analyses of conductors of other than plane shape, and may be thought of as a constant of the material at frequency f. Curves of R_s versus frequency are given on Fig. 6·05b for several materials. The values are also summarized in the table below.

	CONDUCTIVITY MHOS/METER σ	PERMEABILITY HENRYS/METER μ	DEPTH OF PENETRATION METERS δ	SURFACE RESISTIVITY OHMS R_s
Silver	6.17×10^7	$4\pi \times 10^{-7}$	$\dfrac{0.0642}{\sqrt{f}}$	$2.52 \times 10^{-7}\sqrt{f}$
Copper	5.80×10^7	$4\pi \times 10^{-7}$	$\dfrac{0.0660}{\sqrt{f}}$	$2.61 \times 10^{-7}\sqrt{f}$
Aluminum	3.72×10^7	$4\pi \times 10^{-7}$	$\dfrac{0.0826}{\sqrt{f}}$	$3.26 \times 10^{-7}\sqrt{f}$
Brass	1.57×10^7	$4\pi \times 10^{-7}$	$\dfrac{0.127}{\sqrt{f}}$	$5.01 \times 10^{-7}\sqrt{f}$
Solder	0.706×10^7	$4\pi \times 10^{-7}$	$\dfrac{0.185}{\sqrt{f}}$	$7.73 \times 10^{-7}\sqrt{f}$

PROBLEM

6·06 Show that R_s as defined by $R_s = \sqrt{\pi f \mu / \sigma}$ does have the dimensions of ohms.

6·07 POWER LOSS IN A PLANE CONDUCTOR

The average power loss for a unit area of the plane conductor may be found by multiplying the surface resistivity R_s by the square of the magnitude of current per unit width, J_z. A factor of $\frac{1}{2}$ is also required since the convention of this text is to use peak instead of rms values for sinusoids. Then

$$W_L = \tfrac{1}{2} R_s \big| J_z \big|^2 \quad \text{watts/meter}^2 \tag{1}$$

This is the usual formula based upon resistance multiplied by square of current magnitude. It is true that we have not justified it for this case of non-uniform current distribution, but it can be justified in at least two ways. One is to find the power loss per unit volume at each point from the conductivity and the known current density for that point, and integrate over the infinite depth. (See Prob. 6·07a.) Another method of justification is through the Poynting theorem, which will be introduced in the next chapter. (See Prob. 7·03b.)

Equation (1) will be found of the greatest usefulness throughout this text for the computation of power loss in the walls of wave guides, cavity resonators, and other electromagnetic structures. Although the walls of these structures are not plane solids of infinite depth, the results of this section may be applied for all practical purposes whenever the conductor thickness and radii of curvature are much greater than δ, depth of penetration. This includes most important cases at high frequencies. In these cases the quantities which are ordinarily known are the fields at the surface of the conductor. The current per unit width can be readily obtained from the surface value of magnetic field, as can be seen by taking the line integral of magnetic field about some path $ABCD$ of Fig. 6·05a (C and D at infinity). Since magnetic field will be in the y direction for this simple case, there is no contribution to $\bar{H} \cdot \overline{dl}$ along the sides BC and DA; there is no contribution along CD since field is zero at infinity. Hence, for a width w,

$$\oint_{ABCD} \bar{H} \cdot \overline{dl} = \int_A^B \bar{H} \cdot \overline{dl} = wH_y \Big|_{x=0} \tag{2}$$

This line integral of magnetic field must be equal to the *conduction* current enclosed, since displacement current has been shown to be negligible in a good conductor. The current is just the width w times the current per unit width, J_z. A negative sign must be introduced since the right-hand sense associated with the direction of circulation $ABCD$ is the negative z direction. Then, utilizing (2),

$$wH_y \Big|_{x=0} = -wJ_z \quad \text{or} \quad J_z = -H_y \Big|_{x=0} \tag{3}$$

This may be written in a vector form which includes the magnitude and sense information of (3), and the fact that $\bar{J}$ and $\bar{H}$ are mutually perpendicular:

$$\bar{J} = \bar{n} \times \bar{H} \tag{4}$$

where $\bar{n}$ is a unit vector perpendicular to the conductor surface, point-ing into the adjoining dielectric region. $\bar{H}$ is the magnetic field at the surface. It is the form (4) in conjunction with (1) which is especially useful in applying the results of this section to wave guides, resonators, etc.

PROBLEMS

6·07a The average power loss per unit volume at any point in the conductor is $|i_z|^2/2\sigma$. Show that (1) is correct by integrating over the conductor depth to obtain the total power loss per unit area.

6·07b Find the magnetic field $\bar{H}$ for any point x in the plane conductor in terms of i_0 by first finding the electric field, and then utilizing the appropriate one of Maxwell's equations to give $\bar{H}$. Check the equation (3) by means of this result.

6·08 CURRENT DISTRIBUTION IN A WIRE OF CIRCULAR CROSS SECTION

Most common of the conductors used in electrical circuits are round wires, wires of circular cross section. If the round wire forms a con-ducting path with no very sharp curvatures, as in many circuit appli-cations, any small portion may be treated as a straight circular cylinder. It will be assumed that external conditions are applied so that current is in the axial direction only, and that any variations in the axial direction or circumferentially are negligible compared with the variations into the wire (radially). The current distribution equa-tion, 6·04(7), written in cylindrical coordinates with no ϕ or z vari-ations is then (Art. 2·39)

$$\frac{d^2 i_z}{dr^2} + \frac{1}{r}\frac{di_z}{dr} = j\omega\mu\sigma i_z$$

$$\frac{d^2 i_z}{dr^2} + \frac{1}{r}\frac{di_z}{dr} + T^2 i_z = 0 \tag{1}$$

where $$T^2 = -j\omega\mu\sigma$$

or $$T = j^{-1/2}\sqrt{\omega\mu\sigma} = j^{-1/2}\sqrt{2}/\delta \tag{2}$$

A direct comparison of (1) with Eq. 3·21(1) shows that both have exactly the form of the zero order Bessel equation, although T is com-plex. A complete solution may be written, as in Eq. 3·22(8):

$$i_z = AJ_0(Tr) + BH_0^{(1)}(Tr) \tag{3}$$

For a solid wire, $r = 0$ is included in the solution, and then it is neces-sary that $B = 0$ since a study of $H_0^{(1)}(Tr)$ shows that this would become infinite at $r = 0$, even though T is complex. Therefore,

$$i_z = AJ_0(Tr) \tag{4}$$

The arbitrary constant A may be evaluated in terms of current density at the surface.   Let

$$i_z = i_0 \quad \text{at} \quad r = r_0$$

Then, from (4),
$$A = \frac{i_0}{J_0(Tr_0)}$$

and
$$i_z = \frac{i_0 J_0(Tr)}{J_0(Tr_0)} \tag{5}$$

T is complex, and it may seem troublesome to find a Bessel function of a complex quantity.   However, as in cases where we are confronted with sines, cosines, and exponentials of complex quantities, we can resort to the power series definition for the proper function.   Referring to the power series for J_0, it is seen that the function will have both real and imaginary parts if the argument is complex.   These may be calculated separately.   Define

$$Ber\ (v) \equiv \text{Real part of } J_0(j^{-1/2}v)$$

$$Bei\ (v) \equiv \text{Imaginary part of } J_0(j^{-1/2}v)$$

That is,
$$J_0(j^{-1/2}v) \equiv Ber\ (v) + jBei\ (v) \tag{6}$$

$Ber\ (v)$ and $Bei\ (v)$ are tabulated in many references.[1]   Using these definitions and (2), (5) may be written

$$i_z = i_0 \frac{Ber\left(\dfrac{\sqrt{2}\,r}{\delta}\right) + j\ Bei\left(\dfrac{\sqrt{2}\,r}{\delta}\right)}{Ber\left(\dfrac{\sqrt{2}\,r_0}{\delta}\right) + j\ Bei\left(\dfrac{\sqrt{2}\,r_0}{\delta}\right)} \tag{7}$$

Plots of current densities as functions of radius in a round wire are shown in Fig. 6·08a.   Actually the magnitude of the ratio of current density to that at the outside of the wire is plotted as a function of the ratio of radius to outer radius of wire, for different values of the parameter (r_0/δ).   Also, for purposes of the physical picture, these are interpreted in terms of current distribution for a 1-millimeter copper wire at different frequencies by the figure in parentheses.

As an example of the applicability of the plane analysis for curved conductors at high frequencies where δ is small compared with radii, we can take the present case of the round wire.   If we are to neglect the curvature and apply the plane analysis, the coordinate x, distance

---

[1] Dwight, *Tables of Integrals*, Macmillan, rev. ed., 1947; Mclachlan, *Bessel Functions for Engineers*, Oxford, 1934.

below the surface, is $(r_0 - r)$ for a round wire.   Then Eq. 6·05(7) gives

$$\left| \frac{i_z}{i_0} \right| = e^{-(r_0-r)/\delta} \tag{8}$$

In Fig. 6·08b are plotted curves of $\left| i_z/i_0 \right|$ by using this formula, and comparisons are made with curves obtained from the exact formula (7). This is done for two cases, $r_0/\delta = 2.39$ and $r_0/\delta = 7.55$.   In the latter, the approximate distribution agrees well with the exact; in the former it does not.   Thus, if ratio of wire radius to δ is large, it seems that there should be little error in analyzing the wire from the results

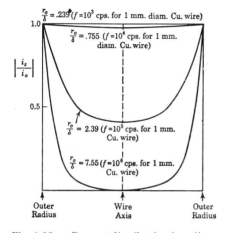

Fig. 6·08a Current distribution in cylindrical wire for different frequencies.

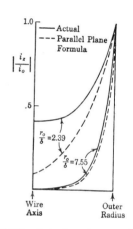

Fig. 6·08b Actual and approximate (parallel plane formula) distribution in cylindrical wire.

developed for plane solids.   This point will be pursued later in impedance calculations.

PROBLEMS

6·08a   Utilizing tables of the Ber and Bei functions, plot the phase of i_z/i_0 versus r/r_0 for $r_0/\delta = 2.39$.

6·08b   Derive Eq. (8) for $r_0/\delta \gg 1$ by utilizing the asymptotic formulas for Bessel functions of large arguments in Eq. (5).

6·09   IMPEDANCE OF A ROUND WIRE AT VERY HIGH OR VERY LOW FREQUENCIES

Very High Frequency.   To show the usefulness of impedance formulas for a semi-infinite plane solid, we shall obtain from them the internal impedance of a round wire at very high frequencies.   It has already been shown that, if the frequency is high enough, the curvature of the wire is unimportant. It may then be considered a plane solid of practically infinite depth, and width equal to its circumference. Thus, if Z_s, Eq. 6·06(3), is the internal impedance of the plane solid per unit square, $Z_s/2\pi r_0$ is the impedance for a width $2\pi r_0$ (the circumference). So, for a round wire of radius r_0 at very high frequencies,

$$Z_{\text{h.f.}} = \frac{(1+j)}{2\pi r_0 \sigma \delta} = \frac{R_s(1+j)}{2\pi r_0}$$

or

$$R_{\text{h.f.}} = (\omega L_i)_{\text{h.f.}} = \frac{R_s}{2\pi r_0} \quad \text{ohms/meter} \tag{1}$$

where R_s is as defined in Eq. 6·06(5).

Very Low Frequency. For very low frequencies the current has essentially a uniform distribution over the cross section, Fig. 6·08(a), and so the d-c resistance formula applies:

$$R_0 = \frac{1}{\pi r_0^2 \sigma} \quad \text{ohms/meter} \tag{2}$$

Internal inductance will be shown in Art. 6·14 to be

$$(L_i)_0 = \frac{\mu}{8\pi} \quad \text{henrys/meter} \tag{3}$$

The first correction term to resistance at moderately low frequencies may be obtained from series expansions of the exact results of the next article. This leads to

$$\frac{R}{R_0} = 1 + \frac{1}{48}\left(\frac{r_0}{\delta}\right)^4 \tag{4}$$

The above equation is good for small values of r_0/δ and has an error of about 6 per cent at $r_0/\delta = 2$ (that is, for a radius twice the depth of penetration).

PROBLEMS

6·09a Show that the ratio of very high-frequency resistance to d-c resistance of a round conductor of radius r_0 and material with depth of penetration δ can be written

$$\frac{R_{\text{h.f.}}}{R_0} = \frac{r_0}{2\delta}$$

6·09b By using the approximate formula 6.09(4), find the value of r_0/δ below which R differs from d-c resistance R_0 by less than 2 per cent. To what size wire does this correspond for copper at 10 kc/sec? For copper at 1 mc/sec? For brass at 1 mc/sec?

6·10   IMPEDANCE OF ROUND WIRES GENERALLY

The internal impedance of the round wire at any frequency is found from total current in the wire and the electric intensity at the surface, according to the ideas of Art. 5·06.   Total current may be obtained from an integration of current density, as for the plane conductor in Art. 6·06; however, it may also be found from the magnetic field at the surface, since the line integral of magnetic field around the outside of the wire must be equal to the total current in the wire:

$$\cdot \oint \bar{H} \cdot \overline{dl} = I$$

or

$$2\pi r_0 H_\phi \big|_{r=r_0} = I \tag{1}$$

Magnetic field is obtained from the electric field by Maxwell's equations:

$$\nabla \times \bar{E} = -j\omega\mu\bar{H} \tag{2}$$

For the round wire with the assumptions made in Art. 6·08, E_z and H_ϕ alone are present, and only r derivatives remain, so (2) is simply

$$H_\phi = \frac{1}{j\omega\mu} \frac{dE_z}{dr} \tag{3}$$

An expression for current density has already been obtained in Eq. 6·08(5).   Electric field is related to this through the conductivity σ:

$$E_z = \frac{i_z}{\sigma} = \frac{i_0}{\sigma} \frac{J_0(Tr)}{J_0(Tr_0)} \tag{4}$$

By substituting in (3) and recalling that $T^2 = -j\omega\mu\sigma$,

$$H_\phi = \frac{i_0 T}{j\omega\mu\sigma} \frac{J_0'(Tr)}{J_0(Tr_0)} = -\frac{i_0}{T} \frac{J_0'(Tr)}{J_0(Tr_0)}$$

$J_0'(Tr)$ denotes $\dfrac{d}{d(Tr)} J_0(Tr)$.   From (1),

$$I \cdot = -\frac{2\pi r_0 i_0}{T} \frac{J_0'(Tr_0)}{J_0(Tr_0)} \tag{5}$$

The internal impedance per unit length is

$$Z_i = \frac{E_z \big|_{r=r_0}}{I} = -\frac{T J_0(Tr_0)}{2\pi r_0 \sigma J_0'(Tr_0)} \tag{6}$$

Z_i will be complex since T is complex [Eq. 6·08(2)]. To separate into real and imaginary parts, use Eq. 6·08(6):

$$Ber\ v + jBei\ v = J_0(j^{-1/2}v)$$

Also let
$$Ber'\ v + jBei'\ v = \frac{d}{dv}(Ber\ v + jBei\ v)$$

$$= j^{-1/2}J_0'(j^{-1/2}v)$$

Then (6) may be written

$$Z_i = R + j\omega L_i = \frac{jR_s}{\sqrt{2}\,\pi r_0}\left[\frac{Ber\ q + jBei\ q}{Ber'\ q + jBei'\ q}\right]$$

where
$$R_s = \frac{1}{\sigma\delta} = \sqrt{\frac{\pi f\mu}{\sigma}} \qquad q = \frac{\sqrt{2}\,r_0}{\delta}$$

or
$$R = \frac{R_s}{\sqrt{2}\,\pi r_0}\left[\frac{Ber\ q\ Bei'\ q - Bei\ q\ Ber'\ q}{(Ber'\ q)^2 + (Bei'\ q)^2}\right] \quad \text{ohms/meter}$$

$$\omega L_i = \frac{R_s}{\sqrt{2}\,\pi r_0}\left[\frac{Ber\ q\ Ber'\ q + Bei\ q\ Bei'\ q}{(Ber'\ q)^2 + (Bei'\ q)^2}\right] \quad \text{ohms/meter}$$

(7)

These are the expressions for resistance and internal reactance of a round wire at any frequency in terms of the parameter q, which is $\sqrt{2}$ times the ratio of wire radius to depth of penetration. Curves giving the ratios of these quantities to the d-c and to the high-frequency values as functions of r_0/δ are plotted in Figs. 6·10a and 6·10b. A careful study of these will reveal the ranges of r_0/δ over which it is permissible to use the approximate formulas for resistance and reactance. For example, if a 10 per cent error can be tolerated, the high-frequency approximation for resistance, Eq. 6·09(1), may be used for $r_0/\delta > 5.5$; the high-frequency approximation for reactance, Eq. 6·09(1), may be used for $r_0/\delta > 2.2$. The d-c resistance formula, Eq. 6·09(2), may be used for $r_0/\delta < 1.5$, and the d-c inductance formula, Eq. 6·09(3), may be used for $r_0/\delta < 1.9$.

PROBLEMS

6·10a For small values of Tr_0 (low frequencies) the Bessel functions may be approximated by only a few terms of the series, Eq. 3·19(8) and Art. 3·26. Using three terms of the series for J_0 and J_0', show that these values, substituted in Eq. 6·10(6), lead to the expressions for low-frequency resistance and inductance stated in Eq. 6·09(3) and Eq. 6·09(4).

6·10b   For large values of Tr_0 (high frequencies) the Bessel functions may be approximated by the asymptotic forms of Art. 3·25.   Show that these, substituted in Eq. 6·10(6), lead to the expressions for resistance and internal inductance at high frequencies obtained in Eq. 6·09(1).

6·10c   From Figs. 6·10a and 6·10b, investigate the ranges of r_0/δ over which it is permissible to use the approximate formulas of Eqs. 6·09(1), 6·09(2), and 6·09(3) if the error must be less than 5 per cent.

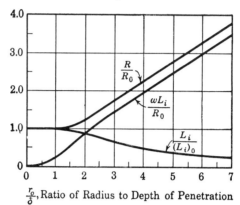

Fig. 6·10a   Solid wire skin effect quantities compared with d-c values.

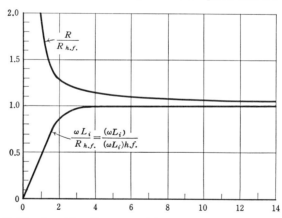

Fig. 6·10b   Solid wire skin effect quantities compared with values from high-frequency formulas.

6·10d   For two geometrically similar systems of good conductors of the same material, show that current distributions will be similar, and current densities equal in magnitude at similar points, if the applied voltage to the small system is $1/K$ in magnitude and K^2 in frequency that of the large system.   Also show that the impedance of the small system will be K times that of the large system under these conditions.   Check these conclusions for the case of two round wires of different radii. K is the ratio of linear dimensions.

6·11   IMPEDANCE OF A COATED CONDUCTOR

Coated conductors appear in radio applications in the form of tinned copper wires, copper-plated iron or iron alloys in vacuum tube leads, silver-plated brass in resonant cavities, etc.   Most often the problem is one of the following.

1. The coating material may be very thick compared with depth of penetration in that material.   This requires no analysis since fields and currents in the coated metal are then negligible, and the impedance is governed only by the metal of the coating; the conductor is as good or as bad as a solid conductor of the coating material.

2. The coating may not be thick enough to prevent currents from flowing in the coated material, but penetration in both materials may be small compared with surface curvature so that the surfaces may be considered as planes, the coated material also being effectively infinite in depth.   An analysis of this second case will follow.

In Fig. 6·11a is shown a plane solid material (conductivity σ_2, permeability μ_2) of effectively infinite depth coated with another material (conductivity σ_1, permeability μ_1) of thickness d. Solutions for the distribution equations must be found for both media and matched at the boundary between the two.   The

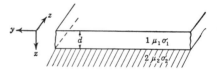

Fig. 6·11a Conductor coated with another conductor.

solution in either material is of the form of Eq. 6·05(5), but there can be no positive exponential term for the lower material since current density must become zero at infinite depth.

$$i_{z_2} = C e^{-\tau_2 x}$$

$$\tau_2 = \frac{(1 + j)}{\delta_2} = (1 + j)\sqrt{\pi f \mu_2 \sigma_2} \qquad (1)$$

In the coating material both exponentials must be present, but it is convenient to write the solution in terms of hyperbolic functions instead of the equivalent exponentials:

$$i_{z_1} = A \sinh \tau_1 x + B \cosh \tau_1 x$$

$$\tau_1 = \frac{(1 + j)}{\delta_1} = (1 + j)\sqrt{\pi f \mu_1 \sigma_1} \qquad (2)$$

For both materials,

$$E_z = \frac{i_z}{\sigma}$$

and, from Maxwell's equations,

$$H_y = \frac{1}{j\omega\mu} \frac{dE_z}{dx} = \frac{\sigma}{\tau^2} \frac{dE_z}{dx}$$

Electric and magnetic fields in the two materials are then

$$E_{z_2} = \frac{C}{\sigma_2} e^{-\tau_2 x} \qquad E_{z_1} = \frac{1}{\sigma_1} [A \sinh \tau_1 x + B \cosh \tau_1 x]$$

$$(3)$$

$$H_{y_2} = -\frac{C}{\tau_2} e^{-\tau_2 x} \qquad H_{y_1} = \frac{1}{\tau_1} [A \cosh \tau_1 x + B \sinh \tau_1 x]$$

The constants may be evaluated since tangential electric and magnetic fields are continuous across the boundary (Art. 4·11):

$$E_{z1} = E_{z2} \qquad H_{y1} = H_{y2} \quad \text{at} \quad x = d$$

Then

$$\frac{B}{A} = -\left[\frac{\sinh \tau_1 d + (\tau_2 \sigma_1 / \tau_1 \sigma_2) \cosh \tau_1 d}{\cosh \tau_1 d + (\tau_2 \sigma_1 / \tau_1 \sigma_2) \sinh \tau_1 d} \right]$$

$$(4)$$

Total current in the two materials is obtainable from Eq. 6·07(4):

$$\bar{J} = \bar{n} \times \bar{H} \qquad \text{or} \qquad J_z = -H_y \big|_{x=0}$$

The impedance per square (per unit width and unit length) is

$$Z = \frac{E_z \big|_{x=0}}{J_z} = -\frac{E_z}{H_y}\bigg|_{x=0} = -\frac{B}{A} \frac{\tau_1}{\sigma_1}$$

$$(5)$$

From (4) with τ_1 and τ_2 substituted,

$$\frac{Z}{R_{s1}} = (1 + j) \left[\frac{\sinh \tau_1 d + (R_{s2}/R_{s1}) \cosh \tau_1 d}{\cosh \tau_1 d + (R_{s2}/R_{s1}) \sinh \tau_1 d} \right]$$

$$(6)$$

Curves of ratio of resistance and reactance of the composite conductor to resistance of a conductor made entirely of the coating material are plotted in Fig. 6·11b for $R_{s2}/R_{s1} = 0.34$, which corresponds roughly to solder on copper. Similar curves are given in Fig. 6·11c for a ratio of 1.6, which corresponds roughly to silver on brass. It is seen that in both cases the composite conductor becomes about as good, or as bad, as though the coating were of infinite depth when the coating thickness is greater than δ_1, depth of penetration for the material of the coating.

PROBLEMS

6·11a For the case of $R_{s2}/R_{s1} = 1.6$, find the ratio of the power loss in the coating material to that in the base when $d/\delta_1 = 1$.

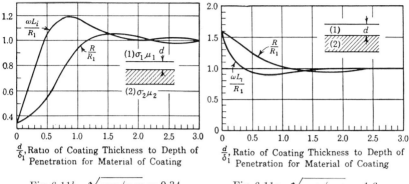

Fig. 6·11b $\sqrt{\mu_2\sigma_1/\mu_1\sigma_2} = 0.34$.   Fig. 6·11$c$ $\sqrt{\mu_2\sigma_1/\mu_1\sigma_2} = 1.6$.

Skin effect quantities for coated conductors.

6·11b   For the conditions of Prob. a, find the ratio of energy stored in magnetic fields for the coating material to that in the base.

6·12   IMPEDANCE OF THIN-WALLED TUBULAR CONDUCTORS

A study of the current distribution in a solid round wire shows that at the higher frequencies the inner part of the conducting material plays little part in the conduction. There should consequently be little difference in impedance under such skin effect conditions between a solid round wire and a hollow tubular conductor of the same outer diameter. Certainly this is true when the wall thickness is very large compared with the depth of penetration of the conducting material, and we would use the same high-frequency equation, Eq. 6·09(1), that was developed for a round wire. If this criterion is not satisfied, the finite wall thickness must be taken into account. An exact solution may be carried through in terms of Bessel functions, but many times the wall thickness is small enough compared with wire radius so that the analysis of a flat plane conductor of finite thickness may be applied well enough. The result for this problem may be lazily found by setting conductivity of the lower material equal to zero in the result for the composite conductor of Art. 6·11. That is, in Eq. 6·11(6), set $R_{s2} = \infty$. Then, the surface impedance per square

$$Z = R + j\omega L_i = (1 + j)R_s \frac{\cosh \tau d}{\sinh \tau d} \tag{1}$$

$$= (1 + j)R_s \coth \left[\frac{d}{\delta} (1 + j) \right] \tag{2}$$

$$\frac{R}{R_s} = \frac{\sinh (2d/\delta) + \sin (2d/\delta)}{\cosh (2d/\delta) - \cos (2d/\delta)} \tag{3}$$

For a tubular conductor satisfying the conditions of wall thickness small compared with radius of tube these results may be used directly to give impedance per unit length by dividing by the circumference:

$$R \approx \frac{R_s}{2\pi r} \left[\frac{\sinh\,(2d/\delta)\,+\,\sin\,(2d/\delta)}{\cosh\,(2d/\delta)\,-\,\cos\,(2d/\delta)} \right] \tag{4}$$

$$\omega L_i \approx \frac{R_s}{2\pi r} \left[\frac{\sinh\,(2d/\delta)\,-\,\sin\,(2d/\delta)}{\cosh\,(2d/\delta)\,-\,\cos\,(2d/\delta)} \right] \tag{5}$$

where r = outer radius if fields are applied along outside of tube; r = inner radius if fields are applied along inside of tube.

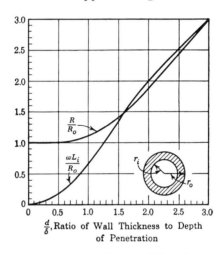

Fig. 6·12a   Thin-walled tubular conductor. Skin effect quantities compared with d-c values.

The high-frequency resistance of the tubular conductor is merely

$$R_{\text{h.f.}} = (\omega L_i)_{\text{h.f.}} = \frac{R_s}{2\pi r}$$

Curves of resistance and internal reactance ratios to high-frequency resistance are given in Fig. 6·12b, and to d-c resistance in Fig. 6·12a.

PROBLEMS

6·12a Explain qualitatively why the ratio of a-c resistance for a tubular conductor to the a-c resistance of a solid conductor of the same outer radius is always less than the ratio of d-c resistances for the two conductors. Explain why the a-c resistance of the tubular conductor is always somewhat greater than the a-c resistance of the solid conductor.

6·12b The analysis of this article is equivalent to solving for the case of a slab conductor of finite depth d, with the boundary condition that tangential magnetic field is zero at $x = d$. Explain why this boundary condition is appropriate for the problem.

6·12c Show that for a tubular conductor of outer radius r_0, inner radius r_i with voltage applied from the outside, the exact expressions for skin effect resistance and reactance are

$$R + j(\omega L_i) = \frac{j^{-1/2}\sqrt{2}R_s}{2\pi r_0}\left[\frac{J_0(Tr_0)H_0^{(1)\prime}(Tr_i) - J_0'(Tr_i)H_0^{(1)}(Tr_0)}{J_0'(Tr_0)H_0^{(1)\prime}(Tr_i) - J_0'(Tr_i)H_0^{(1)\prime}(Tr_0)}\right]$$

T as in Eq. 6·08(2).

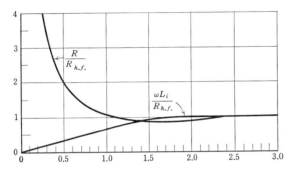

Fig. 6·12b   Thin-walled tubular conductor.   Skin effect quantities compared with values from high-frequency formulas.

6·12d For a case with $r_0/\delta = 1.25$ and $r_i/\delta = 1.0$, calculate the skin effect resistance from the result of the preceding problem and compare with that calculated from the approximate expression, Eq. 6·12(4).

6·12e Show that the result of Prob. 6·12c may be used for a tubular conductor with voltage applied at the inner radius, if r_0 and r_i are interchanged.

Calculation of Inductance

6·13 INDUCTANCE FROM FLUX LINKAGES; SELF-INDUCTANCE OF COAXIAL LINE

It is the purpose of this section of the chapter to demonstrate by example the several methods for finding the self- and mutual inductance coefficients of classical circuit theory discussed in Chapter 5. The examples to be chosen will be those for which results are of great interest in themselves.   The first example will be the important one of a coaxial transmission line, and the method to be used will be the most familiar one of finding inductance from the flux linkages per unit current.

From Eq. 5·07(4), the inductance of a closed circuit is

$$L = \frac{1}{I} \int_S \bar{B} \cdot \overline{dS} \tag{1}$$

or, in words, it is the magnetic flux linking current I, per unit of current I. For a coaxial line as pictured in Fig. 6·13 with axial current I flowing in the inner conductor and returning in the outer, the magnetic

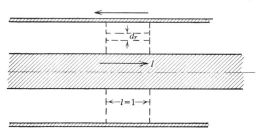

Fig. 6·13   Coaxial transmission line.

field is circumferential and for $a < r < b$ is (Art. 2·29)

$$H_\phi = \frac{I}{2\pi r} \tag{2}$$

For a unit length the magnetic flux between radii a and b is

$$\int_S \bar{B} \cdot \overline{dS} = \int_a^b \mu \left(\frac{I}{2\pi r}\right) dr = \frac{\mu I}{2\pi} \ln \frac{b}{a}$$

So, from (1), the inductance per unit length is

$$L = \frac{\mu}{2\pi} \ln \frac{b}{a} \quad \text{henrys/meter} \tag{3}$$

The value obtained in (3) is of course the *external inductance* of the line, giving the contribution to inductance from flux external to conductors (in this case, between the two conductors). If total inductance is desired, the internal inductance of the solid inner conductor and of the tubular outer conductor (Arts. 6·10 and 6·12) must be added.

PROBLEMS

6·13a   A coaxial transmission line has a solid copper inner conductor of radius 0.20 cm and a tubular copper outer conductor of inner radius 1 cm, wall thickness 0.1 cm.   Find the total impedance per unit length of line for a frequency of 10 kc/sec, including the internal impedance of both conductors.   Accuracy obtainable from curves given in the text will be acceptable.

6·13b   For a coaxial transmission line as described in Prob. *a*, find the ratio of internal inductance from both conductors to the external inductance of the line for a frequency of 3000 mc/sec.

6·14   INDUCTANCE FROM ENERGY STORAGE; INTERNAL INDUCTANCE OF ROUND WIRE

An alternative method for computing inductance which is more convenient for many cases arises from a consideration of energy stored in the magnetic fields. From a circuit point of view, this is known to be $\frac{1}{2}LI^2$, where I is the instantaneous current flow through the inductance. From field theory, it will be shown in the next chapter that the magnetic energy may be found by integrating an energy density of $\frac{1}{2}\mu H^2$ throughout the volume of significant fields. Equating these two forms gives

$$\frac{1}{2}LI^2 = \int_V \frac{\mu}{2} H^2 \, dV \tag{1}$$

The form of (1) is especially convenient for problems that would require consideration of partial linkages if done by the method of flux linkages of the preceding article. As an example, consider the calculation of internal inductance of a round wire of radius r_0 at frequencies low enough so that current distribution may be considered uniform. The magnetic field (Prob. 2·29a and Prob. 2·34c) is

$$H_\psi = \frac{Ir}{2\pi r_0{}^2} \qquad r < r_0 \tag{2}$$

For a unit length, substituting in (1),

$$\frac{1}{2}LI^2 = \int_0^{r_0} \frac{\mu}{2}\left(\frac{Ir}{2\pi r_0{}^2}\right)^2 2\pi r \, dr = \frac{\mu I^2}{4\pi r_0{}^4}\cdot\frac{r_0{}^4}{4}$$

or

$$L = \frac{\mu}{8\pi} \quad \text{henrys/meter} \tag{3}$$

This is the result cited as Eq. 6·09(3), and is also obtainable as a limiting case from the a-c analysis of Art. 6·10.

PROBLEMS

6·14a   Derive the formula for external inductance of the coaxial line by the energy method.

6·14b   Derive the expression for internal inductance of the tubular outer conductor of Fig. 6·13 for low frequencies.

6·14c   Derive the formula for internal inductance of the plane conductor of infinite depth (Art. 6·05) by the energy method. *Suggestion:* Use average values of stored energy.

6·15   MUTUAL INDUCTANCE FROM VECTOR POTENTIAL

The mutual inductance between two circuits 1 and 2 expresses the voltage induced in circuit 1 by unit rate of change of current in circuit 2, and vice versa.

$$M = M_{12} = M_{21} \tag{1}$$

This coefficient was discussed in Art. 5·10, and several equations were given which might be used for its calculation. We wish to stress here the method making use of vector potential $\bar{A}$. From Eq. 5·10(3),

$$M = \frac{1}{I_2} \oint_{C_1} \bar{A}_2 \cdot \overline{dl}_1 \tag{2}$$

where $\bar{A}_2$ is the vector potential arising from the current I_2 of circuit 2, and the integration is taken about circuit 1.

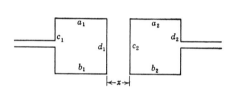

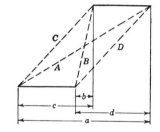

Fig. 6·15a   Two square coupling loops.   Fig. 6·15b   Parallel current elements displaced from one another.

The use of vector potentials directly is especially helpful in the calculation or estimate of mutual inductances for current paths having straight line portions. Consider, for instance, the rectangular circuits of Fig. 6·15a. We know that for a straight current element the potential $\bar{A}$ arising from that element must have just the direction of that element, and may be computed from Eq. 5·10(2) when circuit 2 may be considered a filamentary path. The induced field from changing magnetic effects,

$$\bar{E} = - \frac{\partial \bar{A}}{\partial t} = -j\omega\bar{A} \tag{3}$$

has the direction of $\bar{A}$. Consequently in the system of Fig. 6·15a there can be no contribution to voltage in the sides a_2 and b_2 from current in the sides c_1 and d_1, nor any contribution in the sides c_2 and d_2 from current in the sides a_1 and b_1. The picture obtained from visualizing these directive relations is frequently valuable where the circuit configuration is quite complex. Often a quick estimate of coupling may be obtained by replacing portions of current paths by straight line sections, estimating the coupling from these.

PROBLEMS

6·15a By integration of Eq. 6·15(2), show that the contribution to mutual inductance from two parallel line segments displaced as shown in Fig. 6·15b is

$$M = \frac{\mu}{4\pi}\left[\ln\left\{\frac{(A+a)^a(B+b)^b}{(C+c)^c(D+d)^d}\right\} + (C+D) - (A+B)\right]$$

6·15b Apply the above result to the calculation of mutual inductance between two square loops used for coupling between open-wire transmission lines as shown in Fig. 6·15a. The length of each side is 0.03 meter; the separation x is 0.01 meter. Assume that the gaps at which the lines enter are small enough to be ignored.

6·15c For the coaxial line of Fig. 6·13, find vector potential for each of three regions by solving the Poisson equation as in Eq. 2·34(4) with proper continuity conditions between the regions. With $\bar{A}$ known, apply formula 5·07(2) to find self-inductance of the coaxial line (external) in terms of the vector potential.

6·16 NEUMANN'S FORM; MUTUAL INDUCTANCE BETWEEN COAXIAL CIRCULAR LOOPS

A second derived form for mutual inductance was the Neumann form of Eq. 5·10(6):

$$M = \frac{\mu}{4\pi}\oint\oint\frac{\overline{dl}_1 \cdot \overline{dl}_2}{r} \tag{1}$$

The integrations are performed about the two circuits 1 and 2, with $\overline{ld}_1$ and $\overline{dl}_2$ representing differential elements of length about 1 and 2 respectively. This form is in reality exactly the same as that of the preceding article when one assumes that $\bar{A}_2$ in the vicinity of circuit 1 may be calculated by taking the current of circuit 2 as flowing in a filament, as in Eq. 5·10(2). That is, (1) is just a combination of Eqs. 5·10(3) and (2) in a single step.

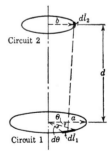

Fig. 6·16 Two coaxial circular loops.

To demonstrate the application of this form, we shall find the mutual inductance between the two coaxial circular loops pictured in Fig. 6·16. If $\overline{dl}_1$ is any element of circuit 1, and $\overline{dl}_2$ is any element of circuit 2,

$$\overline{dl}_1 \cdot \overline{dl}_2 = dl_2\, a\, d\theta \cos\theta$$

$$r = \sqrt{d^2 + (a\sin\theta)^2 + (a\cos\theta - b)^2}$$

By substituting $\theta = \pi - 2\phi$ and

$$k^2 = \frac{4ab}{d^2 + (a + b)^2}$$

the integral then will be found to become

$$M = \mu \sqrt{ab} \, k \int_0^{\pi/2} \frac{(2 \sin^2 \phi - 1) \, d\phi}{\sqrt{1 - k^2 \sin^2 \phi}}$$

This can be broken into two integrals:

$$M = \mu \sqrt{ab} \left[\left(\frac{2}{k} - k \right) \int_0^{\pi/2} \frac{d\phi}{\sqrt{1 - k^2 \sin^2 \phi}} \right. $$
$$\left. - \frac{2}{k} \int_0^{\pi/2} \sqrt{1 - k^2 \sin^2 \phi} \, d\phi \right]$$

$$= \mu \sqrt{ab} \left[\left(\frac{2}{k} - k \right) K(k) - \frac{2}{k} E(k) \right]$$

where

$$E(k) = \int_0^{\pi/2} \sqrt{1 - k^2 \sin^2 \phi} \, d\phi \qquad (2)$$

$$K(k) = \int_0^{\pi/2} \frac{d\phi}{\sqrt{1 - k^2 \sin^2 \phi}} \qquad (3)$$

The definite integrals (2) and (3) are tabulated in tables[2] as functions of k and are called complete elliptic integrals of the first and second kinds respectively. Thus

$$M = \mu \sqrt{d^2 + (a + b)^2} \left[\left(1 - \frac{k^2}{2} \right) K(k) - E(k) \right] \qquad (4)$$

where

$$k = 2 \sqrt{\frac{ab}{d^2 + (a + b)^2}}$$

PROBLEMS

6·16a From tables of the complete elliptic integrals given in the references, plot the form of mutual inductance against d/a for $b/a = 1$.

6·16b Investigate the properties of the complete elliptic integrals from the references for $k \ll 1$ and for $k \approx 1$, and obtain approximate expressions for mutual inductance for these two cases.

6·17   MUTUAL INDUCTANCE FROM FLUX LINKAGES

The third and most common form of mutual inductance is that giving M as the flux linking circuit 1 from current in circuit 2, per

[2] Dwight, *Tables of Integrals*, Macmillan, 1947.

unit of current in circuit 2, or vice versa. From Eq. 5·10(5),

$$M = \frac{\int_{S_1} \bar{B}_2 \cdot \overline{dS}_1}{I_2} \tag{1}$$

If inductance is to be calculated from flux enclosed, any of the appropriate methods studied in Chapters 2 and 3 may be used for calculating fields in the region of circuit 2. For instance, suppose this method were to be applied to the two coaxial circular conductors of Fig. 6·16. Magnetic field has been given in spherical coordinates as a series of spherical harmonics, Eq. 3·33(6):

$$H_z = \frac{I_2}{2b}\left[1 - \frac{3}{2}\left(\frac{r}{b}\right)^2 P_2(\cos\theta) + \cdots\right] \tag{2}$$

This expression may then be integrated over the region of circuit 1. If d/b is much greater than a/b, or if a/b is much less than unity with any value of d, a study of the series of (2) shows that H_z does not vary much over the region of 1, and a good approximation may be had by assuming that H_z is substantially constant at its axial value over the area of the first loop. Then

$$\int_{S_1} \bar{B}_2 \cdot \overline{dS}_1 = \mu\pi a^2 \frac{b^2 I_2}{2(d^2 + b^2)^{3/2}}$$

and
$$M \approx \frac{\mu\pi a^2 b^2}{2(d^2 + b^2)^{3/2}} \quad \text{henrys} \tag{3}$$

PROBLEMS

6·17a Set up the integral for determining flux through circuit 1 when the complete series (2) is to be used.

6·17b A coaxial line has the radius of the inner conductor as a and inside radius of outer conductor as b, and is closed by a conducting plane at $z = 0$. A square loop is introduced for coupling, lying in a longitudinal plane and extending from $z = 0$ to $z = d$ in length and from $r = r_1$ to $r = r_2$ in radius ($a < r_1 < r_2 < b$). Find the mutual between loop and line.

6·18   SELF-INDUCTANCE BY SELECTED MUTUAL INDUCTANCE; INDUCTANCE OF A CIRCULAR LOOP

In order to discuss the external inductance of an arbitrary closed circuit formed by a conductor of circular cross section, let us refer to Fig. 5·07a. The induced voltage about a path taken along the surface of the conductor following the inner contour of the loop (which is appropriate to the external inductance as discussed in Art. 5·07) is obtained from the flux enclosed by that path. To compute the flux we need the magnetic field, but we note that, for a point P some distance from the wire, the field is much the same for a given current in the conductor no matter how that current may be distributed over the conductor's cross section. For such a point it is nearly correct to calculate field intensity by assuming all current concentrated at the center of the conductor. Similarly, at point Q near the wire the field is $I/2\pi r$, where I is the total current in the conductor, *provided other portions of the conducting path are not near enough to disturb the circular symmetry.* Field near the wire is then also very nearly the same as though current were concentrated at the axis. We conclude that field at any point inside the loop may be calculated approximately by assuming a current concentrated along the axis of the wire so long as the proximity effect from other portions of the conducting path is not great enough to disturb the current distribution in the conductor. Then the problem of finding the contribution to self-inductance from the external flux is very nearly that of finding the mutual inductance between a line current along the axis of the wire and a line circuit selected along the inner surface of the wire. Any of the methods of the past three articles may be used for the calculation.

As an example of this method, which might be called the selected mutual inductance method, let us find the inductance of a circular loop of wire. The wire radius is a, and the loop radius is r. The contribution to inductance from external flux, given by the mutual inductance between two concentric circles of radii r and $(r - a)$ may be obtained from Eq. 6·16(4):

$$L_0 = \mu(2r - a)\left[\left(1 - \frac{k^2}{2}\right)K(k) - E(k)\right] \tag{1}$$

$$k^2 = \frac{4r(r - a)}{(2r - a)^2}$$

$K(k)$ and $E(k)$ are complete elliptic integrals of first and second kinds as defined by Eqs. 6·16(2) and 6·16(3). If a/r is very small, k is nearly unity, and K and E may be approximated by

$$K(k) \cong \ln\left(\frac{4}{\sqrt{1 - k^2}}\right)$$

$$E(k) \cong 1$$

so
$$L_0 \cong r\mu\left[\ln\left(\frac{8r}{a}\right) - 2\right] \quad \text{henrys} \tag{2}$$

To find total L, values of internal inductance, as listed in Arts. 6·09 or 6·10, must be added.

6·19 INDUCTANCE OF PRACTICAL COILS

A study of the inductance of coils at low frequencies involves no new concepts but only new troubles because of the complications in geometry. Certain special cases are simple enough for calculation by a straightforward application of previously outlined methods. For example, for a circular coil of N turns formed into a circular cross section (Fig. 6·19a) we may modify the formula for a circular loop of one turn, Eq. 6·18(2), provided the cross section is small compared with the coil radius. Magnetic field must be computed on the basis of a current NI; in addition, to compute the total induced voltage about

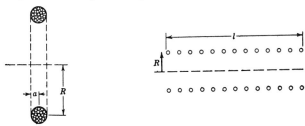

Fig.6·19a   Cross section of a coil.   Fig. 6·19b   Longitudinal section of long solenoid.

the coil, N integrations must be made about the loop. Equation 6·18(2) is thus modified by a factor N^2. The external inductance for this coil is then

$$L_0 = N^2 R \mu \left[\ln \left(\frac{8R}{a} \right) - 2 \right] \quad \text{henrys} \qquad (1)$$

For the other extreme, the inductance of a very long solenoid (Fig. 6·19b) may be computed. If the solenoid is ong enough, the magnetic field on the inside is essentially constant, as for the infinite solenoid (Prob. 2·29c):

$$H_z = \frac{NI}{l}$$

where N is the total number of turns and l the length. The flux linkages for N turns is then $N\pi R^2 \mu H_z$, and the inductance is

$$L_0 = \frac{\pi \mu R^2 N^2}{l} \quad \text{henrys} \qquad (2)$$

For coils of intermediate length to radius ratio, empirical or semi-empirical formulas frequently have to be used.[3, 4] The famous

[3] Circular 74, "Radio Instruments and Measurements," National Bureau of Standards, 1918.

[4] F. W. Grover, *Inductance Calculations*, Van Nostrand, 1946.

Nagaoka formula[5] applies a correction factor K to the formula for the long solenoid, (2).   The factor K or its equivalent is tabulated in the references cited and in many standard handbooks.[6]   Another simple approximate form useful for $l > 0.8R$ is[7]

$$L_0 = \frac{\pi\mu R^2 N^2}{l + 0.9R} \quad \text{henrys} \tag{3}$$

At higher frequencies the problem becomes more complex.   When turns are relatively close together, the assumption made previously in calculating internal impedance (other portions of the circuit so far away that circular symmetry of current in the wire is not disturbed) certainly does not apply.   Current elements in neighboring turns will be near enough to produce nearly as much effect upon current distribution in a given turn as the current in that turn itself.   Values of skin effect resistance and internal inductance are then not as previously calculated.   External inductance may also be different since changes in external fields result when current loses its symmetrical distribution with respect to the wire axis.   In fact, the strict separation of internal and external inductance may not be possible for these coils, for a given field line may be sometimes inside and sometimes outside of the conductor.

Self- and Mutual Capacitances

6·20   THE COEFFICIENTS OF POTENTIAL, CAPACITANCE, AND INDUCTION

The capacitance term of circuit theory was discussed in terms of field theory in Art. 5·08.   Under the assumptions applicable to classical circuit theory, the term for a two-conductor capacitor assumed its common form with capacitance defined as the charge on one conductor divided by the difference of scalar potential between the two.   This definition is so well known that it has been used for many electrostatic examples in Chapters 2 and 3, and no additional examples need be given here.   However, the case of several conductors with capacitance coupling between them is also of interest, and will be discussed in this section.

In engineering practice, a problem of capacitance coupling between several conductors, as in Fig. 6·20a, is commonly handled by drawing an equivalent circuit with a capacitance between each pair of conductors, and from each conductor to ground if the latter coupling is

---

[5] Nagaoka, *J. Coll. Sci. Tokyo*, **27**, Art. 6 (1909).

[6] For example, F. E. Terman, *Radio Engineers' Handbook*, McGraw-Hill, 1943.

[7] H. A. Wheeler, *Proc. I.R.E.*, **16**, 1398–1400 (Oct. 1928).

of importance. This is illustrated for the problem of Fig. 6·20a in Fig. 6·20b. The classical discussion of the several-conductor problem is that of Maxwell[8] in terms of defined coefficients of potential, capacitance, and induction. Since both points of view have usefulness, it is desirable to discuss the relation between the two. The present article will define the coefficients of Maxwell, and give certain of their properties.

From the basic equation for scalar potential Φ, Eq. 4·16(3), it is evident that, for a system with charge $Q_1, Q_2, \cdots, Q_n$ on n conductors,

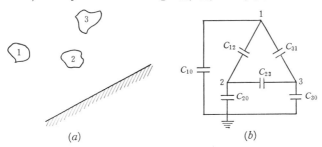

(a) (b)

Fig. 6·20 (a) Three bodies in the presence of ground; (b) the equivalent circuit.

the potential at any point will be linearly related to the several charges. Thus, for the potentials $\Phi_1, \Phi_2, \cdots, \Phi_n$ on the n conductors, we may write the set of linear equations

$$\Phi_1 = p_{11}Q_1 + p_{21}Q_2 + \cdots + p_{n1}Q_n$$
$$\Phi_2 = p_{12}Q_1 + p_{22}Q_2 + \cdots + p_{n2}Q_n \qquad (1)$$
$$\cdots \cdots \cdots \cdots \cdots \cdots \cdots \cdots \cdots \cdots$$
$$\Phi_n = p_{1n}Q_1 + p_{2n}Q_2 + \cdots + p_{nn}Q_n$$

The coefficients p_{rs} are the coefficients of potential, and are all real if retardation may be neglected in the computation of Φ.

The linear set of equations (1) may be solved for the charges, leading to another linear set relating charges to potentials:

$$Q_1 = c_{11}\Phi_1 + c_{21}\Phi_2 + \cdots + c_{n1}\Phi_n$$
$$Q_2 = c_{12}\Phi_1 + c_{22}\Phi_2 + \cdots + c_{n2}\Phi_n \qquad (2)$$
$$\cdots \cdots \cdots \cdots \cdots \cdots \cdots \cdots \cdots \cdots$$
$$Q_n = c_{1n}\Phi_1 + c_{2n}\Phi_2 + \cdots + c_{nn}\Phi_n$$

where
$$c_{rs} = (-1)^{s+r} \frac{M_{sr}(p)}{\Delta(p)} \qquad (3)$$

[8] James Clerk Maxwell, *A Treatise on Electricity and Magnetism*, Oxford, 3rd ed., 1892, Vol. I, pp. 107–118.

$\Delta(p)$ is the determinant of the coefficients p_{rs}, and $M_{sr}(p)$ is the minor of the rth row and sth column. Above coefficients of the form c_{rr} are called coefficients of self-capacitance since such a term represents the ratio of charge on the rth body to potential on that body, all other conductors being grounded. A term of the form c_{rs} ($r \neq s$) represents the ratio of charge on s to potential on r when all conductors but r are grounded. Coefficients of the latter form are called coefficients of induction and are related to the mutual capacitances of the equivalent circuit, as will be shown in the following article.

Important properties of the coefficients of potential, capacitance, and induction are:

1. Reciprocity: $c_{rs} = c_{sr}$ and $p_{rs} = p_{sr}$.
2. All p's are positive or zero.
3. c_{rr} is positive or zero.
4. c_{rs} ($r \neq s$) is negative or zero.
5. The sum $c_{r1} + c_{r2} + \cdot\cdot\ \ + c_{rn}$ is positive or zero.

6·21 CAPACITANCE ELEMENTS IN THE EQUIVALENT CIRCUIT

To study the relation between the coefficients of potential, capacitance, and induction, and the capacitances appearing in an equivalent circuit such as Fig. 6·20b, the first step is that of writing the charge equation for the various nodes of the equivalent circuit in terms of the potentials. Let us write them for the three-conductor problem of Figs. 6·20a, b:

$$Q_1 = C_{10}\Phi_1 + C_{13}(\Phi_1 - \Phi_3) + C_{12}(\Phi_1 - \Phi_2)$$

$$Q_2 = C_{20}\Phi_2 + C_{12}(\Phi_2 - \Phi_1) + C_{23}(\Phi_2 - \Phi_3)$$

$$Q_3 = C_{30}\Phi_3 + C_{23}(\Phi_3 - \Phi_2) + C_{13}(\Phi_3 - \Phi_1)$$

By comparison with the set of equations 6·20(2),

$$c_{11} = C_{10} + C_{12} + C_{13} \qquad c_{12} = -C_{12}$$

$$c_{22} = C_{20} + C_{12} + C_{23} \qquad c_{13} = -C_{13}$$

$$c_{33} = C_{30} + C_{13} + C_{23} \qquad c_{23} = -C_{23}$$

or

$$C_{10} = c_{11} + c_{12} + c_{13} \qquad C_{12} = -c_{12}$$

$$C_{20} = c_{22} + c_{12} + c_{23} \qquad C_{13} = -c_{13}$$

$$C_{30} = c_{33} + c_{13} + c_{23} \qquad C_{23} = -c_{23}$$

Generalizing, the capacitance from the rth conductor to ground is just the sum of the coefficient of self-capacitance and all the coefficients of induction for that conductor:

$$C_{r0} = \sum_{s=1}^{n} c_{rs} \qquad (1)$$

By the property 5 of Art. 6·20, each of these capacitances to ground is positive or zero. The mutual capacitance between element r and s is just the negative of the corresponding coefficient of induction:

$$C_{rs} = -c_{rs} \qquad (2)$$

6·22   ELECTROSTATIC SHIELDING

In electrostatic shielding between two bodies, as 1 and 3 of Fig. 6·22a, it is desired to decrease the capacity coupling between these bodies to as small a value as possible. Of course, if a new conductor 2 is intro-

Fig. 6·22a   Electrostatic shielding by a grounded sphere.

Fig. 6·22b   Partial shielding by a grounded conducting plane.

duced into the field and made to surround either body 1 or 3 completely, as in Fig. 6·22a, it is evident that a change in potential of 3 can in no way influence the charge on 1 and the mutual capacitance $C_{13} = 0$. Also, for the case pictured $C_{10} = 0$, and from Eq. 6·21(1)

$$c_{11} = -c_{12} = C_{12}$$

These characteristics are typical of cases of perfect shielding.

More often the added conductor may not completely enclose any body, so that the capacitance coupling may not be made zero, but may only be reduced from its original value. It can be shown that any finite conductor as 2 introduced into the field acts to decrease the mutual capacitance C_{13} from its value prior to the introduction of 2, and hence provides some decrease in the capacity coupling between 1 and 3 *provided 2 is grounded*. However, if 2 is insulated and C_{20} negligible, the effective capacitance between 1 and 3 is seen from the equivalent circuit of Fig. 6·20b to be given by C_{13} in parallel with C_{12} and C_{23} in series:

$$(C_{13})_{\text{eff}} = C_{13} + \frac{C_{12}C_{23}}{C_{12} + C_{23}}$$

This value is generally greater than the value of C_{13} prior to the introduction of 2 (though it need not be if 2 lies along an equipotential surface of the original field); so, if insulated, the additional conductor may act to increase the effective capacitive coupling between 1 and 3. It often happens that electrodes, although grounded for direct current, may be effectively insulated or floating at radio frequencies because of impedance in the grounding leads. In such cases the new electrodes do not accomplish their shielding purposes but may in fact increase capacity coupling.

PROBLEMS

6·22a Discuss qualitatively the case of Fig. 6·22b in which two bodies, 1 and 3, which are relatively far apart have a conducting plane brought in their vicinity. How can you prove that C_{13} is decreased when the plane is added? What happens to the effective capacity between 1 and 3 if the plane is insulated?

6·22b Suppose that the bodies 1 and 3 of Fig. 6·22b are spheres of radii a separated by a distance d with $a/d \ll 1$. If the added plane is parallel to the line joining their centers and distance b from it $(a/b \ll 1)$, find C_{13} before and after introduction of the plane, and the effective C_{13} with the plane present and insulated.

6·23   EXAMPLE: INTERELECTRODE CAPACITANCES OF TRIODE

Consider the idealized triode with plane cathode, plane anode, and a grid of parallel wires as sketched in Fig. 6·23a. With the coordinates

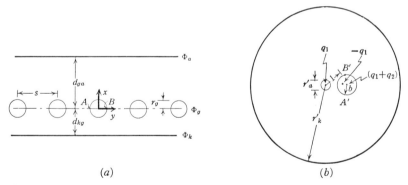

(a) (b)

Fig. 6·23   Planar triode with parallel-wire grids and its transformed figure in the Z' plane.

and dimensions as shown on the figure, this two-dimensional problem may be transformed to that of Fig. 6·23b by the complex function

$$Z' = e^{-2\pi Z/s} = e^{-2\pi x/s}e^{-j(2\pi y/s)} \tag{1}$$

In the transformed figure, the anode and cathode have become coaxial cylinders of radii r_a' and r_k', respectively, and each of the grid wires has transformed to a single nearly-circular cylindrical figure centered at $Z' = 1$. It will be assumed that r_g/s is less than about 0.2, in which case the transformed grid figure may be approximated well enough by a circle of radius b. Then, from (1),

$$r_k' = e^{2\pi d_{gk}/s} \tag{2}$$

$$r_a' = e^{-2\pi d_{ga}/s} \tag{3}$$

$$b = 2 \sin \left(\frac{\pi r_g}{s}\right) \tag{4}$$

The value of b in (4) is found by making the points A and B in the Z plane correspond to A' and B' in the Z' plane.

The problem in the Z' plane may be solved by utilizing a series of line images. Actually, for typical triode dimensions, r_k' as given by (2) is very large and r_a' from (3) is very small, so that the transformed anode may be considered a line charge and a single imaging of this in the transformed grid cylinder may be sufficient. The image is at distance $b^2/1$ from the center of the grid wire (Art. 2·21) so that the three line charges consist of q_1 at the origin, $-q_1$ at $Z' = 1 - b^2$, and $q_1 + q_2$ at $Z' = 1$. (The choice of the last value is made so that the net charge strength on the grid is q_2.) Potential is then (Art. 2·16)

$$\Phi = -\frac{1}{2\pi\epsilon} [q_1 \ln r_1 - q_1 \ln r_2 + (q_1 + q_2) \ln r_3] + C \tag{5}$$

Since r_k' is large, the potential on the cathode may be found by concentrating all charges at the axis. Since r_a' is small, potential on the anode may be found by considering only the charge q_1 on the axis. To find potential on the grid, some point such as $Z' = 1 - b$ on the grid wire is chosen:

$$\Phi_k = -\frac{1}{2\pi\epsilon} (q_1 + q_2) \ln r_k' + C \tag{6}$$

$$\Phi_a = -\frac{1}{2\pi\epsilon} q_1 \ln r_p' + C \tag{7}$$

$$\Phi_g = -\frac{1}{2\pi\epsilon} [q_1 \ln (1 - b) - q_1 \ln b (1 - b) + (q_1 + q_2) \ln b] + C$$

$$= -\frac{q_2}{2\pi\epsilon} \ln b + C \tag{8}$$

Although this is a three-conductor problem, one of the conductors may be taken as the ground provided coupling to any external ground is negligible. Let this be the cathode so that Φ_k of (6) is set equal to zero. The value of C thus determined may be substituted in (7) and (8):

$$\Phi_1 = \Phi_a = -\frac{1}{2\pi\epsilon}\left[q_1 \ln\left(\frac{r_p{'}}{r_k{'}}\right) - q_2 \ln r_k{'} \right] \tag{9}$$

$$\Phi_2 = \Phi_g = -\frac{1}{2\pi\epsilon}\left[-q_1 \ln r_k{'} + q_2 \ln\left(\frac{b}{r_k{'}}\right) \right] \tag{10}$$

By comparing (9) and (10) with the set of equations 6·20(1), the coefficients of potential for this problem may be written

$$p_{11} = \frac{1}{2\pi\epsilon} \ln\left(\frac{r_k{'}}{r_p{'}}\right) = \frac{1}{2\pi\epsilon}\left[\frac{2\pi d_{kg}}{s} + \frac{2\pi d_{ag}}{s} \right] = \frac{d_{ka}}{\epsilon s} \tag{11}$$

$$p_{12} = p_{21} = \frac{1}{2\pi\epsilon} \ln r_k{'} = \frac{d_{kg}}{\epsilon s} \tag{12}$$

$$p_{22} = \frac{1}{2\pi\epsilon} \ln\left(\frac{r_k{'}}{b}\right) = \frac{d_{kg}}{\epsilon s} - \frac{1}{2\pi\epsilon} \ln\left(2 \sin\frac{\pi r_g}{s} \right) \tag{13}$$

Then by Eq. 6·20(3) the coefficients of capacity and induction are

$$c_{11} = \frac{p_{22}}{\Delta(p_{rs})} = \frac{\dfrac{d_{kg}}{\epsilon s} - \dfrac{1}{2\pi\epsilon} \ln\left(2 \sin\dfrac{\pi r_g}{s} \right)}{\Delta(p_{rs})} \tag{14}$$

$$c_{12} = -\frac{p_{12}}{\Delta(p_{rs})} = -\frac{d_{kg}}{\epsilon s\, \Delta(p_{rs})} \tag{15}$$

$$c_{22} = \frac{p_{11}}{\Delta(p_{rs})} = \frac{d_{ka}}{\epsilon s\, \Delta(p_{rs})} \tag{16}$$

where

$$\Delta(p_{rs}) = p_{11}p_{22} - p_{12}{}^2 = \frac{d_{ka}}{\epsilon s}\left[\frac{d_{kg}}{\epsilon s} - \frac{1}{2\pi\epsilon} \ln\left(2 \sin\frac{\pi r_g}{s} \right) \right] - \left(\frac{d_{kg}}{\epsilon s} \right)^2 \tag{17}$$

Finally, the interelectrode capacitances of the equivalent circuit (recalling that the cathode is taken as the ground) are obtainable from

Eqs. 6·21(1) and (2):

$$C_{ka} = C_{10} = c_{11} + c_{12} = -\frac{\ln\left(2 \sin \frac{\pi r_g}{s}\right)}{2\pi\epsilon \, \Delta(p_{rs})} \tag{18}$$

$$C_{kg} = C_{20} = c_{22} + c_{12} = \frac{d_{ga}}{\epsilon s \, \Delta(p_{rs})} \tag{19}$$

$$C_{ga} = C_{12} = -c_{12} = \frac{d_{kg}}{\epsilon s \, \Delta(p_{rs})} \tag{20}$$

It is also of interest to note the electrostatic amplification factor of the triode (an approximation to the amplification factor defined from tube characteristics) defined as the ratio C_{kg}/C_{ka}:

$$\mu_0 = \frac{C_{kg}}{C_{ka}} = -\frac{2\pi d_{ga}}{s \ln\left(2 \sin \frac{\pi r_g}{s}\right)} \tag{21}$$

This equation is a useful approximation for reasonably large values of s/r_g, $2\pi d_{kg}/s$, and $2\pi d_{ga}/s$.

PROBLEMS

6·23a Suppose that $2\pi d_{kg}/s$ is not large enough to justify the approximation used in computing Φ_k for Eq. (6). Describe the additional image charges that should be added for a next approximation. Describe the image charges that should be added if $2\pi d_{ga}/s$ is not large enough to justify the approximation used in computing Φ_a for (7).

6·23b Repeat the problem of this article, using the transformation $Z' = e^{2\pi Z/s}$ so that the cathode transforms to the inner cylinder, the anode to the outer.

7 PROPAGATION AND REFLECTION OF ELECTROMAGNETIC WAVES

7·01 INTRODUCTION

As soon as Maxwell's equations are applied to physical systems, as in the circuits of Chapter 5, it is observed that, in general, effects from all currents and charges are characterized by a retardation or phase delay. The ideas of conventional circuit theory, which assume that the effects of currents and charges are felt instantaneously over all the circuit, are practically exact if we confine ourselves to circuits or regions small compared with wavelength. In a large portion of the problems of modern radio engineering, the discussion cannot be restricted to such small regions. A study of the fields in the region between a transmitting antenna and a receiving antenna, to mention one example, must involve a region extremely large compared with wavelength. Efficient antenna systems themselves must be at least comparable with wavelength in size. At frequencies of the order of billions of cycles per second, almost any circuit element large enough to be of practical use must .have dimensions comparable with wavelength.

The retardation effect leads directly to the regarding of electromagnetic effects as a wave phenomenon. For, when currents and charges change with time, the fields which they cause also change, but with a time delay that depends upon the choice of the distances between the point at which fields are being determined and the points at which the various charges and currents are located. Thus the effect of this change travels outward from the charges or currents with a finite velocity, depending upon the configuration of the conductors and the dielectric constant and permeability of the surrounding medium. This is much the same situation as that in the transmission lines studied in

Chapter 1, for a change in current or voltage at one point of a line is not felt instantaneously over all the line. Instead, it causes an effect which travels away from the point of change with a finite velocity, depending upon the distributed inductance and capacitance of the transmission line.

Waves propagate along a transmission line, according to the simple concepts described in Chapter 1, because a change in current in the line produces a voltage drop through the distributed inductance of the line, and a change in voltage produces a current through the distributed capacitance of the line. Similarly, now that displacement currents are included in the equations, it is apparent that a change in electric field produces a magnetic field in any dielectric medium; through Faraday's law we know that a change in magnetic field produces an electric field in any medium with finite permeability. By this analogy, such a wave propagation of electric and magnetic fields through any medium with finite permeability and dielectric constant should be expected. This analogy between transmission line waves and waves in space will be seen to be a very complete one, and it allows us to apply directly many of the concepts of energy transmission and reflection developed for transmission lines to the study of waves in general.

The reader may well ask at this point how we can bring legitimately into a discussion of retardation electromagnetics the transmission line theory outlined in Chapter 1, when that whole study was based on circuit analysis of the conventional type. It is a good question and one that will be answered when Maxwell's equations are applied to transmission lines; but first skill must be developed in the use of wave ideas to solve electromagnetic field problems.

This first chapter on wave study will be devoted to the ideas of wave propagation in unbounded media and reflection of this wave energy at discontinuities. This theory applies directly to the propagation of radio waves in space, and their reflection from dielectric, conducting, and semi-conducting objects such as the earth. It will, in addition, form the foundation for later study of waves guided or enclosed by all forms of conducting and dielectric boundaries, for it will develop pictures of all boundary condition problems. The wave concepts of this and the two following chapters, quite apart from the electromagnetics, are largely applications and extensions of those built up in the first chapter on oscillations and waves. The mathematics of these chapters consists of the solution of a single differential equation, the wave equation, subject to the initial conditions describing the manner in which the wave was originated, and the boundary conditions imposed upon it by the dielectric and conducting media.

Waves in Unbounded Regions

7·02   THE WAVE EQUATION

It has been stated that electromagnetic phenomena in free space may frequently best be regarded as wave phenomena. Now Maxwell's equations must be applied to a free dielectric to see the quantitative nature of these effects. Consider a dielectric containing no charges and with zero conductivity so that there are no conduction currents in the dielectric. The field equations are then (Art. 4·07)

$$\nabla \cdot \bar{D} = 0 \tag{1}$$

$$\nabla \cdot \bar{B} = 0 \tag{2}$$

$$\nabla \times \bar{E} = -\frac{\partial \bar{B}}{\partial t} \tag{3}$$

$$\nabla \times \bar{H} = \frac{\partial \bar{D}}{\partial t} \tag{4}$$

$$\bar{B} = \mu \bar{H} \tag{5}$$

$$\bar{D} = \epsilon \bar{E} \tag{6}$$

Notice that for completeness Eqs. (1) and (2) have been included, showing zero divergence of the fields, although they are not required if the interest is in steady state a-c components (Prob. 4·07b). If the dielectric is homogeneous, isotropic, and linear, ϵ and μ are constants and do not have space or time derivatives.

To attempt a solution of a group of simultaneous equations, it is usually a good plan to separate the various functions of space, such as $\bar{D}$ and $\bar{B}$, to arrive at equations that give the distributions of each.

First let us take the curl of (3)

$$\nabla \times \nabla \times \bar{E} = -\mu \nabla \times \frac{\partial \bar{H}}{\partial t}$$

Then, expanding,

$$\nabla(\nabla \cdot \bar{E}) - \nabla^2 \bar{E} = -\mu \nabla \times \left(\frac{\partial \bar{H}}{\partial t}\right)$$

By remembering that $\nabla \cdot \bar{E} = 0$ from (1) and that time and space partial derivatives may be taken in any order, and, obtaining $\nabla \times \bar{H}$

from (4), we find

$$-\nabla^2 \bar{E} = -\mu \frac{\partial}{\partial t} \left(\epsilon \frac{\partial \bar{E}}{\partial t} \right)$$

or

$$\nabla^2 \bar{E} = \mu \epsilon \frac{\partial^2 \bar{E}}{\partial t^2} \tag{7}$$

This is the general form of the wave equation. This form applies as well to the magnetic field, as is readily shown by taking first the curl of (4) and then substituting (2) and (3):

$$\nabla^2 \bar{H} = \mu \epsilon \frac{\partial^2 \bar{H}}{\partial t^2} \tag{8}$$

From the simple special case of space variation in one dimension only, many of the characteristics of electromagnetic waves can be found that will aid in studying more complex cases. If we take the x component of (7) and have space variations only in the z direction, the equation becomes simply

$$\frac{\partial^2 E_x}{\partial z^2} = \mu \epsilon \frac{\partial^2 E_x}{\partial t^2} \tag{9}$$

This is exactly the form of the one-dimensional wave equation studied in Chapter 1. It was shown there that the equation has a general solution of the form

$$E_x = f_1 \left(t - \frac{z}{v} \right) + f_2 \left(t + \frac{z}{v} \right) \tag{10}$$

where

$$v = \frac{1}{\sqrt{\mu \epsilon}}$$

The first term of (10) represents the wave or function f_1 traveling with velocity v and unchanging form in the positive z direction; the second term represents the wave or function f_2 traveling with velocity v and unchanging form in the negative z direction. It will be helpful to anticipate following discussions by pointing out that the commonest radio waves at some distance from the antenna and the ground are approximately of this simple form with space variations in one direction only.

For more general cases involving variations in more than one direction, the solution of the wave equation is not quite so simple, yet the general idea of waves propagating with definite velocities can always be obtained from it. Many of these more complicated cases will be treated later.

PROBLEMS

7·02a Show that the wave equation of the form of Eq. 7·02(7) or 7·02(8), applies to scalar potential Φ and vector potential $\bar{A}$ in a charge-free dielectric.

7·02b Show that the wave equation may be written directly in terms of any of the components of $\bar{H}$, $\bar{E}$, or $\bar{A}$ in rectangular coordinates, or to the axial component of $\bar{H}$, $\bar{E}$, or $\bar{A}$ in any coordinate system, but not to other components, such as radial and tangential components in cylindrical coordinates, or any component in spherical coordinates. That is,

$$\nabla^2 E_x = \mu\epsilon \frac{\partial^2 E_x}{\partial t^2} \qquad \nabla^2 H_z = \mu\epsilon \frac{\partial^2 H_z}{\partial t^2}, \text{ etc.}$$

but

$$\nabla^2 E_r \neq \mu\epsilon \frac{\partial^2 E_r}{\partial t^2} \qquad \nabla^2 H_\phi \neq \mu\epsilon \frac{\partial^2 H_\phi}{\partial t^2}, \text{ etc.}$$

7·03 POYNTING'S THEOREM FOR ENERGY RELATIONS IN AN ELECTROMAGNETIC FIELD

The simple transmission line waves studied in Chapter 1 were primarily of interest because of their ability to transfer energy from one point to another. Energy transfer may also be accomplished through more general types of electromagnetic waves, the amount of the energy depending upon the magnitudes, distribution, and phases of the electric and magnetic fields of the wave. This dependence will now be investigated.

Let us take a region in which dielectric constant and permeability may be functions of position but not of time. Maxwell's equations, written in terms of the total fields, currents, and charges of a region, describe the electromagnetic behavior of the region. The two curl equations are:

$$\nabla \times \bar{E} = -\frac{\partial \bar{B}}{\partial t} \tag{1}$$

$$\nabla \times \bar{H} = \bar{\imath} + \frac{\partial \bar{D}}{\partial t} \tag{2}$$

An equivalence of vector operations, Art. 2·39, shows that

$$\bar{H} \cdot (\nabla \times \bar{E}) - \bar{E} \cdot (\nabla \times \bar{H}) = \nabla \cdot (\bar{E} \times \bar{H}) \tag{3}$$

If products in (1) and (2) are taken as indicated by this equivalence and added,

$$-\bar{H} \cdot \frac{\partial \bar{B}}{\partial t} - \bar{E} \cdot \frac{\partial \bar{D}}{\partial t} - \bar{E} \cdot \bar{\imath} = \nabla \cdot (\bar{E} \times \bar{H}) \tag{4}$$

Note that, if ϵ is constant,

$$\frac{1}{2}\frac{\partial(\bar{D} \cdot \bar{E})}{\partial t} = \frac{1}{2}\frac{\partial(\epsilon\bar{E}^2)}{\partial t} = \bar{E} \cdot \frac{\partial\bar{D}}{\partial t}$$

Similarly,

$$\frac{1}{2}\frac{\partial(\bar{B} \cdot \bar{H})}{\partial t} = \bar{H} \cdot \frac{\partial\bar{B}}{\partial t}$$

These may be substituted in (4) and all terms integrated over the volume enclosed:

$$\int_V \left[\frac{\partial}{\partial t}\left(\frac{\bar{B} \cdot \bar{H}}{2}\right) + \frac{\partial}{\partial t}\left(\frac{\bar{D} \cdot \bar{E}}{2}\right) + \bar{E} \cdot \bar{\imath}\right] dV = -\int_V \nabla \cdot (\bar{E} \times \bar{H}) \, dV$$

From the divergence theorem, Art. 2·14, the volume integral of div $(\bar{E} \times \bar{H})$ must be the same as the surface integral of $\bar{E} \times \bar{H}$ over the surrounding surface:

$$\int_V \left[\frac{\partial}{\partial t}\left(\frac{\bar{B} \cdot \bar{H}}{2}\right) + \frac{\partial}{\partial t}\left(\frac{\bar{D} \cdot \bar{E}}{2}\right) + \bar{E} \cdot \bar{\imath}\right] dV = -\int_S (\bar{E} \times \bar{H}) \cdot d\bar{S}$$

$$(5)$$

The term $\epsilon E^2/2$ was shown (Art. 2·23) to represent the energy storage per unit volume for an electrostatic field. If this interpretation is extended by definition to any electric field,[1] the second term of (5) represents the time rate of increase of the stored energy in the electric fields of the region. Similarly, if $\mu H^2/2$ is defined as the density of energy storage for any magnetic field, the first term represents the time rate of increase of the stored energy in the magnetic fields of the region. The third term is the usual ohmic term and so represents energy dissipated in heat per unit time. (Or, if $\bar{\imath}$ is made up of a motion of free charges, $\rho\bar{v}_\rho$, $\bar{E} \cdot \rho\bar{v}_\rho$ represents the energy of acceleration given these charges; and, if there are sources, $\bar{E} \cdot \bar{\imath}$ for these sources is of opposite sign and will represent energy added by them.) All the net energy term must have been supplied externally. Thus the term on the right represents the energy flow into the volume per unit time. Changing sign, the rate of energy flow out through the enclosing surface is

$$W = \int_S \bar{P} \cdot d\bar{S} \tag{6}$$

where

$$\bar{P} = \bar{E} \times \bar{H} \tag{7}$$

[1] For an excellent discussion of the arbitrariness of these definitions, refer to J. A. Stratton, *Electromagnetic Theory*, McGraw-Hill, 1941, p. 133.

Although it is known from the proof only that total energy flow out of a region per unit time is given by the total surface integral (6), it is often convenient to think of the vector $\bar{P}$ defined by (7) as the vector giving direction and magnitude of energy flow at any point in space. Though this step does not follow strictly, it will not lead us into pitfalls for present applications.

To demonstrate the interpretation of the theorem, let us take the simple example of a round wire carrying direct current I_z (Fig. 7·03).

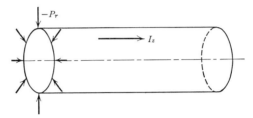

Fig. 7·03.

If R is the resistance per unit length, the electric field in the wire is known from Ohm's law to be

$$E_z = I_z R \tag{8}$$

The magnetic field at the surface, or at any radius r outside the wire, is

$$H_\phi = \frac{I_z}{2\pi r} \tag{9}$$

The Poynting vector $\bar{P} = \bar{E} \times \bar{H}$ is everywhere radial, directed toward the axis:

$$P_r = -E_z H_\phi = -\frac{R I_z{}^2}{2\pi r} \tag{10}$$

If we then make an integration over a cylindrical surface of unit length and radius equal to that of the wire, there is no flow through the ends of the cylinder since $\bar{P}$ has no component normal to the ends.   All the flow is through the cylindrical surface, giving a power flow inward of amount

$$W = 2\pi r(-P_r) = I_z{}^2 R \tag{11}$$

We know that this result does represent the correct power flow into the conductor, being dissipated in heat.   If we accept the Poynting vector as giving the correct *density* of power flow at each point, we must then picture the battery or other source of energy as setting up the electric and magnetic fields, so that the energy flows through the field and into the wire through its surface. If one happens to like this interpretation, it is fine, but the Poynting theorem cannot be considered a proof of its correctness, for it says only that the *total* power balance for a given region will be computed correctly in this manner.

It is also instructive to consider the cases for which there will be no power flow through the electromagnetic field. Accepting the above interpretation of the Poynting vector, we see that it will be zero when either $\bar{E}$ or $\bar{H}$ is zero, or when the two vectors are mutually parallel. Thus, for example, there is no power flow in the vicinity of a system of static charges which has electric field but no magnetic field. Another very important case is that of a perfect conductor which by definition must have a zero tangential component of electric field at its surface. Then $\bar{P}$ can have no component normal to the conductor and there can be no power flow through the perfect conductor.

Finally, we shall give a useful form for the average power in steady state a-c problems using the complex notation. If $\bar{E}$ and $\bar{H}$ are the complex vectors representing the electric and magnetic fields in the time-periodic case, the average Poynting vector is

$$\bar{P}_{av} = \tfrac{1}{2} \operatorname{Re} (\bar{E} \times \bar{H}^*) \tag{12}$$

The construction of this is exactly similar to that for voltage and current in Art. 1·12.

PROBLEMS

7·03a Describe the Poynting vector and discuss its interpretation for the case of a static point charge Q located at the center of a small loop of wire carrying direct current I.

7·03b Utilize the solution for electric and magnetic fields for a semi-infinite solid as given in Chapter 6 to determine the instantaneous Poynting vector at the surface. What does its average value represent? Check the average value by using the complex form (12).

7·03c Show that, if $\bar{E}$ and $\bar{H}$ are the complex multipliers of $e^{j\omega t}$, the instantaneous Poynting vector may be found as follows:

$$\bar{P} = \tfrac{1}{2} \operatorname{Re} \{(\bar{E} \times \bar{H}^*) + (\bar{E}e^{j\omega t}) \times (\bar{H}e^{j\omega t})\}$$

7·04 UNIFORM PLANE WAVES IN A PERFECT DIELECTRIC

Consider now the simple case in which there are no variations except in one direction, which we shall take as the z direction. Let us expand the curl equations of Maxwell in rectangular coordinates with x and y variations set equal to zero:

$$\nabla \times \bar{E} = -\mu \frac{\partial \bar{H}}{\partial t} \qquad\qquad \nabla \times \bar{H} = \epsilon \frac{\partial \bar{E}}{\partial t}$$

$$\frac{\partial E_y}{\partial z} = \mu \frac{\partial H_x}{\partial t} \qquad (1) \qquad\qquad \frac{\partial H_y}{\partial z} = -\epsilon \frac{\partial E_x}{\partial t} \qquad (4)$$

$$\frac{\partial E_x}{\partial z} = -\mu \frac{\partial H_y}{\partial t} \qquad (2) \qquad\qquad \frac{\partial H_x}{\partial z} = \epsilon \frac{\partial E_y}{\partial t} \qquad (5)$$

$$0 = \mu \frac{\partial H_z}{\partial t} \qquad (3) \qquad\qquad 0 = \epsilon \frac{\partial E_z}{\partial t} \qquad (6)$$

We see first from (3) and (6) that E_z and H_z must both be zero, except possibly for constant (static) parts which are not of interest to us in the wave solution.   That is, the electric and magnetic fields of this simple wave are both transverse to the direction of propagation.

Next, if (2) is differentiated with respect to z, (4) with respect to t, and the two results combined, we obtain the one-dimensional form of the wave equation in E_x as written in Eq. 7·02(9).   This is to be expected, for the specializations leading to Eq. 7·02(9) are exactly the same as in this article, though the steps of the derivation are somewhat different.   Then the solution is as in Eq. 7·02(10) and represents a wave traveling with velocity v in the positive z direction and another traveling with the same velocity in the negative z direction.

$$v = \frac{1}{\sqrt{\mu\epsilon}} \quad \text{meters/sec} \qquad (7)$$

For free space,

$$v_0 = \frac{1}{\sqrt{\mu_0\epsilon_0}} \approx 3 \times 10^8 \quad \text{meters/sec} \qquad (8)$$

which is the approximate value of the velocity of light.

Let us concentrate for the moment on the positively traveling component of E_x:

$$E_x{}^+ = f_1\left(t - \frac{z}{v}\right) \qquad (9)$$

From (2) we may find a relation for H_y in the positive wave:

$$\frac{\partial H_y{}^+}{\partial t} = -\frac{1}{\mu} \frac{\partial E_x{}^+}{\partial z} = \sqrt{\frac{\epsilon}{\mu}} f_1'\left(t - \frac{z}{v}\right)$$

Integrating, and again ignoring static constants of integration,

$$H_y{}^+ = \sqrt{\frac{\epsilon}{\mu}} f_1 \left(t - \frac{z}{v} \right) = \frac{E_x{}^+}{\eta} \tag{10}$$

where

$$\eta = \sqrt{\frac{\mu}{\epsilon}} \tag{11}$$

The quantity η is thus seen to be the ratio of E_x to H_y in a single traveling wave of this simple type, and as defined by (11) it may also be considered a constant of the medium, and will be a useful parameter in the analysis of more complicated waves.   It has dimensions of ohms and is known as the *intrinsic impedance* of the medium.   For free space,

$$\eta_0 = \sqrt{\frac{\mu_0}{\epsilon_0}} \approx 120\pi \approx 377 \quad \text{ohms} \tag{12}$$

If we start with the one-dimensional wave equation in E_y and utilize (1), we find that H_x for the positive wave is just $-E_y/\eta$.   Combining this result with (10), we may write

$$\frac{E_x{}^+}{H_y{}^+} = - \frac{E_y{}^+}{H_x{}^+} = \eta \tag{13}$$

Similarly, repeating the steps for a negatively traveling wave,

$$\frac{E_x{}^-}{H_y{}^-} = - \frac{E_y{}^-}{H_x{}^-} = -\eta \tag{14}$$

These results show a number of things.   First, relations (13) and (14) are sufficient to require that $\bar{E}$ and $\bar{H}$ shall be perpendicular to one another in each of the traveling waves.   They also require that the value of E at any instant must be η times the value of H at that instant, for each wave.   Finally we note that, if $\bar{E} \times \bar{H}$ is formed, it points in the positive z direction from (13), and in the negative z direction from (14), or in the direction of travel for each wave.   These relations are indicated for a positively traveling wave in Fig. 7·04.

The energy relations are also of interest.   The stored energy in electric fields per unit volume is

$$U_E = \frac{\epsilon E^2}{2} = \frac{\epsilon}{2} (E_x{}^2 + E_y{}^2) \tag{15}$$

and that in magnetic fields is

$$U_H = \frac{\mu H^2}{2} = \frac{\mu}{2} (H_x{}^2 + H_y{}^2) \tag{16}$$

By (13) or (14), U_E and U_H are equal, so the energy density at each point at each instant is equally divided between electric and magnetic energy. The Poynting vector for the positive traveling wave is

$$P_z{}^+ = E_x{}^+H_y{}^+ - E_y{}^+H_x{}^+ = \frac{1}{\eta}(E_x{}^{+2} + E_y{}^{+2}) \tag{17}$$

and is always in the positive z direction except at particular planes where it may be zero for a given instant. Similarly, the Poynting vector for the negatively traveling wave is always in the negative z direction except where it is zero. The time-average value of the Poynting vector must be the same for all planes along the wave since no energy can be dissipated in the perfect dielectric, but the instantaneous values may be different at two different planes, depending upon whether or not there is a net instantaneous rate of increase or decrease in the stored energy between those planes.

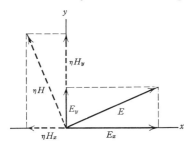

Fig. 7·04 Relations between E and H for a wave propagating in positive z direction (out of paper).

To summarize the properties for a single wave of this simple type, which may be described as a *uniform plane wave*,

1. Velocity of propagation, $v = 1/\sqrt{\mu\epsilon}$.

2. No electric or magnetic field in direction of propagation.

3. Electric field normal to magnetic field.

4. Value of electric field η times that of magnetic field at each instant.

5. Direction of propagation given by direction of $\bar{E} \times \bar{H}$.

6. Energy stored in electric field per unit volume at any instant and any point is equal to energy stored in magnetic field per unit volume at that instant and that point.

7. Instantaneous value of Poynting vector given by $E^2/\eta = \eta H^2$, where E and H are the instantaneous values of total electric and magnetic field strengths.

PROBLEMS

7·04a Draw a sketch similar to Fig. 7·04 demonstrating the relations in a negatively traveling wave.

7·04b A step-function uniform plane wave is generated by suddenly impressing a constant electric field $E_x = C$ at $z = 0$ at time $t = 0$ and maintaining it thereafter. A perfectly conducting plane is placed normal to the z direction at $z = 600$ meters. Sketch total E_x and ηH_y versus z at $t = 1$ microsec and at $t = 3$ microsec.

7·05 UNIFORM PLANE WAVES OF SINUSOIDAL FORM

Although it is of interest to know the characteristics of uniform plane waves having arbitrary functions of time as in the last article, the most important cases in radio engineering are those having to do with steady state sinusoids of a single frequency. If the function of time is represented in the complex notation by $e^{j\omega t}$, the form for positively and negatively traveling wave may be written

$$E_x = E e^{j\omega\left(t-\frac{z}{v}\right)} + E' e^{j\omega\left(t+\frac{z}{v}\right)} \tag{1}$$

or, with the factor $e^{j\omega t}$ understood,

$$E_x = E e^{-jkz} + E' e^{jkz} \tag{2}$$

where

$$k = \frac{\omega}{v} = \omega \sqrt{\mu\epsilon} \quad \text{meters}^{-1} \tag{3}$$

This constant is the phase constant for the uniform plane wave, since by (2) it gives the change in phase per unit length for each wave component. It may also be considered a constant of the medium at a particular frequency defined by (3), known as the *wave number*, and will be found useful in the analysis of all waves, as will be seen.

The value of H_y may be found from (2) and the relations of the preceding article:

$$\eta H_y = E e^{-jkz} - E' e^{jkz} \tag{4}$$

Similar expressions may be written for E_y and ηH_x. If the instantaneous value of E_x is desired, the real part of (1) is taken (Art. 4·09), and if the instantaneous value of H_y is desired, $e^{j\omega t}$ must be put back in (4) and the real part taken. Most often these instantaneous values are not required.

The *wavelength* is defined as the distance the wave propagates in one period. It is then the value of z which causes the phase factor to change by 2π:

$$k\lambda = 2\pi \qquad \text{or} \qquad k = \frac{2\pi}{\lambda} \tag{5}$$

or

$$\lambda = \frac{2\pi}{\omega \sqrt{\mu\epsilon}} = \frac{v}{f} \tag{6}$$

This is the common relation between wavelength, phase velocity, and frequency. The *free-space wavelength* is obtained by using the velocity of light in free space in (6) and is frequently used at the higher frequencies as an alternative to giving the frequency.

It is also of interest to note the average value of the Poynting vector in this case. From Eq. 7·03(12),

$$(P_z)_{\mathrm{av}} = \frac{1}{2} \operatorname{Re}\,(E_x H_y{}^* - E_y H_x{}^*) = \frac{1}{2\eta}\,(E_x{}^2 + E_y{}^2) = \frac{1}{2\eta}\,|\,E\,|^2 \quad (7)$$

where $|\,E\,|$ is the peak magnitude of the sinusoidal electric field vector. Relation (7) could also be deduced directly from the facts that E and H are everywhere at right angles and in time phase and that the average value of a $\sin^2$ term is $\frac{1}{2}$.

7·06 POLARIZATION

Since the wave equation is a linear equation any solution to it may be built up as the sum of other solutions. Many complex electromagnetic wave distributions might, if desired, be considered as made up of a large number of the simple plane waves with different magnitudes, phases, and directions of propagation. For most purposes this viewpoint is of little value except as a concept, and other methods to be given later will serve better for actual analysis. However, if we are studying the important practical case where a combination of plane waves exists such that all have the same direction of propagation, there is a definite advantage in considering these as a superposition of the individual plane waves and analyzing by obtaining the behavior of each individual wave. The orientations of the field vectors in these waves are often described by the *polarization* of the wave. In this discussion we are primarily concerned with sinusoidal waves of the same frequency.

For a single uniform plane wave, it has been seen that electric and magnetic field.vectors are always at right angles and always maintain their respective orientations at every point along the wave. A combination of plane waves all propagating in the same direction, with arbitrary orientations of the field vectors, arbitrary magnitudes, and random phases is called an *unpolarized* wave (Fig. 7·06a).

If the electric field vector of the wave lies always in a given direction, the wave is said to be *plane polarized* (or, sometimes, *linearly polarized*). This condition results when all the superposed waves have electric field in the same direction, or if they are in different directions but of exactly the same phase (Fig. 7·04). In radio engineering, it is common to describe the polarization by the plane of the electric vector, so that a case as described in Figs. 7·06b,c would be described as *vertical* and *horizontal polarization*, respectively.   In optics the convention utilizes the magnetic field to define the plane of polarization, but in either case it is best to avoid ambiguity by specifying explicitly, as "polarized with electric field in the vertical plane."

If there is a combination of two uniform plane waves of the same frequency, but of different phases, magnitudes, and orientations of the field vectors, the resultant combination is said to be an *elliptically polarized* wave.   To see the reason for this, we may first break each wave into its two separate component waves, one with electric vector in the x direction, the other with electric vector in the y direction. The two x components add to produce a wave of given magnitude and

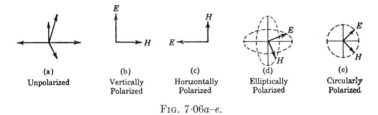

(a)	(b)	(c)	(d)	(e)
Unpolarized	Vertically Polarized	Horizontally Polarized	Elliptically Polarized	Circularly Polarized

Fig. 7·06a–e.

phase angle.   This will be written for this study directly in terms of cosines rather than in the exponential or complex form:

$$E_x = E_1 \cos \omega \left(t - \frac{z}{v} \right) \tag{1}$$

The two y components add to produce a wave of different magnitude and phase angle.

$$E_y = E_2 \cos \left[\omega \left(t - \frac{z}{v} \right) + \psi \right] \tag{2}$$

In any given plane, say $z = 0$, these reduce to equations of the form

$$E_x = E_1 \cos \omega t$$
$$E_y = E_2 \cos (\omega t + \psi) \tag{3}$$

These are the parametric equations for an ellipse.   The terminus of the electric field vector then traces an elliptic path in a plane normal to the direction of propagation.   This is the reason for the name elliptic polarization (Fig. 7·06d).

If the two waves above combine so that total x and y components are equal and 90° out of time phase, the ellipse reduces to a circle, and the wave is said to be *circularly polarized.* Thus, if

$$\psi = \pm \frac{\pi}{2} \quad \text{and} \quad E_1 = E_2$$

$$E_x{}^2 + E_y{}^2 = E_1{}^2 \tag{4}$$

which is the equation of a circle (Fig. 7·06e). The instantaneous angle α between the electric vector and the x axis can be found simply (Fig. 7·06f):

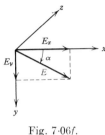

$$\alpha = \tan^{-1}\frac{E_y}{E_x} = \tan^{-1}\left[\frac{\mp E_1 \sin \omega t}{E_1 \cos \omega t}\right] = \mp \omega t \tag{5}$$

Thus the vector is seen to rotate at a uniform rate with angular velocity equal to $2\pi f$. It rotates in a clockwise sense, looking in the direction of propagation, if ψ is $-\pi/2$, and in a counterclockwise sense if ψ is $+\pi/2$. The former

Fig. 7·06f.

is said to be *right-hand* circular polarization, and the latter is called *left-hand* circular polarization.

PROBLEMS

7·06a   Show that any arbitrary elliptically polarized wave may be broken up into right-hand and left-hand circularly polarized components instead of the two plane-polarized components.

7·06b   Write the expressions corresponding to (1) and (2) in complex notation. Show that the general representation for an elliptically polarized wave in complex notation may then be written

$$\bar{E} = (\bar{E}_a + j\bar{E}_b)e^{-jkz}$$

where $\bar{E}_a$ and $\bar{E}_b$ are two real vectors, not in general mutually perpendicular. Relate $\bar{E}_a$ and $\bar{E}_b$ to E_1, E_2, and ψ.

7·06c   Starting with the general complex representation for $\bar{E}$ of Prob. *b*, use Maxwell's equations to obtain the corresponding form for $\bar{H}$.

7·06d   Sketch the locus of the vector for $E_1 = 1$, $E_2 = \frac{1}{2}$, and $\psi = \pi/2$; also for $E_1 = E_2 = 1$ and $\psi = \pi/4$.

Reflection of Waves from Conductors and Dielectrics

7·07   REFLECTION OF NORMALLY INCIDENT PLANE WAVES FROM PERFECT CONDUCTORS

If a single-frequency uniform plane wave is normally incident on a plane perfect conductor located at $z = 0$, we know that there must be some reflected wave in addition to the incident wave. One reason for this is that the boundary conditions cannot be satisfied by a single one of the traveling wave solutions, but will require just enough of the two so that the resultant electric field at the conductor surface will be zero for all time. From another point of view, we would expect the reflected wave since we know that energy cannot pass the perfect conductor from the Poynting theorem. Hence all energy brought by the incident wave must be returned in a reflected wave. In this simple case the incident and reflected waves·are of equal amplitudes, and together form a standing wave pattern whose properties will now be studied.

For a single plane wave, select the orientation of axes so that total electric field lies in the x direction and include waves traveling in both

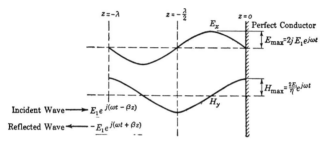

Fig. 7·07   Reflection of a uniform plane wave from a perfect conductor.

the positive and negative z directions (Fig. 7·07):

$$E_x = E e^{j(\omega t - \beta z)} + E' e^{j(\omega t + \beta z)}$$

If $E_x = 0$ at $z = 0$ for all values of time, $E' = -E$.

$$E_x = E(e^{-j\beta z} - e^{j\beta z})e^{j\omega t}$$

but

$$e^{jx} = \cos x + j \sin x$$

So

$$E_x = -2jE \sin \beta z \, e^{j\omega t} \tag{1}$$

The relation of the magnetic field to the electric field for the incident and reflected waves is given by Eqs. 7·04(13) and (14). Hence,

$$H_y = \left(\frac{E}{\eta} e^{j(\omega t - \beta z)} - \frac{E'}{\eta} e^{j(\omega t + \beta z)} \right)$$

$$= \frac{E}{\eta} (e^{-j\beta z} + e^{j\beta z})e^{j\omega t}$$

$$= \frac{2E}{\eta} \cos \beta z \, e^{j\omega t} \tag{2}$$

Equations (1) and (2) state that, although total electric and magnetic fields for the combination of incident and reflected waves are still mutually perpendicular in space and related in magnitude by η, they are now in time quadrature. The pattern is a standing wave pattern since a zero of electric field is always at the conductor surface, and also always at $\beta z = -n\pi$ or $z = -n\lambda/2$. Magnetic field has a maximum at the conductor surface, and there are other maxima each time there are zeros of electric field. Similarly, zeros of magnetic field and maxima of electric field are at $\beta z = (2n + 1)\pi/2$, or $z = -(2n + 1)\lambda/4$. This situation is sketched in Fig. 7.07, which shows a typical standing wave pattern such as was found for the shorted transmission line in Chapter 1. At an instant in time, occurring twice each cycle, all the energy of the line is in the magnetic field; 90° later the energy is stored entirely in the electric field. The *average* value of Poynting vector is zero at every cross-sectional plane; this emphasizes the fact that on the average as much energy is carried away by the reflected wave as is brought by the incident wave.

PROBLEM

7·07   Write expressions for the instantaneous values of E_x, H_y, and the Poynting vector P_z. Evaluate the instantaneous stored energy in electric fields and in magnetic fields for a region extending from $z = -\lambda/4$ to $z = 0$. Note that the sum of these two energies is constant.

7·08   TRANSMISSION LINE ANALOGY OF WAVE PROPAGATION; THE IMPEDANCE CONCEPT

In the above problem of wave reflections from a perfect conductor, we found all the properties previously studied for standing waves on an ideal transmission line. The analogy between the plane wave solutions and the waves along an ideal line is in fact an exact and complete one. It is desirable to make use of this whether one starts with a study of classic transmission line theory and then undertakes the solution of wave problems, or proceeds in the reverse order. In either case the algebraic steps worked out for the solution of one system need not be repeated in analyzing the other; any graphical aids (such as the Smith transmission line chart) developed for one may be used for the other; any experimental techniques applicable to one system will in general have their counterparts in the other system. We wish now to show the basis for this analogy.

Let us write side by side the equations for the field components in positively and negatively traveling uniform plane waves and the corresponding expressions found in Chapter 1 for an ideal transmission line.

For simplicity we orient the axes so that the wave has E_x and H_y components only:

$$E_x(z) = Ee^{-jkz} + E'e^{jkz} \qquad (1) \qquad V(z) = Ve^{-j\beta z} + V'e^{j\beta z} \qquad (5)$$

$$H_y(z) = \frac{1}{\eta}[Ee^{-jkz} - E'e^{jkz}] \quad (2) \qquad I(z) = \frac{1}{Z_0}[Ve^{-j\beta z} - V'e^{j\beta z}] \quad (6)$$

$$k = \omega\sqrt{\mu\epsilon} \qquad (3) \qquad\qquad \beta = \omega\sqrt{LC} \qquad (7)$$

$$\eta = \sqrt{\frac{\mu}{\epsilon}} \qquad (4) \qquad\qquad Z_0 = \sqrt{\frac{L}{C}} \qquad (8)$$

We see that, if in the field equations we replace E_x by voltage V, H_y by current I, permeability μ by inductance per unit length L, and dielectric constant ϵ by capacitance per unit length C, we get exactly the transmission line equations (5) to (8). To complete the analogy, we must consider the continuity conditions at a discontinuity between two regions. For the boundary between two dielectrics, we know that total tangential electric and magnetic field components must be continuous across this boundary. For the case of normal incidence (other cases will be considered separately later), E_x and H_y are the tangential components, so these continuity conditions are in direct correspondence to those of transmission lines which require that total voltage and current be continuous at the junction between two transmission lines.

In order to exploit this analogy fully, it is desirable to consider the ratio of electric to magnetic fields in the wave analysis, analogous to the ratio of voltage to current which is called impedance and used so extensively in the transmission line analysis. It is of course a good idea to use ratios such as this in the analysis, quite apart from the transmission line analogy or the name given these ratios, but in this case it will be especially useful to make the identification with impedance because of the large body of technique existing under the heading of "impedance matching" in transmission lines, most of which may be applied to problems in plane wave reflections. Credit for properly evaluating the importance of the wave impedance concept to engineers and making its use clear belongs to S. A. Schelkunoff.[2]

At any plane z, we shall define the field or wave impedance as the ratio of total electric field to total magnetic field at that plane:

$$Z(z) = \frac{E_x(z)}{H_y(z)} \qquad (9)$$

[2] See, for instance, *Bell Sys. Tech. J.*, **17**, 17–48 (Jan. 1938).

For a single positively traveling wave this ratio is η at all planes, so that η, which has been called the intrinsic impedance of the medium, might also be thought of as a *characteristic wave impedance* for uniform plane waves.   For a single negatively traveling wave the ratio (9) is $-\eta$ for all z.   For combinations of positively and negatively traveling waves, it will vary with z.   The input value Z_i distance l in front of a plane at which the "load" value of this ratio is given as Z_L may be found from the corresponding transmission line formula, Eq. 1·21(10), taking advantage of the exact analogy.   The intervening dielectric has intrinsic impedance η:

$$Z_i = \eta \left[\frac{Z_L \cos kl + j\eta \sin kl}{\eta \cos kl + jZ_L \sin kl} \right] \tag{10}$$

It may be argued that in wave problems one is primarily concerned with reflections and not with impedances directly.   This is true, but as in the transmission line case there is a one-to-one correspondence between reflection coefficient and impedance mismatch ratio.   The analogy may again be invoked to adapt Eqs. 1·19(4) and (5) to give the reflection and transmission coefficients for a dielectric medium of intrinsic impedance η when it is terminated with some known load value of field impedance Z_L:

$$\rho = \frac{E_x^-}{E_x^+} = \frac{Z_L - \eta}{Z_L + \eta} \tag{11}$$

$$\tau = \frac{E_{x2}}{E_{x1}^+} = \frac{2Z_L}{Z_L + \eta} \tag{12}$$

We see from this that there is no reflection when $Z_L = \eta$ (i.e., when impedances are matched).   There is complete reflection, $|\rho| = 1$, when Z_L is zero, infinity, or is purely imaginary (reactive).   Other important uses of formulas (10) and (11) will follow in succeeding articles.

PROBLEMS

7·08a   Obtain the expression for the field impedance for any point z to the left of the conducting plane in Art. 7·07.

7·08b   Write the formulas for a uniform plane wave with E_y and H_x only, and give the correspondence to voltage and current in the transmission line equations.

7·09   NORMAL INCIDENCE ON A PERFECT DIELECTRIC

If a uniform plane wave is normally incident on a single dielectric boundary from a medium with $\sqrt{\mu_1/\epsilon_1} = \eta_1$ to one with $\sqrt{\mu_2/\epsilon_2} = \eta_2$, the wave reflection and transmission may be found from the concepts and equations of the last article. Select the direction of the electric field as the x axis, and the direction of propagation of the incident wave as the positive z direction, with the boundary at $z = 0$ (Fig. 7·09a). The medium to the right is assumed to be effectively infinite in extent, so that there is no reflected wave in that region. The field impedance there is then just the intrinsic impedance η_2 for all planes, and in particular this becomes the known load impedance at the plane

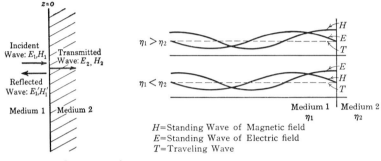

Fig. 7·09a Reflection and transmission at a plane boundary between two media.

H=Standing Wave of Magnetic field
E=Standing Wave of Electric field
T=Traveling Wave

Fig. 7·09b.

$z = 0$. Applying Eq. 7·08(11) to give the reflection coefficient for medium 1 referred to $z = 0$,

$$\rho = \frac{E_{x1}'}{E_{x1}} = -\frac{H_{y1}'}{H_{y1}} = \frac{\eta_2 - \eta_1}{\eta_2 + \eta_1} \tag{1}$$

The transmission coefficient giving the amplitude of transmitted wave into the second dielectric, from Eq. 7·08(12), is·

$$\frac{E_{x2}}{E_{x1}} = \frac{\eta_2}{\eta_1}\frac{H_{y2}}{H_{y1}} = \frac{2\eta_2}{\eta_2 + \eta_1} \tag{2}$$

From (1), we see that there is no reflection if there is a match of impedances, $\eta_1 = \eta_2$. This would of course occur for the trivial case of identical dielectrics, but also for the case of different dielectrics if they could be made with the same *ratio* of μ to ϵ. This latter case is not of practical importance since we do not commonly find high-frequency dielectric materials with permeability different from that of free space, but it is interesting since we might not intuitively expect a reflectionless transmission in going from free space to a dielectric with both dielectric constant and permeability increased by, say, ten times.

In the general case there will be a finite value of reflection in the first region, and from (1) we can show that the magnitude of ρ is always less than unity. (It approaches unity as η_2/η_1 approaches zero or infinity.) The reflected wave could then be combined with a part of the incident wave of equal amplitude to form a standing wave pattern as in the case of complete reflection studied in Art. 7·07. The remaining part of the incident wave could then be thought of as a traveling wave carrying the energy that passes on into the second medium. The combination of the traveling and standing wave parts then produces a space pattern with maxima and minima, but with the minima not zero in general. As in the corresponding transmission line case, it is convenient to express the ratio of a-c amplitude at the electric field maximum to the minimum a-c amplitude (occurring a quarter-wavelength away) as a standing wave ratio S:

$$S = \frac{\left| E_x(z) \right|_{\max}}{\left| E_x(z) \right|_{\min}} = \frac{1 + \left| \rho \right|}{1 - \left| \rho \right|} \tag{3}$$

By utilizing (1), it may be shown for this case that

$$S = \begin{cases} \eta_2/\eta_1 & \text{if} \quad \eta_2 > \eta_1 \\ \eta_1/\eta_2 & \text{if} \quad \eta_1 > \eta_2 \end{cases} \tag{4}$$

Since η_1 and η_2 are both real for perfect dielectrics, ρ is real and the plane $z = 0$ must be a position of a maximum or minimum. It is a maximum of electric field if ρ is positive, since reflected and incident waves then add, so it is a maximum of electric field and minimum of magnetic field if $\eta_2 > \eta_1$. The plane $z = 0$ is a minimum of electric field and a maximum of magnetic field if $\eta_1 > \eta_2$. These two cases are sketched in Fig. 7·09b.

PROBLEMS

7·09a Write the total electric field and total magnetic field for $z < 0$ and for $z > 0$ for the case of reflection from a single dielectric boundary as studied above.

7·09b For a certain dielectric material of effectively infinite depth, reflections of an incident plane wave from free space are observed to produce a standing wave ratio of 2.7 in the free space. The face is an electric field minimum. Find the dielectric constant.

7·10 REFLECTION PROBLEMS WITH SEVERAL DIELECTRICS

We shall next be interested in considering the case of several parallel dielectric discontinuities with a uniform plane wave incident in some material to the left, as pictured in the case for three dielectric materials in Fig. 7·10. One might at first be tempted to treat the problem by considering a series of wave reflections, the incident wave breaking into one part reflected and one part transmitted at the first plane; of the part transmitted into region 2 some is transmitted at the second plane and some is reflected back toward the first plane; of the latter part some is transmitted and some reflected, and so on through an infinite series of wave reflections. This lengthy procedure can be avoided by considering total quantities at each stage of the discussion, and again the impedance formulation is useful in writing down the solution.

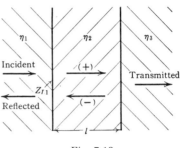

Fig. 7·10.

If the region to the right has only a single outwardly propagating wave, the wave or field impedance at any plane in this medium is η_3, which then becomes the load impedance to place at $z = l$. The input impedance for region 2 is then given at once by Eq. 7·08(10), and, since this is the impedance at $z = 0$, it may also be considered the load impedance for region 1:

$$Z_{L1} = Z_{i2} = \eta_2 \left[\frac{\eta_3 \cos k_2 l + j\eta_2 \sin k_2 l}{\eta_2 \cos k_2 l + j\eta_3 \sin k_2 l} \right] \tag{1}$$

The reflection coefficient in region 1, referred to $z = 0$, is given by Eq. 7·08(11):

$$\rho = \frac{Z_{L1} - \eta_1}{Z_{L1} + \eta_1} \tag{2}$$

In such problems we are often most interested in the ratio of power in the reflected wave to that in the incident wave, and this ratio is given by the square of the magnitude of (2), as can be shown by considering the Poynting vectors:

$$\frac{P_z^-}{P_z^+} = |\rho|^2 \tag{3}$$

If there are more than the two parallel dielectric boundaries, the process is simply repeated, the input impedance for one region becoming the load value for the next, until one arrives at the region in which reflection is to be computed. It is of course desirable in many cases to utilize the Smith chart described in Art. 1·23 in place of (1) to transform load to input impedances, and to compute reflection coefficient or standing wave ratio once the impedance mismatch ratio is known, just as the chart is used in transmission line calculations.

We now wish to consider several special cases which are of importance.

A. *Half-Wave Dielectric Window.* If the input and output dielectrics are the same in Fig. 7·10, $\eta_1 = \eta_3$, and the intervening dielectric window is some multiple of a half-wavelength referred to medium 2, $k_2 l = m\pi$, (1) gives

$$Z_{L1} = \eta_3 = \eta_1$$

and from (2)

$$\rho = 0 \tag{4}$$

Hence, there is no reflection from such a window since the impedance seen at the input face is the same as that at the output.

B. *Electrically Thin Window.* If $\eta_1 = \eta_3$ and $k_2 l$ is so small compared with unity that all powers higher than the first may be neglected, (1) becomes to this approximation

$$Z_{L1} \approx \eta_2 \left[\frac{\eta_1 + j\eta_2 k_2 l}{\eta_2 + j\eta_1 k_2 l} \right] \approx \eta_1 \left[1 + jk_2 l \left(\frac{\eta_2}{\eta_1} - \frac{\eta_1}{\eta_2} \right) \right]$$

Substituting in (2),

$$\rho \approx j \frac{k_2 l}{2} \left(\frac{\eta_2}{\eta_1} - \frac{\eta_1}{\eta_2} \right) \tag{5}$$

The magnitude of reflection coefficient is thus proportional to the electrical length of the dielectric window for small values of $k_2 l$; and the fraction of incident power reflected is then proportional to the square of this length.

C. *Quarter-Wave Coating for Eliminating Reflections.* Another important case is that of a quarter-wave coating placed between two different dielectrics. If its intrinsic impedance is the geometric mean of those on the two sides, it will eliminate all wave reflections for energy passing from the first medium into the third. To show this, let

$$k_2 l = \frac{\pi}{2} \qquad \eta_2 = \sqrt{\eta_1 \eta_3} \tag{6}$$

From (1),

$$Z_{L1} = \frac{\eta_2^{\,2}}{\eta_3} = \frac{\eta_1 \eta_3}{\eta_3} = \eta_1$$

and from (2)

$$\rho = 0 \tag{7}$$

This technique is used, for example, in coating optical lenses to decrease the amount of reflected light, and is exactly analogous to the technique of matching transmission lines of different characteristic impedances by introducing a quarter-wave section having characteristic impedance the geometric mean of those on the two sides.   In all cases the matching is perfect only at specific frequencies for which the length is an odd multiple of a quarter wave, but is approximately correct for bands of frequencies about these values.

PROBLEMS

7·10a   Calculate the reflection coefficient and per cent of incident energy reflected, when a uniform plane wave is normally incident on a Plexiglas radome (dielectric window) of thickness $\frac{3}{8}$ in., dielectric constant $\epsilon' = 2.8$, with free space on both sides.   Frequency corresponds to free-space wavelength of 20 cm.   Repeat for 10 cm; for 3 cm.

7·10b   For a sandwich-type radome consisting of two identical thin sheets (thickness 1.5 mm, dielectric constant $\epsilon' = 4$) on either side of a thicker foam-type dielectric (thickness 1.81 cm, dielectric constant $\epsilon' = 1.1$), calculate the reflection coefficient for waves striking at normal incidence.   Take frequency 3×10^9 cps; repeat for 6×10^9 cps.   *Suggestion:* Use the Smith chart of Art. 1·23.

7·10c   A quarter-wave matching coating is designed to eliminate reflections for waves of frequency 3000 mc/sec passing normally from space into the body of a material with relative dielectric constant 16.   Find the thickness of the coating and its dielectric constant.   Plot a curve showing percentage of incident energy reflected as a function of frequency for normally incident waves of frequencies in the range 1000 mc/sec to 6000 mc/sec.

7·11   INCIDENCE AT ANY ANGLE ON PERFECT CONDUCTORS

We now wish to remove the restriction to normal incidence which has been assumed in all the preceding examples.   It is possible and desirable to extend the impedance concept to apply to this case also, but before doing this we shall consider the reflection of uniform plane waves at arbitrary incidence from a perfect conductor in order to develop certain ideas of the behavior at oblique incidence.   It is also convenient to separate the discussion into two cases, polarization with electric field in the plane of incidence, and normal to the plane of incidence.   Other cases may be considered a superposition of these two.   The plane of incidence is defined by a normal to the surface on which the wave impinges, and a ray following the direction of propagation of the incident wave.   That is, it is the plane of the paper as we have drawn sketches in this chapter.

A. Polarization with Electric Field in the Plane of Incidence.   In Fig. 7·11a the ray drawn normal to the incident wave front makes an angle θ with the normal to the conductor.   We know that, since energy cannot pass the perfect conductor, there must be some reflected wave, and we draw its direction of propagation at some unknown angle θ'. The electric and magnetic fields of both incident and reflected wave must lie perpendicular to their respective directions of propagation by the properties of uniform plane waves (Art. 7·04), so the electric fields may be drawn as shown by $\bar{E}$ and $\bar{E}'$.   The corresponding magnetic fields $\bar{H}$ and $\bar{H}'$ are then both normally out of the paper, so that $\bar{E} \times \bar{H}$ will give the direction of propagation for each wave.   Moreover, with the senses as shown,

$$\frac{E}{H} = \frac{E'}{H'} = \eta \tag{1}$$

If we draw a ζ direction in the actual direction of propagation for the incident wave as shown, and a ζ' direction so that the reflected

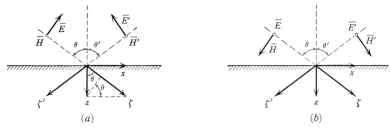

Fig. 7·11.

wave is traveling in the negative ζ' direction, we know that the phase factors for the two waves may be written as $e^{-jk\zeta}$ and $e^{jk\zeta'}$, respectively. The sum of incident and reflected waves at any point $x,z(z < 0)$ could be written

$$\bar{E}(x,z) = \bar{E}e^{-jk\zeta} + \bar{E}'e^{jk\zeta'} \tag{2}$$

where $\bar{E}$ and $\bar{E}'$ are reference values at the origin.   We wish, however, to express all coordinates in terms of the rectangular system aligned with the conductor surface.   The conversion of ζ and ζ' from the diagram is

$$\zeta = x \sin \theta + z \cos \theta \tag{3}$$

$$\zeta' = -x \sin \theta' + z \cos \theta' \tag{4}$$

so that, if these are substituted in the phase factors of (2), and the two waves broken into their x and z components, we have

$$E_x(x,z) = E \cos \theta e^{-jk(x \sin \theta + z \cos \theta)} - E' \cos \theta' e^{jk(-x \sin \theta' + z \cos \theta')} \tag{5}$$

$$E_z(x,z) = E \sin \theta e^{-jk(x \sin \theta + z \cos \theta)} + E' \sin \theta' e^{jk(-x \sin \theta' + z \cos \theta')} \tag{6}$$

The magnetic field in the two waves is

$$H_y(x,z) = He^{-jk(x \sin \theta + z \cos \theta)} + H'e^{jk(-x \sin \theta' + z \cos \theta')} \tag{7}$$

The next step is the application of the boundary condition of the perfect conductor, which is that, at $z = 0$, E_x must be zero for all x. From (5),

$$E_x(x,0) = E \cos \theta e^{-jkx \sin \theta} - E' \cos \theta' e^{-jkx \sin \theta'} = 0 \tag{8}$$

This equation can be satisfied for all x only if the phase factors in the two terms are equal, and this in turn requires that

$$\theta = \theta' \tag{9}$$

That is, *the angle of reflection is equal to the angle of incidence.* With this result in (8), it follows that the two amplitudes must be equal:

$$E = E' \tag{10}$$

If the results (9) and (10) are substituted in (5), (6), and (7), we have the final expressions for field components at any point $z < 0$:

$$E_x(x,z) = -2jE \cos \theta \sin (kz \cos \theta)e^{-jkx \sin \theta} \tag{11}$$

$$E_z(x,z) = 2E \sin \theta \cos (kz \cos \theta)e^{-jkx \sin \theta} \tag{12}$$

$$\eta H_y(x,z) = 2E \cos (kz \cos \theta)e^{-jkx \sin \theta} \tag{13}$$

The above field has the character of a traveling wave with respect to the x direction, but that of a standing wave with respect to the z direction. That is, E_x is zero for all time at the conducting plane, and also in parallel planes distance nd in front of the conductor, where

$$d = \frac{\lambda_1}{2 \cos \theta} = \frac{1}{2f \sqrt{\mu \epsilon} \cos \theta} \tag{14}$$

The a-c amplitude of E_x is a maximum in planes an odd multiple of $d/2$ in front of the conductor. H_y and E_z are maximum where E_x is zero, are zero where E_x is maximum, and are everywhere 90° out of time phase with respect to E_x. Perhaps the most interesting result from this analysis is that the distance between successive maxima and minima, measured normal to the plane, becomes *greater* as the incidence becomes more oblique. A superficial survey of the situation might lead one to believe that they would be at projections of the wavelength in this direction, which would become smaller with increasing θ. This point will be pursued more in the following article.

B. Polarization with Electric Field Normal to the Plane of Incidence.
In this case (Fig. 7·11b) $\bar{E}$ and $\bar{E}'$ are normal to the plane of the paper,
and $\bar{H}$ and $\bar{H}'$ are then as shown. Proceeding exactly as above, we
can write the components of the two waves in the x,z system of coordinates as

$$E_y(x,z) = Ee^{-jk(x \sin \theta + z \cos \theta)} + E'e^{jk(-x \sin \theta' + z \cos \theta')} \tag{15}$$

$$\eta H_x(x,z) = -E \cos \theta e^{-jk(x \sin \theta + z \cos \theta)} + E' \cos \theta' e^{jk(-x \sin \theta' + z \cos \theta')} \tag{16}$$

$$\eta H_z(x,z) = E \sin \theta e^{-jk(x \sin \theta + z \cos \theta)} + E' \sin \theta' e^{jk(-x \sin \theta' + z \cos \theta')} \tag{17}$$

The boundary condition at the perfectly conducting plane is that E_y
is zero at $z = 0$ for all x, which by the same reasoning as above leads
to the conclusion that $\theta = \theta'$ and $E = -E'$. The field components,
(15) to (17), then become

$$E_y = -2jE \sin (kz \cos \theta)e^{-jkx \sin \theta} \tag{18}$$

$$\eta H_x = -2E \cos \theta \cos (kz \cos \theta)e^{-jkx \sin \theta} \tag{19}$$

$$\eta H_z = -2jE \sin \theta \sin (kz \cos \theta)e^{-jkx \sin \theta} \tag{20}$$

This set again shows the behavior of a traveling wave in the x direction and a standing wave pattern in the z direction with zeros of E_y
and H_z and maxima of H_x at the conducting plane and at parallel
planes distance nd away, with d given by (14).

PROBLEMS

7·11a   Write the instantaneous values of the field components corresponding to
(11) to (13) above.   Write the average and instantaneous component of Poynting
vector in the x direction; in the z direction.

7·11b   Repeat Prob. *a* for the other polarization, (18) to (20).

7·12   PHASE VELOCITY AND IMPEDANCE FOR WAVES AT OBLIQUE INCIDENCE

A. Phase Velocity.   Let us consider an incident wave, such as that
of the last article, traveling with velocity $v = 1/\sqrt{\mu\epsilon}$ in a positive
direction, which makes angle θ with a desired z direction aligned normally to some reflecting surface.   We saw that it was possible to
express the phase factor in terms of the x and z coordinates:

$$\bar{E}(x,z) = \bar{E}e^{-jk\xi} = \bar{E}e^{-jk(x\sin\theta + z \cos \theta)} \tag{1}$$

For many purposes it is desirable to concentrate on the change in phase
as one moves in the x direction, or in the z direction.   We may then

define the two phase constants for these directions:

$$\beta_x = k \sin \theta \tag{2}$$

$$\beta_z = k \cos \theta \tag{3}$$

Wave (1) may then be written (putting in $e^{j\omega t}$ explicitly)

$$\bar{E}(x,z,t) = \bar{E}e^{j(\omega t - \beta_x x - \beta_z z)} \tag{4}$$

If we wish to keep the instantaneous phase constant as we move in the x direction, we keep $\omega t - \beta_x x$ constant (the last term does not change if we move only in the x direction), and the velocity required for this is defined as the phase velocity referred to the x direction:

$$v_{px} = \left.\frac{\partial x}{\partial t}\right|_{(\omega t - \beta_x x) = \text{const}} = \frac{\omega}{\beta_x}$$

or

$$v_{px} = \frac{\omega}{k \sin \theta} = \frac{1}{\sqrt{\mu\epsilon} \sin \theta} = \frac{v}{\sin \theta} \tag{5}$$

Similarly for the z direction,

$$v_{pz} = \frac{\omega}{\beta_z} = \frac{v}{\cos \theta} \tag{6}$$

where v is the velocity normal to its wave front, $1/\sqrt{\mu\epsilon}$.

We see that in both cases the phase velocity is *greater* than the velocity measured normal to the wave front, and will in fact be so for any oblique direction. There is no violation of relativistic principles by this result, since no material object moves at this velocity. It is the velocity of a fictitious point of intersection of the wave front and a line drawn in the selected direction. Thus in Fig. 7·12, if a plane of constant phase aa moves to $a'a'$ in a given interval of time, the distance moved normal to the wave front is

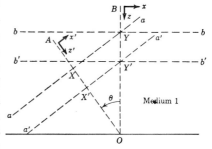

Fig. 7·12   Uniform plane wave moving at angle θ toward a plane.

XX', but the distance moved by this constant phase reference along the z direction BO is the greater distance YY'. Since

$$YY' = XX' \sec \theta$$

this picture would again lead to the result (6) for phase velocity in the z direction.

The concept of a phase velocity, and the understanding of why it may be greater than the velocity of light, is very necessary to the discussion of guided waves in later chapters, as well as to the remainder of this chapter.

B. Wave Impedance. In the problems of oblique incidence on a plane boundary between different media, it is also useful to define the wave or field impedance as the ratio of electric to magnetic field components in planes parallel to the boundary. The reason for this is the continuity of the *tangential* components of electric and magnetic fields at a boundary, and the consequent equality of the above defined ratio on the two sides of the boundary. That is, if the value of this ratio is computed as an input impedance for a region to the right in some manner, it is also the value of load impedance at that plane for the region to the left, just as in the examples of normal incidence.

Thus, for incident and reflected waves making angle θ with the normal as in Art. 7·11, we may define a characteristic wave impedance referred to the z direction in terms of the components in planes transverse to that direction. From Eqs. 7·11(5) and (7) *for waves polarized with electric field in the plane of incidence,*

$$Z_z = \frac{E_x{}^+}{H_y{}^+} = -\frac{E_x{}^-}{H_y{}^-} = \eta \cos \theta \qquad (7)$$

Superscripts $+$ and $-$ refer, respectively, to incident and reflected wave; the sign of the ratio is chosen for each wave to yield a positive result. From Eqs. 7·11(15) and (16) *for waves polarized with electric field normal to the plane of incidence,*

$$Z_z = -\frac{E_y{}^+}{H_x{}^+} = \frac{E_y{}^-}{H_x{}^-} = \eta \sec \theta \qquad (8)$$

We see that, for the first type of polarization, the characteristic wave impedance is always less than η, as we would expect since only a component of total electric field lies in the transverse x-y plane, whereas the total magnetic field lies in that plane. In the latter polarization, the reverse is true and Z_z is always greater than η.

The interpretation of the example of the last article from the above point of view is then that the perfect conductor amounts to a zero impedance or short to the transverse field component E_x. We would then expect a standing wave pattern in the z direction with other zeros at multiples of a half-wavelength away, this wavelength being computed from phase velocity in the z direction. This leads again to the result Eq. 7·11(14).

7·13 INCIDENCE AT ANY ANGLE ON PERFECT DIELECTRICS

A. Law of Reflection. For a uniform plane wave incident at angle θ with the normal to the plane boundary between two dielectrics ϵ_1 and ϵ_2, Fig. 7·13, there will be a reflected wave at some angle θ' with the normal, and a transmitted (or refracted) wave into the second medium which is drawn at some angle θ'' with the normal. For either type of polarization, the continuity condition on tangential components of electric and magnetic field at the boundary $z = 0$ must be satisfied for all values of x. As in the argument applied to the problem of reflection from the perfect conductor, this is possible for all x only if incident, reflected, and refracted waves all have the same phase factor with respect to the x direction, and hence the same phase velocity in the x direction. Using the result of Eq. 7·12(5), we conclude that

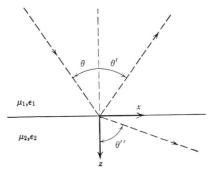

$$\frac{v_1}{\sin \theta} = \frac{v_1}{\sin \theta'} = \frac{v_2}{\sin \theta''} \quad (1)$$

The first pair in (1) gives the result

$$\theta' = \theta \quad (2)$$

Fig. 7·13   Oblique incidence on boundary between two dielectrics.

or the angle of reflection is equal to the angle of incidence.

B. Snell's Law of Refraction. From the last pair of (1) we find a relation between the angle of refraction θ'' and the angle of incidence θ:

$$\frac{\sin \theta''}{\sin \theta} = \frac{v_2}{v_1} = \sqrt{\frac{\mu_1 \epsilon_1}{\mu_2 \epsilon_2}} \quad (3)$$

This relation is a familiar one in geometrical optics and is known as Snell's law. It is especially interesting to note that electromagnetic theory provides a proof of this and the well-known law of reflection. Note that for all common dielectric materials the permeability is not different from that of space, $\mu_1 = \mu_2 = \mu_0$.

C. Reflection and Transmission for Polarization with E in Plane of Incidence. To compute the amount of the wave reflected and the amount transmitted, we may use the impedance concept as extended for oblique incidence in the last article. To show the validity of this procedure, we write the continuity conditions for total E_x and H_y, including both incident (unprimed) and reflected (primed) components in region 1:

$$E_{x1} + E_{x1}' = E_{x2} \tag{4}$$

$$H_{y1} + H_{y1}' = H_{y2} \tag{5}$$

Following Art. 7·12, if we define wave impedances in terms of the tangential components,

$$Z_{z1} = \frac{E_{x1}}{H_{y1}} = -\frac{E_{x1}'}{H_{y1}'} \tag{6}$$

$$Z_L = \frac{E_{x2}}{H_{y2}} \tag{7}$$

Equation (5) may be written

$$\frac{E_{x1}}{Z_{z1}} - \frac{E_{x1}'}{Z_{z1}} = \frac{E_{x2}}{Z_L} \tag{8}$$

An elimination between (4) and (8) results in equations for reflection and transmission coefficients:

$$\rho = \frac{E_{x1}'}{E_{x1}} = \frac{Z_L - Z_{z1}}{Z_L + Z_{z1}} \tag{9}$$

$$\tau = \frac{E_{x2}}{E_{x1}} = \frac{2Z_L}{Z_L + Z_{z1}} \tag{10}$$

For the present case, since there is no returning wave in medium 2, the load impedance Z_L is just the characteristic wave impedance for the refracted wave referred to the z direction, obtainable from Eq. 7·12(7):

$$Z_L = \eta_2 \cos \theta'' = \eta_2 \sqrt{1 - \left(\frac{v_2}{v_1}\right)^2 \sin^2 \theta} \tag{11}$$

And the characteristic wave impedance for medium 1 referred to the z direction is

$$Z_{z1} = \eta_1 \cos \theta \tag{12}$$

The second form of (11) is obtained by substituting the Snell's law relation (3) between θ'' and θ, and is applicable even when the result for Z_L is imaginary. Note that, for dielectrics with $\mu_1 = \mu_2$,

$$\frac{\eta_2}{\eta_1} = \frac{v_2}{v_1} = \sqrt{\frac{\epsilon_1}{\epsilon_2}} \tag{13}$$

The total fields in region 1 may then be written as the sum of incident and reflected waves, utilizing (9) and the basic properties of uniform plane waves. We shall use H_y (denoted H) of the incident wave as the reference component since it is parallel to the boundary.

$$E_x = \eta_1 H \cos \theta e^{-j\beta_x x}[e^{-j\beta_z z} + \rho e^{j\beta_z z}] \tag{14}$$

$$H_y = H e^{-j\beta_x x}[e^{-j\beta_z z} - \rho e^{j\beta_z z}] \tag{15}$$

$$E_z = \eta_1 H \sin \theta e^{-j\beta_x x}[-e^{-j\beta_z z} + \rho e^{j\beta_z z}] \tag{16}$$

$$\beta_x = k_1 \sin \theta \qquad \beta_z = k_1 \cos \theta \tag{17}$$

This field again has the character of a traveling wave field in the x direction and a standing wave field in the z direction, but here the minima in the z direction do not in general reach zero. The ratio of maxima to minima could be expressed as a standing wave ratio and would be related to the magnitude of reflection coefficient by the usual expression, Eq. 7·09(3).

D. *Reflection and Transmission for Polarization with E Normal to Plane of Incidence.* For this polarization also, the basic relations (9) and (10) between impedances and reflection or transmission may be shown to apply. Note that they were first introduced in connection with transmission line waves in Chapter 1, but have now found usefulness for many wave problems through the impedance concept applied to wave phenomena.

$$\rho = \frac{E_{y1}'}{E_{y1}} = \frac{Z_L - Z_{z1}}{Z_L + Z_{z1}} \tag{18}$$

$$\tau = \frac{E_{y2}}{E_{y1}} = \frac{2Z_L}{Z_L + Z_{z1}} \tag{19}$$

For this polarization, the proper wave impedances are obtained from Eq. 7·12(8):

$$Z_L = \eta_2 \sec \theta'' = \eta_2 \left[1 - \left(\frac{v_2}{v_1}\right)^2 \sin^2 \theta\right]^{-\frac{1}{2}} \tag{20}$$

$$Z_{z1} = \eta_1 \sec \theta \tag{21}$$

The total fields in region 1 are (E denotes the value of E_y in the incident wave)

$$E_y = E e^{-j\beta_x x}[e^{-j\beta_z z} + \rho e^{j\beta_z z}] \tag{22}$$

$$H_x = -\left(\frac{E \cos \theta}{\eta}\right) e^{-j\beta_x x}[e^{-j\beta_z z} - \rho e^{j\beta_z z}] \tag{23}$$

$$H_z = \left(\frac{E \sin \theta}{\eta}\right) e^{-j\beta_x x}[e^{-j\beta_z z} + \rho e^{j\beta_z z}] \tag{24}$$

$$\beta_x = k_1 \sin \theta \qquad \beta_z = k_1 \cos \theta \tag{25}$$

PROBLEMS

7·13a   Write the expressions for field components in region 2 for both types of polarization.

7·13b   For the first type of polarization, evaluate the average Poynting vector in both regions, and show the power balance.

7·13c   For both polarizations, give the conditions for which the standing wave pattern in z shows a minimum of tangential electric field at the boundary surface; repeat for a maximum of tangential E at the surface.

7·13d   Derive formulas (18) and (19) for polarization with electric field normal to the plane of incidence.

7·14   TOTAL REFLECTION

A study of the general results from the preceding article shows that there are several particular conditions of incidence of special interest. The first of these is one which leads to a condition of total reflection. From the basic formula for reflection coefficient, Eq. 7·13(9) or (18), we know that there is complete reflection ($|\,\rho\,| = 1$) if the load impedance Z_L is zero, infinity, or purely imaginary.   To show the last condition, let $Z_L = jX_L$ and note that Z_{z1} is real:

$$|\,\rho\,| = \left|\frac{jX_L - Z_{z1}}{jX_L + Z_{z1}}\right| = \frac{\sqrt{X_L{}^2 + Z_{z1}{}^2}}{\sqrt{X_L{}^2 + Z_{z1}{}^2}} = 1 \tag{1}$$

The value of Z_L for polarization with electric field in the plane of incidence, given by Eq. 7·13(11), is seen to become zero for some critical angle $\theta = \theta_c$ such that

$$\sin\,\theta_c = \frac{v_1}{v_2} \tag{2}$$

The value of Z_L for polarization with electric field normal to the plane of incidence, given by Eq. 7·13(20), becomes infinite for this same condition.   For both polarizations, Z_L would be imaginary for angles of incidence greater than θ_c, so there would be total reflection for such angles of incidence.

For common dielectrics having $\mu_1 = \mu_2$, (2) reduces to

$$\sin\,\theta_c = \sqrt{\frac{\epsilon_2}{\epsilon_1}} \tag{3}$$

It is seen that there are real solutions for the critical angle in this case only when $\epsilon_1 > \epsilon_2$, or when the wave passes from an optically dense to an optically rarer medium.   From Snell's law, Eq. 7·13(3), we would find that the angle of refraction would be $\pi/2$ for $\theta = \theta_c$, and would become imaginary for greater angles of incidence. So from this point of view also we would expect no transfer of energy into the second medium. Although there is no energy transfer, there are finite values of field in the second region as required by the continuity conditions at the boundary. These die off exponentially with distance from the boundary as the phase constant β_z becomes imaginary.

Although the reflected wave has the same amplitude as the incident wave for angles of incidence greater than the critical, it does not in general have the same phase. The phase relation between E_{x1}' and E_{x1} for the first type of polarization is also different from that between E_{y1}' and E_{y1} for the second type of polarization incident at the same angle. Thus, if the incident wave has both types of polarization components, the reflected wave under these conditions will be elliptically polarized (Art. 7·06).

PROBLEMS

7·14a Calculate the critical angle for an electromagnetic wave passing from the following dielectrics into air.

Material	ϵ/ϵ_0 (ratio of dielectric constant to that of air)
Distilled water	81.1
Ethyl alcohol	25.8
Glass (high-density)	9
Glass (low-density)	6
Mica	6
Quartz	5
Petroleum oil	2.1

7·14b Defining ψ as the phase of E_{x1}'/E_{x1} and ψ' as the phase of E_{y1}'/E_{y1}, find expressions for ψ and ψ' under conditions of total reflection. Show that the phase difference between these two polarization components, $\delta = \psi - \psi'$, is given by

$$\tan\left(\frac{\delta}{2}\right) = \frac{\dfrac{\eta_2}{\eta_1}\left[\left(\dfrac{v_2}{v_1}\right)^2 - 1\right]\sin^2\theta}{\left[\left(\dfrac{\eta_2}{\eta_1}\right)^2 - 1\right]\cos\theta\sqrt{\left(\dfrac{v_2}{v_1}\right)^2\sin^2\theta - 1}}$$

7·14c Find, in such form as to disclose the exponential decay of fields with penetration into the second dielectric, the expressions for the fields in the second dielectric when the incident angle is such as to yield imaginary K.

7·15 POLARIZING ANGLE

Let us next ask under what conditions there might be no reflected wave when the uniform plane wave is incident at angle θ on the dielectric boundary. We know that this occurs for a matching of impedances between the two media, $Z_L = Z_{z1}$. For the wave polarized with electric field in the plane of incidence, and for a medium with $\mu_1 = \mu_2$, Eqs. 7·13(11) and (12) become

$$Z_L = \sqrt{\frac{\mu_1}{\epsilon_2}} \sqrt{1 - \left(\frac{\epsilon_1}{\epsilon_2}\right) \sin^2 \theta} \tag{1}$$

$$Z_{z1} = \sqrt{\frac{\mu_1}{\epsilon_1}} \cos \theta \tag{2}$$

These two quantities may be made equal for a particular angle $\theta = \theta_p$ such that

$$\cos \theta_p = \frac{\epsilon_1}{\epsilon_2} \sqrt{1 - \left(\frac{\epsilon_1}{\epsilon_2}\right) \sin^2 \theta_p} \tag{3}$$

This equation has a solution:

$$\theta_p = \sin^{-1} \sqrt{\frac{\epsilon_2}{\epsilon_1 + \epsilon_2}} = \tan^{-1} \sqrt{\frac{\epsilon_2}{\epsilon_1}} \tag{4}$$

Note that (4) yields real values of θ_p for either $\epsilon_1 > \epsilon_2$ or $\epsilon_2 > \epsilon_1$, and so, for polarization with electric field in the plane of incidence, there is always some angle for which there is no reflection; all energy incident at this angle passes into the second medium.

For polarization with electric field normal to the plane of incidence, a study of Eqs. 7·13(20) and (21) would show that there is no angle yielding an equality of impedances for materials with different dielectric constants but like permeabilities. Hence, a wave incident at angle θ_p with both polarization components present has some of the second polarization component but none of the first reflected. The reflected wave at this angle is thus plane polarized with electric field normal to the plane of incidence, and the angle θ_p is correspondingly known as the *polarizing angle*. It is also alternatively known as the *Brewster angle*.

PROBLEMS

7·15a For the dielectrics listed in Prob. 7·14a, determine the polarizing angle for waves passing from each of the dielectrics into air, and also for waves passing from air into the dielectrics.

7·15b Imagine a material with $\epsilon_1 = \epsilon_2$, but $\mu_1 \neq \mu_2$. Which polarization component would then yield a solution for incident angle giving no reflections? Give the angle.

7·15c For the wave with E polarized in the plane of incidence, note the change of phase between E_x in reflected and incident waves for angles in the vicinity of θ_p. What effect does this have on the standing wave pattern in the z direction in the first dielectric?

7·16 MULTIPLE DIELECTRIC BOUNDARIES WITH OBLIQUE INCIDENCE

If there are several dielectric regions with parallel boundaries, the problem may be solved by successively transforming impedances through the several regions, using the standard transmission line formula, Eq. 1·21(10), or a graphical aid such as the Smith chart. For each region the phase constant and characteristic wave impedance must include the function of angle from the normal as well as the properties of the dielectric material. Thus for the ith region, from the concepts of Art. 7·12, the phase constant is

$$\beta_{zi} = k_i \cos \theta_i \qquad (1)$$

and the characteristic wave impedance is

$$Z_{zi} = \eta_i \cos \theta_i \qquad \text{for } E \text{ in plane of incidence} \qquad (2)$$

$$Z_{zi} = \eta_i \sec \theta_i \qquad \text{for } E \text{ normal to plane of incidence} \qquad (3)$$

When the impedance is finally transformed to the surface at which it is desired to find reflection, the reflection coefficient is calculated from the basic reflection formula, Eq. 7·13(9), and the fraction of the incident power reflected is just the square of its magnitude. The angles in the several regions are found by successively applying Snell's law, starting from the first given angle of incidence.

PROBLEMS

7·16a A uniform plane wave of free-space wavelength 3 cm is incident from space on a window of dielectric constant 3, and thickness equal to a half-wavelength referred to the dielectric material so that it gives no reflections for normal incidence. For general angles of incidence, plot the fraction of incident energy reflected versus θ for polarization with E in the plane of incidence, and also for polarization normal to the plane of incidence.

7·16b An incident wave in medium 1 of dielectric constant ϵ_1 makes angle θ_1 with the normal. Find the proper length and dielectric constant of a medium 2 to form a "quarter-wave matching section" to a medium of dielectric constant ϵ_3.

Waves in Imperfect Conductors and Dielectrics

7·17 WAVES IN CONDUCTING MATERIALS

From Poynting's theorem it is known that no energy can be transmitted into a perfect conductor, and so no wave can exist inside such a conductor.   Furthermore, no fields of any kind, waves or otherwise, can be in such a conductor.   If the conductivity is not perfect, electric and magnetic fields may exist inside the conductor, as was shown in the past chapter, and under certain conditions it may be desirable to consider these as waves.

For a conductor, the equations corresponding to Eq. 7·02(3) and Eq. 7·02(4), assuming sinusoidal time variations, are

$$\nabla \times \bar{E} = -j\omega\mu\bar{H}$$

$$\nabla \times \bar{H} = (\sigma + j\omega\epsilon)\bar{E} = j\omega\epsilon \left[1 + \frac{\sigma}{j\omega\epsilon} \right] \bar{E}$$

It is apparent from these equations that all mathematical manipulations of previous sections are valid if

$$\epsilon_c = \epsilon \left[1 + \frac{\sigma}{j\omega\epsilon} \right] \tag{1}$$

is substituted in place of ϵ for solutions applying inside the conducting material.   In other words, as far as the use of previously derived mathematical relations are concerned, a conductor is simply another dielectric with a complex dielectric constant ϵ_c and with its conductivity never appearing explicitly.   Of course, we are interested in more than the mathematical relations, so we shall return soon to see what this means physically.

Thus, taking γ again as the propagation constant for a uniform plane wave, Eq. 7·05(3),

$$\gamma = jk_c = j\omega \sqrt{\mu\epsilon_c}$$

Since ϵ_c is complex, γ will have real and imaginary parts.   Thus

$$\gamma = \alpha + j\beta = j\omega \sqrt{\mu\epsilon \left(1 + \frac{\sigma}{j\omega\epsilon} \right)} \tag{2}$$

$$\alpha = \omega \sqrt{\frac{\mu\epsilon}{2} \left(\sqrt{1 + \frac{\sigma^2}{\omega^2\epsilon^2}} - 1 \right)} \tag{3}$$

$$\beta = \omega \sqrt{\frac{\mu\epsilon}{2} \left(\sqrt{1 + \frac{\sigma^2}{\omega^2\epsilon^2}} + 1 \right)} \tag{4}$$

There is thus attenuation as the wave progresses into the conductor:

$$e^{-\gamma z} = e^{-\alpha z} e^{-j\beta z}$$

This is as would be expected since energy is lost by currents flowing in the imperfect conductor.

The intrinsic impedance, or ratio of electric to magnetic field for a uniform plane wave, becomes

$$\eta_c = \sqrt{\frac{\mu}{\epsilon_c}} = \sqrt{\frac{\mu}{\epsilon(1 + \sigma/j\omega\epsilon)}} \tag{5}$$

Since η_c is complex, it follows that electric and magnetic fields are out of phase in a conducting material. Moreover, if we wish to compute the reflection coefficient (ratio of tangential electric field in the reflected wave to that in the incident wave) for a wave normally incident from a perfect dielectric of intrinsic impedance η onto a conducting material of intrinsic impedance η_c, the basic wave reflection formula, Eq. 7·08(11), becomes

$$\rho = \frac{\eta_c - \eta}{\eta_c + \eta} \tag{6}$$

And, since ρ is complex, there will be a phase shift between incident and reflected waves on reflection.

The special cases of greatest interest are those in which the material is either a reasonably good dielectric, or a reasonably good conductor, and of these more detailed analysis will follow.

7·18 WAVES IN IMPERFECT CONDUCTORS

A good conductor will be regarded as a conductor in which displacement currents are negligibly small compared with conduction currents for the frequency of interest but in which the resistivity cannot be neglected. That is,

$$\frac{\sigma}{\omega\epsilon} \gg 1$$

Then Eq. 7·17(2) reduces to

$$\gamma = j\omega\sqrt{\frac{\mu\sigma}{j\omega}} = (1 + j)\sqrt{\pi f\mu\sigma} = \frac{1 + j}{\delta} \tag{1}$$

δ is the depth of penetration used extensively in Chapter 6 and defined by Eq. 6·05(4). The propagation function for the wave,

$$e^{-\gamma z} = e^{-z/\delta}e^{-j(z/\delta)}$$

shows that the wave decreases in magnitude exponentially, and has decreased to $1/e$ of its original value after propagating a distance equal to depth of penetration of the material. The phase factor corresponds to a very small phase velocity,

$$v = \frac{\omega}{\beta} = \omega\delta = c\,\frac{2\pi\delta}{\lambda_0} \tag{2}$$

where c = velocity of light in free space; λ_0 = free-space wavelength. Since δ/λ_0 is usually very small (see Art. 6·05), this phase velocity is usually much less than the velocity of light.

Equation 7·17(5) gives, for a good conductor,

$$\eta_c = \sqrt{\frac{j\omega\mu}{\sigma}} = (1 + j)\sqrt{\frac{\pi f\mu}{\sigma}} = (1 + j)R_s \tag{3}$$

R_s is the surface resistivity or high-frequency skin effect resistance per square of a plane conductor of great depth. Equation (3) shows that electric and magnetic fields are 45° out of time phase for the wave propagating in a good conductor. Also, since R_s is very small (see Art. 6·06), the ratio of electric field to magnetic field in the wave is small.

Since R_s is much less than unity for ordinary conducting materials (0.014 ohm for copper at 3000 mc/sec) and since the intrinsic impedance of most dielectrics is much greater than unity (377 ohms for air), the reflection coefficient as computed from Eq. 7·17(6) is very nearly unity and for many purposes accurate enough results are obtained by considering the conductor as perfect. However, there is a small fraction of the incident energy transmitted to the conductor, and therefore a small departure of the magnitude of reflection coefficient from unity. There is also a small phase shift on reflection from the 180° value applying to the perfect conductor. For some purposes it is necessary to take these quantities into consideration.

The results of this article are identical with those derived in the discussion of skin effect for the plane solid (Art. 6·05), as they should be since Maxwell's equations are utilized in both analyses with the same simplifying assumptions. The point of view taken at the outset is somewhat different, for here we picture the decrease in current density and field strengths as one progresses into the conductor as the attenuation of a wave propagating into the conductor. The transmission line analogy for a wave in this good conductor would require a line with distributed inductance and conductance, but not series resistance or shunt capacitance.

PROBLEMS

7·18a   Derive a formula for the fraction of incident energy passing into a conductor of conductivity σ, permeability μ, when a uniform plane wave is normally incident from a dielectric with intrinsic impedance η.   Make approximations based on $\eta \gg R_s$.   Compute the values for incidence from air to copper at 30 mc/sec and 3000 mc/sec.

7·18b   Check the formula derived in Prob. a by assuming that the magnetic field at the surface is the same as for reflection from a perfect conductor, and computing the conductor losses due to currents compatible with this magnetic field.

7·18c   Derive an approximate formula for the ratio of quadrature component in the reflected wave to the real component for a wave normally incident from a perfect dielectric onto a good conductor.   Compute the ratios for incidence from air to copper at 30 and 3000 mc/sec.

7·18d   Derive the expression for group velocity of a uniform plane wave propagating in a good conductor.

7·19   IMPERFECT DIELECTRICS

In a dielectric material with finite conductivity, it is not possible to neglect displacement currents as was done for good conductors, since displacement currents will usually be much greater than conduction currents if the material is to be useful as a dielectric.   Neither can we completely neglect conductive currents if any information is to be obtained on the effect of losses.   It seems necessary to give both the conductivity σ and the dielectric constant ϵ to determine the complex dielectric constant defined in Eq. 7·17(1).   However, for reasons having to do with measurement and variation of properties with frequency, it is more common to express the properties of a dielectric in terms of two quantities, ϵ' and ϵ'', such that

$$\epsilon_c = \epsilon_0[\epsilon' - j\epsilon''] \tag{1}$$

ϵ_0 is the dielectric constant of free space in mks units, ϵ' is the familiar value of dielectric constant for the material, based on air or space as unity, and ϵ'' is called the loss factor.   By comparing (1) and Eq. 7·17(1) we see that

$$\epsilon'' = \frac{\sigma}{\omega\epsilon_0} = \frac{36\pi\sigma}{\omega \times 10^{-9}} \tag{2}$$

where σ is in mhos per meter.

The ratio ϵ''/ϵ' is also a common constant for dielectrics, since it is a direct measure of the ratio of conduction current to displacement current in the dielectric:

$$\frac{\epsilon''}{\epsilon'} = \frac{\sigma}{\omega\epsilon_0\epsilon'} = \frac{\sigma}{\omega\epsilon} \tag{3}$$

This ratio is tabulated in certain tables as tan δ. The properties of a lossy dielectric are also sometimes given by the *power factor*, which is defined as sin δ. For small values, it is very nearly equal to ϵ''/ϵ'.

It should be emphasized that any of the properties used to describe a lossy dielectric, ϵ', ϵ'', σ, or power factor, may vary with frequency, and a typical curve of dielectric constant and loss factor might be as

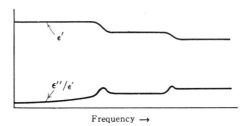

Frequency →

Fig. 7·19 Form of dielectric constant and loss factor variations with frequency typical of some dielectrics. The peaks of loss and steps of dielectric constant occur at resonances of the material.

shown in Fig. 7·19. Values of ϵ' and ϵ''/ϵ' for several materials at three different frequencies are given in Table 7·19.

TABLE 7·19

Material	Relative Dielectric Constant			Loss Tangent, $10^4\epsilon''/\epsilon'$		
	$f = 10^6$	$f = 10^8$	$f = 10^{10}$	$f = 10^6$	$f = 10^8$	$f = 10^{10}$
Glass, Corning 707.....	4.00	4.00	4.00	8	12	21
Fused quartz.........	3.78	3.78	3.78	2	1	1
Ruby Mica...........	5.4	5.4	....	3	2	....
Ceramic Alsimag 393..	4.95	4.95	4.95	10	10	9.7
Titania..............	100	100	....	3	2.5	....
Polystyrene...........	2.56	2.55	2.54	0.7	1	4.3
Neoprene............	5.7	3.4	....	950	1600	....

7·20 WAVES IN IMPERFECT DIELECTRICS

It will be assumed here that the dielectric is good enough so that conduction currents are small compared with displacement currents, $\epsilon''/\epsilon' \ll 1$. With this assumption, the attenuation and phase constants for a uniform plane wave, Eqs. 7·17(3) and (4), reduce to

$$\alpha \approx \frac{k\epsilon''}{2\epsilon'} = \frac{\pi\epsilon''}{\lambda\epsilon'} \tag{1}$$

$$\beta \approx k\left[1 + \frac{1}{8}\left(\frac{\epsilon''}{\epsilon'}\right)^2\right] \tag{2}$$

It is seen from the attenuation constant that the wave would decrease to $1/e$ of its initial value in a distance $\lambda\epsilon'/\pi\epsilon''$. If $\pi\epsilon''/\epsilon'$ is small compared with unity, this distance is large compared with wavelength. From (2) we see that the phase constant is increased by a small but finite amount due to the losses, so the phase velocity would be decreased by losses. The intrinsic impedance of the medium is given by Eq. 7·17(5):

$$\eta_c = \sqrt{\frac{\mu}{\epsilon(1 - j\epsilon''/\epsilon')}} \approx \eta\left\{\left[1 - \frac{3}{8}\left(\frac{\epsilon''}{\epsilon'}\right)^2\right] + j\frac{\epsilon''}{2\epsilon'}\right\} \tag{3}$$

In utilizing the impedance concept for reflection calculations, the impedance through a lossy dielectric region would be computed from the transmission line formula which includes losses, Eq. 1·24(13), using η_c for the characteristic impedance, and propagation constant $\gamma = \alpha + j\beta$.

$$Z_i = \eta_c\left[\frac{Z_L \cosh \gamma l + \eta_c \sinh \gamma l}{\eta_c \cosh \gamma l + Z_L \sinh \gamma l}\right] \tag{4}$$

Thus, for a lossy dielectric window of thickness l, having free space on both sides, the impedance Z_L would be that of free space, η_0. Input impedance is computed from (4), and the reflection coefficient from the front face would be

$$\rho = \frac{Z_i - \eta_0}{Z_i + \eta_0} \tag{5}$$

PROBLEMS

7·20a For a uniform plane wave of frequency 10^{10} cps propagating in polystyrene, calculate the attenuation constant, phase velocity, and intrinsic impedance.

7·20b A dielectric window of polystyrene is made a half-wavelength thick (referred to the dielectric) at 10^8 cps, so that there would be no reflections for normally incident uniform plane waves from space, neglecting losses in the dielectric. Considering the finite losses, compute the reflection coefficient and fraction of incident energy reflected from the front face   Also determine the fraction of the incident energy lost in the dielectric window.

7·20c A slab of dielectric of length l, constants ϵ' and ϵ'', is backed by a conducting plane at $z = l$ which may be considered perfect. Determine the expression for field impedance at the front face, $z = 0$. Calculate the value for $\epsilon' = 4$, $\epsilon'' = 0.01$, $f = 3 \times 10^9$ cps, $l = 1.25$ cm.

7·20d Determine the group velocity for uniform plane waves in a lossy dielectric, assuming σ and ϵ' independent of frequency; assuming ϵ''/ϵ' independent of frequency.

7·21 PROPERTIES AND CLASSIFICATION OF POOR CONDUCTORS

There are certain materials with properties in between those we have called good conductors on the one hand, and good dielectrics on the other. For many of these poor conductors, the displacement currents may be negligible at low frequencies so that the analysis of Art. 7·18 would be applicable; whereas at very high frequencies the conduction currents might be considerably less than the displacement currents so that the analysis of Art. 7·20 would be applicable. For intermediate frequencies, the two terms might be comparable, and both would have to be taken into account as in Art. 7·17. In the table below, some of the materials of this type which are of special importance to radio engineering are listed with approximate values of conductivity, dielectric constant, and frequency at which conduction and displacement currents are comparable. For much lower frequencies they may be analyzed as good conductors; for much higher frequencies they may be analyzed as imperfect dielectrics; for intermediate frequencies both terms must be taken into account.

Material	Conductivity σ, mhos/meter	ϵ'	Frequency at Which $\sigma = \omega\epsilon$
Sea water	4	81	8.9×10^8
Fresh water	10^{-3}	81	2.2×10^5
Wet earth	10^{-3}	10	1.8×10^6
Dry earth	10^{-5}	5	3.6×10^4

PROBLEM

7·21 Plot a curve showing attenuation constant in sea water from 10^4 cps to 10^9 cps, assuming that the constants given do not vary over this range. Comment on the implications of the results to the problem of communicating by radio waves through sea water.

7·22 ELIMINATION OF WAVE REFLECTIONS FROM GOOD CONDUCTORS

For high-frequency applications it is often desirable to reduce or eliminate spurious reflections from metallic objects placed in the vicinity of radiating systems. We shall show[3] that a thin conducting film may be utilized for this purpose if removed a quarter- wavelength from the metallic surface. This example will again serve to illustrate the usefulness of the transmission line analogy and impedance concepts.

The uniform plane wave normally incident upon a good conductor, (4) of Fig. 7·22a, will be considered. It has been shown (Art. 7·07) that a standing wave pattern is set up which is due to the combination

[3] S. A. Schelkunoff, "The Electromagnetic Theory of Coaxial Transmission Lines and Cylindrical Shields," *Bell Sys. Tech. J.*, **13**, 532 (Oct. 1934).

of reflected and incident waves, so that a quarter-wavelength in front of the conductor there is a minimum of magnetic field and a maximum of electric field.   This represents a point of very high impedance, E/H. Suppose that a given thickness, d, of any material is placed at that point.   The impedance viewed from the front surface of the material, where the wave strikes, may be expressed in terms of the terminating impedance, the thickness, and the propagation constant through that material, Eq. 7·20(4).   If the back surface of the film is placed exactly at the node of magnetic field, the terminating impedance is practically

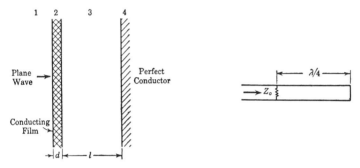

Fig. 7·22a   Impedance sheet for termi-   Fig. 7·22b   Transmission line equiv-
nation of a wave region.   alent of Fig. 7·22a.

infinite.   (It is of course exactly infinite if the conductor 4 is perfect.) The impedance at the front surface is then

$$Z_i = \eta_2 \coth \gamma_2 d \approx \frac{\eta_2}{\gamma_2 d} \tag{1}$$

The last approximation is valid for thin films with $|\gamma_2 d| \ll 1$.   Let us take the material of the film as one in which displacement currents are negligible and use Eqs. 7·18 (1) and (3) for γ_2 and η_2.

$$Z_i = \left[(1 + j) \sqrt{\frac{\pi f \mu_2}{\sigma_2}} \right] \left[\frac{1}{d(1 + j) \sqrt{\pi f \mu_2 \sigma_2}} \right] = \frac{1}{\sigma_2 d}$$

For a perfect match to the wave coming from medium 1, this input impedance should be equal to η_1.   Hence, the film should be designed so that

$$\frac{1}{\sigma_2 d} = \eta_1 \tag{2}$$

This corresponds to a thin film of resistive material whose resistance per square is equal to the intrinsic impedance η_1.   This is analogous in transmission line terms to the characteristic impedance of a transmission line placed a quarter-wavelength in front of a short-circuited end (Fig. 7·22b). Since the short-circuited quarter-wave line has infinite impedance, this represents perfect matching for a wave approaching from the left.

Note that the conductivity σ_2 must be quite small if d is not to be unreasonably small in thickness. Thus, if material 1 is air or space ($\eta = 120\pi$ ohms), σ_2 must be 26.5 mhos per meter to make $d = 0.1$ mm. This corresponds to a conductivity about 0.5×10^{-6} times that of copper. Note also that the spacing l between film and conductor is a quarter-wavelength in the dielectric material of 3, so that this spacing may be decreased if a material of higher dielectric constant is used.

$$l = \frac{\lambda_3}{4} = \frac{1}{4f \sqrt{\mu_3 \epsilon_3}} \tag{3}$$

The perfect matching was possible because the film, which must absorb the incident wave, was placed a quarter-wavelength from the conductor where the electric field was high. Matching is not possible with a film of simple electrical properties if it is attempted to place the film on the surface of the conductor itself, since this is a region of low electric field. The dielectric and conductivity properties of the film would then be unimportant.

PROBLEMS

7·22a A conducting film of impedance 377 ohms per square is placed a quarter-wave in air from a plane conductor to eliminate wave reflections for a 9000 mc/sec wave as described in the above article. Plot a curve showing the fraction of incident power reflected versus frequency for frequencies from 6000 to 18,000 mc/sec.

7·22b For the design described in Prob. a, plot a curve showing fraction of incident power reflected versus angle of incidence for 9000 mc/sec waves at oblique incidence and polarized with electric field in the plane of incidence. Repeat for electric field normal to plane of incidence.

7·22c The common materials used for the conducting films in the application of this article may not have a negligible dielectric constant. Study the effect of finite dielectric constant on a design that would otherwise produce no reflection.

7·22d By use of the transmission line analogies, determine the spacing between a film and a good conductor, and the conductivity properties of that film if reflections are to be perfectly eliminated for a wave incident at an angle θ from the normal for the two types of polarization.

8 GUIDED ELECTROMAGNETIC WAVES

8·01 INTRODUCTION

In the preceding chapter we were interested primarily in electromagnetic waves in boundless dielectrics except in so far as reflecting discontinuities were concerned. Actually, no wave is ever truly free from the effect of conductors and dielectrics, but one may be to a good approximation, as in the example of a radio wave at a great distance from the ground in the region between transmitter and receiver. However, we now wish to study specifically the behavior of electromagnetic waves in the immediate vicinity of conducting and dielectric boundaries when the configurations of these boundaries have the effect of guiding the waves along their surfaces.

By a guided wave, we mean first that the direction of energy flow must be primarily along the direction of the guiding system, although there must of course be some energy flow from the wave into the imperfectly conducting metal and dielectric boundaries for any real system. But, more important, if the wave is said to be guided by the boundaries, we infer that a change in the direction of these boundaries, within reasonable limits, will cause the wave to follow the new direction of the guide. We know, for example, that this is true for the transmission line used to transfer energy between the transmitter and an antenna, where the wave energy follows the path of the line, at least for paths with only reasonable discontinuities. This guiding of the wave is accomplished in all such systems by an intimate connection between the fields of the wave and the currents and charges of the boundary, or by some condition of special reflection at the boundary.

In the field picture, we imagine the energy as being transmitted through the electromagnetic fields of the wave in the dielectric region between boundaries, those boundaries being of primary importance in forming the characteristics of a particular wave. In the mathematical analysis, we wish to find solutions of the wave equation which fit the boundary conditions imposed by the conducting and dielectric boundaries of the guides, concentrating on those solutions which represent energy transfer along the direction of the guide and which are intimately tied to the guide through some condition of current flow, charge induction, or special reflection at the boundary of the guide. Analysis will be confined here to guides which are straight and uniform, with the recognition that the waves will follow these with little change in characteristics if there are only reasonable changes in direction of the guides.

In the two articles following this, we shall write the relations from Maxwell's equations in the special form suitable for studying guided waves, and consider the classification of basic wave types. We shall then try to develop many of the important physical pictures and techniques of analysis for guided waves by considering the simple boundary conditions imposed by parallel conducting planes. We shall devote the remainder of the chapter to the discussion of some of the general properties of the basic wave types applicable to any shape of a guiding boundary before going on in the next chapter to the most commonly used shapes of guides for electromagnetic energy.

8·02 BASIC EQUATIONS FOR WAVES ALONG UNIFORM SYSTEMS

In view of the concept of guided waves discussed in Art. 8·01, we would like to describe the waves propagating along a uniform guiding system in terms of a propagation factor $e^{(j\omega t - \gamma z)}$, such as was found for transmission line waves in Chapter 1. The character of the propagation constant γ tells much about the properties of the wave, such as the degree of attenuation, the phase velocity, and the group velocity. We shall begin by writing Maxwell's equations for the dielectric region in rectangular coordinates (without inferring here any limitation to rectangular shapes of boundaries), with the factor $e^{(j\omega t - \gamma z)}$ substituted. Then by solution subject to the boundary conditions of particular guides we may find what waves, if any, exist in this propagating form, and the character of γ as well as the distributions of electric and magnetic fields in the wave.

The curl equations with the assumed functions $e^{(j\omega t - \gamma z)}$ are written below for fields in the dielectric of the system.

$$\nabla \times \bar{E} = -j\omega\mu\bar{H} \qquad\qquad \nabla \times \bar{H} = j\omega\epsilon\bar{E}$$

$$\frac{\partial E_z}{\partial y} + \gamma E_y = -j\omega\mu H_x \quad (1) \qquad\qquad \frac{\partial H_z}{\partial y} + \gamma H_y = j\omega\epsilon E_x \quad (4)$$

$$-\gamma E_x - \frac{\partial E_z}{\partial x} = -j\omega\mu H_y \quad (2) \qquad\qquad -\gamma H_x - \frac{\partial H_z}{\partial x} = j\omega\epsilon E_y \quad (5)$$

$$\frac{\partial E_y}{\partial x} - \frac{\partial E_x}{\partial y} = -j\omega\mu H_z \quad (3) \qquad\qquad \frac{\partial H_y}{\partial x} - \frac{\partial H_x}{\partial y} = j\omega\epsilon E_z \quad (6)$$

It must be remembered, in all analysis to follow, that these coefficients, E_x, H_x, E_y, etc., are functions of x and y only, by our agreement to take care of the z and time functions in the assumed $e^{(j\omega t - \gamma z)}$.

From the above equations, it is possible to solve for E_x, E_y, H_x, or H_y in terms of E_z and H_z. For example, H_x is found by eliminating E_y from (1) and (5), and a similar procedure gives the other components.

$$H_x = \frac{1}{\gamma^2 + k^2}\left[j\omega\epsilon\,\frac{\partial E_z}{\partial y} - \gamma\,\frac{\partial H_z}{\partial x}\right] \tag{7}$$

$$H_y = -\frac{1}{\gamma^2 + k^2}\left[j\omega\epsilon\,\frac{\partial E_z}{\partial x} + \gamma\,\frac{\partial H_z}{\partial y}\right] \tag{8}$$

$$E_x = -\frac{1}{\gamma^2 + k^2}\left[\gamma\,\frac{\partial E_z}{\partial x} + j\omega\mu\,\frac{\partial H_z}{\partial y}\right] \tag{9}$$

$$E_y = \frac{1}{\gamma^2 + k^2}\left[-\gamma\,\frac{\partial E_z}{\partial y} + j\omega\mu\,\frac{\partial H_z}{\partial x}\right] \tag{10}$$

where $k^2 = \omega^2\mu\epsilon$.

If the dielectric has finite conductivity, σ, it is merely necessary to substitute $\epsilon(1 + \sigma/j\omega\epsilon)$ for ϵ in the above expressions (Art. 7·17).

All waves propagating in the positive z direction according to the factor $e^{(j\omega t - \gamma z)}$ must have components related by these equations, since nothing has been assumed but this factor and Maxwell's equations. [For a wave traveling in the negative z direction, substitute $-\gamma$ for γ in (1) to (6) or (7) to (10).] The total electric and magnetic intensities in the charge-free regions between the conducting boundaries must also satisfy the wave equation (Art. 7·02):

$$\nabla^2\bar{E} = -k^2\bar{E} \qquad \nabla^2\bar{H} = -k^2\bar{H}$$

The three-dimensional ∇^2 may be broken into two parts:

$$\nabla^2\bar{E} = \nabla_{xy}^2\bar{E} + \frac{\partial^2\bar{E}}{\partial z^2}$$

The last term is the contribution to ∇^2 from derivatives in the axial direction. The first term is the two-dimensional Laplacian in the transverse plane, representing contributions to ∇^2 from derivatives in this plane. By the assumed propagation function, $e^{-\gamma z}$, in the axial direction,

$$\frac{\partial^2\bar{E}}{\partial z^2} = \gamma^2\bar{E}$$

The above wave equations may then be written

$$\nabla_{xy}{}^2\bar{E} = -(\gamma^2 + k^2)\bar{E} \tag{11}$$

$$\nabla_{xy}{}^2\bar{H} = -(\gamma^2 + k^2)\bar{H} \tag{12}$$

Equations (11) and (12) are the differential equations that must be satisfied in the dielectric region bounded by the conductors of the transmission lines or guides. The boundary conditions imposed on these differential equations follow from the configuration and the electrical properties of the conducting guides. Equations (1) to (6) or (7) to (10) then give the relations between any desired components in the wave.

8·03 BASIC WAVE TYPES

In studying guided waves along uniform systems, it is common to classify the wave solutions into the following types:

1. Waves that contain neither electric nor magnetic field in the direction of propagation. Since electric and magnetic field lines both lie entirely in the transverse plane, these may be called *transverse electromagnetic waves* (abbreviated *TEM*). They are the usual *transmission line waves* along a multi-conductor guide, and are also known as *principal waves*.

2. Waves that contain electric field but no magnetic field in the direction of propagation. Since the magnetic field lies in transverse planes, they are known as *transverse magnetic* (*TM*) waves. They have also been referred to in the literature as *E* waves, or waves of electric type.

3. Waves that contain magnetic field but no electric field in the direction of propagation. These are known as *transverse electric* (*TE*) waves, and have also been referred to as *H* waves or waves of magnetic type.

The above is not the only way in which the possible wave solutions may be broken into types, but it is a useful one in that any general field distribution excited in an ideal guide may be broken up into a number (possibly an infinite number) of the above types with suitable amplitudes and phases. The propagation constants of these tell how the individual waves change phase and amplitude as they travel down the guide, so that they may be superposed at any later position and time to give the total resultant field there. Of course, only one of the possible infinite number may propagate along the guiding system if it alone is excited and if conditions are favorable for its propagation. This is in fact the condition we try to approximate in most practical uses of wave guiding systems.

Simple Waves Guided by Parallel Planes

8·04 *TEM* WAVES GUIDED BY IDEAL PARALLEL PLANE CONDUCTORS

We wish to develop our physical pictures and techniques for analysis of guided waves by considering the simplest of all guiding systems, that of two infinite parallel conducting planes separated by a dielectric. Although this is an idealization, there are physical systems for which it is a good approximation. One of these is represented by the region between two coaxial conducting cylinders with only slightly different radii. Following the division of Art. 8·03, we shall begin with a study

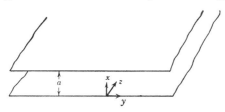

Fig. 8·04   Infinite parallel plane guide.

of those waves which have both electric and magnetic fields confined to the transverse plane.

Without explicitly solving the equations of Art. 8·02, it is evident that, if the planes are perfectly conducting, there is a solution of the transverse electromagnetic type (TEM) for the region between planes, for we may introduce a portion of a uniform plane wave as studied in Chapter 7, propagating in the z direction and polarized with its electric field in the x direction (Fig. 8·04). This is known to be a solution of the wave equation, and it obviously fulfills the requirements for a TEM wave. We know also that it must propagate with the velocity of light in the dielectric and that it has a ratio of electric field to magnetic field given by the intrinsic impedance η of the dielectric. We may then write the expressions for the fields ($e^{j\omega t}$ understood):

$$E_x(z) = E_0 e^{\mp jkz} \tag{1}$$

$$\eta H_y(z) = \pm E_0 e^{\mp jkz} \tag{2}$$

where $\qquad \eta = \sqrt{\mu/\epsilon} \qquad k = \omega \sqrt{\mu\epsilon} \tag{3}$

The upper signs in the above equations apply to a wave propagating in the positive z direction, and the lower signs to one propagating in the negative z direction.

The electric field E_x passing normally between planes induces equal and opposite charge densities on the two planes at a given value of z;

the uniform magnetic field H_y corresponds to equal and opposite currents flowing in the z direction in the two planes. These are properties we commonly associate with a two-conductor transmission line, so the wave studied here is recognized as the ordinary transmission line wave for this two-conductor system. The identification may be completed by deriving voltage and current from the field solution, comparing with the results from a classical transmission line solution. The voltage of the upper plate with respect to the lower may be found by integrating the electric field, .

$$V(z) = - \int_0^a E_x(z)\ dx = -aE_0 e^{\mp jkz} \tag{4}$$

Note that this result is independent of the path of integration *for all paths confined to the transverse plane*, since there is no H_z (Art. 4·18). The current per unit width in the upper plane is found from the rule $\bar{J} = \bar{n} \times \bar{H}$ developed in Art. 6·07,

$$J_z = -H_y$$

Thus, if a width b is taken in the y direction, the current in the upper plane is

$$I(z) = -bH_y = \mp \frac{bE_0}{\eta} e^{\mp jkz} \tag{5}$$

A direct solution of the transmission line equations (Art. 1·21) yields

$$V(z) = V_0 e^{\mp j\beta z} \tag{6}$$

$$I(z) = \left(\pm \frac{V_0}{Z_0} \right) e^{\mp j\beta z} \tag{7}$$

$$Z_0 = \sqrt{L/C} \qquad \beta = \omega \sqrt{LC} \tag{8}$$

But, for the parallel planes, the capacitance and inductance per unit length, for a width b, are

$$C = \frac{\epsilon b}{a} \quad \text{farads/meter} \tag{9}$$

$$L = \frac{\mu a}{b} \quad \text{henrys/meter} \tag{10}$$

So, from (8),

$$Z_0 = \sqrt{\left(\frac{\mu a}{b} \right)\left(\frac{a}{\epsilon b} \right)} = \frac{\eta a}{b} \quad \text{ohms} \tag{11}$$

$$\beta = \omega \sqrt{\left(\frac{\mu a}{b} \right)\left(\frac{\epsilon b}{a} \right)} = k \tag{12}$$

With these values and $V_0 = -aE_0$, (6) and (7) become identical with the results of the field solution, (4) and (5).

The power transferred by the wave may be calculated from the fields or from the classical transmission line solution. From the field viewpoint, the Poynting vector is found and integrated over the dielectric region between planes. Here it has a z component only, so that the average power transmitted by a single positive traveling wave is

$$W_T = b \int_0^a \frac{1}{2} \operatorname{Re} (E_x H_y{}^*) \, dx = \frac{ba}{2} \frac{E_0{}^2}{\eta} \quad \text{watts} \tag{13}$$

From the voltage-current viewpoint, the average power transmitted by a single positively traveling wave is

$$W_T = \frac{1}{2} \operatorname{Re} (VI^*) = \frac{V_0{}^2}{2Z_0} = \frac{E_0{}^2 ab}{2\eta} \tag{14}$$

so that the expressions for power computed from these two points of view are also identical.

PROBLEM

8·04 Starting from the equations of Art. 8·02, obtain the TEM wave solutions for this parallel-plane system and compare with (1) and (2) above. Show that there can be no TEM solution for this case with finite E_y.

8·05 *TEM* WAVES BETWEEN LOSSY PARALLEL PLANES; PHYSICAL APPROXIMATIONS

In the analysis of the preceding article, the conductor and dielectric were taken as ideal. For any actual guide, conductor and dielectric must have finite conductivities, and the resulting loss effects, which may be negligible for some applications, may not be for others. An exact solution will be set up in the following article. We are most often interested in guides for which the losses are small, so that approximations may be made which greatly simplify the solution and which provide good physical pictures for the effects of losses. The approximate techniques to be applied will be of great importance in the analysis of all guides to follow.

If the dielectric region between planes has a conductivity σ, as well as dielectric constant ϵ, we may proceed as in Art. 7·17, replacing $j\omega\epsilon$ by $(\sigma + j\omega\epsilon)$ in the loss-free solution. The propagation constant and wave impedance E_x/H_y are then

$$\gamma = \alpha + j\beta = \sqrt{j\omega\mu(\sigma + j\omega\epsilon)} \tag{1}$$

$$Z_z = \sqrt{\frac{j\omega\mu}{\sigma + j\omega\epsilon}} \tag{2}$$

For low-loss dielectrics, $\sigma/\omega\epsilon = \epsilon''/\epsilon' \ll 1$, these become

$$\alpha \approx \frac{\eta\sigma}{2} = \frac{k\epsilon''}{2\epsilon'} \tag{3}$$

$$\beta \approx k\left[1 + \frac{\sigma^2}{8\omega^2\epsilon^2}\right] = k\left[1 + \frac{1}{8}\left(\frac{\epsilon''}{\epsilon'}\right)^2\right] \tag{4}$$

$$Z_z \approx \eta\left\{\left[1 - \frac{3}{8}\left(\frac{\sigma}{\omega\epsilon}\right)^2\right] + j\frac{\sigma}{2\omega\epsilon}\right\} \tag{5}$$

If the conductor has a finite conductivity, the main effect will be an attenuation caused by the power loss in the conducting boundaries. The value of this attenuation may be estimated by the method of Art. 1·26, if the ratio of power loss per unit length to the average power transferred by the wave can be found. For a good conductor, it is reasonable to assume that the expression for power transfer derived for the ideal guide in Art. 8·04 applies well enough to the actual guide, and that power loss may be computed by taking the current flow of the ideal guide as flowing in the walls of the actual guide with known conductivity.

Let us assume that the conducting plates are thick compared with depth of penetration in the conducting material, and that the surface resistivity R_s is known. The average power loss per unit area would be $\frac{1}{2}R_s|J_z|^2$, so for a unit length and width b, counting both plates,

$$W_L = 2b\left[\frac{1}{2}R_s|J_z|^2\right] = bR_s|H_y|^2 = \frac{bR_sE_0^2}{\eta^2} \tag{6}$$

The average power transfer is given by Eq. 8·04(13). Attenuation constant is then

$$\alpha = \frac{W_L}{2W_T} \tag{7}$$

$$\alpha = \frac{1}{2}\left(\frac{bR_sE_0^2}{\eta^2}\right)\left(\frac{2\eta}{abE_0^2}\right) = \frac{R_s}{\eta a} \tag{8}$$

Note that the wave we are considering in the presence of finite conducting boundaries is not strictly a transverse electromagnetic wave since a small but finite axial electric field E_z is required to force the axial current flow along the conductors. The designation TEM is still ordinarily retained, since the fields are so nearly the same as those for the TEM wave of the ideal guide. The ratio of longitudinal to transverse electric field can be estimated. At the surface of the upper conductor,

$$E_z = J_z Z_s = -H_y R_s (1 + j) = -(1 + j) \frac{R_s E_0}{\eta}$$

or
$$\frac{E_z}{E_x} = \frac{E_z}{E_0} = -(1 + j) \frac{R_s}{\eta} \qquad (9)$$

This ratio is around 4×10^{-5} for copper conductor and air dielectric at 3000 megacycles per second and is thus exceedingly small for most practical systems.

If losses are present in both conductor and dielectric, attenuation may be found by adding (3) and (8) so long as both are small. The result is the same as would be obtained from the approximate transmission line formula, Eq. 1·24(14):

$$\alpha \approx \frac{R}{2Z_0} + \frac{GZ_0}{2} \qquad (10)$$

The proof of this will be left for a problem.

PROBLEMS

8·05a Show that the transmission line formula for attenuation constant (10) gives precisely the same result as the approximate wave analysis of this article for the wave under consideration.

8·05b Derive the approximate formula for attenuation constant due to dielectric losses by using Eq. (7).

8·05c Since E_z is equal and opposite at top and bottom conductors, it is reasonable to assume a linear variation between the two values,

$$E_z = (1 + j) \frac{R_s E_0}{\eta} \left(1 - \frac{2x}{a} \right)$$

Find the modification in the distribution for E_x to satisfy the divergence equation for $\bar{E}$. Find the corresponding modification in H_y from Maxwell's equations. Describe qualitatively the average Poynting vector as a function of position in the guide.

8·06　TEM WAVES BETWEEN LOSSY PARALLEL PLANES; MATHEMATICAL APPROXIMATIONS

The physical approximations for low-loss guides utilized in the preceding article are of first importance since they will be applied to nearly all the types of wave guiding systems to be studied in this book. It is consequently well to compare it with a rigorous solution for this simple case where one can be performed. The model is that of Fig. 8·06, in which the upper and lower conductors are infinite in depth, and the origin of x has been moved to the middle of the guide in order to take advantage of the symmetry. Variations of all quantities in the y direction are neglected. Dielectric constant, permeability, and conductivity for the two regions are ϵ_1, μ_1, σ_1, and ϵ_2, μ_2, σ_2, respectively.

For the dielectric region 1, let us solve Equation 8·02(11) for E_z:

$$\nabla_{xy}{}^2 E_z = \frac{d^2 E_z}{dx^2} = -K_1{}^2 E_z \tag{1}$$

$$K_1{}^2 = \gamma^2 - j\omega\mu_1(\sigma_1 + j\omega\epsilon_1) \tag{2}$$

Note that $(\sigma_1 + j\omega\epsilon_1)$ has been substituted for $j\omega\epsilon_1$ in Eq. 8·02(11). The solution may be written in sinusoids. We shall look for a solution

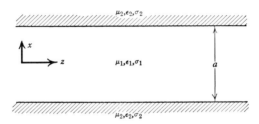

Fig. 8·06   Model for mathematical solution of waves between imperfectly conducting planes.

with E_z odd in x and so retain only the sine term:

$$E_{z1} = C_1 \sin K_1 x \tag{3}$$

E_x and H_y may be found from Eqs. 8·02(9) and (8), respectively:

$$E_{x1} = -\frac{\gamma}{K_1} C_1 \cos K_1 x \tag{4}$$

$$H_{y1} = \frac{-(\sigma_1 + j\omega\epsilon_1)}{K_1} C_1 \cos K_1 x \tag{5}$$

For the conducting region 2, we also write Eq. 8·02(11), using the same γ as in region 1, since continuity relations between the fields of the two regions must be satisfied at the boundary for all values of z:

$$\frac{d^2 E_z}{dx^2} = -K_2{}^2 E_z \tag{6}$$

$$K_2{}^2 = \gamma^2 - j\omega\mu_2(\sigma_2 + j\omega\epsilon_2) \tag{7}$$

Let us write the solution for (6) in terms of exponentials, retaining only the negative exponential terms so that fields will die off properly as x approaches infinity. [This means that we select the square root of (7) so that jK_2 has a positive real part.]

$$E_{z2} = C_2 e^{-jK_2 x} \tag{8}$$

The fields E_x and H_y from Eqs. 8·02(8) and (9) are then

$$E_{x2} = \frac{j\gamma}{K_2} C_2 e^{-jK_2 x} \tag{9}$$

$$H_{y2} = \frac{j(\sigma_2 + j\omega\epsilon_2)}{K_2} C_2 e^{-jK_2 x} \tag{10}$$

At the boundary between conductor and dielectric, $x = a/2$, the tangential fields E_z and H_y must be continuous. For the continuity of E_z, (3) and (8) give

$$C_1 \sin\left(\frac{K_1 a}{2}\right) = C_2 e^{-jK_2 a/2} \tag{11}$$

For the continuity of H_y, (5) and (10) give

$$-\frac{(\sigma_1 + j\omega\epsilon_1)}{K_1} C_1 \cos\left(\frac{K_1 a}{2}\right) = \frac{j(\sigma_2 + j\omega\epsilon_2)}{K_2} C_2 e^{-jK_2 a/2} \tag{12}$$

Substituting the value of C_2 from (11), we have

$$\tan\left(\frac{K_1 a}{2}\right) = \frac{(\sigma_1 + j\omega\epsilon_1) jK_2}{(\sigma_2 + j\omega\epsilon_2) K_1} \tag{13}$$

Since in (13) all quantities are known but γ, the equation in principle determines the value of propagation constant. However, since the equation is a transcendental containing complex quantities, it is not easy to solve in the general case. We shall then go to the special low-loss case which is of greatest interest to us. Let us take the conductivity of the dielectric as negligible, and the displacement currents in the conductor as negligible, so that we may neglect σ_1 and ϵ_2. Since we know from the preceding articles that γ^2 should turn out to be of the same order as $\omega^2 \mu\epsilon$, it is also consistent to neglect γ^2 in (7) compared with $j\omega\mu_2\sigma_2$ (i.e., this means that $\omega\epsilon_1/\sigma_2 \ll 1$). K_2 may then be written in terms of the depth of penetration δ defined in Art. 6·05:

$$jK_2 = (j\omega\mu_2\sigma_2)^{\frac{1}{2}} = \frac{(1+j)}{\delta_2} \tag{14}$$

From (2), $$K_1{}^2 = \gamma^2 + \omega^2\mu_1\epsilon_1 = \gamma^2 + k_1{}^2 \tag{15}$$

Since from the approximate analysis we expect γ^2 to be near the value $(-k_1{}^2)$ found for the ideal case, K_1 should be very small, and it is reasonable for first order analysis to approximate the tangent by the angle in (13). (This point can be checked when final results are obtained.)

$$\frac{K_1{}^2 a}{2} = \left(\frac{j\omega\epsilon_1}{\sigma_2}\right) jK_2$$

$$(\gamma^2 + k_1{}^2) = \frac{2j\omega\epsilon_1(1 + j)}{a(\sigma_2\delta_2)} = \frac{2j(1 + j)\omega\epsilon_1 R_{s2}}{a}$$

$$\gamma^2 = -k_1{}^2\left[1 - \frac{2j(1 + j)R_{s2}}{k_1 a\eta_1}\right]$$

It can be checked that the last term is small so long as frequency is high enough so that $k_1 a$ is not less than, say, 10^{-3}, so the square root may be approximated by two terms of the binomial expansion.

$$\gamma \approx jk_1\left[1 - \frac{j(1 + j)R_{s2}}{k_1 a\eta_1}\right]$$

$$\alpha + j\beta \approx \frac{R_{s2}}{a\eta_1} + jk_1\left[1 + \frac{R_{s2}}{k_1 a\eta_1}\right] \tag{16}$$

The expression for α is the same as that of the last article where approximations were made on a physical basis. By the analysis of this article we can see that these approximations are justified whenever

$$\frac{\sigma_1}{\omega\epsilon_1} \ll 1 \qquad \frac{\omega\epsilon_2}{\sigma_2} \ll 1 \tag{17}$$

That is, conduction current should be small compared with displacement current in the dielectric, but displacement current should be small compared with conduction current in the conductor. A study of the field expressions shows that electric field is very nearly transverse in the dielectric ($E_{z1} \ll E_{x1}$) and very nearly longitudinal in the conductor ($E_{x2} \ll E_{z2}$).

PROBLEMS

8·06a   Find the ratios E_{z1}/E_{x1} and E_{x2}/E_{z2} for the low-loss case at $x = a/2$. What type of polarization is represented in each case?

8·06b   For the low-loss case show that the fields in the dielectric have nearly the form assumed in Prob. 8·05c.

8·07 TRANSVERSE MAGNETIC WAVES BETWEEN PARALLEL PLANES

In the second classification given in Art. 8·03, the waves are to have an electric field component but no magnetic field in the direction of propagation. We can find many of the important properties for these TM waves by studying them in the simple guiding system formed by parallel-plane conductors, as we did for the TEM waves in preceding articles. We shall first give a fairly straightforward solution of the equations subject to the boundary conditions of the planes, and then give a physical picture for arriving at the same results by considering the waves as made up of a superposition of uniform plane waves.

Since the TM wave is to have a non-zero E_z, let us write Eq. 8·02(11) in terms of E_z. We are assuming no variations with y.

$$\nabla_{xy}{}^2 E_z = \frac{d^2 E_z}{dx^2} = -K^2 E_z \tag{1}$$

$$K^2 = \gamma^2 + k^2 = \gamma^2 + \omega^2 \mu \epsilon \tag{2}$$

The solution to (1) may be written in terms of either sinusoids or exponentials, but, since the perfectly conducting planes require that E_z be zero at $x = 0$ and $x = a$, we shall select the sinusoidal form because of its repeated zeros. The cosine terms may also be eliminated if the bottom plate is taken as $x = 0$.

$$E_z = A \sin Kx \tag{3}$$

But E_z must also be zero at the upper plate, $x = a$. There must then be a half-period of the sine wave or a multiple thereof between the planes.

$$Ka = n\pi \tag{4}$$

The remaining field components may be found from Eqs. 8·02(7) to (10), remembering that $H_z = 0$ and $\partial/\partial y = 0$.

$$
\begin{aligned}
E_z &= A \sin\left(\frac{n\pi x}{a}\right) \\[2mm]
E_x &= -\frac{\gamma}{K^2}\frac{\partial E_z}{\partial x} = -\frac{\gamma}{K} A \cos\left(\frac{n\pi x}{a}\right) \\[2mm]
H_y &= -\frac{j\omega\epsilon}{K^2}\frac{\partial E_z}{\partial x} = -\frac{j\omega\epsilon}{K} A \cos\left(\frac{n\pi x}{a}\right) \\[2mm]
H_x &= 0 \\[2mm]
E_y &= 0
\end{aligned}
\tag{5}
$$

The above set of fields satisfies Maxwell's equations for the dielectric region, and for n an integer fulfills the boundary condition that electric field tangential to the planes shall be zero.   Hence, there are many "modes" of this TM type, one for each integer n.   A particular one with n half-sine variations between the plates may be designated as TM_{n0} (the zero to denote that there are no variations with y).

The propagation constant for the nth mode may now be found from (2) and (4):

$$\gamma = \sqrt{K^2 - k^2} = \sqrt{\left(\frac{n\pi}{a}\right)^2 - \omega^2\mu\epsilon} \tag{6}$$

A study of this form reveals a very important characteristic which we will find for TM and TE waves in all closed guides.   For a particular spacing, a and mode number n, $(n\pi/a)^2$ is a real number.   For frequencies low enough so that $k < n\pi/a$, γ will have a real result representing attenuation only.   As frequency is increased, we come to a condition (called the cut-off of the mode) where $k = n\pi/a$ and $\gamma = 0$, so that there is neither phase shift nor attenuation along the guide. As frequency is increased more, $k > n\pi/a$ and (6) yields a purely imaginary result so that the mode propagates without attenuation. From the above, the cut-off condition may be written

$$k_c = 2\pi f_c \sqrt{\mu\epsilon} = \frac{2\pi}{\lambda_c} = \frac{n\pi}{a} \tag{7}$$

where λ_c is the wavelength of a uniform plane wave in the dielectric at the cut-off frequency.   We can then write (6) in terms of the cut-off frequency for the particular mode of interest.

$$\gamma = \alpha = \frac{n\pi}{a} \sqrt{1 - (f/f_c)^2} \qquad f < f_c \tag{8a}$$

$$\gamma = j\beta = jk \sqrt{1 - (f_c/f)^2} \qquad f > f_c \tag{8b}$$

For the propagating range $(f > f_c)$, phase and group velocities are (Art. 1·27)

$$v_p = \frac{\omega}{\beta} = v/\sqrt{1 - (f_c/f)^2} \tag{9}$$

$$v_g = \frac{d\omega}{d\beta} = v \sqrt{1 - (f_c/f)^2} \tag{10}$$

The wavelength measured along the guide in the z direction is the distance represented by a phase shift of 2π, and is denoted λ_g:

$$\lambda_g = \frac{\lambda}{\sqrt{1 - (f_c/f)^2}} \tag{11}$$

The wave or field impedance is another useful concept (Art. 7·12) and is here defined as the ratio of transverse electric to magnetic field components:

$$Z_z = \frac{E_x}{H_y} = \frac{\gamma}{j\omega\epsilon} = \frac{-jn\pi}{a\omega\epsilon}\sqrt{1 - (f/f_c)^2} \qquad f < f_c \qquad (12a)$$

$$Z_z = \eta\sqrt{1 - (f_c/f)^2} \qquad\qquad\qquad f > f_c \qquad (12b)$$

Note that it is real in the propagating range and imaginary in the attenuating range, so that there is average power transferred in the former case but not in the latter.

8·08   PHYSICAL DISCUSSION OF TRANSVERSE MAGNETIC WAVE

Let us study the field distribution in a single positively traveling TM mode having one half-sine variation in x (i.e., $n = 1$). It will be convenient to write the field expressions in true instantaneous form by taking the real part of the complex expressions of Art. 8·07 (see Art. 4·09):

$$E_z(x,z,t) = \mathrm{Re}\left[A \sin\frac{\pi x}{a} e^{j(\omega t - \beta z)} \right] = A \sin\frac{\pi x}{a}\cos(\omega t - \beta z)$$

$$E_x(x,z,t) = \mathrm{Re}\left[-\frac{j\beta a}{\pi} A \cos\frac{\pi x}{a} e^{j(\omega t - \beta z)} \right] = \frac{\beta a}{\pi} A \cos\frac{\pi x}{a}\sin(\omega t - \beta z)$$

$$H_y(x,z,t) = \mathrm{Re}\left[-\frac{j\omega\epsilon a A}{\pi} \cos\frac{\pi x}{a} e^{j(\omega t - \beta z)} \right] = \frac{\omega\epsilon a}{\pi} A \cos\frac{\pi x}{a}\sin(\omega t - \beta z)$$

Let us consider the distribution at a particular instant of time, say $t = 0$:

$$E_z(x,z,0) = A \sin\frac{\pi x}{a}\cos\beta z \qquad\qquad (1)$$

$$E_x(x,z,0) = \frac{-\beta a A}{\pi}\cos\frac{\pi x}{a}\sin\beta z \qquad\qquad (2)$$

$$H_y(x,z,0) = \frac{-\omega\epsilon a A}{\pi}\cos\frac{\pi x}{a}\sin\beta z \qquad\qquad (3)$$

The slope of the electric field lines in the x-z plane are

$$\frac{dx}{dz} = \frac{E_x}{E_z} = -\frac{\beta a}{\pi}\cot\frac{\pi x}{a}\tan\beta z \qquad\qquad (4)$$

The lines may be sketched either by drawing in the direction of the tangents at a number of points throughout the field, or by integrating

(4) to give the equation of the family of electric field lines (Prob. 8·08a). A few of these field lines are shown in Fig. 8·08a.

Note that in this mode electric field lines start from charges on the guide walls, and pass to charges of opposite sign, not on the opposite plane as in the TEM mode, but on the same plane a half guide wavelength along in the z direction. The axial displacement currents are surrounded by magnetic field lines (considering the magnetic field lines as closing at $y = \pm \infty$). Note that displacement current and H_y are maximum, not at $\beta z = 0$ where E_z is a maximum, but at $\beta z = \pm \pi/2$ where its rate of change is a maximum.

A somewhat different physical picture in terms of wave reflections may be developed for the TM modes between parallel planes by reference to Art. 7·11. That article was concerned with the reflection of a uniform plane wave from a perfectly conducting plane when incident at any angle θ from the normal. It was found that the tangential component of electric field was zero at the conductor, and also at planes parallel to the conductor and distance $n\lambda/2 \cos \theta$ away. Hence, a second perfectly conducting plane could be placed at any of the positions characterized by a given value of n without disturbing the fields. The field solution found in that article, Eqs. (11) to (13), should then apply directly to the parallel-plane guide. (The x and z coordinates must be interchanged to correspond to the coordinate system set up for the present analysis.)

Thus, if the spacing between plates is a,

$$a = \frac{n\lambda}{2 \cos \theta}$$

or
$$\cos \theta = \frac{n\lambda}{2a} \tag{5}$$

For the $n = 1$ mode, for example, θ will be zero if the spacing between plates is just a half-wavelength; the wave will bounce back and forth between the plates with nodes at $x = 0$ and $x = a$; and there will be no tendency for propagation in the z direction. This is the condition we have called cut-off. As frequency is raised (λ decreased), $\lambda/2a$ will be less than unity and θ will take on a finite value representing some component of propagation in the z direction as pictured in Figs. 8·08b, c. That is, since the spacing a is greater than a half-wavelength measured normal to a wave front, the wave must tip somewhat to make the distance between zeros of E_z still correspond to a. This is accomplished since the phase velocity measured in the x direction is $v/\cos \theta$ and is consequently greater than v (where $v = 1/\sqrt{\mu\epsilon}$). If frequency is raised so that $\lambda/2a$ is very small, $\cos\theta$ must also be small and the plane wave components propagate nearly in the axial direction of the guide (Fig. 8·08d).

The phase velocity in the z direction may be obtained from this picture:

$$v_{pz} = \frac{v}{\sin\theta} = v/\sqrt{1 - \cos^2\theta} \tag{6}$$

But

$$\cos\theta = \frac{n\lambda}{2a} = \frac{\lambda}{\lambda_c} = \frac{f_c}{f}$$

so

$$v_{pz} = v/\sqrt{1 - (f_c/f)^2} \tag{7}$$

Therefore this result is the same as that obtained by the detailed analysis of Art. 8·07. In fact, all the properties of the TM mode in

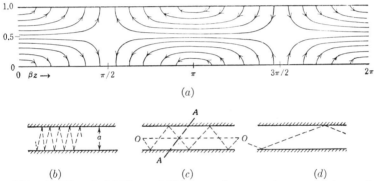

(a)

(b) $\qquad$ (c) $\qquad$ (d)

Fig. 8·08 $\quad(a)$ Electric field lines of TM_{10} wave between plane conductors. (bcd) Waves guided by two parallel conducting planes.

the propagating range could be similarly derived from this analysis of the TM wave into component uniform plane waves propagating and reflecting at an angle from the boundary.

PROBLEMS

8·08a Show that the curve of an electric field line corresponding to (1) and (2) is expressed by

$$\cos\beta z = \frac{\cos(\pi x_0/a)}{\cos(\pi x/a)}.$$

Plot a few lines for selected values of x_0/a. (x_0 is the value of x for a particular curve at $z = 0$.)

8·08b Sketch the form of electric and magnetic field lines, showing sense, for a single positively traveling TM mode between planes with $n = 2$.

8·08c By suitably changing coordinates and notation, show that the field distributions of Art. 8·07 for the TM wave and of Eqs. 7·11(11) to (13) for uniform plane waves reflected at oblique incidence are identical.

8·08d Obtain the expressions for wave impedance, using the picture of uniform plane waves reflecting at an angle.

8·09 EFFECT OF LOSSES ON *TM* WAVES BETWEEN PLANES

It will be assumed that dielectric and conductor are reasonably good so that attenuation may be calculated in the approximate manner demonstrated previously for the TEM wave (Art. 8·05).

Losses in the dielectric may be taken into account by substituting $(\sigma + j\omega\epsilon)$ for $j\omega\epsilon$ in the loss-free analysis. The expression for propagation constant, Eq. 8·07(6), becomes

$$
\gamma = \left[\left(\frac{n\pi}{a} \right)^2 - \omega^2\mu\epsilon \left(1 - \frac{j\sigma}{\omega\epsilon} \right) \right]^{1/2}
$$

$$
\approx \left[\left(\frac{n\pi}{a} \right)^2 - \omega^2\mu\epsilon \right]^{1/2} \left\{ 1 + \frac{j\omega\mu\sigma}{2} \left[\left(\frac{n\pi}{a} \right)^2 - \omega^2\mu\epsilon \right]^{-1} \right\} \tag{1}
$$

The above approximation retains only two terms of the binomial expansion and is valid for

$$
\omega\mu\sigma \ll \left| \left(\frac{n\pi}{a} \right)^2 - \omega^2\mu\epsilon \right| \tag{2}
$$

Utilizing the cut-off frequency defined in Eq. 8·07(7),

$$
\left(\frac{n\pi}{a} \right) = 2\pi f_c \sqrt{\mu\epsilon}
$$

$$
\gamma = \frac{\omega\mu\sigma}{2\omega \sqrt{\mu\epsilon} \sqrt{1 - (f_c/f)^2}} + j\omega \sqrt{\mu\epsilon} \sqrt{1 - (f_c/f)^2} \tag{3}
$$

The phase constant (imaginary part of γ) is the same as that obtained in the loss-free case to the extent of this approximation. The attenuation constant (real part of γ) is

$$
\alpha_d = \frac{\eta\sigma}{2 \sqrt{1 - (f_c/f)^2}} = \frac{k\epsilon''}{2\epsilon' \sqrt{1 - (f_c/f)^2}} \quad \text{nepers/meter} \tag{4}
$$

where $\qquad \eta = \sqrt{\mu/\epsilon} \qquad \epsilon'' = \sigma/\omega\epsilon_0 \qquad k = \omega \sqrt{\mu\epsilon}$

Note that α apparently approaches infinity as the frequency approaches cutoff, but this does not actually happen since condition (2) breaks down for any finite σ as the cut-off frequency is approached.

To compute the attenuation caused by conductor losses, the power transfer for the loss-free case will be found, and also the power loss per unit length, taking the currents flowing in the actual conductors the same as in the ideal conductors. The average power transfer for a width b is found by a Poynting integration:

$$
\begin{aligned}
W_T &= b \int_0^a \tfrac{1}{2}(E_x H_y{}^*) \, dx \\
&= \frac{b}{2} \int_0^a \left(-\frac{j\beta a}{n\pi} A \cos \frac{n\pi x}{a} e^{-j\beta z} \right) \left(\frac{j\omega\epsilon a}{n\pi} A \cos \frac{n\pi x}{a} e^{j\beta z} \right) dx \\
&= \frac{b}{2} \frac{\omega\epsilon\beta a^2 A^2}{n^2\pi^2} \int_0^a \cos^2 \frac{n\pi x}{a} \, dx = \left(\frac{b\omega\epsilon\beta a^2 A^2}{2\pi^2 n^2} \right) \frac{a}{2}
\end{aligned} \tag{5}
$$

The current flow in upper and lower planes has the same magnitude. For the lower plane the current per unit width is

$$
\left| J_z \right| = \left| H_y \right|_{x=0} = \frac{\omega\epsilon a A}{n\pi}
$$

The total power loss for a unit length and width b, counting both planes, is

$$
W_L = \frac{2bR_s \left| J_z \right|^2}{2} = \frac{bR_s \omega^2 \epsilon^2 a^2 A^2}{n^2 \pi^2} \tag{6}
$$

The attenuation arising from conductor losses is then approximately

$$
\alpha_c = \frac{W_L}{2W_T} = \frac{2R_s \omega\epsilon}{\beta a}
$$

$$
\alpha_c = \frac{2R_s \omega\epsilon}{a\omega \sqrt{\mu\epsilon} \sqrt{1 - (f_c/f)^2}} = \frac{2R_s}{\eta a \sqrt{1 - (f_c/f)^2}} \quad \text{nepers/meter} \tag{7}
$$

where, in terms of μ_2 and σ_2 of the conductor,

$$
R_s = \sqrt{\pi f \mu_2 / \sigma_2}
$$

The expression for attenuation caused by conductor losses also approaches infinity at cut-off, but again the approximations entering into its derivation break down in that region so that the expression does not apply there. The attenuation will, however, be high at cut-off and decrease with frequency until a frequency of $\sqrt{3} f_c$ is reached beyond which the surface resistivity in the numerator takes over and attenuation again increases with frequency. The form of the curve is shown in Fig. 8·09.

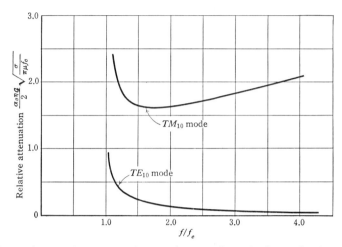

Fig. 8·09   Attenuation curves of waves between imperfectly conducting planes.

PROBLEM

8·09   Prove that the frequency of minimum attenuation due to conductor losses for the TM mode is at $f = \sqrt{3} f_c$, and find the expression for this minimum attenuation.   Calculate its value for copper conductors 5 cm apart with air dielectric for the $n = 1, 2,$ and 3 modes.

8·10 TRANSVERSE ELECTRIC WAVES BETWEEN PARALLEL PLANES

Since the analysis and characteristics of the transverse electric waves are very similar to those for the transverse magnetic waves, they will be treated more briefly.   Equation 8·02(12) may be written in terms of the non-zero H_z:

$$\nabla_{xy}{}^2 H_z = \frac{d^2 H_z}{dx^2} = -K^2 H_z \tag{1}$$

$$K^2 = \gamma^2 + k^2 \tag{2}$$

The solution will again be written in terms of sinusoids, but this time only the cosine term is retained since E_y, proportional to the derivative of H_z with x, must become zero at the perfectly conducting plane $x = 0$:

$$H_z = B \cos Kx \tag{3}$$

From Eqs. 8·02(7) to (10), remembering that E_z is zero,

$$H_x = -\frac{\gamma}{K^2}\frac{\partial H_z}{\partial x} = \frac{\gamma}{K} B \sin Kx \tag{4}$$

$$E_y = \frac{j\omega\mu}{K^2}\frac{\partial H_z}{\partial x} = -\frac{j\omega\mu}{K} B \sin Kx \tag{5}$$

$$E_x = 0 \tag{6}$$

$$H_y = 0 \tag{7}$$

E_y must be zero at the conducting plane $x = a$ also, so K is determined from (4) as some multiple of π/a. As with the TM wave, this is identified from (2) as the value of k at cut-off.

$$K = 2\pi f_c \sqrt{\mu\epsilon} = n\pi/a \tag{8}$$

Propagation constant from (2) may then be written

$$\gamma = \alpha = (n\pi/a) \sqrt{1 - (f/f_c)^2} \qquad f < f_c \tag{9}$$

$$\gamma = j\beta = jk \sqrt{1 - (f_c/f)^2} \qquad f > f_c \tag{10}$$

The forms for attenuation constant in the cut-off range and phase constant in the propagating range are thus exactly the same as for the TM waves, and by (8) conditions for cut-off are the same for TE modes as for TM modes of the same order. The expressions for phase velocity, group velocity, and guide wavelength in the propagating range follow from (10) and are exactly the same as Eqs. 8·07(9) to (11).

Wave or field impedance for the TE wave is

$$Z_z = -\frac{E_y}{H_x} = \frac{j\omega\mu}{\gamma} = \frac{j\omega\mu}{j\omega \sqrt{\mu\epsilon} \sqrt{1 - (f_c/f)^2}}$$

$$Z_z = \eta/\sqrt{1 - (f_c/f)^2} \tag{11}$$

For frequencies below cut-off this wave impedance is imaginary, but for frequencies above cut-off it is real and always greater than η, as contrasted to the wave impedance for TM waves, which is always less than η.

The form of the field lines for the first order TE mode is indicated in Fig. 8·10. Here the magnetic field lines form closed curves surrounding the y-direction displacement current. There is no charge induced on the conducting plates and only a y component of current corresponding to the finite H_z tangential to the plates. The TE waves may also be considered as made up of uniform plane waves propagating and reflecting from the planes at an angle θ from the normal, as pictured in Figs. 8·08b–d, but here the component plane waves are polarized with the electric field normal to the plane of incidence so that Eqs. 7·11(18) to (20) apply. The relation between angle θ and f_c/f is, as for the TM waves, Eq. 8·08(5).

If the dielectric is lossy, the approximate expression for attenuation constant is the same as for TM waves, Eq. 8·09(4), since this was derived from the formula for propagation constant which is common to both types of waves.

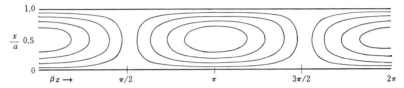

Fig. 8·10   Magnetic field lines of TE_{10} wave between plane conductors.

If the conductor has finite conductivity, the attenuation constant may be computed in terms of power loss and power transfer as before. The power loss per unit length, for a width b of both planes, is

$$W_L = 2bR_s \frac{\left| H_z \right|^2_{x=0}}{2} = bR_s B^2 \tag{12}$$

The average power transferred by the wave is

$$W_T = \frac{b}{2} \int_0^a (-E_y H_x{}^*)\,dx = \frac{b}{2}\frac{a}{2}\frac{\beta a}{\pi}\frac{\omega\mu a}{\pi} B^2 \tag{13}$$

So the attenuation constant arising from conductor losses is

$$\alpha_c = \frac{W_L}{2W_T} = \frac{4\pi^2 R_s}{2\beta\omega\mu a^3} = \frac{4R_s\omega_c{}^2\mu\epsilon\,\sqrt{\epsilon}}{2\omega^2\mu\epsilon\,\sqrt{\mu}\,a\,\sqrt{1-(f_c/f)^2}}$$

$$= \frac{2R_s f_c{}^2}{\eta a f^2\,\sqrt{1-(f_c/f)^2}} \tag{14}$$

Note that, unlike that for TM waves, this expression shows a continually decreasing attenuation with increasing frequency (Fig. 8·09).

PROBLEMS

8·10a   Derive the expression for the curves in the x-z plane corresponding to the magnetic field lines. Sketch a few for a single positively traveling $n = 2$ TE mode. Show sense and indicate position and sense of electric field.

8·10b By suitably changing coordinates and notation, show that the expressions 7·11(18) to (20) for plane waves reflecting from a plane at an oblique angle give exactly the fields of the TE modes of this article.

8·10c In the curve showing the attenuation caused by conductor losses as a function of f/f_c (Fig. 8·09), explain qualitatively the reason for the decrease of attenuation with increasing frequency.

General Analysis of Guided Waves

8·11   TRANSVERSE ELECTROMAGNETIC OR TRANSMISSION LINE WAVES

Now that certain points of view toward guided waves have been developed through the study of the special case of parallel-plane conductors, it is desirable to study those properties of TEM, TM, and TE waves which can be found independently of the shape of the cylindrical guiding conductor. The general analysis follows quite closely that given by Schelkunoff.[1]

The first of the basic wave types to be studied is that with neither electric nor magnetic field in the direction of propagation. This has been termed a transverse electromagnetic wave. In the simple case of propagation between perfectly conducting parallel planes, such a wave was identified exactly with the ordinary wave expected from transmission line theory. It will now be shown that this must be true for any general cross section of a uniform guiding line with perfect conductors along which this wave type may exist. (The types of guides on which it may not exist will be apparent once its characteristics are found.)

The general relations between wave components as expressed by Eq. 8·02(7) to Eq. 8·02(10) show that, with E_z and H_z zero, all other components must of necessity also be zero, unless $\gamma^2 + k^2$ is at the same time zero. Thus, a transverse electromagnetic wave must satisfy the condition

$$\gamma^2 + k^2 = 0$$

or $\qquad\qquad \gamma = \pm jk = \pm j\omega/v = \pm j\omega \sqrt{\mu\epsilon} \qquad\qquad (1)$

For a perfect dielectric, the propagation constant γ is thus a purely imaginary quantity, signifying that any completely transverse electromagnetic wave must propagate unattenuated, and with velocity v, the velocity of light in the dielectric bounded by the guide.

With (1) satisfied, the wave equations, as written in the form of Eqs. 8·02(11) and 8·02(12), reduce to

$$\nabla_{xy}^2 \bar{E} = 0 \qquad \nabla_{xy}^2 \bar{H} = 0 \qquad\qquad (2)$$

[1] S. A. Schelkunoff, "Transmission Theory of Plane Electromagnetic Waves," *Proc. I.R.E.*, **25**, 1457–1492 (Nov. 1937).

These are exactly the form of the two-dimensional Laplace's equation written for $\bar{E}$ and $\bar{H}$ in the transverse plane. Since E_z and H_z are zero, $\bar{E}$ and $\bar{H}$ lie entirely in the transverse plane. In Art. 3·02 it was found that electric and magnetic fields both satisfy Laplace's equation under static conditions. Consequently it may be concluded that the field distribution in the transverse plane is exactly a static distribution, if it can be shown that boundary conditions to be applied to the differential equations (2) are the same as those for a static field distribution. The boundary condition for the TEM wave on a perfect conducting guide is that electric field at the surface of the conductor can have a normal component only, which is the same as the condition at a conducting boundary in statics. The line integral of the electric field between conductors is the same for all paths lying in a given transverse plane,

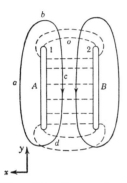

Fig. 8·11 Two-conductor transmission line with integration paths.

and may be thought of as corresponding to a potential difference between the conductors for that value of z.

To study the character of the magnetic field, note Eqs. 8·02(1) and 8·02(4) with zero E_z and H_z.

$$H_y = \frac{j\omega\epsilon}{\gamma} E_x = \frac{E_x}{\eta} \tag{3}$$

and

$$H_x = -\frac{\gamma}{j\omega\mu} E_y = -\frac{E_y}{\eta} \tag{4}$$

[The signs of (3) and (4) are for a positively traveling wave; for a negatively traveling wave they are opposite.] Study shows that (3) and (4) are conditions which require that electric and magnetic field be everywhere normal to each other. In particular, magnetic field must be tangential to the conducting surfaces since electric field is normal to them. The magnetic field pattern in the transverse plane then corresponds exactly to that arising from static currents flowing entirely on the surfaces of the perfect conductors.

The above characteristics show that a transverse electromagnetic wave may be guided by two or more conductors, or outside a single conductor, but not inside a closed conducting region, since it can have only the distributions of the corresponding two-dimensional static problem, and no electrostatic field can exist inside a source-free region completely closed by a conductor. (See Problem 8·11b.)

In addition to the above general properties of TEM waves along perfectly conducting guides for which this type may exist, we may show an exact identity with the ordinary transmission line equations for such cases.   In order that a definite example may be referred to, consider a line consisting of two conductors A and B of any general shape, Fig. 8·11.   We shall, for the demonstration, be quite general regarding time and z functions, merely requiring that E_z and H_z be zero.   The voltage between the two lines may be found by integrating electric field over any path between lines, such as that shown, 1-0-2.   It will have the same value no matter which path is chosen, since $\bar{E}$ does satisfy Laplace's equation in the transverse plane and so may be considered the gradient of a scalar potential in so far as variations in the transverse plane are concerned.

$$V = - \int_1^2 \bar{E} \cdot \overline{dl} = - \int_1^2 (E_x \, dx + E_y \, dy)$$

Differentiate the above equation with respect to z.

$$\frac{\partial V}{\partial z} = - \int_1^2 \left(\frac{\partial E_x}{\partial z} \, dx + \frac{\partial E_y}{\partial z} \, dy \right)$$

But the curl relation,

$$\nabla \times \bar{E} = - \frac{\partial \bar{B}}{\partial t}$$

shows that, if E_z is zero,

$$\frac{\partial E_y}{\partial z} = \frac{\partial B_x}{\partial t} \qquad \text{and} \qquad \frac{\partial E_x}{\partial z} = - \frac{\partial B_y}{\partial t}$$

By substituting these in the above equation,

$$\frac{\partial V}{\partial z} = - \frac{\partial}{\partial t} \int_1^2 (-B_y \, dx + B_x \, dy)$$

A study of Fig. 8·11 reveals that the quantity inside the integral is the magnetic flux flowing across the path 1-0-2, per unit length in the z direction.   According to the usual definition of inductance, this may be written as the product of inductance L per unit length and the current I:

$$\frac{\partial V}{\partial z} = \frac{\partial}{\partial t} (LI) = -L \frac{\partial I}{\partial t} \qquad (5)$$

The above is one of the differential equations used as a starting point for conventional transmission line analysis (Art. 1·16).   The other may be developed by starting with current in line A as the integral of magnetic field about a path a-b-c-d-a. (There is no contribution from displacement current since there is no E_z.)

$$I = \oint \bar{H} \cdot \bar{dl} = \oint (H_x\,dx + H_y\,dy)$$

Differentiate with respect to z.

$$\frac{\partial I}{\partial z} = \oint \left(\frac{\partial H_x}{\partial z}\,dx + \frac{\partial H_y}{\partial z}\,dy \right)$$

From the curl equation,

$$\nabla \times \bar{H} = \frac{\partial \bar{D}}{\partial t}$$

it follows that, if $H_z = 0$,

$$\frac{\partial H_y}{\partial z} = -\frac{\partial D_x}{\partial t} \quad \text{and} \quad \frac{\partial H_x}{\partial z} = \frac{\partial D_y}{\partial t}$$

Substituting,

$$\frac{\partial I}{\partial z} = -\frac{\partial}{\partial t} \oint (D_x\,dy - D_y\,dx)$$

Inspection of the figure shows that this must be the electric displacement flux per unit length of line crossing from one conductor to the other. Since it corresponds to the charge per unit length on the conductors, it may be written as the product of capacity per unit length and the voltage between lines:

$$\frac{\partial I}{\partial z} = -C\frac{\partial V}{\partial t} \tag{6}$$

Equations (5) and (6) are exactly the equations used as a beginning for transmission line analysis, neglecting losses (Art. 1·16). It is seen that they may be derived exactly from Maxwell's equations provided the conductors are perfect, and, since fields in the transverse plane satisfy Laplace's equation, the inductance and capacitance appearing in the equations are the same as those computed in statics. So, in this very important case of guiding of electromagnetic energy (transmission lines with negligible imperfections in conductivity of conductors), the well-known method of analysis based upon low-frequency circuit notions gives the correct answer, since it is actually equivalent to an analysis starting from Maxwell's equations, this despite the use of *static* L's and C's for a problem certainly not static.

As we shall see, this situation will not be true for other more general types of waves.

PROBLEMS

8·11a Demonstrate that, although in a *TEM* wave $\bar{E}$ does satisfy Laplace's equation in the transverse plane and so may be considered a gradient of a scalar in so far as variations in the transverse plane are concerned, $\bar{E}$ is *not* the gradient of a scalar when variations in all directions (x, y, and z) are included.

8·11b Demonstrate that electrostatic field will be zero inside any source-free region closed by a conductor at constant potential C. *Hint:* Make use of the uniqueness theorem, Art. 3·03.

8·12   TRANSMISSION LINE WAVES ALONG IMPERFECT LINES

We have found that the classical analysis for a transmission line wave (TEM), made in terms of voltage and current along the line and the distributed inductance and capacitance calculated for direct current, is equivalent to one made directly from Maxwell's equations provided the conductor and dielectric are perfect.

This conclusion might not have been expected, for, if one had wished to be skeptical, it would have been easy to question the validity of the transmission line equations on at least two counts.

1. A voltage drop due to current flow through the distributed inductance of the line is calculated, but none is included because of mutual effects from any other part of the line; similarly, no mutual charging effects are considered.

2. Inductance and capacitance used in the equations are those calculated for direct current. It might seem doubtful that such constants could be of any use for extremely high frequencies; certainly we found that it is not permissible to neglect frequency effects when considering lumped inductances and capacitances at the highest frequencies in circuit equations (Chapter 5).

The first objection is answered once it is found from the field equations that there are no axial field components in the wave, and consequently no mutual effects. The second objection is answered by the discovery that the field distribution for the wave in the transverse plane is actually one corresponding to the static field pattern for that configuration, no matter what the frequency may be. The necessary condition is that the propagation be with light velocity in the dielectric of the line, a condition the conventional approach to transmission lines is very happy to grant.

If the transmission line is not ideal, but has resistance and conductance of finite amount, classical transmission line theory would have us take account of these by setting the voltage change along the line equal to a resistance plus an inductance drop, and the current change equal to a capacitance plus a conductance leakage current (Art. 1·24):

$$\frac{\partial V}{\partial z} = -(j\omega LI + RI)$$

$$\frac{\partial I}{\partial z} = -(j\omega CV + GV)$$

It is usually assumed that inductance and capacitance calculated on the basis of d-c distributions are still used in these equations. Although it is true that a contribution to inductance from the flux inside the conductors (the internal inductance of Chapter 6) may now be included, that part of the inductance arising from flux in the space between conductors is still calculated from the d-c distributions.

It will now be shown that such an analysis is equivalent to one made from Maxwell's equations if a line has uniform conductance but no resistance; it will also be shown that, if resistance of the conductors is important, the two analyses cannot be exactly equivalent. However, we should not undermine our confidence in the usual transmission line expressions too quickly, for the error will be infinitesimal for efficient transmission lines.

If the transmission line has a dielectric with uniform conductivity σ, occupying all the space between conductors, previous field analyses can be corrected by replacing $j\omega\epsilon$ by $(\sigma + j\omega\epsilon)$ in all results (Art. 7·17). However, this is exactly what is done in a conventional analysis, where $j\omega C$ for the ideal line is replaced by $(G + j\omega C)$ for the line with conductance. For a line with uniform dielectric, G has the same form as C, with conductivity in place of dielectric constant:

$$(G + j\omega C) = (\sigma + j\omega\epsilon) \times \text{function of configuration}$$

It follows that the two analyses have then actually considered the effect of conductivity of the dielectric in the same manner.

If the current-carrying conductors of the transmission line have finite conductivity, one trouble is immediately apparent. There must be at least some small component of electric field in the direction of propagation to force the current through the conductors. By referring again to Eqs. 8·02(7) to 8·02(10), it is seen that with E_z finite, $\gamma^2 + k^2$ must then also be finite. The quantity on the right of the wave equation cannot then be exactly zero, but must be some small but finite amount.

$$\nabla_{xy}{}^2 \bar{E} = \text{finite quantity}$$

This indicates that the field distributions are disturbed from the Laplace distributions somewhat by the axial field required to produce current flow.   It is then no longer correct to calculate values of capacitance and inductance from the static distributions.

Although the nature of an exact analysis from Maxwell's equations is apparent, it is difficult to apply to practical lines.   One must first obtain the wave solutions which apply inside the dielectric and those which apply inside the conductor, matching the two at the boundary. The difficulties with most geometrical configurations are obvious. Schelkunoff has carried through this attack for coaxial lines,[2] determining the extent of the approximations which must be made to reduce the problem to the classical analysis.   We have carried through the similar procedure for the parallel-plane transmission line in Art. 8·06.   Studies of more general configurations might be made by the method of successive perturbations.   That is, the first correction to the perfect conductor case is the required axial electric field, which may be estimated simply from the resistivity times the approximate current flow.   An idea is thus obtained of E_z's distribution and magnitude and consequently of $\nabla^2 E_z$.   A next approximation is then obtained for the distribution of E_x, H_y, etc., as well as γ.   From the new H's thus computed, a new current is computed and the whole process is again repeated.   From the results of such studies it becomes apparent that an exact analysis from Maxwell's equations is fortunately unnecessary for lines which are at all efficient for energy transfer.   The difference in results between such an exact analysis and the usual classical analysis including distributed resistance is extremely small.[3]

The classical transmission line analysis for imperfectly conducting boundaries is similar to methods previously introduced in this book, in which the first correction arising from the resistance is applied, but the major field distributions are assumed essentially unchanged.   When this type of approximation was used for a wave analysis in Art. 8·06, the two criteria for its use were

1. Displacement currents in the conductor negligible compared to conduction currents.

2. The intrinsic impedance of the dielectric much greater than the skin effect surface resistivity of the conductor.

These are also a measure of the excellence of the conventional trans-

[2] S. A. Schelkunoff, "The Electromagnetic Theory of Coaxial Transmission Lines and Cylindrical Shields," *Bell Sys. Tech. J.*, **13**, 532–579 (Oct. 1934).

[3] J. R. Carson, "The Guided and Radiated Energy in Wire Transmission," *J.A.I.E.E.*, **43**, 906–913 (Oct. 1924).

mission line analysis including distributed resistance. Stated in another way, such an analysis assumes that transverse electric field components *in the conductor* are negligible compared with the axial, and that axial electric field components *in the dielectric* are small compared with the transverse. These are equivalent to the above. Thus

$$\frac{\sigma_2}{\omega\epsilon_2} \gg 1 \qquad \frac{R_s}{\eta} \ll 1$$

R_s is surface impedance of the conductor, and η intrinsic impedance of the dielectric. These inequalities are nearly always satisfied by the materials of common transmission lines, but, if they are not, one must examine critically any results predicted by the usual transmission line equations.

PROBLEMS

8·12a Two perfectly conducting cylinders of arbitrary cross-sectional shape are parallel and separated by a dielectric of conductivity σ and dielectric constant ϵ. Show that the ratio of electrostatic capacitance per unit length to d-c conductance per unit length is ϵ/σ.

8·12b If conductors are perfect but dielectric has conductivity σ as well as dielectric constant ϵ, show that γ must have the following value in order for a *TEM* wave to exist ($E_z = 0$, $H_z = 0$):

$$\gamma = \pm[j\omega\mu(\sigma + j\omega\epsilon)]^{\frac{1}{2}}$$

Explain why the distribution of fields may be a static distribution as in the loss-free line, unlike the case for a lossy conducting boundary.

8·13   TRANSVERSE MAGNETIC WAVES

As the next possibility, let us consider generally those waves that may exist with electric field but no magnetic field in the direction of propagation. These have been named transverse magnetic (TM) waves, and examples have been given for the parallel-plane guide (Arts. 8·07 to 8·09).

The Differential Equation. With the assumed propagation constant $e^{(j\omega t - \gamma z)}$, the finite axial component of electric field for the TM waves must satisfy the wave equation in the form of Eq. 8·02(11):

$$\nabla_{xy}^2 E_z = -k_c^2 E_z \tag{1}$$

$$k_c^2 = (\gamma^2 + k^2) = \gamma^2 + \omega^2\mu\epsilon \tag{2}$$

The value of k_c, which should be a constant for a particular mode, is determined by the boundary condition to be applied to (1).

Boundary Condition for a Perfectly Conducting Guide. As in the examples, the first step in the solution of a practical wave guide problem is to assume that ·the wave guide boundaries are perfectly conducting. E_z must then certainly be zero at the conducting boundary of the guide:

$$E_z = 0 \quad \text{at boundary} \tag{3}$$

There are transverse components of electric field in the waves which must enter the conducting boundaries normally, but this need not be put on as a separate condition since it turns out to follow from (3). To show this, let us write all field components from the general relations of Art. 8·02 with H_z set equal to zero. Upper and lower signs are for positively and negatively traveling waves, respectively.

$$E_x = \mp \frac{\gamma}{k_c^2} \frac{\partial E_z}{\partial x} \qquad E_y = \mp \frac{\gamma}{k_c^2} \frac{\partial E_z}{\partial y} \tag{4}$$

$$H_x = \frac{j\omega\epsilon}{k_c^2} \frac{\partial E_z}{\partial y} \qquad H_y = -\frac{j\omega\epsilon}{k_c^2} \frac{\partial E_z}{\partial x} \tag{5}$$

Relation (4) may be written in the vector form:

$$\bar{E}_t = \mp \frac{\gamma}{k_c^2} \nabla_t E_z \tag{6}$$

where $\bar{E}_t$ is the transverse part of the electric field vector, and ∇_t represents the transverse part of the gradient. By the nature of the gradient, the transverse electric vector $\bar{E}_t$ is normal to any line of constant E_z. It is then normal to the conducting boundary, as required, once the boundary is made a curve of constant $E_z = 0$. Thus (3) is the only required boundary condition for solutions of (1).

Cut-Off Properties of TM Waves. Solution of the homogeneous differential equation (1) subject to the boundary condition (3) at a given boundary is possible only for discrete values of the constant k_c. These are the *characteristic values, allowed values,* or *eigenvalues* of the problem, any one of which determines a particular *TM mode* for the given guide. In the example of the plane conductors (Art. 8·07), the allowed values of k_c were defined by $n\pi/a$, and a particular mode was described by the appropriate integer n. It will be shown below that, for any dielectric region which is completely closed by perfect conductors, the allowed values, k_c, must always be real. Hence the propagation constant from (2),

$$\gamma = \sqrt{k_c^2 - k^2} \tag{7}$$

always exhibits cut-off properties.   That is, for a particular mode γ is real for the range of frequencies such that $k < k_c$, γ is zero for $k = k_c$, and γ is imaginary for $k > k_c$.   The cut-off frequency of a given mode is then given by

$$2\pi f_c \sqrt{\mu\epsilon} = \frac{2\pi}{\lambda_c} = k_c \tag{8}$$

and (7) may be written in terms of frequency f and cut-off frequency f_c:

$$\gamma = \alpha = k_c \sqrt{1 - (f/f_c)^2} \qquad f < f_c \tag{9}$$

$$\gamma = j\beta = jk \sqrt{1 - (f_c/f)^2} \qquad f > f_c \tag{10}$$

The phase velocity for all TM modes in an ideal guide then has the form

$$v_p = \frac{\omega}{\beta} = v[1 - (f_c/f)^2]^{-\frac{1}{2}} \tag{11}$$

The group velocity is

$$v_g = \frac{d\omega}{d\beta} = v[1 - (f_c/f)^2]^{\frac{1}{2}} \tag{12}$$

Universal curves for attenuation constant, phase velocity, and group velocity as functions of f/f_c are shown in Fig. 8·13a.   Phase velocity is infinite at cut-off frequency and is always greater than the velocity of light in the dielectric; group velocity is zero at cut-off and is always less than the velocity of light in the dielectric.   As the frequency increases far beyond cut-off, phase and group velocities both approach the velocity of light in the dielectric.

It remains to be shown that k_c is real for all TM modes in a dielectric region completely enclosed by perfect conductors.   To do this, let us write the divergence theorem (Art. 2·14) in a form applicable to the two-dimensional case by applying the original theorem to a cylindrical region of unit length:

$$\int_{c.s.} (\nabla_t \cdot \bar{F}) \, dS = \oint F_n \, dl \tag{13}$$

In the above, the integral on the left is taken over the cross-sectional area of the cylindrical region, and the integral on the right is the line integral of the component of $\bar{F}$ normal to the boundary, taken about the boundary of the region.   All vector operations are confined to the transverse plane, and $\bar{F}$ may be any vector which does not vary in the axial direction.   In particular, let it   be the vector $E_z \nabla_t E_z$

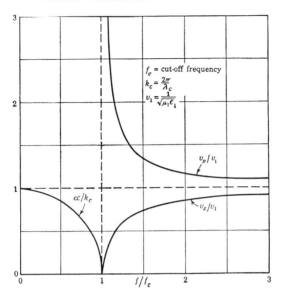

Fig. 8·13a   Frequency characteristics of all TE and TM wave types.

(Recall that E_z is the multiplier of $e^{(j\omega t - \gamma z)}$ and so does not vary with z.)

$$\int_{c.s.} \nabla_t \cdot (E_z \nabla_t E_z) \, dS = \oint E_z \frac{\partial E_z}{\partial n} \, dl = 0$$

The right-hand integral is zero since E_z is zero on the perfectly conducting boundary.   The left side may be transformed (Art. 2·39):

$$\int_{c.s.} [(\nabla_t E_z)^2 + E_z \nabla_t^2 E_z] \, dS = 0$$

The value of $\nabla_t^2 E_z$ is supplied by (1).

$$\int_{c.s.} (\nabla_t E_z)^2 \, dS = k_c^2 \int_{c.s.} E_z^2 \, dS \tag{14}$$

For plane waves which are of the same phase in any given transverse section, E_z^2 and $(\nabla_t E_z)^2$ are real and positive, so k_c^2 must also be real and positive.   Hence, k_c is real under the conditions stated.

Magnetic Fields of the Waves.   Once the distribution of E_z is found by solution of the differential equation (1) subject to the boundary condition (3), the transverse electric field of a given mode may be found from relation (6), or (4).   The transverse magnetic field may be found from relations (5).   By comparing (4) and (5), it is seen that

$$\frac{E_x}{H_y} = -\frac{E_y}{H_x} = \pm \frac{\gamma}{j\omega\epsilon} \tag{15}$$

These relations show that transverse electric and magnetic fields are at right angles, and that their magnitudes are related by the quantity $\gamma/j\omega\epsilon$, which may be thought of as the wave impedance or field impedance of the mode. The usefulness of this type of quantity has already been demonstrated, and will appear in additional discussions.

$$Z_{TM} = \frac{\gamma}{j\omega\epsilon} = \eta \sqrt{1 - (f_c/f)^2} \tag{16}$$

$$\eta = \sqrt{\mu/\epsilon}$$

The latter form is found by substitution of relation (10).

The wave impedance is imaginary (reactive) for frequencies less than the cut-off frequency, and purely real for frequencies above cut-off, approaching the intrinsic impedance of the dielectric at infinite frequency. This type of behavior is also found in the study of lumped-element filters, and again emphasizes that the wave can produce no average power transfer for frequencies below cut-off where the impedance is imaginary.

The relations between electric and magnetic fields may also be expressed in the following vector form, which expresses the properties described above:

$$\bar{H} = \pm \frac{\bar{a}_z \times \bar{E}_t}{Z_{TM}} \tag{17}$$

$\bar{a}_z$ is the unit vector in the z direction. The upper sign is for positively traveling waves, the lower sign for negatively traveling waves.

Power Transfer in the Waves. The power transfer down the guide has been shown to be zero below cut-off if the conductor of the guide is perfect. Above cut-off it may be obtained in terms of the field components by integrating the axial component of the Poynting vector over the cross-sectional area. Since it has been shown that transverse components of electric and magnetic fields are in phase and normal to each other, the axial component of the average Poynting vector is one half the product of the transverse field magnitudes. For a positively traveling wave,

$$W_T = \int_{c.s.} \frac{1}{2} \operatorname{Re} [\bar{E} \times \bar{H}^*]_z \, dS = \frac{1}{2} \int_{c.s.} |E_T||H_T| \, dS$$
$$= \frac{Z_{TM}}{2} \int_{c.s.} |H_T|^2 \, dS \tag{18}$$

By (5), this may be written

$$W_T = \frac{Z_{TM}\omega^2\epsilon^2}{2k_c^4} \int_{c.s.} |\nabla E_z|^2 \, dS$$

By substitution of (14), this is

$$W_T = \frac{Z_{TM}\omega^2\epsilon^2}{2k_c^2} \int_{\text{c.s.}} E_z^2 \, dS = \frac{Z_{TM}}{2\eta^2} \left(\frac{f}{f_c}\right)^2 \int_{\text{c.s.}} E_z^2 \, dS \qquad (19)$$

It is often as easy to use the transverse field distributions of a mode in the Poynting integration (18) as to use the form (19). However, the latter form does emphasize that, for a given power transfer in the mode, the axial component of field E_z must decrease as f/f_c approaches infinity.

Attenuation due to Imperfectly Conducting Boundaries. When the conducting boundaries are imperfect, an exact solution would require solution of Maxwell's equations in both the dielectric and conducting regions as was done for the parallel-plane guide in Art. 8·06. As this procedure is impractical for most geometrical configurations, we take advantage of the fact that most practical conductors are good enough to cause only a slight modification of the ideal solution, and the approximate formula 8·05(7) may be used. To compute the average power loss per unit length, we require the current flow in the guide walls, which is taken the same as that in the ideal guide. By the $\bar{n} \times \bar{H}$ rule, the current in the boundary is equal to the transverse magnetic field at the boundary, and flows in the axial direction since magnetic field is entirely transverse:

$$W_L = \oint_{\text{bound}} \frac{R_s}{2} \, |J_z|^2 \, dl = \frac{R_s}{2} \oint_{\text{bound}} |H_t|^2 \, dl \qquad (20)$$

The attenuation constant is then approximately

$$\alpha = \frac{W_L}{2W_T} = \frac{R_s \oint_{\text{bound}} |H_t|^2 \, dl}{2Z_{TM} \int_{\text{c.s.}} |H_t|^2 \, dS} \qquad (21)$$

If desired, the power loss and hence the attenuation constant may be written in terms of the distribution of E_z only. By (5),

$$W_L = \frac{R_s}{2} \frac{\omega^2\epsilon^2}{k_c^4} \oint_{\text{bound}} |\nabla E_z|^2 \, dl \qquad (22)$$

Since E_z is zero at all points along the boundary, there is no tangential derivative of E_z there; E_z consists merely of the derivative normal to the conductor:

$$W_L = \frac{R_s\omega^2\epsilon^2}{2k_c^4} \oint_{\text{bound}} \left[\frac{\partial E_z}{\partial n}\right]^2 \, dl = \frac{R_s}{2\eta^2 k_c^2} \left(\frac{f}{f_c}\right)^2 \oint \left[\frac{\partial E_z}{\partial n}\right]^2 \, dl \qquad (23)$$

An alternative form for the attenuation constant is then

$$\alpha = \frac{R_s}{2k_c^2 Z_{TM}} \left[\oint \left[\frac{\partial E_z}{\partial n} \right]^2 dl \Big/ \int_{\text{c.s.}} E_z{}^2 \, dS \right] \qquad (24)$$

Attenuation due to Imperfect Dielectric. It is noted that the general form for propagation constant (7) is exactly the same as that for the special case of the parallel-plane guide, Eq. 8·07(6). Hence, the modification caused by an imperfect dielectric, taken into account by replacing $j\omega\epsilon$ by $\sigma + j\omega\epsilon$, yields the same form for attenuation as Eq. 8·09(4):

$$\alpha_d = \frac{k\epsilon''/\epsilon'}{2 \sqrt{1 - (f_c/f)^2}} = \frac{\sigma\eta}{2 \sqrt{1 - (f_c/f)^2}} \quad \text{nepers/meter} \qquad (25)$$

It is especially interesting to note that the form of the attenuation due to an imperfect dielectric is the same for all modes and all shapes of guides, though of course the amount of attenuation is a function of the cut-off frequency, which does depend upon the guide and the mode.

Summary. For TM modes, the differential equation (1) is solved subject to the boundary condition (3). This determines certain allowed distributions of E_z (modes) and corresponding allowed values of the constant k_c. The latter determine cut-off frequencies for the various modes, which, placed in (9), (11), (12), (16), (24), and (25), determine attenuation below cut-off, phase and group velocities above cut-off, wave impedance, attenuation due to conductors, and attenuation due to dielectric, respectively. All this may be done without explicitly finding the transverse fields. However, it is usually desirable to study the form of the transverse components of field, which may be done by means of (6) and (17). These may in turn be used to compute power transfer, power loss, and attenuation due to conductors by (18), (20), and (21), as alternatives to (19), (22), and (24).

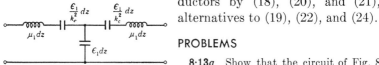

Fig. 8·13b Equivalent circuit for the transverse magnetic wave.

PROBLEMS

8·13a Show that the circuit of Fig. 8·13b may be used to represent the propagation characteristics of the transverse magnetic wave, if the characteristic wave impedance and propagation constant are written by analogy with transmission line results in terms of an impedance Z_1, and an admittance Y_1 per unit length.

$$Z_{TM} = \sqrt{Z_1/Y_1} \qquad \gamma = \sqrt{Z_1 Y_1}$$

Note the similarity between this and the circuits of conventional filter sections, remembering of course that all constants in this circuit are in reality distributed constants.

8·13b Show that all field components for a TM wave may be derived from the axial component of the vector potential $\bar{A}$. Obtain the expressions relating E_x, H_x, etc., to A_z, the differential equation for A_z, and the boundary conditions to be applied at a perfect conductor.

8·13c Repeat Prob. b, using the axial component of the Hertz potential as defined in Prob. 4·15.

8·13d Show that the magnetic field distribution in the transverse plane can be derived from a scalar flux function, and relate this to E_z. With transverse electric field derivable from a scalar potential function and transverse magnetic field derivable from a scalar flux function, does it follow that both are static type distributions as in the TEM wave? Explain.

8·13e Note that we have essentially used E_z as a potential function for derivation of other components in the preceding article. How is this related to the A_z of Prob. b and the Π_z of Prob. c?

8·14 TRANSVERSE ELECTRIC WAVES

Finally, we consider those waves which have magnetic field but no electric field in the axial direction. Because of the similarity of treatment to that of TM waves in the preceding article, it will be given more briefly.

The Differential Equation. The finite H_z of the waves must satisfy the wave equation in the form of Eq. 8·02(12):

$$\nabla_t^2 H_z = -k_c^2 H_z \qquad (1)$$

$$k_c^2 = \gamma^2 + k^2 \qquad (2)$$

Boundary Conditions for a Perfectly Conducting Guide. Allowable solutions to (1) are determined by the single boundary condition that at perfect conductors the normal derivative of H_z must be zero:

$$\frac{\partial H_z}{\partial n} = 0 \quad \text{at boundary} \qquad (3)$$

To show that this is the required boundary condition, write the transverse fields of the wave from Eqs. 8·02(7) to (10).

$$E_x = -\frac{j\omega\mu}{k_c^2}\frac{\partial H_z}{\partial y} \qquad E_y = \frac{j\omega\mu}{k_c^2}\frac{\partial H_z}{\partial x} \qquad (4)$$

$$H_x = \mp\frac{\gamma}{k_c^2}\frac{\partial H_z}{\partial x} \qquad H_y = \mp\frac{\gamma}{k_c^2}\frac{\partial H_z}{\partial y} \qquad (5)$$

Relation (5) may be written in the vector form,

$$\bar{H}_t = \mp\frac{\gamma}{k_c^2}\nabla_t H_z \qquad (6)$$

If H_z has no normal derivative at the boundary, its transverse gradient has only a component tangential to the boundary, so, by (6), $\bar{H}_t$ does also. Comparison of (4) and (5) shows that transverse electric and magnetic field components are normal to one another, so electric field is normal to the conducting boundary as required.

Cut-Off Properties of TE Waves. If in the two-dimensional divergence theorem, Eq. 8·13(13), the general vector $\bar{F}$ is set equal to $H_z \nabla_t H_z$, the following relation may be derived for a cylindrical region closed by a perfectly conducting boundary:

$$\int_{c.s.} (\nabla_t H_z)^2 \, dS = k_c^2 \int_{c.s.} H_z^2 \, dS \tag{7}$$

For plane waves, H_z and $\nabla_t H_z$ are real, so k_c^2 must be real and positive. By (2), γ then shows cut-off properties exactly the same as for TM waves:

$$\gamma = \sqrt{k_c^2 - k^2} \tag{8}$$

Formulas for attenuation constant below cut-off, phase constant, phase and group velocities above cut-off then follow exactly as in Eqs. 8·13(9) to (12).

$$\gamma = \alpha = k_c \sqrt{1 - (f/f_c)^2} \qquad f < f_c \tag{9}$$

$$\gamma = j\beta = jk \sqrt{1 - (f_c/f)^2} \qquad f > f_c \tag{10}$$

$$v_p = v[1 - (f_c/f)^2]^{-\frac{1}{2}} \tag{11}$$

$$v_g = v[1 - (f_c/f)^2]^{\frac{1}{2}} \tag{12}$$

where

$$2\pi f_c \sqrt{\mu\epsilon} = k_c = 2\pi/\lambda_c \tag{13}$$

The universal curves of Fig. 8·13a then apply directly.

Electric Field of the Wave. The electric field is everywhere transverse, and everywhere normal to the transverse magnetic field components. Transverse components of electric and magnetic field may again be related through a field or wave impedance:

$$\frac{E_x}{H_y} = -\frac{E_y}{H_x} = Z_{TE} \tag{14}$$

where, from (4) and (5),

$$Z_{TE} = \frac{j\omega\mu}{\gamma} = \eta \left[1 - \left(\frac{f_c}{f}\right)^2 \right]^{-\frac{1}{2}} \tag{15}$$

This impedance is imaginary for frequencies below cut-off, infinite at cut-off, and purely real for frequencies above cut-off, approaching the intrinsic impedance η as f/f_c becomes large.

Electric field may also be written in the vector form,

$$\bar{E} = \mp Z_{TE}(\bar{a}_z \times \bar{H}_t) \tag{16}$$

where $\bar{a}_z$ is the unit vector in the z direction, and the upper and lower signs apply respectively to positively and negatively traveling waves.

Power Transfer in TE Waves. Average power transfer in the propagating range is, as usual, obtained from the Poynting vector:

$$W_T = \tfrac{1}{2} \int_{\text{c.s.}} \text{Re} \, [\bar{E} \times \bar{H}^*] \cdot \overline{dS} = \tfrac{1}{2} \int_{\text{c.s.}} | \, E_T \, || \, H_T \, | \, dS$$

$$= \frac{Z_{TE}}{2} \int | \, H_T \, |^2 \, dS \tag{17}$$

By (6) and (7), this may be transformed to

$$W_T = \frac{\eta^2 (f/f_c)^2}{2Z_{TE}} \int_{\text{c.s.}} H_z{}^2 \, dS \tag{18}$$

Attenuation due to Imperfectly Conducting Boundaries. As with the *TEM* mode, there cannot be a true transverse electric wave in most guides with imperfect conductors, since most (but not all) of the *TE* modes have axial currents which require a certain finite axial electric field when conductivity is finite. However, this axial field is very small compared with the transverse field, so that one does not bother to rename the waves.

The axial component of current arises from the transverse component of magnetic field at the boundary:

$$| \, J_z \, | = | \, H_t \, | = \frac{\beta}{k_c{}^2} | \, \nabla_t H_z \, | = \frac{\beta}{k_c{}^2} \frac{\partial H_z}{\partial l} \tag{19}$$

The last form follows since it has been shown that the transverse gradient of H_z has only a tangential component $(\partial/\partial l)$ at the boundary. There is in addition a transverse current arising from the axial magnetic field:

$$| \, J_t \, | = | \, H_z \, | \tag{20}$$

The power loss per unit length is then

$$W_L = \frac{R_s}{2} \oint [| \, H_z \, |^2 + | \, H_t \, |^2] \, dl \tag{21}$$

$$W_L = \frac{R_s}{2} \oint \left\{ H_z{}^2 + \left(\frac{f}{f_c}\right)^2 \frac{[1 - (f_c/f)^2]}{k_c{}^2} \left[\frac{\partial H_z}{\partial l}\right]^2 \right\} \, dl \tag{22}$$

Attenuation due to the loss is

$$\alpha = \frac{R_s Z_{TE}}{2\eta^2} \frac{\oint \left\{ (f_c/f)^2 H_z{}^2 + 1/k_c{}^2 [1 - (f_c/f)^2] \left[\frac{\partial H_z}{\partial l} \right]^2 \right\} dl}{\displaystyle\int_{\text{c.s.}} H_z{}^2 \, dS} \qquad (23)$$

If the transverse field components have been calculated explicitly, it is usually as easy to use forms (17) and (21) as the derived forms (18) and (22).

Attenuation due to Imperfect Dielectrics. Since propagation constant of the TE waves has the same form as for the TM waves, it follows that the form for attenuation due to an imperfect dielectric does also. For a reasonably good dielectric, the approximate form, Eq. 8·13(25), may be used:

$$\alpha_d = \frac{k\epsilon''/\epsilon'}{2\sqrt{1 - (f_c/f)^2}} = \frac{\sigma\eta}{2\sqrt{1 - (f_c/f)^2}} \qquad (24)$$

PROBLEMS

8·14a   As in Prob. 8·13a, show that the equivalent circuit for transverse electric waves in terms of distributed constants is as pictured in Fig. 8·14.

8·14b   Show that fields satisfying Maxwell's equations in a homogeneous, charge-free, current-free dielectric may be derived from a vector potential $\bar{F}$,

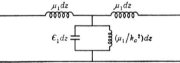

$$\bar{E} = -\frac{1}{\epsilon} \nabla \times \bar{F}$$

$$\bar{H} = \frac{1}{j\omega\mu\epsilon} \nabla(\nabla \cdot \bar{F}) - j\omega\bar{F}$$

Fig. 8·14   Equivalent circuit for the transverse electric wave.

$$(\nabla^2 + k^2)\bar{F} = 0$$

Obtain expressions for all field components of a TE wave from the axial component F_z of the above potential function, and give the differential equation and boundary conditions for F_z.

8·14c   Show that, if one utilizes the potential function $\bar{A}$ instead of the $\bar{F}$ of Prob. b for derivation of a TE wave, more than one component is required.

8·14d   Show that transverse distribution of electric field can be derived from a scalar flux function.   How is this related to H_z?

8·15   GENERAL WAVE TYPES IN RECTANGULAR COORDINATES

The general solutions for guided waves may be written in rectangular coordinates for application to waves between parallel planes, parallel bar transmission lines, wave guides of rectangular section, etc.

For transverse magnetic waves, Eq. 8·13(1) in rectangular coordinates is

$$\nabla_{xy}^2 E_z = \frac{\partial^2 E_z}{\partial x^2} + \frac{\partial^2 E_z}{\partial y^2} = -k_c^2 E_z \tag{1}$$

This is a partial differential equation which may be solved by the method used in Chapter 3. Assume that the solution may be written as a product of two terms, one a function of x only, the other a function of y only:

$$E_z = XY$$

where X is a function of x only and Y is a function of y only. Substitute in (1):

$$X''Y + XY'' = -k_c^2 XY$$

or
$$\frac{X''}{X} + \frac{Y''}{Y} = -k_c^2 \tag{2}$$

The primes indicate derivatives. If this equation is to hold for all values of x and y, since x and y may be changed independently of each other, each of the ratios X''/X and Y''/Y can be only a constant. There are then several forms for the solutions, depending upon whether these ratios are both taken as negative constants, both positive, or one negative and one positive. If both are taken as negative, say k_x^2 and k_y^2 respectively, then

$$\frac{X''}{X} = -k_x^2$$

$$\frac{Y''}{Y} = -k_y^2$$

The solutions to the above ordinary differential equations are sinusoids, and by (2) the sum of k_x^2 and k_y^2 is k_c^2.

Thus three forms of the wave solution for rectangular coordinates in the transverse plane are listed below, with $e^{j(\omega t - \gamma z)}$ understood. They apply as well to H_z in transverse electric or H waves, since H_z satisfies an equation identical to (1).

$$\left.\begin{array}{l} E_z \quad \text{for } TM \text{ waves} \\ H_z \quad \text{for } TE \text{ waves} \end{array}\right\} = XY \tag{3}$$

where
$$X = A \cos k_x x + B \sin k_x x$$
$$Y = C \cos k_y y + D \sin k_y y \tag{4}$$
$$k_x^2 + k_y^2 = k_c^2$$

or
$$X = A_1 \cos k_x x + B_1 \sin k_x x$$
$$Y = C_1 \cosh K_y y + D_1 \sinh K_y y \tag{5}$$
$$k_x{}^2 - K_y{}^2 = k_c{}^2$$

or
$$X = A_2 \cosh K_x x + B_2 \sinh K_x x$$
$$Y = C_2 \cosh K_y y + D_2 \sinh K_y y \tag{6}$$
$$- (K_x{}^2 + K_y{}^2) = k_c{}^2$$

Note that solutions in the form of (6) have a negative value of $k_c{}^2$, which does not violate previous proofs that $k_c{}^2$ must be positive for solutions applying within a closed region, since (6) would not be applicable inside a region closed by a perfect conductor.

All other components, H_x, H_y, E_x, and E_y, are obtained from the above and Eqs. 8·02(7) to (10). For a negatively traveling wave, reverse the sign of all terms containing γ in those equations.

PROBLEM

8·15 Discuss the types of geometrical configurations to which each of the forms of Eqs. 8·15(4) to (6) might be applied.

8·16 GENERAL WAVE TYPES IN CYLINDRICAL COORDINATES

In cylindrical structures, such as coaxial lines or wave guides of circular sections, the wave components will be most conveniently expressed in terms of cylindrical coordinates. The two-dimensional Laplacian $\nabla_{xy}{}^2$ in Eq. 8·13(1) should be written in cylindrical coordinates:

$$\nabla_{xy}{}^2 E_z = \nabla_{r\phi}{}^2 E_z = \frac{\partial^2 E_z}{\partial r^2} + \frac{1}{r} \frac{\partial E_z}{\partial r} + \frac{1}{r^2} \frac{\partial^2 E_z}{\partial \phi^2}$$

So that
$$\frac{\partial^2 E_z}{\partial r^2} + \frac{1}{r} \frac{\partial E_z}{\partial r} + \frac{1}{r^2} \frac{\partial^2 E_z}{\partial \phi^2} = -k_c{}^2 E_z \tag{1}$$

For this partial differential equation, we shall again substitute an assumed product solution and attempt to separate variables in order to obtain two ordinary differential equations.

Assume
$$E_z = R F_\phi$$

where R is a function of r alone and F_ϕ is a function of ϕ alone.

$$R'' F_\phi + \frac{R' F_\phi}{r} + \frac{F_\phi'' R}{r^2} = -k_c{}^2 R F_\phi$$

Separating variables,

$$r^2 \frac{R''}{R} + \frac{rR'}{R} + k_c^2 r^2 = \frac{-F_\phi''}{F_\phi}$$

The left side of the equation is a function of r alone; the right of ϕ alone. If both sides are to be equal for all values of r and ϕ, both sides must equal a constant. Let this constant be ν^2. There are then the two ordinary differential equations

$$\frac{-F_\phi''}{F_\phi} = \nu^2 \tag{2}$$

and

$$r^2 \frac{R''}{R} + \frac{rR'}{R} + k_c^2 r^2 = \nu^2$$

or

$$R'' + \frac{1}{r} R' + \left(k_c^2 - \frac{\nu^2}{r^2}\right) R = 0 \tag{3}$$

The solution to (2) is in sinusoids. By comparing with Eq. 3·24(3), it is seen that solutions to (3) may be written in terms of Bessel functions of order ν. Since H_z for transverse electric or H waves satisfies the same equation as (1), solutions to H_z will also be in the same form. Thus, with $e^{j(\omega t - \gamma z)}$ understood,

$$\left. \begin{array}{l} E_z \quad \text{(for } TM \text{ waves)} \\ H_z \quad \text{(for } TE \text{ waves)} \end{array} \right\} = RF_\phi \tag{4}$$

where

$$R = AJ_\nu(k_c r) + BN_\nu(k_c r)$$
$$F_\phi = C \cos \nu\phi + D \sin \nu\phi \tag{5}$$

or

$$R = A_1 H_\nu^{(1)}(k_c r) + B_1 H_\nu^{(2)}(k_c r)$$
$$F_\phi = C \cos \nu\phi + D \sin \nu\phi \tag{6}$$

or

$$R = A_2 J_\nu(k_c r) + B_2 H_\nu^{(1)}(k_c r)$$
$$F_\phi = C \cos \nu\phi + D \sin \nu\phi \tag{7}$$

The Hankel function form of (6) is useful when it is desired to look at waves as though propagation were in the radial direction, as will be seen in the study of radial transmission lines. The form of (7) is useful for problems in which the constant k_c may be imaginary, since J_ν and $H_\nu^{(1)}$ of imaginary quantities are tabulated.[4]

[4] See Jahnke-Emde, *Tables of Functions*, Dover Publications, reprint, 1943.

Other components, E_r, E_ϕ, H_r, and H_ϕ, are obtainable from the above solutions by the following equations, which are the cylindrical coordinate equivalents of Eqs. 8·02(7) to (10).

$$E_r = -\frac{1}{k_c^2}\left[\gamma\frac{\partial E_z}{\partial r} + \frac{j\omega\mu}{r}\frac{\partial H_z}{\partial \phi}\right] \tag{8}$$

$$E_\phi = \frac{1}{k_c^2}\left[-\frac{\gamma}{r}\frac{\partial E_z}{\partial \phi} + j\omega\mu\frac{\partial H_z}{\partial r}\right] \tag{9}$$

$$H_r = \frac{1}{k_c^2}\left[\frac{j\omega\epsilon}{r}\frac{\partial E_z}{\partial \phi} - \gamma\frac{\partial H_z}{\partial r}\right] \tag{10}$$

$$H_\phi = -\frac{1}{k_c^2}\left[j\omega\epsilon\frac{\partial E_z}{\partial r} + \frac{\gamma}{r}\frac{\partial H_z}{\partial \phi}\right] \tag{11}$$

For a negatively traveling wave, reverse the sign of all terms containing γ in the above.

PROBLEM

8·16 Demonstrate, making use of the form of Eq. 8·16(7), that a solution with k_c imaginary cannot apply inside a closed region.

8·17 COMPARISONS OF GENERAL WAVE BEHAVIOR AND PHYSICAL EXPLANATIONS OF WAVE TYPES

Many characteristics have been found in the past articles for waves along uniform guiding systems by mathematical analyses starting from Maxwell's equations.   It has been found, for instance, that transverse electromagnetic waves (waves with no field components in the direction of propagation) may propagate along an ideal guide with the velocity of light for the dielectric of the guide.   In the transverse plane, these may have any field distributions which correspond to static field distributions.   Thus such waves may propagate along a system of two or more conductors, or outside a single conductor, but not inside any hollow pipe, since a static field distribution cannot exist inside an infinitely long, hollow, closed conductor.   Moreover, it has been verified that the usual transmission line equations written with distributed inductance and capacitance calculated for direct current are exact for ideal lines, and the usual equations with distributed inductance, capacitance, resistance, and conductance are excellent approximations for any practical transmission line efficient for energy transfer.

So much for these principal or transmission line waves we have known of, if without assurance, from the conventional line equations, which Maxwell's equations actually verified. In addition, waves have been found which could not have been predicted from the classical transmission line equations based on circuit notions. These waves have either electric or magnetic field components in the direction of propagation. They may propagate inside closed hollow conductors, but only above certain critical or cut-off frequencies for which cross-sectional dimensions between conductors are of the order of a half-wavelength. Below these cut-off frequencies the waves, even if started, attenuate extremely rapidly, so that, for ordinary transmission lines where spacing between conductors is much smaller than a half wavelength, these waves should not enter into energy propagation. They may be important at discontinuities, end effects, or in the radiation field at a long distance from the line. However, above the cut-off frequency, these waves may be quite satisfactory for energy transfer in any system, and are the only waves which may exist inside closed hollow conductors.

These and other characteristics were obtained by mathematical analysis. It will be profitable to pause now, attempting to understand physically the basis for this behavior and the comparisons between the several types of waves.

It should first be recalled that at the frequencies of interest—at least for the profitable use of hollow pipe wave guides—current flow in the conducting walls will be completely governed by skin effect. For many purposes the conductors may be considered perfect, so that there is no penetration whatever into the conductors, but all currents and charges reside on the surface. Even when actual conductivities of practical conducting materials are taken into account, it is found that at such frequencies depth of penetration is of the order of 10^{-4} inch, and the outside of the pipe is perfectly shielded from the fields which are being retained on the interior.

For the dielectric space inside the pipe, it should be recalled that:

1. Electric field lines may begin and end on charges. If an electric field ends on a conductor, it must represent a charge induced on that conductor.

2. Magnetic field lines can never end since magnetic charges are not known physically. Magnetic fields must always form continuous closed paths, surrounding either a conduction current or a changing electric field (displacement current).

3. Electric field lines may form continuous closed paths, surrounding a changing magnetic field.

In a transverse electromagnetic field, by definition, there are no axial field components; both electric and magnetic fields must lie in the transverse plane.   Since electric field is transverse, it would be impossible for magnetic field to surround it without having a component in the axial direction.   Consequently all magnetic fields must surround axial conduction currents and not displacement currents.   This is the result checked by the analysis for these waves and explains physically why the magnetic fields satisfy a Laplacian equation in the transverse plane outside of the current-carrying region.   Similarly, since magnetic fields are transverse, electric fields could not enclose them without

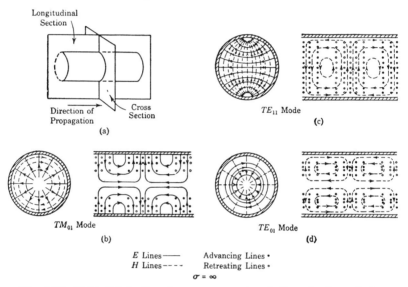

Longitudinal
Section

Direction of   Cross
Propagation   Section

(a)

TE_{11} Mode

(c)

TM_{01} Mode

(b)

TE_{01} Mode

(d)

E Lines ——   Advancing Lines •
H Lines ----   Retreating Lines •
$\sigma = \infty$

Fig. 8·17   Field distributions for some waves in a hollow circular cylinder.

having an axial component of electric field.   Consequently, in a given transverse plane, all electric field lines must begin on a certain number of positive charges and end on the same number of negative charges. So electric field also must satisfy Laplace's equation in the transverse plane for the region between conductors.

We can also see quite easily that there can be no transverse electromagnetic waves inside hollow closed conductors.   Consider, for a specific case, the round hollow pipe of Fig. 8·17a.   If the conductor of the pipe is perfect, magnetic field must be tangential to the conductor. Since magnetic field must also form closed lines, any magnetic field line just inside the pipe would have to be a closed circle tangential to the pipe.   It could cut no part of the conductor, and so could surround no conduction current.   For a wave with no axial electric field, it cannot surround displacement current (or changing electric field). Consequently, it cannot exist at all.

It is evident as an extension of the above reasoning that there may be a value of magnetic field inside the pipe if there is an axial electric field, since the axial displacement current could then account for magnetic field. The electric field might start from positive charges at one section of the guide, turn and go down the guide axially, and finally end on negative charges farther down the guide (Fig. 8·17b). It is recognized that such a wave is a transverse magnetic wave analyzed in Art. 8·13. (The subscript notation will be defined in Chapter 9.) Note particularly that, since the line integral of magnetic field is proportional to *rate of change* of electric flux enclosed, magnetic field for a single traveling wave is a maximum, not in the plane where axial electric field is a maximum, but rather in the plane where rate of change of axial electric field is a maximum as the entire pattern moves down the guide. If this wave is symmetrical, there must be only axial current flow, produced by the transverse magnetic field at the conductor surface. This is also evident by the current which must flow to account for the lumps of induced charge. From still another point of view, we have agreed that the conducting wall acts as a perfect shield so that no magnetic field due to influences on the inside can exist outside it. Thus, at any section, there must flow a current in the conductor exactly equal and opposite to the total axial displacement current inside the guide at that section.

Let us now consider the field distribution for waves with axial magnetic field and transverse electric field. First, as in Fig. 8·17c, notice that, if electric field lines start from positive charges on one side of the hollow pipe and go directly across to negative charges on the opposite side, magnetic field lines may exist inside the hollow pipe if they surround these electric field lines. In this type of wave there must exist currents flowing circumferentially between the positive and negative charges at any given section in addition to those which flow axially. The former are accounted for by the axial magnetic field at the surface of the conductor; the latter are accounted for by the transverse component of magnetic field at the surface of the conductor.

The wave described above is, of course, a transverse electric or H wave. However, another wave of this same type may appear if the electric field lines in the transverse plane do not end on any charges, but always close upon themselves. In this wave (Fig. 8·17d) the electric field lines and the magnetic field lines surround each other. There are then no charges induced on the conductors and no axial currents. There are circulating currents arising from the axial component of magnetic field. Since we have found that this axial component becomes very small for frequencies far above cut-off, so will the circulating current become small, and under this condition there will be but slight losses in the guide even though conductors are imperfect. Of course, such a situation indicates that the type of wave described is not so intimately tied to the guide. If it is attempted to make a bend in such a guide, current must flow at the discontinuity, and the new wave generated at the bend may be of an entirely different type. Because of this reason it is often pointed out that the type of wave is unstable. This is the TE_0 wave of circular guide which will be studied in more detail later.

We might next·ask if it is possible to have a transverse magnetic or E wave with no charges induced on the guide, but with electric and magnetic fields surrounding each other. A little study of this shows that, although it may be possible for the fields to surround each other on the interior of the guide for the higher order TM waves, the field nearest the conductor must turn to enter the conductor normally, thus inducing charges as described previously.

All the above general characteristics will be further clarified in later study of the specific waves which may propagate inside guides of circular and rectangular shapes. However, the preceding general study is particularly important in showing that similar types of waves should be found in guides of different cross sections, since the above discussions did not require the specification of the shape of guide.

9 CHARACTERISTICS

OF COMMON WAVE GUIDES

AND TRANSMISSION LINES

Common Transmission Lines

9·01 COAXIAL LINES, PARALLEL-WIRE LINES, AND SHIELDED PAIRS

From the conclusions of Arts. 8·11 and 8·12 the analysis for ordinary transmission line waves along practical transmission systems may be correctly made from the distributed circuit constant concepts of Chapter 1. For use of the formulas of Chapter 1, it is necessary to calculate values for the inductance, capacitance, resistance, and conductance per unit length. The calculation of such constants was studied in Chapter 6. However, for convenience, some results for the commonly used transmission lines will be listed.

Coaxial lines are among the most commonly used of all transmission lines, particularly at the higher frequencies. This is largely because of the convenient construction and the practically perfect shielding between fields inside and outside of the line. The range of impedances that may be obtained most conveniently by coaxial lines (see Table 9·01) is about 30 to 100 ohms.

Somewhat higher impedances may be obtained conveniently with parallel-wire lines, and these find wide application, although the shielding and radiation problems make them undesirable at the highest frequencies. It is also difficult to attain the lowest impedances conveniently with them. Unlike the coaxial line, the parallel-wire line is a balanced line, which is sometimes desirable.

If the parallel-wire line is placed inside a conducting pipe as shield, the radiation and shielding difficulties are eliminated. The impedance of the line with shield is in general somewhat lower than the same line without the shield. The resulting shielded pair is also a balanced line, assuming symmetrical location of the lines in the shield.

The parallel-bar transmission line is sometimes used when balanced lines of low impedance are desired. Like the parallel-wire line, it is not perfectly shielded.

In Table 9·01 are listed some of the constants for the above lines. Many of these formulas are approximate, applying at the highest frequencies. For lower frequencies, values of resistance and internal inductance should be calculated by the methods of Chapter 6 and substituted in the formulas of Chapter 1.

$$\gamma = \alpha + j\beta = \sqrt{(R + j\omega L)(G + j\omega C)}$$

$$Z_0 = \sqrt{\frac{(R + j\omega L)}{(G + j\omega C)}} \quad \text{ohms}$$

9·02   COAXIAL LINES—HIGHER ORDER WAVES

In addition to the ordinary transmission line wave in a coaxial line, there may exist under certain conditions higher order waves with electric or magnetic field in the direction of the line axis. Such waves

Fig. 9·02a
Cross section of
a coaxial line.

would be expected from the study of the simple case of parallel planes, and by the general study of waves along uniform systems in Chapter 8, where TM and TE waves were found in addition to the principal or transmission line waves. The general forms for the TM and TE waves in cylindrical coordinates are listed in Art. 8·16. The boundary conditions require that E_z for the TM waves be zero at the inner radius and, at the outer radius, assuming perfect conductors. (These, of course, refer to radii measured at the boundary between conductors and dielectric, as in Fig. 9·02a.)

   TM waves

$$A_n J_n(k_c r_i) + B_n N_n(k_c r_i) = 0$$

$$A_n J_n(k_c r_0) + B_n N_n(k_c r_0) = 0$$

or
$$\frac{N_n(k_c r_i)}{J_n(k_c r_i)} = \frac{N_n(k_c r_0)}{J_n(k_c r_0)} \qquad (1)$$

For TE waves, the derivative of H_z normal to the two conductors must be zero at the inner and outer radii. Then, in place of (1),

$$\frac{N_n'(k_c r_i)}{J_n'(k_c r_i)} = \frac{N_n'(k_c r_0)}{J_n'(k_c r_0)} \qquad (2)$$

Solutions to the transcendental equations (1) and (2) determine the values of k_c and hence cut-off frequency, for any wave type and any

Capacitance C, farads/meter	$\dfrac{2\pi\epsilon}{\ln\left(\dfrac{r_0}{r_i}\right)}$	cosh
External inductance L, henrys/meter	$\dfrac{\mu}{2\pi}\ln\left(\dfrac{r_0}{r_i}\right)$	$\dfrac{\mu}{\pi}\cos$
Conductance G, mhos/meter	$\dfrac{2\pi\sigma}{\ln\left(\dfrac{r_0}{r_i}\right)} = \dfrac{2\pi\omega\epsilon_0\epsilon''}{\ln\left(\dfrac{r_0}{r_i}\right)}$	$\dfrac{\pi\sigma}{\cosh^{-1}\left(\dfrac{s}{d}\right)}$
Resistance R, ohms/meter	$\dfrac{R_s}{2\pi}\left(\dfrac{1}{r_0}+\dfrac{1}{r_i}\right)$	$\dfrac{2R_s}{\pi d}\left[\dfrac{}{\sqrt{\;}}\right.$
Internal inductance L_i, henrys/meter (for high frequency)	$\longleftarrow$	
Characteristic impedance at high frequency Z_0, ohms	$\dfrac{\eta}{2\pi}\ln\left(\dfrac{r_0}{r_i}\right)$	$\dfrac{\eta}{\pi}\cos$
Z_0 for air dielectric	$60\ln\left(\dfrac{r_0}{r_i}\right)$	$120\cosh^{-1}\left(\dfrac{s}{}\right)$
Attenuation due to conductor α_c	$\longleftarrow$	
Attenuation due to dielectric α_d	$\longleftarrow$	
Total attenuation db/meter	$\longleftarrow$	
Phase constant for low-loss lines β	$\longleftarrow$	

All units above are mks.

$\epsilon = \epsilon'\epsilon_0 =$ dielectric constant, farads/meter
$\mu = \mu'\mu_0 =$ permeability, henrys/meter $\left.\begin{array}{c}\\\\\end{array}\right\}$ for the dielectric
$\eta = \sqrt{\mu/\epsilon}$ ohms

Formulas for shielded pair obtai
Tech. Journ., **15**, pp. 248–284 (April,

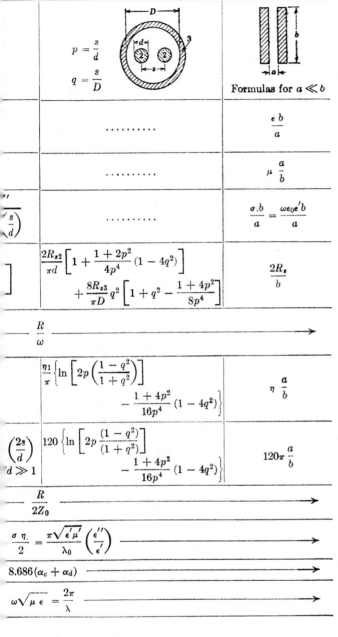

$$p = \frac{s}{d}$$

$$q = \frac{s}{D}$$

Formulas for $a \ll b$

. . . .	$\dfrac{\epsilon\, b}{a}$
. . . .	$\mu\, \dfrac{a}{b}$
. . . .	$\dfrac{\sigma\, b}{a} = \dfrac{\omega\epsilon_0\epsilon'\, b}{a}$
$\dfrac{2R_{s2}}{\pi d}\left[1 + \dfrac{1+2p^2}{4p^4}(1-4q^2)\right] + \dfrac{8R_{s3}}{\pi D}q^2\left[1 + q^2 - \dfrac{1+4p^2}{8p^4}\right]$	$\dfrac{2R_s}{b}$

$$\frac{R}{\omega} \longrightarrow$$

$\dfrac{\eta_1}{\pi}\left\{\ln\left[2p\left(\dfrac{1-q^2}{1+q^2}\right)\right] - \dfrac{1+4p^2}{16p^4}(1-4q^2)\right\}$	$\eta\, \dfrac{a}{b}$
$120\left\{\ln\left[2p\dfrac{(1-q^2)}{(1+q^2)}\right] - \dfrac{1+4p^2}{16p^4}(1-4q^2)\right\}$	$120\pi\, \dfrac{a}{b}$

$$\frac{R}{2Z_0} \longrightarrow$$

$$\frac{\sigma\, \eta}{2} = \frac{\pi\sqrt{\epsilon'\mu'}}{\lambda_0}\left(\frac{\epsilon''}{\epsilon'}\right) \longrightarrow$$

$$8.686(\alpha_c + \alpha_d) \longrightarrow$$

$$\omega\sqrt{\mu\,\epsilon} = \frac{2\pi}{\lambda} \longrightarrow$$

ϵ'' = loss factor of dielectric = $\sigma\cdot/\omega\epsilon_0$

R_s = skin effect surface resistivity of conductor, ohms

λ = wavelength in dielectric = $\lambda_0/\sqrt{\epsilon'\mu'}$

reen, Leibe, and Curtis, *Bell System*

particular values of r_i and r_0. Solution of the transcendental equations is accomplished by graphical methods or by consulting published tables. By analogy with the parallel-plane guide, we would expect to find certain modes with a cut-off such that the spacing between conductors is of the order of p half-wavelengths. Figure 9·02b shows that this is so for the TM modes so long as radii of curvature are large.

$$\lambda_c \approx \frac{2}{p}(r_0 - r_i) \qquad p = 1, 2, 3, \cdots \tag{3}$$

This is verified by Fig. 9·02b for values of r_0/r_i near unity.

Probably more important is the lowest order TE wave with circumferential variations. This is analogous to the TE_{10} wave of a rectangu-

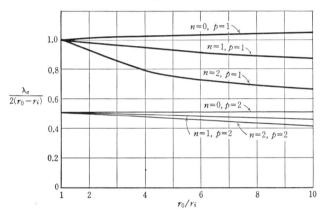

Fig. 9·02b Cut-off wavelength for some higher order TM waves in coaxial lines.

lar wave guide, and physical reasoning from the analogy leads one to expect cut-off for this wave type when the average circumference is about equal to wavelength. (The later discussion of Art. 9·04 will indicate this more clearly.) Solution of (2) reveals this simple rule to be within about 4 per cent accuracy for r_0/r_i up to 5. In general, for the nth order TE wave with circumferential variations,

$$\lambda_c \approx \frac{2\pi}{n}\left(\frac{r_0 + r_i}{2}\right) \qquad n = 1, 2, 3, \cdots \tag{4}$$

There are, of course, other TE waves with further radial variations, and the lowest order of these has a cut-off about the same as the lowest order TM wave.

Once cut-off is found by solution of (1) and (2) or the above approximations, propagation characteristics are determined by the expressions of Arts. 8·13, 8·14. Of course, for the majority of coaxial line applications, dimensions are small enough compared with wavelength so that the waves are far below cut-off. They then do not propagate energy, but attenuate rapidly so that they are important only at end effects, discontinuities, or in the radiation field. For microwave applications, however, the line size may sometimes be large enough to propagate the circumferential mode determined by $n = 1$ in (4). Care must then be taken to avoid its excitation or its interference with the desired mode.

Common Wave Guides

9·03   RECTANGULAR WAVE GUIDES

Hollow conducting pipes of rectangular cross section are the most commonly used of the hollow-pipe wave guides. It has been pointed out in Chapter 8 that for such hollow pipes the dielectric interior can

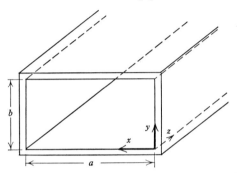

Fig. 9·03a   Coordinate system for rectangular guide.

support TM and TE waves, but not TEM waves. With the coordinate system chosen as in Fig. 9·03a, the wave equation may be solved in rectangular coordinates as in Art. 8·15. For TM waves the boundary conditions require zero E_z at $x = 0$ and at $y = 0$, so only sine terms can be present. Other components are derived by the relations 8·02(7) to (10).

$$
\begin{array}{ll}
\textit{Transverse Magnetic Waves} & \textit{Transverse Electric Waves} \\[4pt]
E_z = A \sin k_x x \sin k_y y & H_z = B \cos k_x x \cos k_y y \\[8pt]
H_x = j \dfrac{k_y f}{k_c \eta f_c} A \sin k_x x \cos k_y y & E_x = j \dfrac{\eta k_y f}{k_c f_c} B \cos k_x x \sin k_y y \\[10pt]
H_y = -j \dfrac{k_x f}{k_c \eta f_c} A \cos k_x x \sin k_y y \quad (1) & E_y = -j \dfrac{\eta k_x f}{k_c f_c} B \sin k_x x \cos k_y y \quad (2) \\[10pt]
E_x = Z_{TM} H_y & H_x = -\dfrac{E_y}{Z_{TE}} \\[10pt]
E_y = -Z_{TM} H_x & H_y = \dfrac{E_x}{Z_{TE}}
\end{array}
$$

In the above, the propagation factor $e^{(j\omega t - \gamma z)}$ is understood, and

$$Z_{TM} = \eta[1 - (f_c/f)^2]^{\frac{1}{2}} \qquad Z_{TE} = \eta[1 - (f_c/f)^2]^{-\frac{1}{2}} \tag{3}$$

$$\gamma = \sqrt{k_c{}^2 - k^2} = j\frac{\omega}{v}\sqrt{1 - \left(\frac{f_c}{f}\right)^2} \tag{4}$$

If the wave is negatively traveling, $e^{(j\omega t + \gamma z)}$ is understood and the signs of terms in Z_{TM} or Z_{TE} should be reversed.

In addition to the boundary conditions utilized above, there remain the conditions at $x = a$ and $y = b$. For the TM waves, E_z must be zero here also, requiring that $k_x a$ and $k_y b$ be multiples of π.

$$k_x = \frac{m\pi}{a} \qquad k_y = \frac{n\pi}{b}$$

The requirement of $\partial H_z/\partial x = 0$ at $x = a$ and $\partial H_z/\partial y = 0$ at $y = b$ leads to the same values of k_x and k_y for TE waves. From Eq. 8·15(4) for either TM or TE waves,

$$(k_c)_{m,n} = \sqrt{k_x{}^2 + k_y{}^2} = \sqrt{\left(\frac{m\pi}{a}\right)^2 + \left(\frac{n\pi}{b}\right)^2} \tag{5}$$

Then cut-off wavelength and frequency may be written

$$(\lambda_c)_{m,n} = \frac{2\pi}{k_c} = \frac{2}{\sqrt{(m/a)^2 + (n/b)^2}} = \frac{2ab}{\sqrt{(mb)^2 + (na)^2}} \tag{6}$$

$$(f_c)_{m,n} = \frac{k_c}{2\pi\sqrt{\mu\epsilon}} = \frac{1}{2\sqrt{\mu\epsilon}}\sqrt{\left(\frac{m}{a}\right)^2 + \left(\frac{n}{b}\right)^2} \tag{7}$$

There are then a doubly infinite number of possible waves of each type, corresponding to all the combinations of the integers m and n. An E or transverse magnetic wave with m half-sine variations in the x direction and n half-sine variations in the y direction is denoted as an E_{mn} or TM_{mn} wave. An H or transverse electric wave with m half-sine variations in x, n in y, is denoted by H_{mn} or TE_{mn}. Note that by (1) and (2) TE waves may exist with either m or n (but not both) zero, whereas in a TM wave neither m nor n can be zero or the entire wave disappears. The lowest order TE wave, TE_{10}, is of enough special engineering interest to be studied in more detail in a following article. For the moment, however, we see from (6)˙ that the cut-off (free space) wavelength of such a wave is

$$[\lambda_c]_{TE_{10}} = 2a \tag{8}$$

That is, the cut-off frequency is that frequency for which the width of the guide is a half-wavelength. It does not depend at all on the other dimensions. This TE_{10} mode is frequently referred to as the *dominant* mode of the rectangular guide.

Figure 9·03b shows a line diagram indicating the cut-off frequencies of several of the lowest order modes for a square guide, $a = b$, referred to the cut-off frequency of the dominant TE_{10} mode, and for a guide of ratio $b/a = \frac{1}{2}$.

The phase and group velocities, attenuation below cut-off, and attenuation due to imperfect dielectrics above cut-off for any wave type are given in terms of the cut-off frequency of that wave type by the

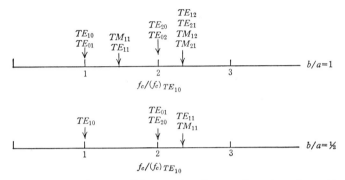

Fig. 9·03b Relative cut-off frequencies of waves in rectangular guides.

general expressions of Art. 8·13. For attenuation above cut-off due to imperfect conductivity, we evaluate the integrals of Eqs. 8·13(19) to (24) in a straightforward manner. The results are

$$(\alpha_c)_{TEm0} = \frac{R_s}{b\eta \sqrt{1 - (f_c/f)^2}} \left[1 + \frac{2b}{a} \left(\frac{f_c}{f}\right)^2 \right] \tag{9}$$

$$(\alpha_c)_{TEmn} =$$

$$\frac{2R_s}{b\eta \sqrt{1 - \left(\dfrac{f_c}{f}\right)^2}} \left\{ \left(1 + \frac{b}{a}\right)\left(\frac{f_c}{f}\right)^2 + \left[1 - \left(\frac{f_c}{f}\right)^2\right] \left[\frac{\dfrac{b}{a}\left(\dfrac{b}{a}m^2 + n^2\right)}{\dfrac{b^2 m^2}{a^2} + n^2} \right] \right\} \tag{10}$$

$$(\alpha_c)_{TMmn} = \frac{2R_s}{b\eta \sqrt{1 - (f_c/f)^2}} \frac{[m^2(b/a)^3 + n^2]}{[m^2(b/a)^2 + n^2]} \tag{11}$$

Curves of attenuation in decibels per meter (8.686 times the values of α in nepers per meter given in the equations above) are plotted for a

TE_{10}

TE_{20}

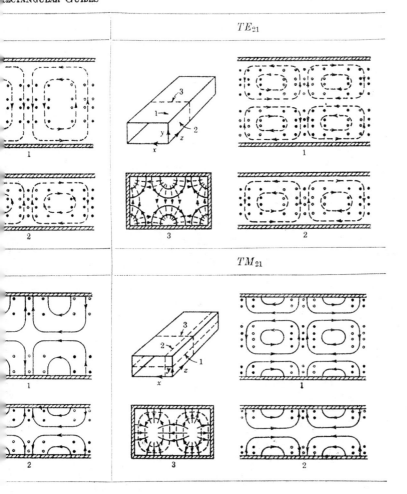

TE_{21}

TM_{21}

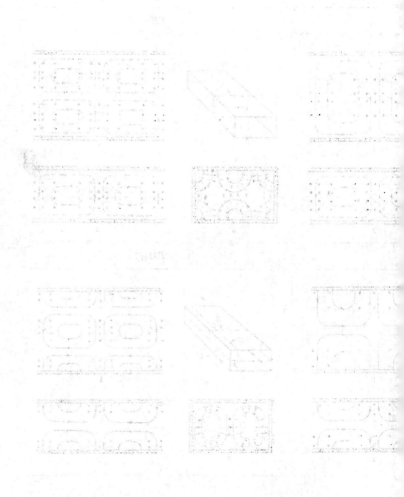

few modes and b/a ratios in Fig. 9·03c.   Note that all curves show a minimum value of attenuation, after which attenuation increases with frequency.   Field distributions in several of the modes are shown in

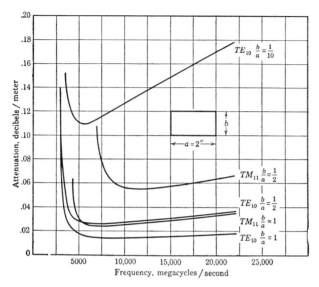

Fig. 9·03c   Attenuation due to copper losses in rectangular wave guides of fixed width.

Table 9·03.   It will be useful to become familiar with this table, and especially to make comparisons with the similar table to be given in Art. 9·05 for circular guides.

PROBLEMS

9·03a   Derive in detail the expressions for attenuation due to imperfect conductors, Eqs. 9·03(9) to (11).

9·03b   Recalling that surface resistivity R_s is a function of frequency, find the frequency of minimum attenuation for a TM_{mn} mode.   Show that the expression for attenuation of a TE_{mn} mode must also have a minimum.

9·03c   Of the wave types studied so far, those transverse magnetic to the axial direction were obtained by setting $H_z = 0$; those transverse electric to the axial direction were obtained by setting $E_z = 0$.   For the rectangular wave guide, obtain the lowest order mode with $H_x = 0$ but all other components present.   This may be called a wave transverse magnetic to the x direction.   Show that it may also be obtained by superposing the TM and TE waves given previously of just sufficient amounts so that H_x from the two waves exactly cancel.   Repeat for a wave transverse electric to the x direction.   The above wave types are also called *longitudinal section waves*.

9·04   THE TE_{10} WAVE IN A RECTANGULAR GUIDE

One of the simplest of all the waves which may exist inside hollow pipe wave guides is the dominant TE_{10} wave in the rectangular guide. It is also of great engineering importance, partly for the following reasons.

1. Cut-off frequency is independent of one of the dimensions of the cross section.   Consequently for a given frequency this dimension may be made small enough so that the TE_{10} wave is the only wave which will propagate, and there is no difficulty with higher order waves which end effects or discontinuities may cause to be excited.

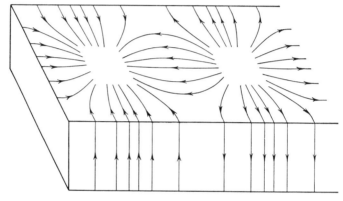

Fig. 9·04a   Current flow in walls of rectangular guide with TE_{10} mode.

2. The polarization of the field is definitely fixed, electric field passing from top to bottom of the guide.   This fixed polarization may be required for certain applications.

3. For a given frequency the attenuation due to copper losses is not excessive compared with other wave types in guides of comparable size.

Let us now rewrite the expressions from the previous article for general TE waves in rectangular guides, Fig. 9·04a, setting $m = 1$, $n = 0$, and substituting the value of cut-off for this combination.

$$E_y = E_0 \sin \frac{\pi x}{a} \tag{1}$$

$$H_x = -\left(\frac{E_0}{Z_{TE}}\right) \sin\left(\frac{\pi x}{a}\right) \tag{2}$$

$$H_z = \frac{jE_0}{\eta}\left(\frac{\lambda}{2a}\right) \cos \frac{\pi x}{a} \tag{3}$$

$$H_y = 0 = E_x \tag{4}$$

$$Z_{TE} = \frac{\eta}{\sqrt{1 - (\lambda/2a)^2}} \tag{5}$$

$$v_p = \frac{1}{\sqrt{\mu\epsilon} \sqrt{1 - (\lambda/2a)^2}} \tag{6}$$

$$v_g = \frac{1}{\sqrt{\mu\epsilon}} \sqrt{1 - \left(\frac{\lambda}{2a}\right)^2} \tag{7}$$

$$\lambda_c = 2a \tag{8}$$

$$f_c = \frac{1}{2a \sqrt{\mu\epsilon}} \tag{9}$$

Attenuation due to imperfect dielectric,

$$\alpha_d = \frac{\sigma\eta}{2 \quad 1 - (f_c/f)^2} = \frac{k\epsilon''/\epsilon'}{2 \sqrt{1 - (f_c/f)^2}} \tag{10}$$

Attenuation due to imperfect conductor,

$$\alpha_c = \frac{R_s}{b\eta \sqrt{1 - (f_c/f)^2}} \left[1 + \frac{2b}{a} \left(\frac{f_c}{f}\right)^2 \right] \tag{11}$$

In the above, v_p is phase velocity, v_g is group velocity, μ, ϵ, and η are permeability, dielectric constant, and intrinsic impedance respectively for the dielectric filling the guide. R_s is the skin effect surface resistivity of the conducting walls, and ϵ''/ϵ' is the ratio of loss factor to relative dielectric constant of the dielectric.

A study of the field distributions (1) to (3) shows the field patterns for this wave sketched in Table 9·03. First it is noted that no field components vary in the vertical or y direction. The only electric field component is that vertical one E_y passing between top and bottom of the guide. This is a maximum at the center and zero at the conducting walls, varying as a half-sine curve. The corresponding charges induced by the electric field lines ending on conductors are:

(a) Charges zero on side walls.
(b) A charge distribution on top and bottom corresponding to E_y.

$$\rho_s = -\epsilon E_y \text{ coulombs/meter}^2 \text{ on top}$$

$$= \epsilon E_y \text{ coulombs/meter}^2 \text{ on bottom}$$

The magnetic field forms closed paths surrounding the vertical electric displacement currents arising from E_y, so that there are components

H_x and H_z. H_x is zero at the two side walls and a maximum in the center, following the distribution of E_y. H_z is a maximum at the side walls and zero at the center. H_x corresponds to a longitudinal current flow down the guide in the top, and opposite in the bottom; H_z corresponds to a current from top to bottom around the periphery of the guide. These current distributions are sketched in Fig. 9·04a.

(a) Longitudinal current flow:

On top $J_z = H_x$ amperes per meter.

On bottom $J_z = -H_x$ amperes per meter.

(b) Transverse current flow from top to bottom:

On walls $J_y = -H_z\big|_{x=0}$ amperes per meter.

On top $J_x = -H_z$ amperes per meter.

On bottom $J_x = H_z$ amperes per meter.

This simple wave type is a convenient one to study in order to strengthen some of our physical pictures of wave propagation. First note that this is one of the types predicted by physical reasoning in Art. 8·17. Electric field is confined to the transverse plane and so passes between equal and opposite charge densities lying on different parts of the walls in the same transverse plane. Currents flow around the periphery of the guide between these opposite charges; currents also flow longitudinally down the guide between a given charge and that of opposite sign, a half-wave farther down the guide. The magnetic fields surround the electric displacement currents inside the guide and so must have an axial as well as a transverse component.

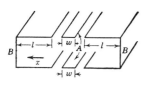

Fig. 9·04b.

As a fairly crude way of looking at the problem, one might also think of this mode being formed by starting with a parallel-plate transmission line of width w to carry the longitudinal current in the center of the guide, and then adding shorted troughs B of depth l on the two sides to close the region, as pictured in Fig. 9·04b. Since one would expect the lengths l to be around a quarter-wavelength to provide a high impedance at the center, the over-all width should be something over a half-wavelength, which we know to be true for propagation. The picture is only a rough one because the fields in the two regions are not separated, and propagation is not purely longitudinal in the center portion or transverse in the side portions.

A third viewpoint follows from that used in studying the higher order waves between parallel planes. Here it was pointed out that one could visualize the TM and TE waves in terms of plane waves bouncing between the two planes at such an angle that the interference pattern maintains a zero of electric field tangential to the two planes. Similarly, the TE_{10} wave in the rectangular guide may be thought of as arising from the interference between incident and reflected plane waves, polarized so that the electric vector is vertical, and bouncing between the two sides of the guide at such an angle with the sides that the zero electric field is maintained at the two sides. One such component uniform plane wave is indicated in Fig. 9·04c. As in the

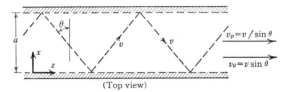

Fig. 9·04c Path of uniform plane wave component of TE_{10} wave in rectangular guide.

result of Art. 8·08, when the width a is exactly $\lambda/2$, the waves travel exactly back and forth across the guide with no component of propagation in the axial direction. At slightly higher frequencies there is a small angle θ such that $a = \lambda/2 \cos \theta$, and there is a small propagation in the axial direction, a very small group velocity in the axial direction $v \sin \theta$, and a very large phase velocity $v/\sin \theta$. At frequencies approaching infinity, θ approaches 90°, so that the wave travels down the guide practically as a plane wave in space propagating in the axial direction.

All the above points of view explain why the dimension b should not enter into the determination of cut-off frequency. Since the electric field is always normal to top and bottom, the placing of these planes plays no part in the boundary condition. However, this dimension b will be important from two other points of view.

(a) The smaller b is (all other parameters constant), the greater is the electric field across the guide for a given power transfer, and so the danger of voltage breakdown is greater.

(b) The smaller b is (all other parameters constant), the greater is the attenuation due to conductor losses.

The first point is easily seen since it was shown that the power transfer can be written as the integral over the cross-sectional area of E^2/Z_{TE}. Z_{TE} does not change with b, so, as cross-sectional area decreases, E must increase, if power is to be constant.

The second point follows from an approximate picture in which the attenuation is roughly proportional to the ratio of perimeter to cross-sectional area. This picture is a logical one as the conductor losses occur on the perimeter, and the power transfer occurs through the cross-sectional area. Of course, field distributions enter, and we can look at this case more rigorously by noting that, if the strength of magnetic field is maintained constant as b is decreased, the magnitude of currents in the walls is maintained constant. A large part of the losses occur along the top and bottom, and this part is consequently unchanged as b decreases, but power transfer for this constant H decreases directly with b. Therefore the ratio of power loss to power transfer increases as b decreases.

PROBLEMS

9·04a   For $\lambda = 10$ cm, design a rectangular wave guide with copper conductor and air dielectric so that the TE_{10} wave will propagate with a 30 per cent safety factor ($f = 1.30f_c$) but also so that the wave type with next higher cut-off will be 30 per cent below its cut-off frequency. Calculate the attenuation due to copper losses in decibels per meter.

9·04b   Repeat the above for $\lambda = 5$ cm.

9·04c   Design a guide for use at 3000 mc/sec with the same requirements as in a except that the guide is to be filled with a dielectric having a dielectric constant 4 times that of air. Calculate the increase in attenuation due to copper losses alone, assuming that the dielectric is perfect. Calculate the additional attenuation due to this dielectric, if $\epsilon''/\epsilon' = 0.01$.

9·05   WAVE GUIDES OF CIRCULAR CROSS SECTION

For a circular guide, cylindrical coordinates will be selected so that the appropriate solutions for the waves may be taken directly from Art. 8·16. There can be no term in $N_n(k_c r)$ since the solution must in this case apply at the origin, $r = 0$ and $N_n(0) = \infty$. For TM waves, E_z is then given by Eqs. 8·16(4) and 8·16(5) with $B = 0$. For TE waves, H_z is given by a like expression. Other field components for the two types of waves follow from Eqs. 8·16(8) to 8·16(11) respectively. General solutions for the two types of waves are then as follows.

Transverse Magnetic Waves

$$E_z = A J_n(k_c r) \begin{cases} \cos n\phi \\ \sin n\phi \end{cases}$$

$$H_r = -j \frac{nf}{k_c \eta r f_c} A J_n(k_c r) \begin{cases} \sin n\phi \\ -\cos n\phi \end{cases}$$

$$H_\phi = -j \frac{f}{f_c \eta} A J_n'(k_c r) \begin{cases} \cos n\phi \\ \sin n\phi \end{cases} \quad (1)$$

$$E_\phi = -H_r Z_{TM}$$

$$E_r = H_\phi Z_{TM}$$

Transverse Electric Waves

$$H_z = B J_n(k_c r) \begin{cases} \cos n\phi \\ \sin n\phi \end{cases}$$

$$E_r = j \frac{n\eta f}{k_c r f_c} B J_n(k_c r) \begin{cases} \sin n\phi \\ -\cos n\phi \end{cases}$$

$$E_\phi = j\eta \frac{f}{f_c} B J_n'(k_c r) \begin{cases} \cos n\phi \\ \sin n\phi \end{cases} \quad (2)$$

$$H_\phi = \frac{E_r}{Z_{TE}}$$

$$H_r = -\frac{E_\phi}{Z_{TE}}$$

In all the above expressions $e^{j\omega t - \gamma z}$ is understood, and γ, Z_{TM}, and Z_{TE} are:

$$\gamma = j(\omega/v)[1 - (f_c/f)^2]^{1/2}$$

$$Z_{TM} = \eta[1 - (f_c/f)^2]^{1/2}$$

$$Z_{TE} = \eta[1 - (f_c/f)^2]^{-1/2}$$

For a negatively traveling wave ($e^{j\omega t + \gamma z}$ understood), the signs of terms in (1) and (2) containing Z_{TM} or Z_{TE} should be reversed.

For transverse magnetic waves, the boundary condition of zero electric field tangential to the conducting boundary, $E_z = 0$ at $r = a$, must require that

$$J_n(k_c a) = 0 \quad (3)$$

Since the Bessel function $J_n(x)$ has an infinite number of values of x for which it becomes zero, (3) may be satisfied by any one of these. That is, if p_{nl} is the lth root of $J_n(x) = 0$, (3) is satisfied if

$$(k_c)_{nl} = \frac{p_{nl}}{a} \quad (4)$$

Equation (4) defines a doubly infinite set of possible values for k_c, one for each combination of the integers n and l. Each of these combinations defines a particular wave type by Eqs. (1), in general differing from all others in field distributions, cut-off frequencies, and propagation properties. A particular E or transverse magnetic wave corresponding to two integers n and l is denoted by E_{nl} or TM_{nl}. The integer n describes the number of variations circumferentially; the integer l describes the number of variations radially. The cut-off wavelength or frequency for a particular wave type follows from (4).

$$(\lambda_c)_{TM_{nl}} = \frac{2\pi}{k_c} = \frac{2\pi a}{p_{nl}} \tag{5}$$

$$(f_c)_{TM_{nl}} = \frac{k_c}{2\pi \sqrt{\mu\epsilon}} = \frac{p_{nl}}{2\pi a \sqrt{\mu\epsilon}} \tag{6}$$

The lowest value of p_{nl} is the first root of the zero order Bessel function, $p_{01} = 2.405$, so that this TM_{01} wave has the lowest cut-off frequency of all transverse magnetic waves in a given circular pipe. From (5), this cut-off wavelength is $2.61a$. Note that this wavelength is measured at velocity of light in the dielectric filling the guide, $1/\sqrt{\mu\epsilon}$.

For transverse electric or H waves the required boundary condition is that normal derivative of H_z be zero at all conducting surfaces. This requires

$$J_n'(k_c a) = 0 \tag{7}$$

So that, if p_{nl}' is the lth root of $J_n'(x) = 0$, (7) is satisfied by

$$(k_c)_{nl} = \frac{p_{nl}'}{a} \tag{8}$$

Equation (8) again defines a doubly infinite number of possible TE wave types corresponding to all the possible combinations of the integers n and l, n describing the number of circumferential variations, l the number of radial variations. A particular H or transverse electric wave type is labeled H_{nl} or TE_{nl}. Cut-off wavelength and frequency are

$$(\lambda_c)_{TE_{nl}} = \frac{2\pi}{p_{nl}'} a \tag{9}$$

$$(f_c)_{TE_{nl}} = \frac{p_{nl}'}{2\pi a \sqrt{\mu\epsilon}} \tag{10}$$

The lowest value of p_{nl}' is p_{11}', which is 1.84, so that the TE_{11} wave has the lowest cut-off frequency of all transverse electric waves in a given diameter of pipe. From (9) this corresponds to a cut-off wavelength of $3·41a$. This is also a lower frequency of cut-off than that found for the lowest order TM wave in a given size of pipe. Stated

Wave Type	TM_{01}	TM_{02}
Field distributions in cross-sectional plane, at plane of maximum transverse fields		
Field distributions along guide		
Field components present	E_z, E_r, H_ϕ	E_z, E_r, H_ϕ
p_{nl} or p'_{nl}	2.405	5.52
$(k_c)_{nl}$	$\dfrac{2.405}{a}$	$\dfrac{5.52}{a}$
$(\lambda_c)_{nl}$	$2.61a$	$1.14a$
$(f_c)_{nl}$	$\dfrac{0.383}{a\sqrt{\mu\,\epsilon}}$	$\dfrac{0.877}{a\sqrt{\mu\,\epsilon}}$
Attenuation due to imperfect conductors	$\dfrac{R_s}{a\eta}\dfrac{1}{\sqrt{1-(f_c/f)^2}}$	$\dfrac{R_s}{a\eta}\dfrac{1}{\sqrt{1-(f_c/f)^2}}$

TM_{11}	TE_{01}	TE_{11}
Distributions Below Along This Plane		Distributions Below Along This Plane
E_r, E_ϕ, H_r, H_ϕ	H_z, H_r, E_ϕ	$H_z, H_r, H_\phi, E_r, E_\phi$
3.83	3.83	1.84
$\dfrac{3.83}{a}$	$\dfrac{3.83}{a}$	$\dfrac{1.84}{a}$
$1.64a$	$1.64a$	$3.41a$
$\dfrac{0.609}{a\sqrt{\mu\,\epsilon}}$	$\dfrac{0.609}{a\sqrt{\mu\,\epsilon}}$	$\dfrac{0.293}{a\sqrt{\mu\,\epsilon}}$
$\dfrac{1}{\sqrt{1-(f_c/f)^2}}$	$\dfrac{R_s}{a\eta}\dfrac{(f_c/f)^2}{\sqrt{1-(f_c/f)^2}}$	$\dfrac{R_s}{a\eta}\dfrac{1}{\sqrt{1-(f_c/f)^2}}\left[\left(\dfrac{f_c}{f}\right)^2+0.420\right]$

in another way, the TE_{11} wave of a given frequency will propagate in a pipe only 76.6 per cent as big as that required to support a TM_{01} wave of the same frequency.

A line diagram showing positions of the cut-off frequencies of some of the lower order modes as compared with the dominant TE_{11} mode is given for a circular guide in Fig. 9·05a. Field distributions for several of the modes with other important data are shown in Table 9·05. In comparing this with the similar table for rectangular guides, note that analogous modes in the two shapes of guides do not have corresponding subscripts. Thus, a TE_{11} circular mode is analogous to the TE_{10} rectangular, a TM_{01} circular is analogous to a TM_{11}

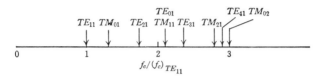

Fig. 9·05a   Relative cut-off frequencies of waves in a circular guide.

rectangular, the TM_{11} circular is analogous to the TM_{21} rectangular, etc.

To demonstrate the calculation of the attenuation arising from imperfect conductors, we will carry through the steps for a TM_{nl} mode. To compute power transfer, the expression for E_z in (1) may be substituted in Eq. 8·13(19).

$$W_T = \frac{Z_{TM}}{2\eta^2}\left(\frac{f}{f_c}\right)^2 \int_{c.s.} E_z^2 \, dS$$
$$= \frac{(f/f_c)^2 \sqrt{1 - (f_c/f)^2}}{2\eta} \int_0^{2\pi}\int_0^a A^2 J_n^2(k_c r)\cos^2(n\phi)\, r\, dr\, d\phi$$

The integral of the $\cos^2$ term gives a value of π. The integral of the Bessel function is evaluated by Eq. 3·28(5).

$$\int_0^a J_n^2(k_c r)r\, dr = \frac{a^2}{2}\left[J_n'^2(k_c a) + \left(1 + \frac{n^2}{k_c^2 a^2}\right)J_n^2(k_c a)\right]$$

The second term in this integral is zero because of (3). So

$$W_T = \frac{\pi(f/f_c)^2 \sqrt{1 - (f_c/f)^2}\, a^2}{4\eta} A^2 J_n'^2(k_c a) \qquad (11)$$

The power loss per unit length due to the conductors, by Eq. 8·13(23), is

$$W_L = \frac{R_s}{2\eta^2 k_c{}^2} \left(\frac{f}{f_c}\right)^2 \oint \left(\frac{\partial E_z}{\partial n}\right)^2 dl$$

$$= \frac{R_s}{2\eta^2 k_c{}^2} \left(\frac{f}{f_c}\right)^2 k_c{}^2 A^2 J_n{}'^2(k_c a) \int_0^{2\pi} \cos^2 (n\phi)\, a\, d\phi$$

$$= \frac{R_s \pi a}{2\eta^2} \left(\frac{f}{f_c}\right)^2 A^2 J_n{}'^2(k_c a) \tag{12}$$

The attenuation is then

$$\alpha_{TM_{nl}} = \frac{W_L}{2W_T} = \frac{R_s}{a\eta} \frac{1}{\sqrt{1 - (f_c/f)^2}}, \quad \text{nepers/meter} \tag{13}$$

A similar use of the equations gives the attenuation for a TE_{nl} wave,

$$\alpha_{TE_{nl}} = \frac{R_s}{a\eta} \frac{1}{\sqrt{1 - (f_c/f)^2}} \left[\left(\frac{f_c}{f}\right)^2 + \frac{n^2}{p_{nl}{}'^2 - n^2} \right] \tag{14}$$

Some representative curves of attenuation versus diameter are plotted in Fig. 9·05b for different wave types at a fixed frequency; and,

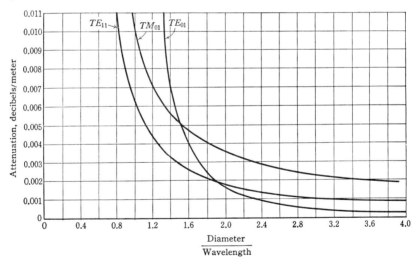

Fig. 9·05b   Attenuation due to copper losses in circular wave guides at 3000 mc/sec.

in Fig. 9·05c, for different wave types in a guide of fixed diameter, attenuation is plotted versus frequency. The TE_{01} wave is interesting because it shows an attenuation which decreases indefinitely with increasing frequency. This is logical, since equations (2) show that the only magnetic field component tangential to the conductors is H_z, if $n = 0$. As frequency increases, H_z decreases for a constant value of transmitted energy and approaches zero at infinite frequency. Currents in the guide walls therefore approach zero, and losses approach zero. As was pointed out in Art. 8·17, this merely means that under such conditions the wave is not tied intimately to

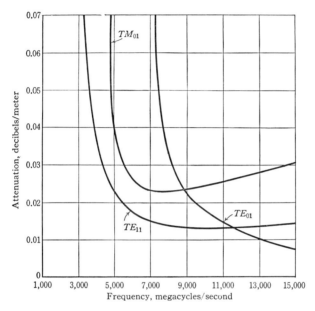

Fig. 9·05c   Attenuation due to copper losses in circular wave guides; diameter = 2 in.

the conducting walls. Any asymmetry or bending of the guide will, of course, produce currents in the walls and a corresponding increase in losses, or may even transform the wave into a type other than the TE_{01}. Although the TE_{01} wave was used as an example, all TE_{0l} waves behave similarly.

PROBLEMS

9·05a Derive Eq. 9·05(14) for attenuation of TE_{nl} waves in an imperfectly conducting guide.

9·05b Show that for all TM_{nl} waves the minimum attenuation arising from imperfect conductors occurs at a frequency,

$$f = \sqrt{3}\,f_c$$

Study the dependence of the value of attenuation at this frequency on f_c.   (Recall that R_s is a function of frequency.)

9·05c   For $\lambda = 7$ cm, select a pipe size to propagate with a reasonable safety factor the TE_{11} wave, but no other wave type.   Compare the dissipative attenuation in this TE_{11} wave (copper guide) with the reactive attenuation in the next highest order wave.

9·06   EXCITATION AND RECEPTION OF WAVES IN GUIDES

The problems of exciting waves in wave guides and of absorbing their energy in a receiver are extremely difficult to analyze if exact quantitative analysis is desired.   Some aspects of the quantitative problem will be given in the discussion of microwave networks in Chapter 11.   Some qualitative ideas will be given here.   In order to excite any particular desired wave, one should study the wave pattern, and then use any of the following methods.

1. Introduce the excitation in a probe or antenna oriented in the direction of electric field, and most often placed near a maximum of the field.   (The exact placing as well as the length and size of the probe is a matter of impedance matching.)

2. Introduce the excitation through a loop oriented in a plane normal to the magnetic field, and near a maximum of magnetic field.

3. Couple to the desired exciting fields by a hole, slit, or iris in the guide wall, chosen so that there is some common field component between the desired mode and the exciting source.

4. Introduce currents from transmission lines or other sources in such a manner that the desired current directions in the guide walls are forcibly excited.   (Or course it is true that, since currents and fields are directly related, any scheme based on exciting currents in the walls may, if preferred, be looked upon as a scheme of exciting fields in the space, but the viewpoint from currents is often more direct.)

5. For higher order waves combine as many of the exciting sources as are required, with proper phasings.

Since any of the above exciting methods are in the nature of concentrated sources, they will not in general excite purely one wave, but all waves which have field components in a favorable direction for the particular exciting source.   From another point of view, we see that one wave alone will not suffice to satisfy the boundary conditions of the guide complicated by the exciting source, so that many higher order waves must be added for this purpose.   If the guide is large enough, several of these waves will then proceed to propagate.   Most often, however, only one of the excited waves is above cut-off.   This will

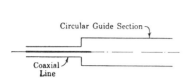

Fig. 9·06a   Antenna in end of circular guide for excitation of TM_{01} wave.

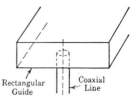

Fig. 9·06b   Antenna in bottom of rectangular guide for excitation of the TE_{10} wave.

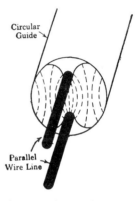

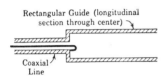

Fig. 9·06c   Loop in end of rectangular guide for excitation of TE_{10} wave.

Fig. 9·06d   Parallel wire line for excitation of TE_{11} wave in circular guide.

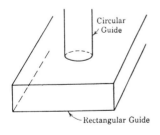

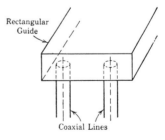

Fig. 9·06e   Junction between circular guide (TM_{01} wave) and rectangular guide (TE_{10} wave).

Fig. 9·06f   Excitation of the TE_{20} wave in rectangular guide by two oppositely phased antennas.

propagate down the guide, and (if absorbed somewhere) will represent a resistive load on the source, comparable to the radiation resistance of antennas which we shall encounter further in Chapter 12. The higher order waves which are excited, if all below cut-off, will be localized in the neighborhood of the source and will represent purely reactive loads on the source. For practical application, it is then necessary to add, in the line which feeds the probe or loop or other exciting means, an arrangement for matching to the load which has a real part representing the propagating wave and an imaginary part representing the localized reactive waves.

The receiving problem is the reverse of the exciting problem, and in general any method which works well for exciting will also work well for receiving.

Some examples of the several excitation methods listed in 1 to 4 are shown in Figs. 9·06a to 9·06f. In Fig. 9·06a an antenna is used to excite a TM_{01} wave in a circular guide. In Fig. 9·06b a similar antenna is used to excite a TE_{10} wave in a rectangular guide. Note that one end of the guide is closed to obtain transmission in one direction only. The position of this closed end may be utilized as one variable in the matching process. In Fig. 9·06c, a TE_{10} wave in a rectangular guide is excited by a loop. In Fig. 9·06d, a TE_{11} wave in a circular guide is excited by the currents of a two-wire transmission line. Similarly, in Fig. 9·06e, the TM_{01} wave in the circular guide is excited by a TE_{10} wave in a rectangular guide, and a study of the patterns and reflections at the closed end shows that currents in the walls are proper here for excitation. From another point of view this example may be considered hole or iris coupling. Other examples of this type will be given in Art. 10·12. Finally in Fig. 9·06f, a TE_{20} wave in a rectangular guide is excited by two antennas, properly phased. Further discussion, with experimental verification, is presented by Southworth.[1]

PROBLEM

9·06 Draw the field and current patterns in the lines and guides of Figs. 9·06a to 9·06f, and explain the coupling mechanism in each of these figures.

9·07 SIMPLE TRANSMISSION LINE TECHNIQUES APPLIED TO GUIDES

Equivalent networks for general junctions such as those of the last article are very important in general impedance-matching problems, and will be discussed in Chapter 11. However, certain simple problems may be handled in terms of the wave impedance, defined as the ratio of transverse electric field to transverse magnetic field, and given

[1] G. C. Southworth, *Proc. I.R.E.*, **25**, 807–822 (July 1937).

for various wave types in preceding articles. These problems are characterized by the fact that any discontinuity should be the same over an entire transverse section of the guide, so that matching of E and H for one point of the transverse plane produces a match for all points of that plane. This is of course similar to the study of plane wave reflection problems by impedance techniques in Chapter 7. Several examples will follow. Guide wavelength λ_g and wave impedances to be used are

$$\lambda_g = \frac{\lambda}{\sqrt{1 - (f_c/f)^2}} = \frac{1}{f \sqrt{\mu\epsilon} \sqrt{1 - (f_c/f)^2}} \tag{1}$$

Transverse electromagnetic waves $Z_{TEM} = \eta = \sqrt{\mu/\epsilon}$ (2)

Transverse magnetic (E) waves $Z_{TM} = \eta \sqrt{1 - (f_c/f)^2}$ (3)

Transverse electric (H) waves $Z_{TE} = \dfrac{\eta}{\sqrt{1 - (f_c/f)^2}}$ (4)

A. Short-Circuited Guide. A wave guide may be considered as truly short-circuited if a conducting plate is placed across the entire section

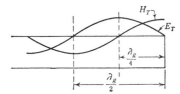

Fig. 9·07a Standing waves of transverse field components in shorted guide.

Fig. 9·07b Guide with dielectric discontinuity.

of the guide so that the transverse component of electric field is reduced to zero over all that section. This corresponds to a shorted transmission line, so that at once we may draw the forms of the resulting standing wave pattern (Fig. 9·07a). Transverse electric field is zero at the conducting plate and at multiples of $\lambda_g/2$ in front of it. It is a maximum at odd multiples of $\lambda_g/4$ in front of the plate. Transverse magnetic field is a maximum at the plate and has other maxima at $n\lambda_g/2$; minima at $(2n + 1)\lambda_g/4$ before the plate. Other phase relations show that E_z for TM waves has the same axial distribution pattern as the magnetic field, and H_z for TE waves has the same axial distribution pattern as the electric field.

B. Guide with Dielectric Discontinuity. If there is a discontinuity from one dielectric to another in a guide (Fig. 9·07b), the amount of reflection into the first region and the transmission to the second region may be determined from the mismatch in impedances Z_1 and Z_2. The expressions in terms of transverse field components are

$$\frac{E_t{'}}{E_t} = \frac{Z_2 - Z_1}{Z_2 + Z_1} = -\frac{H_{t1}{'}}{H_{t1}}$$

$$\frac{E_{t2}}{E_{t1}} = \frac{2Z_2}{Z_2 + Z_1} = \frac{Z_2 H_{t2}}{Z_1 H_{t1}}$$

(5)

Region (1) then has both a standing wave and a traveling wave. The other standard expressions for input impedance, and voltage and current along the line, from Chapter 1, may be applied to calculation of input impedance on a field basis and of values of electric and magnetic fields along the guide.

C. Quarter-Wave Matching Sections. It is of course possible to match between one section of a guide and another section with different dielectric constant for any of the wave types at any single frequency. This is accomplished by the technique of quarter-wave matching sections developed for transmission lines in Prob. 1·21(*b*) and for plane waves in Art. 7·10. Thus in Fig. 9·07*c* it is possible to match between the regions 1 and 3, if a region 2 is introduced, a quarter wavelength long (measured at the phase velocity in that region) and having an impedance the geometric mean of those on the two sides. Note that, in calculating these impedances, the different cut-off frequencies for the three sections must be taken into account in (3) or (4).

This matching may be used, for instance, in a case where it is desired to absorb power in the third section, which may be filled with water or some other material with a small but finite conductivity. A quarter-wave section of a proper material (certain special glasses, for example) may then be used to match this section to the portion of the guide with air dielectric.

D. Elimination of Reflections from Dielectric Slabs. If dielectric slabs must be placed in an otherwise uniform guide (for example, because a section must be evacuated), these may be designed in certain ways so that they cause no reflections, just as may insulators in transmission lines. The simplest arrangement is to make the dielectric slabs a half-wavelength in thickness ($\lambda_g/2$ for the material of the slab). The impedance at the front is then exactly the impedance of the guide following the slab. From another point of view, the reflections from the front and back surfaces exactly cancel under these conditions.

The above method of eliminating reflections requires that the dielectric slab be a half-wavelength in thickness, measured in the material of that slab.   For certain applications it may be undesirable to use slabs of that thickness.   For slabs of any thickness, reflections may be eliminated by cancelling the reflected wave from one slab by that from another placed a proper distance from it.   For slabs of thickness small compared with wavelength, or of a material with properties not too greatly different from that of region 1, this spacing is such that the total phase angle corresponding to the length of guide between insulators and one insulator is very nearly 90°.

E. Termination of Wave Guides.   Another important technique of transmission lines is the termination of a line by means of a proper resistor to eliminate the reflected wave.   All energy is completely absorbed according to the simple line theory if this resistor is equal to

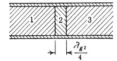

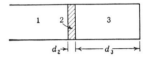

Fig. 9·07c   Insertion of matching section in a guide.

Fig. 9·07d   Conducting film for terminating a guide.

the characteristic wave impedance of the line.   If the line must be closed at the end, the terminating resistor may be placed a quarter-wavelength from the shorted end, since for perfect conductors the shorted quarter-wave line represents an infinite impedance in parallel with the resistance.   Similarly, a wave guide may be terminated by a conducting sheet having a resistance per unit square equal to the characteristic wave impedance of the wave type to be matched.   This sheet is placed a quarter-wavelength from the shorted end (Fig. 9·07d).

$$d_3 = \frac{\lambda_{g3}}{4}$$

$$\frac{1}{\sigma_2 d_2} = Z_1$$

Notice that the conducting film must be made of some material of relatively low conductivity if its thickness is not to be absurdly small.   That is, for a material like copper, d_2 would be only of the order of 10^{-10} meter.

PROBLEMS

9·07a   Show, for a *TM* wave in any shape of guide passing from one dielectric material to another, that at one frequency the change in cut-off factor may cancel the change in η, and the wave may pass between the two media without reflection, even though no intervening matching section is present. Identify this condition with the case of incidence at polarizing angle in Art. 7·15. Determine the requirement for a similar situation with TE waves, and show why it is not practical to obtain this.

9·07b A rectangular wave guide of inside dimensions 4 cm by 2 cm is to propagate a TE_{10} mode of frequency 5000 mc/sec. A dielectric of constant $\epsilon' = 4$ fills the guide for $z > 0$, with an air dielectric for $z < 0$. Assuming the dielectric-filled part is to be matched, find the reflection coefficient at $z = 0$ and the standing wave ratio in the air-filled part.

9·07c Find the length and dielectric constant of a quarter-wave matching section to be placed between the air and given dielectric of Prob. 9·07b.

9·08 WAVES BELOW AND NEAR CUT-OFF

The higher order waves which may exist in coaxial lines and all waves which may exist in hollow pipe wave guides are characterized by cut-off frequencies. If the waves are to be used for propagating energy, we are of course interested only in the behavior above cut-off. However, the behavior of these reactive or local waves below cut-off is important in at least two practical cases:

1. Application to wave guide attenuators.
2. Effects at discontinuities in transmission systems.

The attenuation properties of these waves below cut-off have been developed in the previous analyses. It has been found that below the cut-off frequency there is an attenuation only and no phase shift in an ideal guide. The characteristic wave impedance is a purely imaginary quantity—a re-emphasis of the fact that no energy can propagate down the guide. This is not a dissipative attenuation as is that due to resistance and conductance in transmission systems with propagating waves. It is a purely reactive attenuation, analogous to that in a filter section made of reactive elements, when this is in the cut-off region. The energy is not lost but is reflected back to the source so that the guide acts as a pure reactance to the source.

The expression for attenuation below cut-off in an ideal guide, Eq. 8·13(9), may be written

$$\gamma = \alpha = k_c \sqrt{1 - \left(\frac{f}{f_c}\right)^2} = \frac{2\pi}{\lambda_c} \sqrt{1 - \left(\frac{f}{f_c}\right)^2} \tag{1}$$

As f is decreased below f_c, α increases from a value of 0 approaching the constant value

$$\alpha = \frac{2\pi}{\lambda_c} \tag{2}$$

when $(f/f_c)^2 \ll 1$.   This is an important point in the use of wave guide attenuators, since it shows that the amount of this attenuation is substantially independent of frequency if the operating frequency is very far below the cut-off frequency.   In addition, the amount of this attenuation is determined only by the cut-off wavelength of the guide, which is in general proportional to the transverse size of the guide, so that the value of α may be made almost as large as one pleases by selecting a low cut-off wavelength (small pipe size).   Since (1) holds for any wave in any shape of guide, it follows that choices of wave type and guide shape cannot influence the attenuation constant except in so far as they fix the cut-off wavelength λ_c.

Note that, if a wave guide attenuator is designed with $(f/f_c) \ll 1$ so that attenuation is independent of frequency, attenuation must necessarily be very great in a wavelength since α will be much greater than the free space phase constant,

$$\frac{\alpha}{k} = \frac{2\pi/\lambda_c}{2\pi/\lambda} = \frac{\lambda}{\lambda_c} \gg 1$$

Now let us look for a moment at the relations among the fields of both transverse magnetic and transverse electric waves below cut-off. If $\gamma = \alpha$ as given by (1) is substituted in the expressions for field components of transverse magnetic waves, Eqs. 8·13(4)-(5),

$$H_x = \frac{j}{\eta}\left(\frac{f}{f_c}\right)\frac{1}{k_c}\frac{\partial E_z}{\partial y} \qquad E_x = -\sqrt{1 - \left(\frac{f}{f_c}\right)^2}\,\frac{1}{k_c}\frac{\partial E_z}{\partial x}$$

$$H_y = -\frac{j}{\eta}\left(\frac{f}{f_c}\right)\frac{1}{k_c}\frac{\partial E_z}{\partial x} \qquad E_y = -\sqrt{1 - \left(\frac{f}{f_c}\right)^2}\,\frac{1}{k_c}\frac{\partial E_z}{\partial y} \tag{3}$$

For a given distribution of E_z across the guide section, which is determined once the guide shape and size and the wave type are determined, it is evident from relations (3) that, as frequency decreases, $f/f_c \rightarrow 0$, the components of magnetic field approach zero whereas the transverse components of electric field approach a constant value.   We draw the conclusion that only electric fields are of importance in transverse magnetic or E waves far below cut-off.   Similarly, only magnetic fields are of importance in transverse electric or H waves far below cut-off.

Suppose that a TM wave is excited by some source in a wave guide, extending down the guide a certain distance to a suitable receiver.   If the frequency is far enough below cut-off so that $(f/f_c)^2$ is negligible compared with unity, the entire problem may be looked upon as one of electric coupling between the source and the receiver, calculated by d-c or low-frequency methods (of course, taking into account the presence of the guide as a shield). Similarly, a TE wave between a source and receiver in a guide far below cut-off may be looked upon as a problem of ordinary magnetic coupling between the source and receiver (of course, taking into account the presence of the guide as a shield). If the waves are far below cut-off, the dimensions of the guide must be small compared with wavelength. For any such region small compared with wavelength, the wave equation will reduce to Laplace's equation so that low-frequency analyses neglecting any tendency toward wave propagation are applicable. Only when $(f/f_c)^2$ is comparable to unity must the effects of magnetic fields be considered in TM waves, and the effects of electric fields in TE waves.

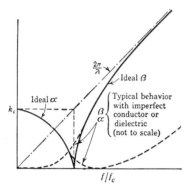

Fig. 9·08 Modification of propagation characteristics due to losses.

The presence of losses in the guide below cut-off causes the phase constant to change from the zero value for an ideal guide to a small but finite value, and modifies slightly the formula for attenuation. These modifications are most important in the immediate vicinity of cut-off, for with losses there is no longer a sharp transition but a more gradual change from one region to another, as indicated by the dotted curves in Fig. 9·08. It should be emphasized again that the approximate formulas developed in previous articles may become extremely inaccurate in this region. For example, the approximate formulas for attenuation caused by conductor or dielectric losses would yield an infinite value at $f = f_c$. The actual value is large compared with the minimum attenuation in the pass range since it is approaching the relatively larger magnitude of attenuation in the cut-off regime, but it is nevertheless finite. Previous formulas have also shown an infinite value of phase velocity at cut-off, and with losses it too will be finite.

Miscellaneous Wave-Guiding Systems

9·09 DIELECTRIC ROD OR SLAB GUIDES

The study of waves in the rectangular guide from the point of view of plane waves reflected between top and bottom (Art. 9·04) suggests that under certain conditions a wave may be guided without loss of energy by a slab of perfect dielectric having no metal boundaries.

This follows from the concept of total reflection of Art. 7·14, where it was found that, if a wave traveling in a dense dielectric strikes the boundary of a less dense dielectric at an angle of incidence greater than a certain critical angle, all energy is reflected. This critical angle, Eq. 7·14(2), where 1 refers to the dense medium and 2 to the less dense medium, is

$$\theta_c = \sin^{-1}\left(\sqrt{\frac{\mu_2\epsilon_2}{\mu_1\epsilon_1}}\right) \tag{1}$$

Thus in a dielectric slab as in Fig. 9·09a, which is assumed infinite in the direction normal to the paper, suppose that plane waves are excited inside the dielectric in some manner so that they travel as shown,

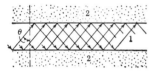

Fig. 9·09a Paths of uniform plane wave   Fig. 9·09b Dielectric rod wave guide.
components in a dielectric slab guide.

striking the surface at an angle of incidence, θ. If $\theta > \theta_c$, all energy will be reflected at each reflection and all will be retained in the slab. There is, for a slab of given thickness, a certain minimum frequency at which such a condition can exist. For frequencies lower than this critical frequency, the angle θ will be less than θ_c and a certain amount of energy will be transmitted into the dielectric medium 2 at each reflection, so that the dielectric does not act as a perfect guide. At frequencies higher than the critical, the angle becomes greater than θ_c, and the only fields in medium 2 are reactive fields that decay exponentially from the boundary in the transverse direction. As the frequency approaches infinity, $\theta \to \pi/2$ and the exponentially decaying fields in medium 2 approach zero. The critical frequency is that for which $\theta = \theta_c$. A study of the incident and reflected waves at this critical angle shows that there is a phase angle of 180° between incident and reflected components of magnetic fields parallel to the surface. It follows (maybe not obviously) that the slab should be exactly a half-wave thick, measured at a phase velocity transverse to the slab.

$$d = \frac{\lambda_1}{2\cos\theta} = \frac{1}{2f\sqrt{\mu_1\epsilon_1}\,\cos\theta} \tag{2}$$

Substitute the value of $\theta = \theta_c$ from (1):

$$\cos\theta_c = \sqrt{1 - \sin^2\theta_c} = \sqrt{1 - (\epsilon_2\mu_2/\mu_1\epsilon_1)}$$

So $\quad f_c = \dfrac{1}{2d \sqrt{\mu_1\epsilon_1} \sqrt{1 - (\epsilon_2\mu_2/\mu_1\epsilon_1)}} = \dfrac{1}{2d \sqrt{\mu_1\epsilon_1 - \mu_2\epsilon_2}}$ $\qquad$ (3)

Note that, if $\mu_1\epsilon_1 \gg \mu_2\epsilon_2$, the requirement for cut-off is that the slab be a half-wave thick, measured for the dielectric material of the slab, so that such a slab will have exactly the same cut-off frequency as though it had conducting walls. If $\mu_2\epsilon_2$ is not negligible compared with $\mu_1\epsilon_1$, the guide must be somewhat thicker than a similar slab with conducting boundaries in order to have the same cut-off frequency.

For exact behavior of the guided wave below and above this critical frequency it would be possible to utilize further the results of reflections at boundaries between dielectrics, but probably it would be as easy to go directly to Maxwell's equations and match solutions on the two sides of the boundary. For variety, let us do this, not for the above example but for a round dielectric rod in a medium of lesser dielectric constant.

Let us investigate the possibilities of propagating a TM wave with circular symmetry in a dielectric rod (medium 1 of Fig. 9·09b) surrounded by the dielectric medium 2 with no intervening conductors. The proper wave solutions may be found from Art. 8·16. If ϕ variations are eliminated, $\nu = 0$. Since medium 1 includes the origin, only the J_0 term can be present in this region; otherwise fields would become infinite at $r = 0$. Since medium 2 extends to infinity, only the $H_0{}^{(2)}$ term can be present in this solution; otherwise fields would become infinite at $r = \infty$. The factor $e^{(j\omega t - \gamma z)}$ is, of course, understood in all terms. Then,

$$E_{z1} = A_1 J_0(k_{c1}r)$$
$$E_{z2} = A_2 H_0{}^{(2)}(k_{c2}r) \qquad (4)$$

Other components follow from the relations of Eqs. 8·16(8) to 8·16(11):

$$E_{\phi 1} = E_{\phi 2} = 0 \qquad\qquad H_{r1} = H_{r2} = 0$$

$$E_{r1} = \frac{\gamma A_1}{k_{c1}} J_1(k_{c1}r) \qquad\qquad E_{r2} = \frac{\gamma A_2}{k_{c2}} H_1{}^{(2)}(k_{c2}r) \qquad (5)$$

$$H_{\phi 1} = \frac{j\omega\epsilon_1 A_1}{k_{c1}} J_1(k_{c1}r) \qquad H_{\phi 2} = \frac{j\omega\epsilon_2 A_2}{k_{c2}} H_1{}^{(2)}(k_{c2}r)$$

where

$$k_{c1}{}^2 = \gamma^2 + \omega^2\mu_1\epsilon_1 \qquad\qquad (6)$$

$$k_{c2}{}^2 = \gamma^2 + \omega^2\mu_2\epsilon_2 \qquad\qquad (7)$$

At the boundary between the two dielectrics, $r = a$, E_z and H_ϕ must be continuous.   If this requirement is placed in (4) and (5),

$$\frac{J_0(k_{c1}a)}{J_1(k_{c1}a)} = \frac{\epsilon_1 k_{c2}}{\epsilon_2 k_{c1}} \frac{H_0^{(2)}(k_{c2}a)}{H_1^{(2)}(k_{c2}a)} \tag{8}$$

We now reason as follows.   If the condition under which all energy is retained in the rod is sought, and no average energy is to be transmitted into the second medium, it is desired to have a solution corresponding to an exponential decay in the outer medium, and from Chapter 3 we find that this is obtained if k_{c2} is imaginary, since $H_0^{(2)}$ of an imaginary quantity is analogous to a negative exponential.   The requirement is then

$$k_{c2}^2 < 0$$

and the critical limiting condition is

$$k_{c2} = 0 \tag{9}$$

From (7), the propagation constant under this critical condition is

$$\gamma^2 = -\omega^2 \mu_2 \epsilon_2$$

$$\gamma = j\beta = j\omega \sqrt{\mu_2 \epsilon_2} \tag{10}$$

Therefore there is propagation with no attenuation and, under this critical condition, at a phase velocity equal to the velocity of light in the outer medium.

If (8) is observed for $k_{c2} = 0$, it is seen that for this critical condition

$$J_0(k_{c1}a) = 0$$

Denote the lth root of $J_0(x) = 0$ by p_{0l}.   Then

$$k_{c1}a = p_{0l}$$

But, from (6) and (10),

$$k_{c1} = \omega \sqrt{\mu_1 \epsilon_1 - \mu_2 \epsilon_2}$$

so

$$f_c = \frac{p_{0l}}{2\pi a \sqrt{\mu_1 \epsilon_1 - \mu_2 \epsilon_2}} \tag{11}$$

The lowest root, p_{01}, is 2.405.   For $\mu_1 \epsilon_1 \gg \mu_2 \epsilon_2$, the cut-off frequency approaches that of a TM_{01} mode in a guide with the dielectric material bounded by a perfect conductor.

If the above analysis were followed through in detail, it would be discovered that large negative values of k_{c2}^2 correspond to very high frequencies, and for these the phase velocity approaches $1/\sqrt{\mu_1 \epsilon_1}$, or the velocity of light for the medium of the rod. The large imaginary values of k_{c2} require that fields attenuate rapidly as one progresses transversely into the outer dielectric, and most of the energy is confined in the rod. Conversely, for the small values of k_{c2} near the critical frequency, the fields extend a long distance into medium 2. These changes in energy distribution check with results from physical reasoning; this would lead us to believe that velocity of propagation would be determined largely by region 2 near cut-off, and by region 1 as frequency approaches infinity.

The most important practical use of dielectric rod guides has been for radiation[2] where a continuous leakage of energy along the rod is permitted in order to form an end-fire array. The mode most often used in such dielectric rod antennas is a bit different from those studied above. It is one with a sinusoidal variation of fields about the circumference, and it turns out that all such modes in the dielectric rod require both E_z and H_z. Most interesting is the fact that for $n = 1$ the cut-off frequency is zero. To analyze the problem of first order circumferential mode in a circular rod of radius a, begin with solutions for E_z and H_z for both regions. (See Art. 8·16.)

$$r < a \qquad\qquad\qquad\qquad r > a$$
$$E_{z1} = AJ_1(\alpha r)\cos\phi \qquad\qquad E_{z2} = CK_1(\beta r)\cos\phi$$

$$H_{z1} = BJ_1(\alpha r)\sin\phi \qquad\qquad H_{z2} = DK_1(\beta r)\sin\phi \qquad (12)$$

$$\alpha^2 = \gamma^2 + k_1^2 \qquad\qquad\qquad \beta^2 = -(\gamma^2 + k_2^2)$$

Other field components $(E_r, H_r, E_\phi, H_\phi)$ may be obtained by application of Eqs. 8·16(8) to (11). Continuity of E_z, H_z, E_ϕ, H_ϕ is required at $r = a$, and there results the following equation which in principle determines γ.

$$\frac{\mu_1\epsilon_1 J_1'^2(\alpha a)}{\alpha^2 J_1^2(\alpha a)} + \frac{(\epsilon_1\mu_2 + \mu_1\epsilon_2)J_1'(\alpha a)K_1'(\beta a)}{\alpha\beta J_1(\alpha a)K_1(\beta a)} + \frac{\mu_2\epsilon_2 K_1'^2(\beta a)}{\beta^2 K_1^2(\beta a)}$$
$$= \left(\frac{1}{\alpha^2} + \frac{1}{\beta^2}\right)\left(\frac{\epsilon_1\mu_1}{\alpha^2 a^2} + \frac{\epsilon_2\mu_2}{\beta^2 a^2}\right) \qquad (13)$$

If cut-off is defined as in the simple modes studied above to be the condition for which there are no transverse variations in the outer dielectric, $\beta = 0$, (13) requires for this condition that $J_1(\alpha a)$ be zero. The lowest root of this is $\alpha a = 0$, and, if $\mu_1\epsilon_1 \neq \mu_2\epsilon_2$, this requires

[2] G. E. Mueller and W. A. Tyrrell, "Polyrod Antennas," *Bell Sys. Tech. J.*, **26,** 837–851 (Oct. 1947).

that $\gamma = 0$ and $\omega = 0$; Hence the conclusion stated above that cut-off frequency is zero for this particular mode.

PROBLEMS

9·09a   For a circular dielectric rod with small but finite losses, $\sigma_1 \ll \omega\epsilon_1$, study equation (8) by means of Taylor series methods from the point of view of attenuation of the TM_{01} mode caused by dielectric losses.

9·09b   Consider the propagation of waves between two infinite parallel conducting planes separated by two regions of different dielectric constant, ϵ_1 extending from $x = 0$ (bottom plate) to $x = d$, ϵ_2 extending from $x = d$ to $x = a$ (top plate). Show that, even for perfectly conducting planes, an E_z component must be present in the principal wave and indicate the extent to which the conventional transmission line equations might be in error in predicting the characteristics of the principal wave. Assume spacings small compared with wavelength.

9·09c   Obtain the equations for all field components of the $n = 1$ mode discussed above in a circular dielectric rod.

9·10   WAVES GUIDED BY A SINGLE CYLINDRICAL CONDUCTOR

If a circular conducting cylinder is surrounded by a dielectric which extends to infinity, the plane wave solutions in cylindrical coordinates for the dielectric region may be obtained from Art. 8·16. The second Hankel function is used since the region extends to infinity. For a transverse magnetic mode,

$$E_z = A_n H_n^{(2)}(k_c r) \cos n\phi$$

$$E_r = \frac{\gamma}{j\omega\epsilon} H_\phi = -\frac{\gamma A_n}{k_c} H_n^{(2)\prime}(k_c r) \cos n\phi \tag{1}$$

$$E_\phi = -\frac{\gamma}{j\omega\epsilon} H_r = \frac{\gamma n A_n}{k_c^2 r} H_n^{(2)}(k_c r) \sin n\phi$$

$$k_c^2 = \gamma^2 + \omega^2 \mu\epsilon$$

If the conducting cylinder of radius a is perfect, the boundary condition is that E_z and E_ϕ shall be zero at $r = a$. As the principal branch of the Hankel function has no zeros,[3] there are apparently no solutions. However, as $k_c \to 0$, it can be shown that the ratio E_z/H_ϕ approaches zero by using the following approximate values for small arguments.

$$H_0^{(2)}(x) \to -\frac{j2}{\pi} \ln (1.572x) \qquad H_n^{(2)}(x) \to j \frac{2^n (n - 1)!}{\pi x^n} \tag{2}$$

[3] Riemann-Weber, *Differentialgleichungen der Physik*, Vieweg, Braunschweig, 7th ed., 1927, Vol. II, p. 461.

For the symmetrical mode, $n = 0$, by redefining the constant, the solution then approaches

$$E_r = \pm \eta H_\phi = \frac{C}{r} e^{j(\omega t \mp kz)} \tag{3}$$

All other field components approach zero. Solution (3) is recognized as the principal or TEM wave having a transverse distribution like the static field about a charged cylinder. The wave propagates unattenuated with the velocity of light in the surrounding dielectric, and might be thought of as the principal mode in a coaxial line with the outer conductor removed to infinity. The mode would not appear to be very useful for energy transmission as it would have infinite energy storage, and in practice the radial electric field would not extend to infinity but would end on the nearest available conductor. The system would be the opposite of a well-shielded system.

With higher values of n and $k_c \to 0$, equations (1), with (2) utilized, reduce to the static "circular harmonics" (Prob. 3·16c). These do not, however, meet the boundary condition of zero E_ϕ when E_r is finite, and so do not represent actual TM modes for the perfectly conducting cylinder. A study of TE modes shows that neither the zero order nor any higher order one of these satisfies the ideal boundary conditions. Hence, for the perfectly conducting cylinder we conclude that the only plane wave solution is the TEM wave represented by (3).

When the conducting cylinder is imperfect, wave solutions can be set up inside the conductor with tangential field components matched to those in the external dielectric. A very complete treatment by Stratton[4] shows the following:

1. For good conductors and normal wire sizes, the principal wave discussed above may propagate with reasonable attenuation. For very poor conductors or very small conductor radii, the attenuation in this wave may be large and the phase velocity may depart markedly from the velocity of light in the surrounding dielectric.

2. Symmetrical TM and TE waves and mixed waves with circumferential variations may exist, but all have a very rapid attenuation and are important only near junctions at which they may be excited.

3. As the conductivity of the wire becomes poorer, the fields penetrate farther into the conductor. When the conductivity has become very small, the wire takes on more the characteristics of a lossy dielectric and the solution approaches the solution for waves guided by a dielectric rod (Art. 9·09).

[4] J. A. Stratton, *Electromagnetic Theory*, McGraw-Hill, 1941, pp. 524–537.

4. The analysis of this case reminds one that there is a transverse electromagnetic or principal wave possible for the parallel-wire line in addition to that already studied. This wave corresponds to like charges on the two wires and equal currents in the same direction in the two lines, with fields extending outward toward infinity. This is the *zero-phase-sequence wave* of power transmission line experience.

In addition to the above, one should note the work by Goubau[5] in showing that addition of a dielectric coating on the outside of the conductor causes localization of the fields in the vicinity of the wire. The most impressive point is that only a thin layer of dielectric is necessary to produce a pronounced localization; attenuation of the wave is then small, so that the system is practical for energy transmission. The addition of corrugations or other surface perturbations has been shown[5,6] to produce similar concentration of energy near the surface, and with the above lead to an important branch of wave phenomena known as *surface guiding*.

PROBLEM

9·10   Show that, as $k_c \to 0$, the transverse distributions (1) approach the form of static fields that may be derived from the "circular harmonic" potential, $\Phi = Br^{-n} \cos n\phi$. Obtain the form of transmission line boundaries that might support the $n = 1$ mode of this type.

9·11   RADIAL TRANSMISSION LINES

Another guide of practical importance consists of two circular, parallel, conducting plates, separated by a dielectric and used for guiding electromagnetic energy radially (Figs. 9·11a and b). The simplest wave that may be guided by these plates is one with no field variations circumferentially or axially. There are then no field components in the radial direction, but field components E_z and H_ϕ only. The component E_z, having no variations in the z direction, corresponds to a total voltage $E_z d$ between plates. The component H_ϕ corresponds to a total radial current $2\pi r H_\phi$, outward in one plate and inward in the other. This wave is then exactly analogous to an ordinary transmission line wave and thus derives its name, radial transmission line.

For the simple wave described above, since there are no radial field components, it is possible to base the analysis on the transmission line equations, except that L and C now vary with radius. However, we

---

[5] G. Goubau, *Proc. I.R.E.*, **39**, 619–624 (1951); *J. Appl. Phys.*, **21**, 1119–1128 (1950).

[6] W. Rotman, *Proc. I.R.E.*, **39**, 952–959 (Aug. 1951).

already have the wave solutions for fields if results of Art. 8·16 are properly interpreted. Since there are no ϕ variations, ν is set equal to zero. Since there are no z variations, γ is also set equal to zero. In order to identify terms as waves traveling radially inward or radially outward, the form of Eq. 8·16(6) is used. We shall see the reasons for

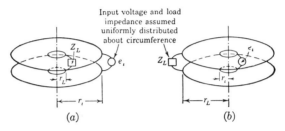

Input voltage and load
impedance assumed
uniformly distributed
about circumference

(a)   (b)

Fig. 9·11a,b   (a) Radial transmission line with input at outer radius.   (b) Radial transmission line with input at inner radius.

this below.   The constant k_c, by Eq. 8·13(2) reduces to $k = \omega \sqrt{\mu\epsilon}$, since $\gamma = 0$.

$$E_z = AH_0^{(1)}(kr) + BH_0^{(2)}(kr) \tag{1}$$

With γ and $\nu = 0$, the only other remaining field component in Eqs. 8·16(8) to 8·16(11) is H_ϕ.

$$H_\phi = \frac{1}{j\omega\mu} \frac{\partial E_z}{\partial r}$$

$$H_\phi = \frac{j}{\eta} [AH_1^{(1)}(kr) + BH_1^{(2)}(kr)] \tag{2}$$

The two terms may be identified definitely as waves traveling inward and outward by employing the asymptotic expressions of the Bessel functions for large arguments (Art. 3·25).   Then

$$E_z\big|_{kr\to\infty} = \sqrt{\frac{2}{\pi kr}} [Ae^{j\left(kr - \frac{\pi}{4}\right)} + Be^{-j\left(kr - \frac{\pi}{4}\right)}]$$

with a similar expression for H_ϕ.   When the above are multiplied by $e^{j\omega t}$, the first term will involve $e^{j(\omega t + kr)}$ and the second $e^{j(\omega t - kr)}$, so that these are identified respectively as waves propagating in the negative r and positive r directions.

The wave impedance of an outward traveling wave may be found by taking the ratio of E_z to H_ϕ in (1) and (2) with $A = 0$.

$$Z_r^+ = -\frac{\eta}{j} \frac{H_0^{(2)}(kr)}{H_1^{(2)}(kr)} \tag{3}$$

This is a function of r.   For the inward traveling wave, $B = 0$,

$$Z_r^- = \frac{\eta}{j} \frac{H_0^{(1)}(kr)}{H_1^{(1)}(kr)} \tag{4}$$

The signs of (3) and (4) are chosen in accordance with the convention discussed in Art. 7·12.

With these definitions of impedance it is possible to evaluate the constants A and B and so find fields at any point along the line if any two field quantities are given, such as a terminating impedance and an electric field, two values of magnetic field, two values of electric field, or one value of electric field and one of magnetic field.   Before giving these formulas, let us define magnitudes and phase angles for the complex Hankel functions as follows.

$$H_0^{(1)}(x) = J_0(x) + jN_0(x) = G_0(x)e^{j\theta(x)}$$

$$H_0^{(2)}(x) = J_0(x) - jN_0(x) = G_0(x)e^{-j\theta(x)}$$

$$jH_1^{(1)}(x) = -N_1(x) + jJ_1(x) = G_1(x)e^{j\psi(x)}$$

$$jH_1^{(2)}(x) = -[-N_1(x) - jJ_1(x)] = -G_1(x)e^{-j\psi(x)}$$

so that

$$G_0(x) = \sqrt{J_0^2(x) + N_0^2(x)} \qquad \theta(x) = \tan^{-1}\left[\frac{N_0(x)}{J_0(x)}\right]$$

$$G_1(x) = \sqrt{J_1^2(x) + N_1^2(x)} \qquad \psi(x) = \tan^{-1}\left[\frac{J_1(x)}{-N_1(x)}\right]$$

Expressions (1) and (2) then become

$$E_z = G_0(kr)[Ae^{j\theta(kr)} + Be^{-j\theta(kr)}] \tag{5}$$

$$H_\phi = \frac{G_1(kr)}{\eta}[Ae^{j\psi(kr)} - Be^{-j\psi(kr)}] \tag{6}$$

Expressions (3) and (4) become

$$Z_r^+ = Z_0(kr)e^{j[\psi(kr)-\theta(kr)]} \tag{7}$$

$$Z_r^- = Z_0(kr)e^{-j[\psi(kr)-\theta(kr)]} \tag{8}$$

where

$$Z_0(kr) = \eta_1 \frac{G_0(kr)}{G_1(kr)} \tag{9}$$

The magnitudes G_0 and G_1, the phase angles θ and ψ, and the impedance Z_0 are plotted in Figs. 9·11c and d.

The constants A and B will now be determined for several different cases. The resulting formulas are quite similar to the familiar formulas of transmission line theory giving voltages, currents, and impedances in terms of input end or loading end values. In the following, the subscript of a quantity indicates the quantity is to be evaluated at the value of r denoted by the subscript.

1. Given electric field E_a at r_a, magnetic field H_b at r_b; for any radius r,

$$E = E_a \frac{G_0}{G_{0a}} \frac{\cos(\theta - \psi_b)}{\cos(\theta_a - \psi_b)} + jZ_{0b}H_b \frac{G_0}{G_{0b}} \frac{\sin(\theta - \theta_a)}{\cos(\theta_a - \psi_b)}$$

$$H = H_b \frac{G_1}{G_{1b}} \frac{\cos(\psi - \theta_a)}{\cos(\theta_a - \psi_b)} + j \frac{E_a}{Z_{0a}} \frac{G_1}{G_{1a}} \frac{\sin(\psi - \psi_b)}{\cos(\theta_a - \psi_b)}$$

(10)

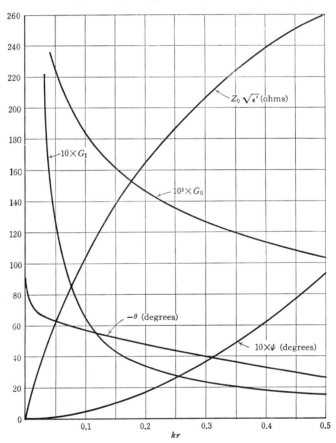

Fig. 9.11c   Radial transmission line quantities.

2. Given electric fields E_a at r_a, E_b at r_b; for any radius r,

$$E = E_a \frac{G_0}{G_{0a}} \frac{\sin (\theta_b - \theta)}{\sin (\theta_b - \theta_a)} + E_b \frac{G_0}{G_{0b}} \frac{\sin (\theta - \theta_a)}{\sin (\theta_b - \theta_a)}$$

$$H = \frac{E_b}{jZ_{0b}} \frac{G_1}{G_{1b}} \frac{\cos (\psi - \theta_a)}{\sin (\theta_b - \theta_a)} - \frac{E_a G_1}{jZ_{0a} G_{1a}} \frac{\cos (\theta_b - \psi)}{\sin (\theta_b - \theta_a)}$$

(11)

3. Given magnetic fields H_a at r_a, H_b at r_b,

$$E = \frac{Z_{0a} H_a}{j} \frac{G_0}{G_{0a}} \frac{\cos (\theta - \psi_b)}{\sin (\psi_a - \psi_b)} - \frac{Z_{0b} H_b}{j} \frac{G_0}{G_{0b}} \frac{\cos (\theta - \psi_a)}{\sin (\psi_a - \psi_b)}$$

$$H = H_a \frac{G_1}{G_{1a}} \frac{\sin (\psi - \psi_b)}{\sin (\psi_a - \psi_b)} + H_b \frac{G_1}{G_{1b}} \frac{\sin (\psi_a - \psi)}{\sin (\psi_a - \psi_b)}$$

(12)

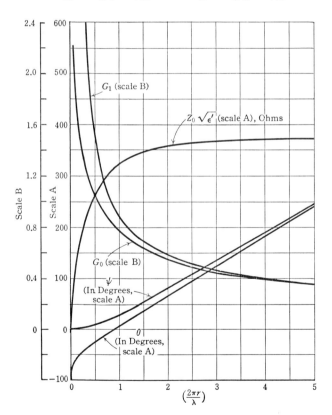

Fig. 9·11d Radial transmission line quantities.

4. Input impedance $Z_i = \dfrac{E_z}{H_\phi}\bigg|_i$ when load impedance $Z_L = \dfrac{E_z}{H_\phi}\bigg|_L$ is given,

$$Z_i = Z_{0i} \left[\frac{Z_L \cos\,(\theta_i - \psi_L) + jZ_{0L} \sin\,(\theta_i - \theta_L)}{Z_{0L} \cos\,(\psi_i - \theta_L) + jZ_L \sin\,(\psi_i - \psi_L)} \right] \qquad (13)$$

5. Input impedance $Z_i = \dfrac{E_z}{H_\phi}\bigg|_i$ when output is shorted $(Z_L = 0)$.

$$Z_i = jZ_{0i} \frac{\sin\,(\theta_i - \theta_L)}{\cos\,(\psi_i - \theta_L)} \qquad (14)$$

6. Input impedance $Z_i = \dfrac{E_z}{H_\phi}\bigg|_i$ when output is open-circuited $(Z_L = \infty)$.

$$Z_i = -jZ_{0i} \frac{\cos\,(\theta_i - \psi_L)}{\sin\,(\psi_i - \psi_L)} \qquad (15)$$

Usually total current and voltage are desired before the problem is regarded as completely solved. They can be obtained from the field expressions. Total voltage and current, defining a higher voltage in the upper plate and outward current in the upper plate as positive, are

$$V = -E_z d \qquad I = 2\pi r H_\phi \qquad (16)$$

The relation between total impedance and the field impedance utilized above is then

$$Z_{\text{total}} = \mp \frac{d}{2\pi r} \left(\frac{E_z}{H_\phi} \right) \qquad (17)$$

The upper sign is for the input radius less than that of the load, $r_i < r_L$, and the lower sign for the reverse, $r_i > r_L$, since then the convention for positive current should be opposite to that of (16).

PROBLEMS

9·11a   For a TM_{01} wave in a circular wave guide it is desired to insert a blocking impedance for a given frequency. To do this, a section of shorted radial line (Fig. 9·11e) is inserted in the guide, its outer radius a chosen so that with the guide radius b given, the impedance looking into the radial line is infinite at the given frequency. Suppose that the radius b is 1.25 times greater than cut-off radius at this frequency for the TM_{01} wave and find the radius a.

9·11b   It is sometimes required to break the outer conductor of a coaxial line for insulation purposes, without interrupting the r-f current flow. This may be accomplished by the radial line as shown (Fig. 9·11f) in which a is chosen so that with b and the operating wavelength specified, the radial line has zero input impedance seen from the line.   Find the value of a, assuming that end effects are negligible, and that

$$\frac{2\pi b}{\lambda} = 1$$

9·11c   Find the voltage at the radius a in terms of the coaxial line's current flowing into the radial line at radius b (Fig. 9·11f).

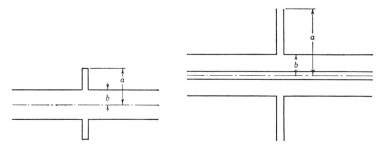

Fig. 9·11e Circular wave guide with shorted radial line in series with cylinder wall.

Fig. 9·11f Coaxial line with open radial line in series with outer conductor.

9·11d   Taking the classical transmission line equations with distributed inductance and capacitance varying with radius as appropriate to the radial line,

$$L = \frac{\mu d}{2\pi r} \quad \text{and} \quad C = \frac{2\pi \epsilon r}{d}$$

show that the equation for voltage as a function of radius is a Bessel equation, and that the solutions for voltage and current obtained in this manner are consistent with (1) and (2).

9·12   CIRCUMFERENTIAL MODES IN RADIAL LINES; SECTORAL HORNS

There are many higher order modes in the radial transmission lines studied in the last article.   All those with z variations require a spacing between plates greater than a half-wavelength for radial propagation of energy.   More interesting are those modes having circumferential variations but no z variations.   The field components may be written

$$E_z = A_\nu Z_\nu(kr) \sin \nu\phi \tag{1}$$

$$H_\phi = -\frac{j}{\eta} A_\nu Z_\nu{}'(kr) \sin \nu\phi \tag{2}$$

$$H_r = \frac{j\nu A_\nu}{kr\eta} Z_\nu(kr) \cos \nu\phi \tag{3}$$

In the above, Z_ν denotes any solution of the ordinary νth order Bessel equation. For example, to stress the concept of radially propagating waves it may again be convenient to utilize Hankel functions.

$$Z_\nu(kr) = H_\nu^{(1)}(kr) + c_\nu H_\nu^{(2)}(kr) \tag{4}$$

These circumferential modes may be important as disturbing effects excited by asymmetries in radial lines intended for use with the symmetrical mode studied in the preceding article, Figs. 9·11a, b. In this case ν must be an integer, n. Waves of the same form may also be supported in a wedge-shaped guide with conducting planes at $\phi = 0$

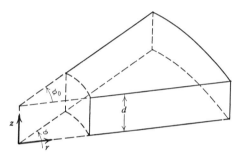

Fig. 9·12a   Wedge-shaped guide or sectoral horn.

and $\phi = \phi_0$ as well as at $z = 0$, d (Fig. 9·12a). The latter case is important as a sectoral electromagnetic horn[7] used for radiation. In this case, since E_z must be zero at $\phi = 0$, ϕ_0,

$$\nu = \frac{m\pi}{\phi_0} \tag{5}$$

The waves discussed here are interesting in one respect especially. If we think of the lowest order mode ($m = 1$) propagating radially inward in the pie-shaped guide of Fig. 9·12a, it would be quite similar to the TE_{10} mode of the rectangular guide, although modified by the convergence of the sides. We would consequently expect a cut-off phenomenon at such a radius r_c that the width $r_c\phi_0$ becomes a half-wavelength. Similarly, for the nth order circumferential mode in the radial line of Figs. 9·11a, b, we would expect a cut-off at such a radius that circumference is n wavelengths.

$$2\pi r_c = n\lambda \text{ for radial line} \qquad \phi_0 r_c = \lambda/2 \text{ for sectoral horn} \tag{6}$$

[7] W. L. Barrow and L. J. Chu, "Sectoral Electromagnetic Horns," *Proc. I.R.E.*, **27**, 51–64 (Jan. 1939).

A casual inspection of Eqs. (1) to (3) would not reveal this cut-off since there is no sudden change of mathematical form as there was in the rectangular guide at cut-off. However, a more detailed study would reveal that there is a very effective cut-off phenomenon at about the radius predicted by (6) in that the reactive energy for a given power transfer becomes very great for radii less than this. For example, the radial field impedances,

$$Z_r^+(kr) = j\eta\, \frac{H_\nu^{(2)}(kr)}{H_\nu^{(2)\prime}(kr)} \tag{7}$$

$$Z_r^-(kr) = -j\eta\, \frac{H_\nu^{(1)}(kr)}{H_\nu^{(1)\prime}(kr)} \tag{8}$$

become predominantly reactive at a value of $kr \approx \nu$, which is compatible with (6). Figure 9·12b shows real and imaginary parts of

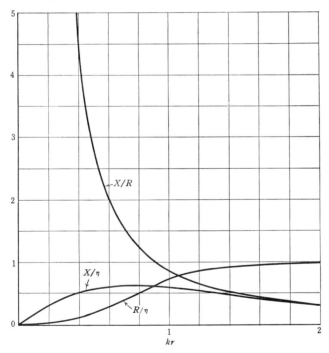

Fig. 9·12b   Wave resistance and reactance for circumferential mode in radial line.

Z_r^+ and Z_r^- for $\nu = 1$. Particular caution must then be taken to guard against circumferential modes for radial lines greater than a wavelength in maximum circumference.

PROBLEMS

9·12a   Sketch lines of current flow for a circumferential mode with $\nu = 1$ in a radial line. (Take $Z_n = J_n$ for this purpose.) Suggest methods of suppressing this mode by judicious cuts without disturbing the symmetrical mode.

9·12b   A section of the wedge-shaped guide as in Fig. 9·12a may be used to join two wave guides of the same height but different width, both propagating the TE_{10} mode, and a good degree of match is obtained by the process so long as the transition is gradual. Discuss qualitatively the transition between the fields of the wave guide and those of the sectoral guide.

9·13   DUALITY; PROPAGATION BETWEEN INCLINED PLANES

Given certain solutions of Maxwell's equations, other useful ones may be obtained by making use of the simple but important principle

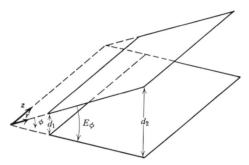

Fig. 9·13   Inclined-plane guide.

of duality. This principle follows from the symmetry of the field equations for charge-free regions,

$$\nabla \times \bar{E} = -j\omega\mu\bar{H} \tag{1}$$

$$\nabla \times \bar{H} = j\omega\epsilon\bar{E} \tag{2}$$

It is evident that, if $\bar{E}$ is replaced by $\bar{H}$, $\bar{H}$ by $-\bar{E}$, μ by ϵ, and ϵ by μ, the original equations are again obtained. It follows that, if we are given any solution for such a dielectric, another may be obtained by interchanging components as above. It may be difficult to supply appropriate boundary conditions for the new solution since the magnetic equivalent of the perfect conductor is not known at high frequencies, so the new solution is not always of practical importance.

One example in which the principle of duality may be utilized to save work in a practical problem is that of the principal mode in the wedge-shaped dielectric region between inclined plane conductors (Fig. 9·13). This mode has electric field E_ϕ representing a radial flow of current in the planes and magnetic field H_z. If there are no variations with ϕ

or z, it is evident that the field distributions can be obtained from those of the radial transmission line mode, Art. 9·11, through the above principle of duality.   Replacing $\bar{E}$ by $\bar{H}$, $\bar{H}$ by $-\bar{E}$, μ by ϵ, and ϵ by μ in Eqs. 9·11(1) to (2),

$$H_z = A H_0^{(1)}(kr) + B H_0^{(2)}(kr) \tag{3}$$

$$E_\phi = -j\sqrt{\frac{\mu}{\epsilon}}\,[A H_1^{(1)}(kr) + B H_1^{(2)}(kr)] \tag{4}$$

The real advantage is that all the derived expressions 9·11(10)–(15) may be used without rederivation, as well as the curves of Fig. 9·11c and d, with the interchange of quantities as above.   Admittance should be read in place of impedance, and the numerical scale of $Z_0\sqrt{\epsilon'}$ in ohms (Figs. 9·11c and d) should be divided by $(377)^2$ to give the characteristic admittance $Y_0/\sqrt{\epsilon'}$ in mhos.   Total admittance is obtained from the field admittance as follows:

$$Y_{\text{total}} = \mp\,\frac{l}{r\phi_0}\left[-\frac{H_z}{E_\phi}\right] \tag{5}$$

where the upper sign is for $r_i < r_L$, the lower for $r_i > r_L$.

One application of the above line might be in impedance matching between parallel-plate transmission lines of different spacings, d_1 and d_2 (Fig. 9·13).   It is known from practical experience that such transitions, if gradual enough, supply a good impedance match over a wide band of frequencies (unlike schemes studied in Art. 1·21, which depend upon quarter-wavelengths of line).   It is seen from Fig. 9·11c that for both kr_i and kr_L large (say greater than 5) the characteristic admittance Y_0 is nearly $1/\eta$ and θ and ψ are nearly equal (i.e., $\theta_i \approx \psi_i$, $\theta_L \approx \psi_L$).   If the parallel-plane line to the right is matched, its characteristic wave admittance is that of a plane wave, $1/\eta$.   Equation 9·11(13) then shows that with the above approximations the input wave admittance is also approximately $1/\eta$, so that the parallel-plane line to the left is also nearly matched.   This gives some quantitative support to the matching phenomenon mentioned above.

PROBLEMS

9·13a   In the use of the inclined plane line for matching as discussed in the last paragraph, suppose that $f = 3000$ mc/sec, $d_1 = 1$ cm, $d_2 = 2$ cm, $kr_1 = 2.5$, and the dielectric is air.   If the line to the right is perfectly matched, obtain the approximate standing wave ratio in the line to the left.   Compare with that which would exist with a sudden transition, considering only the impedance discontinuity.

9·13b   Discuss the approximation in the above procedure at the junctions in view of the curved wave fronts in the tapered line and the plane wave fronts in the parallel-plane line.

9·13c   Apply the principle of duality to the TE_{11}, TE_{01}, and TM_{01} modes in circular cylindrical wave guides to obtain qualitatively the fields of the "dual" modes.   For which of these might boundary conditions be supplied, allowing changes in the conductor position or shape from those of the original mode?

9·13d   A wedge-shaped dielectric region is bounded by conducting planes at $\phi = 0$ and ϕ_0, $z = 0$ and d.   Find the field components of the lowest order mode with E_ϕ, H_r, and H_z.   Is this the dual of the mode discussed for sectoral horns in Art. 9·12?

9·13e   Discuss the application of the mode of Prob. 9·13d to the matching between rectangular wave guides of different height, both propagating the TE_{10} mode.

9·14   WAVES GUIDED BY CONICAL SYSTEMS

The problem of waves guided by conical systems (Fig. 9·14) is important to a basic understanding of waves along dipole antennas and

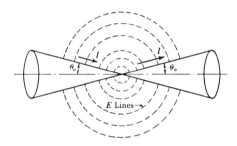

Fig. 9·14   Biconical guide.

in certain classes of cavity resonators.   In particular, one very important wave propagates along the cones with the velocity of light and has no field components in the radial direction, and so is analogous to the transmission line wave on cylindrical systems.   This basic wave is symmetric about the axis of the guiding cones, so that, if the two curl relations of Maxwell's equations are written in spherical coordinates with all ϕ variation eliminated, it is seen that there is one independent set containing E_θ and H_ϕ and E_r only:

$$\frac{1}{r}\frac{\partial(rE_\theta)}{\partial r} - \frac{1}{r}\frac{\partial E_r}{\partial \theta} + j\omega\mu H_\phi = 0 \tag{1}$$

$$\frac{1}{r\sin\theta}\left[\frac{\partial}{\partial\theta}(\sin\theta H_\phi)\right] - j\omega\epsilon E_r = 0 \tag{2}$$

$$-\frac{1}{r}\frac{\partial(rH_\phi)}{\partial r} - j\omega\epsilon E_\theta = 0 \tag{3}$$

Although we might proceed to a direct attack on these equations, it can be checked by substitution that the following solution does satisfy the three equations.

$$E_r = 0 \tag{4}$$

$$rE_\theta = \frac{\eta}{\sin \theta} [A e^{j(\omega t - kr)} + B e^{j(\omega t + kr)}] \tag{5}$$

$$rH_\phi = \frac{1}{\sin \theta} [A e^{j(\omega t - kr)} - B e^{j(\omega t + kr)}] \tag{6}$$

These equations show the now familiar propagation behavior, the first term representing a wave traveling radially outward with the velocity of light in the dielectric material surrounding the cones, the second term representing a radially inward traveling wave of the same velocity. The ratio of electric to magnetic field is given by $+\eta$ for the positively traveling wave, by $-\eta$ for the negatively traveling wave. There is no field component in the radial direction, which is the direction of propagation.

The above wave looks much like the ordinary transmission line waves of uniform cylindrical systems. This resemblance is stressed if we note that the E_θ corresponds to a voltage difference between the two cones,

$$V = -\int_{\theta_0}^{\pi - \theta_0} E_\theta r \, d\theta = -\eta \int_{\theta_0}^{\pi - \theta_0} \frac{d\theta}{\sin \theta} [A e^{j(\omega t - kr)}) + B e^{j(\omega t + kr)}]$$

$$= 2\eta \ln \cot \frac{\theta_0}{2} [A e^{j(\omega t - kr)} + B e^{j(\omega t + kr)} \tag{7}$$

where the case treated is that of equal angle cones (Fig. 9·14). This is a voltage which is independent of r, except through the propagation term, $e^{\pm jkr}$. Similarly the azimuthal magnetic field corresponds to a current flow in the cones,

$$I = 2\pi r H_\phi \sin \theta$$

$$= 2\pi [A e^{j(\omega t - kr)} - B e^{j(\omega t + kr)}] \tag{8}$$

This current is also independent of radius, except through the propagation term. A study of the sign relations shows that it is in opposite directions in the two cones at any given radius.

The ratio of voltage to current in a single outward-traveling wave, a quantity which we call characteristic impedance in an ordinary transmission line, is obtained by setting $B = 0$ in (7) and (8):

$$Z_0 = \frac{\eta \ln \cot \theta_0/2}{\pi} \tag{9}$$

For a negatively traveling wave, the ratio of voltage to current is the negative of this quantity. This value of impedance is a constant, independent of radius, unlike those defined for a radial transmission line in Art. 9·11. We might have guessed this had we started from the familiar concept of Z_0 as $\sqrt{L/C}$, since inductance and capacitance between cones per unit radial length are independent of radius. This comes about since surface area increases proportionally to radius, and distance separating the cone, along the path of the electric field, also increases proportionally to radius.

So far as this wave is concerned, the system arising from two ideal coaxial conical conductors can be considered a uniform transmission line. All the familiar formulas for input impedances and voltage and current along the line hold directly with Z_0 given by (9) and phase constant corresponding to velocity of light in the dielectric.

$$\beta = \frac{2\pi}{\lambda} = \omega \sqrt{\mu\epsilon} \tag{10}$$

If the conducting cones have resistance, there is a departure from uniformity due to this resistance term, but this is usually not serious in any practical cases where such conical systems are used.

Of course a large number of higher order waves may exist in this conical system and in similar systems. These will in general have field components in the radial direction and will not propagate at the velocity of light. We shall consider such general wave types for spherical coordinates later.

PROBLEMS

9·14a It has been seen that along cones, cylinders, planes, etc., a principal wave can exist in which, at least for perfect conductors, it is possible to analyze the problem correctly by dealing with distributed L's and C's per unit length, these distributed constants being computed from static field distributions. It is not always true that the electric and magnetic field lines over the cross section of the wave, for the principal wave, will be as in the static case. This does not mean that the distributed constant technique fails for such lines, but it does mean that it is no longer exact to use L and C as computed from the static field equations. Illustrate the above statement by considering waves propagating symmetrically between concentric spheres in the θ direction ($\partial/\partial\phi = 0$). Show that no wave can exist containing only E_r and H_ϕ; E_θ must also be present. Show also that, if the distance between spheres is small compared with wavelength, the presence of E_θ has a negligible effect on the wave distribution and distributed L and C (computed from statics) may be used for good approximate results.

9·14b Derive the basic characteristics of the principal waves on a transmission line consisting of two coaxial, common-apex cones of unequal angles.

9·14c Write the dual of the mode studied in this article. Can it be supported by physical boundaries using perfect conductors?

9·15   RIDGE WAVE GUIDE

Of the miscellaneous shapes of cylindrical guides that have been utilized, one rather important one is the ridge wave guide, which has a central ridge added either to the top or bottom or both of a rectangular section, Fig. 9·15a. It is interesting from an electromagnetic

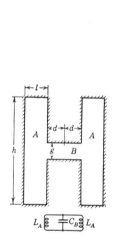

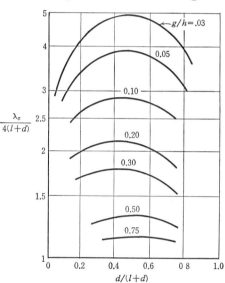

Fig. 9·15a   Cross section of ridge wave guide and approximate equivalent circuit for cut-off calculation.

Fig. 9·15b   Curves giving cut-off wavelength for a ridge wave guide as in Fig. 9·15a. Data from Cohn.

point of view since the cut-off frequency is lowered because of the capacitive effect at the center, and could in principle be made as low as desired by decreasing the gap width g sufficiently. Of course, the effective impedance of the guide also decreases as g is made smaller. One of the important applications is as a non-uniform transmission system for matching purposes (see Art. 9·13) obtained by varying the depth of ridge as one progresses along the guide.

The calculation of cut-off frequency, which has been found to be one of the very important parameters for any shape of guide, also illustrates an interesting approach that may be applied to many guide shapes which cannot be solved exactly. At cut-off, there is no variation in the z direction ($\gamma = 0$), so one may think of this as the condition for waves propagating only transversely in the given cross section, according to the desired mode. For example, the TE_{10} wave in a rectangular guide has a cut-off frequency equal to the resonant frequency for a plane wave propagating only in the x direction across the guide, thus corresponding to a half-wavelength in the x direction. A very approximate calculation of cut-off frequency for the ridge guide might then be made as in Fig. 9·15a by considering the gap a capacitance and the side sections inductances, and writing the condition for resonance.

$$f_c = \frac{1}{2\pi}\left(C_B \frac{L_A}{2}\right)^{-\frac{1}{2}} = \frac{1}{2\pi}\left(\frac{2d\epsilon}{g}\right)^{-\frac{1}{2}}\left(\frac{\mu l h}{2}\right)^{-\frac{1}{2}} = \frac{1}{2\pi}\left(\frac{g}{\mu\epsilon l h d}\right)^{\frac{1}{2}} \quad (1)$$

A better equivalent circuit for calculation of the transverse resonance is one in which the two sections A and B are considered parallel-plane transmission lines with a discontinuity capacitance C_d placed at the junction between them. (This junction effect will be discussed in Chapter 11.) Curves of cut-off frequency and a total impedance for the guide have been calculated in this manner by Cohn.[8] Some results are shown in Fig. 9·15b. Definitions of total impedance of wave guides will also be discussed in Chapter 11.

PROBLEMS

9·15a Demonstrate that the cut-off frequency of a TM_{01} mode in circular guide may be found by considering transverse resonance of a radial line mode.

9·15b Calculate by the approximate formula (1) the cut-off frequency of some of the ridge wave guides for which better results may be obtained from Fig. 9·15b, and make comparisons. Choose at least one with a small gap and at least one with a wide one.

9·16   THE IDEALIZED HELIX AND OTHER SLOW-WAVE STRUCTURES

A wire wound in the form of a helix (Fig. 9·16a) makes a type of guide that has been found useful for antennas[9] and as slow-wave structures in traveling-wave tubes.[10] It is interesting as an example

---

[8] S. B. Cohn, *Proc. I.R.E.*, **35**, 783–788 (Aug. 1947).

[9] J. D. Kraus, *Antennas*, McGraw-Hill, 1950, Chapter 7.

[10] J. R. Pierce, *Traveling-Wave Tubes*, Van Nostrand, 1950, Chapter III and Appendix II.

of a general class of structures which possess waves with a phase velocity along the axis much less than the velocity of light, as contrasted to most of the waves so far studied, which have phase velocities greater than the velocity of light. A rough picture would convince one that the wave should follow the wire with about the velocity of

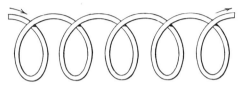

Fig. 9·16a   Wire helix.

light, so that its rate of progress along the axis should correspond to a phase velocity

$$v_p \approx c \sin \psi \qquad (1)$$

where ψ is the pitch angle. It is rather surprising that this represents a good approximation over a wide range of parameters. It is also interesting to find that a useful analysis can be made by considering an idealization of the actual helix.

The idealization commonly analyzed,[10] referred to as the *helical sheet*, is a cylindrical surface in which the component of electric field along the direction of ψ is assumed to be zero *at all points of the sheet* (Fig. 9·16b). Moreover, the component of electric field lying in the cylindrical surface normal to the direction of ψ is assumed to be continuous through the surface, as is the component of magnetic field along ψ (the latter because there is to be no current flow normal to the direction of ψ). Since the idealization takes these conditions to be the same over all the sheet, it would be expected to give best results for fine-wire helices of small pitch angle or for multifilar helices with fine wires close together.

The solutions inside and outside the surface are taken with no ϕ variations. They require both TM and TE modes and may be written

$$
\begin{array}{ll}
\quad\quad r < a & \quad\quad r > a \\
E_{z1} = A_1 I_0(\tau r) & E_{z2} = A_2 K_0(\tau r) \quad\quad (2)
\end{array}
$$

$$
E_{r1} = \frac{j\beta}{\tau} A_1 I_1(\tau r) \qquad E_{r2} = -\frac{j\beta}{\tau} A_2 K_1(\tau r) \qquad (3)
$$

$$
H_{\phi 1} = \frac{j\omega\epsilon}{\tau} A_1 I_1(\tau r) \qquad H_{\phi 2} = -\frac{j\omega\epsilon}{\tau} A_2 K_1(\tau r) \qquad (4)
$$

$$H_{z1} = B_1 I_0(\tau r) \qquad\qquad H_{z2} = B_2 K_0(\tau r) \qquad (5)$$

$$H_{r1} = \frac{j\beta}{\tau} B_1 I_1(\tau r) \qquad\qquad H_{r2} = -\frac{j\beta}{\tau} B_2 K_1(\tau r) \qquad (6)$$

$$E_{\phi1} = -\frac{j\omega\mu}{\tau} B_1 I_1(\tau r) \qquad\qquad E_{\phi2} = \frac{j\omega\mu}{\tau} B_2 K_1(\tau r) \qquad (7)$$

where all variations have been taken as $e^{j(\omega t - \beta z)}$ and

$$\tau^2 = -(\gamma^2 + k^2) = \beta^2 - k^2 \qquad (8)$$

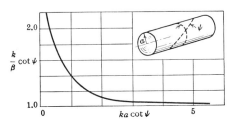

Fig. 9·16b   Idealized conducting sheet and curve giving propagation constant. From Pierce.[10]

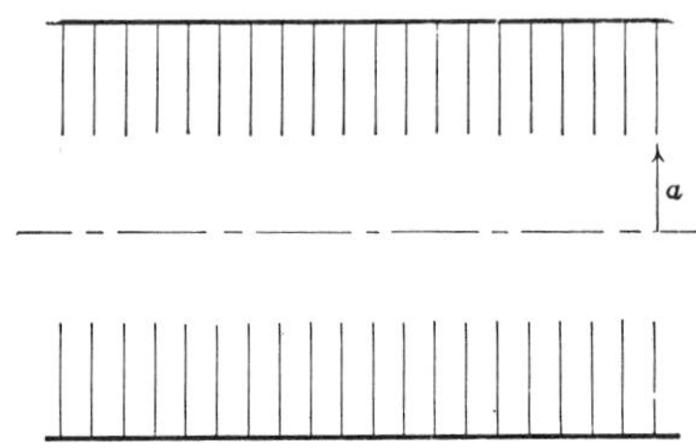

Fig. 9·16c   Section of disk-loaded wave guide.

The idealized boundary conditions described above are

$$E_{z1} \sin\psi + E_{\phi1} \cos\psi = 0 \qquad (9)$$

$$E_{z2} \sin\psi + E_{\phi2} \cos\psi = 0 \qquad (10)$$

$$E_{z1} \cos\psi - E_{\phi1} \sin\psi = E_{z2} \cos\psi - E_{\phi2} \sin\psi \qquad (11)$$

$$H_{z1} \sin\psi + H_{\phi1} \cos\psi = H_{z2} \sin\psi + H_{\phi2} \cos\psi \qquad (12)$$

Application of (9)–(12) to (2)–(7) yields the equation

$$(\tau a)^2 \frac{I_0(\tau a)K_0(\tau a)}{I_1(\tau a)K_1(\tau a)} = (ka \cot\psi)^2 \qquad (13)$$

A solution of this taken from Pierce[10] is shown in Fig. 9·16b. It is seen that, for $ka \cot\psi > 4$, the approximation (1) gives good results.

Some general comments about slow-wave structures are in order. In these we will neglect attenuation, assuming $\gamma = j\beta$. If it is desired to produce an electric field along the axis propagating with a phase velocity less than that of light (as in a traveling-wave tube where the phase velocity should be of the order of the beam velocity for efficient interaction with the electrons), we see that the combination $\gamma^2 + k^2$, which we have called $k_c{}^2$ in Chapter 8, will be negative, since $\beta > k$.

$$\tau^2 = -k_c{}^2 = \beta^2 - k^2 \tag{14}$$

$$\tau = \beta(1 - v_p{}^2/c^2)^{\frac{1}{2}} \tag{15}$$

It is consequently necessary in a cylindrically symmetric system that the Bessel function solutions (Art. 8·16) have imaginary arguments, and they may therefore be written as modified Bessel functions. For a TM wave,

$$E_z = AI_0(\tau r) \tag{16}$$

$$H_\phi = \frac{\omega\epsilon}{\beta} E_r = \frac{j\omega\epsilon}{\tau} I_1(\tau r) \tag{17}$$

If we ask about the boundary conditions that might be supplied at a cylindrical surface $r = a$ in order to support such waves, we see that, if uniform, it should be of the nature of a reactive sheet with

$$jX = -\frac{E_z}{H_\phi}\bigg|_{r=a} = j\eta\,\frac{\tau}{k}\,\frac{I_0(\tau a)}{I_1(\tau a)} \tag{18}$$

The helical sheet studied above may be considered as supplying this required reactance through the interaction with the TE waves and external fields caused by the helical cuts. The short-circuited sections of radial lines of a disk-loaded wave guide (Fig. 9·16c) may also be considered as supplying an approximation to the above required uniform reactance at $r = a$, and will therefore support a slow wave also. The approximate reactance supplied by this structure is

$$X = \eta\left[\frac{J_0(ka)N_0(kb) - J_0(kb)N_0(ka)}{J_1(ka)N_0(kb) - J_0(kb)N_0(ka)}\right] \tag{19}$$

Note that, if $(v_p/c)^2 \ll 1$, τ is substantially equal to β. By the nature of the I_0 functions (Fig. 3·23), the field on the axis of such slow-wave structures is much less than that on the boundary when βa is large. This is of course undesirable when it is the field on the axis that is to act on electrons as in a traveling-wave tube. Of course the presence of electron space charge will modify the forms of solution somewhat.

PROBLEMS

9.16a Imagine a parallel-plane transmission line of spacing $2a$ in which both upper and lower planes are cut with many fine cuts at angle ψ from the y direction (coordinate system as in Fig. 8·04). Assume no variations with y, and apply approximations as utilized in the helical sheet analysis, obtaining the field components for propagation in the z direction, the complete equation determining β, and the approximate solution of this for $ka \cot \psi \gg 1$.

9.16b   Assuming $(v_p/c)^2 \ll 1$, plot kaX/η versus βa for a slow-wave structure. State the requirements on the reactance in order that there may be any slow-wave solution of this type.   What should X/η be for βa large?

9.16c   Show that a reactance sheet might be used as the boundary condition on fast waves of the TM_{01} type studied in Art. 9·05.   Plot the required value of kaX/η as a function of $k_c a$.   Under what conditions might there be a slow wave and a series of fast waves in a given guide of this type?

10 RESONANT CAVITIES

10·01 INTRODUCTION

At extremely high frequencies (wavelengths, say, below 1 meter) ordinary lumped-circuit elements are hardly suitable for practical use. As was seen in Chapter 5, a conventional circuit with dimensions comparable to wavelength may lose energy by radiation. In Chapter 6 it was found that resistance of ordinary wire circuits may become high because of skin effect behavior. Both of these phenomena give rise to definite modifications in elements that are to serve as efficient circuits for ultra-high frequencies. It is immediately suggested that the circuit region should be shielded, completely surrounded by a good conductor, to prevent radiation. It is also suggested that the current paths be made with as large area as possible. The result was a hollow conducting box with the electromagnetic energy confined on the inside.[1] The conducting walls act effectively as perfect shields, so that this inner region is perfectly shielded from the outside, and no radiation is possible. Since the inner walls of the box serve as current paths, the desired large area for current flow is provided and losses are extremely small. The resulting element is known as a cavity resonator.

In this chapter we shall study electromagnetic waves in regions closed by conductors, with particular application to such cavity resonators. It will first be observed that such high-frequency elements might be arrived at by extension of conventional transmission line and circuit ideas. Exact analyses will be made of certain of the simpler shapes of cavity resonators, and at least approximate analyses will be made of some of the more complex shapes of such resonators. All mathematical analyses will be based on the solution of Maxwell's equations subject to the boundary conditions, and in general will follow directly from the results of the last several chapters on propagating waves, since the waves inside the conducting boxes may be considered standing wave patterns arising from reflections of the

[1] W. W. Hansen, *J. Appl. Phys.*, **9**, 654–663 (Oct. 1938).

appropriate traveling waves from the walls of the enclosure.   Certain circuit ideas useful in the discussion of cavity resonators, especially that of Q, will be treated in this chapter, but the more detailed circuit analysis for such resonators will be left for the following chapter.

Elemental Concepts of Cavity Resonators

10·02   THE RESONANT TRANSMISSION LINE AS A CAVITY RESONATOR

Before the solution of the wave equation inside regions closed by conductors is attempted, there are several physical analogies that should make the concept of such wave regions more meaningful, particularly in their function as "circuits" at ultra-high frequencies.

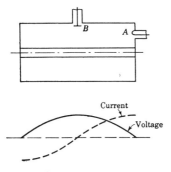

Fig. 10·02   Resonant coaxial system and standing waves of voltage and current.

For the first analogy, let us consider something which is not ordinarily thought of as a cavity resonator, but which certainly may be.   This is a section of coaxial transmission line shorted at both ends.   From the transmission line analysis of Chapter 1, it is known that such a shorted line may support a standing wave of frequency such that the length of line is exactly a half-wave.   The line may be thought of as resonant at that frequency, since the standing wave pattern set up has constant total energy in that section of line, that energy oscillating between the electric and magnetic fields of the line.   Thus, as in Fig. 10·02, the standing wave of voltage has a zero at each end and a maximum at the center.   The standing wave of current is 90° out of time phase with the voltage wave, and has maxima at the two ends, a zero at the center.   These waves may exist inside this completely enclosed region without interference from, or radiation to, the outside. The shielding is complete if conductors are perfect, and practically so for any practical conductors at ultra-high frequencies.   This viewpoint is verified by the previous analyses (Chapter 6) of skin effect phenomena, where it was found that depth of penetration at high frequencies is so small (of the order of 10^{-4} inch for copper at 3000 megacycles per second) that almost any practical thickness acts essentially as an infinite thickness.   Fields applied on the inside of a conducting wall die out to a completely negligible value at the outside of the conductor.

Since the inside of the region is completely shielded from the outside, it will be necessary to excite the waves by some source, such as the small loop A (Fig. 10·02), designed to excite the magnetic field of the line at its maximum value, or the small probe B introduced at the maximum of electric field.   If one of these means is used to stimulate the line exactly at its resonant frequency, the oscillations may build up to a large value.   In the steady state limit, the exciting source need supply only the relatively small amount of energy lost to the finite conductivity of the walls, the relatively large stored energy being essentially constant and passing back and forth between electric and magnetic fields.   If the source excites the line at a frequency somewhat off resonance, the energies in electric and magnetic fields do not balance.   Some extra energy must be supplied over one part of the cycle which is given back to the source over another part of the cycle, and the line acts as a reactive load on the exciting source in addition to its small loss component.   The similarity to ordinary tuned circuit operation is evident, and it seems likely that many of the same considerations concerning effect of losses on band width, expressed in terms of a Q, will hold, at least qualitatively.

The above simple example requires essentially only a knowledge of transmission line theory, yet it holds all the fundamental characteristics of cavity resonators, and differs from others only in the types of waves that are utilized.

10·03 CAVITY RESONATORS AS EXTENSIONS OF LUMPED RESONANT CIRCUITS

Since closed resonant cavities take the place of lumped L-C circuits at high frequencies, we shall see as a next example how a closed cavity might be considered the logical evolution of such a circuit as it is extended to these frequencies.   If a parallel resonant circuit with lumped L and C, such as that of Fig. 10·03, is to be extended to high

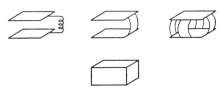

Fig. 10·03   Evolution from resonant circuit with lumped elements to a closed cavity.

frequencies, a decrease must be made in the magnitudes of C and L. Capacitance may be decreased simply by moving the plates of the condenser farther apart.   To decrease inductance, fewer and fewer turns might be used in the inductance until this has degenerated to a single straight wire. Next, to eliminate stray lead inductances, this might be moved to the condenser plates and connected directly between them at the edges. The final step suggested is the paralleling of many of these single-wire inductances about the outside of the plates, until in the limit the two plates are connected by a solid conducting wall. We are now left with a hollow cylindrical conducting box, completely enclosed, or in other words, another example of a cavity resonator.

The above example is, of course, not exactly rigorous. It is significant in demonstrating a logical evolution from lumped-circuit ideas to the concept of cavity resonators, but if only a knowledge of lumped circuits without any background in wave phenomena were available, there would be reason to doubt that the system arrived at in the limit would even work. Certainly there is a point in the evolution where one realizes that the fields of the capacity and the inductances are becoming intimately related, and at best it is a problem with distributed rather than lumped constants with perhaps mutual impedances also present. It would appear safe to conclude that the condenser plates have actually been shorted in the limit, so that, if any voltage can exist between them, it can only exist at the center and must form a standing wave pattern inside the box, falling to zero at the shorting walls, and so requiring that the box have a diameter at least comparable to wavelength. Here it may be protested that the side walls have been imagined to act as an inductance. How can there be always zero voltage across these walls then, since there is a voltage drop across an inductance whose current is changing? The answer involves recognizing that we are speaking of total voltage, and that total voltage across any inductance made of a perfect conductor must be zero, the applied voltage being exactly balanced by that induced from the changing magnetic fields of the inductance. But these are all tentative and preliminary pictures. We will not try to press further conclusions from the present analogy, since it is realized that the wave picture is in reality the correct one and will determine whether any particular result or physical picture is legitimate. However, it will prove useful to recall this analogy from time to time in seeking circuit ideas that may be employed in discussing resonator behavior.

10·04 CAVITY RESONATORS FROM THE POINT OF VIEW OF WAVE REFLECTIONS

A picture which is in fact an exact one and one which we will utilize in following sections, considers the resonant standing wave pattern of electromagnetic fields in the resonator as the interference pattern produced by the superposition of various waves reflected from the walls of the resonator. Thus, for cylindrical resonators of any section, one may consider the standing wave produced by any of the wave guide modes appropriate to that cross section as resonant if the length between conducting end plates (shorts) is a multiple of a half guide wavelength for that mode. An example is given in Fig. 10·04a, in which fields are indicated for a circular cylindrical resonator which is one half guide wavelength for the TM_{01} mode. It is evident from this picture that a particular cavity of fixed shape and size will have many different modes (actually an infinite number) corresponding to all the

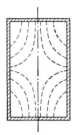

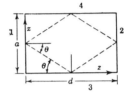

Fig. 10·04a Cylindrical cavity and electric field pattern on a longitudinal section plane.

Fig. 10·04b Paths of component uniform plane waves in a closed resonant box.

wave types that may exist in the corresponding wave guide, and to different numbers of half-waves between shorting ends. This picture will be pursued in detail for cylindrical resonators of circular and square section in the following articles.

One may go farther, analyzing the standing wave pattern in a resonator into component plane waves reflected from the walls of the enclosure. It is evident that in the general case these will be reflected continuously from the walls of the box. Certain conditions of dimensions proper compared with wavelength may exist such that standing wave patterns may be set up inside the box with constant total energy, this energy passing naturally between the electric and magnetic fields of the box. The simplest example of this may be found in a rectangular box with a plane wave bouncing between only four of the walls, as pictured in Fig. 10·04b. For the simplest case, this wave may be polarized with electric vector in the vertical or y direction and with no variations in that direction. If the path of the plane wave makes an angle θ with the normal to side 1, as shown, some general conclusions may be drawn at once from the concepts of Chapter 7 without a detailed study of the wave paths. It would be expected, for example, that since the vertical electric field should be zero at the conducting sides 1 and 2, the dimension d should be a half-wavelength *measured at the phase velocity in the z direction.*

$$d = \frac{1}{2f \sqrt{\mu\epsilon} \cos \theta} \tag{1}$$

where μ and ϵ are the constants for the dielectric filling the guide. Similarly, the dimension a should be a half-wavelength measured at the phase velocity in the x direction, so that the vertical electric field may be zero at the two conducting sides 3 and 4.

$$a = \frac{1}{2f \sqrt{\mu\epsilon} \sin \theta} \tag{2}$$

The top and bottom raise no problem, since the only electric field component is vertical and so ends on top and bottom normally as required, no matter how far apart these are placed. The two conditions (1) and (2) might be combined to eliminate θ, giving

$$\omega^2\mu\epsilon = \left(\frac{\pi}{a}\right)^2 + \left(\frac{\pi}{d}\right)^2 \tag{3}$$

This expression shows that the natural frequency necessary to set up the assumed standing wave pattern is fixed by the dimensions a and d, and by the dielectric material filling the box. This expression will be derived in other ways in later articles, where it will be studied more completely. For the moment, it should be noted that (3) has been derived from wave solutions to Maxwell's equations and is therefore completely correct.

A final analogy that should not be overlooked comes from another branch of science. In the study of sound, one finds resonators for the sound waves which are quite similar to the cavity resonators for electromagnetic waves. This analogy may be appreciated from the pictures of the standing waves arising because of reflections of waves from the box walls. The phenomena of reflections and standing wave patterns obviously occur also for sound waves. The analogy is exact for certain modes so far as resonant frequency is concerned, and may be practically useful for predicting resonant frequencies by model studies. However, the velocity and pressure fields of a sound wave may be derived from a scalar potential, and we have seen that a general electromagnetic field requires a vector potential also (Chapter 4), so the analogy is not always complete.

Each of the several analogies discussed supplies background for understanding electromagnetic energy storage inside a hollow closed conducting box of practically any shape and for appreciating the usefulness of this arrangement in place of the usual tuned circuit of low frequencies.   It should be recognized that, except for extraneous holes or leaks that may be added in constructing the cavity practically, the region is perfectly shielded from the outside, so that there is no radiation to or interference from the outside.   The behavior of the cavity for frequencies on and near resonance will be similar to that of lumped circuits with, as we shall see later, extremely high values of Q.   A given cavity should have many possible modes (actually an infinite number), and for each mode the resonant frequency is determined by the mode, the cavity dimensions, and the constants of the dielectric filling the cavity.   Coupling to the cavity may be either to the electric or the magnetic fields of the mode it is desired to excite, or to both.

Resonators of Simple Shape

10·05   FIELDS OF SIMPLE RECTANGULAR RESONATOR

For the first mode to be studied in some detail, we shall choose that mode in a rectangular conducting box which may be considered the standing wave pattern corresponding to the TE_{10} mode in rectangular guide.   As was done in the study of wave guides, the conducting walls will be taken as perfect, and losses in an actual resonator will be computed approximately by taking the current flow of the ideal mode as flowing in the walls of known conductivity.

In the rectangular conducting box of Fig. 10·05a, imagine a TE_{10} wave guide mode oriented with its electric field in the y direction and propagating in the z direction.   The condition that E_y shall be zero at $z = 0$ and d, as required by the perfect conductors, is satisfied if the dimension d is a half guide wavelength.   Using Eq. 9·04(6),

$$d = \frac{\lambda_g}{2} = \frac{\lambda}{2 \sqrt{1 - (\lambda/2a)^2}}$$

or
$$\lambda = \frac{2ad}{\sqrt{a^2 + d^2}} \tag{1}$$

By recalling that $\omega^2 \mu\epsilon = (2\pi/\lambda)^2$, condition (1) may be shown to be equivalent to Eq. 10·04(3), which was derived by considering plane wave reflections.

To obtain the field distributions in the dielectric interior, we add positive and negative propagating waves of the form of Eqs. 9·04(1)–(3).

$$E_y = [E_0^+ e^{-j\beta z} + E_0^- e^{j\beta z}] \sin \frac{\pi x}{a} \tag{2}$$

$$H_x = -\frac{1}{Z_{TE}} [E_0^+ e^{-j\beta z} - E_0^- e^{j\beta z}] \sin \frac{\pi x}{a} \tag{3}$$

$$H_z = \frac{j}{\eta} \left(\frac{\lambda}{2a}\right) [E_0^+ e^{-j\beta z} + E_0^- e^{j\beta z}] \cos \frac{\pi x}{a} \tag{4}$$

Since E_y must be zero at $z = 0$, $E_0^- = -E_0^+$, as we would expect, since the reflected wave from the perfectly conducting wall should

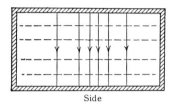

Side

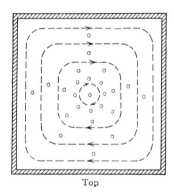

Top

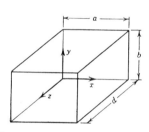

Fig. 10·05a   Rectangular cavity.

Fig. 10·05b   Electric and magnetic fields in rectangular resonator with TE_{101} mode.

be equal to the incident wave. E_y must also be zero at $z = d$, so that $\beta = \pi/d$, which may be shown to yield again the condition (1) or Eq. 10·04(3).   Then (2)–(4) may be simplified, letting $E_0 = 2jE_0^+$:

$$E_y = E_0 \sin \frac{\pi x}{a} \sin \frac{\pi z}{d} \tag{5}$$

$$H_x = -j \frac{E_0}{\eta} \frac{\lambda}{2d} \sin \frac{\pi x}{a} \cos \frac{\pi z}{d} \tag{6}$$

$$H_z = j \frac{E_0}{\eta} \frac{\lambda}{2a} \cos \frac{\pi x}{a} \sin \frac{\pi z}{d} \tag{7}$$

In studying the expressions above, we find that electric field passes vertically from top to bottom, entering top and bottom normally and becoming zero at the side walls as required by the perfect conductors. The magnetic field lines lie in horizontal (x-z) planes and surround the vertical displacement current resulting from the time rate of change of E_y. Fields are sketched roughly in Fig. 10·05b. There are equal and opposite charges on top and bottom because of the normal electric field ending there. A current flows between top and bottom, becoming vertical in the side walls. Here we are reminded of a conventional resonant circuit with the top and bottom acting as capacitor plates and the side walls as the current path between them, as in the elemental analogy of Art. 10·03.

Because the mode studied here has one half-sine variation in the x direction, none in the y direction, and one in the z direction, it is sometimes known as a TE_{101} mode. The coordinate system is of course arbitrary, but some choice must be made before the mode can be described in this manner.

PROBLEMS

10·05a Show that the mode described above (resonant condition and field expressions) would be obtained if one started with the point of view that it was a TE_{10} mode propagating in the x direction; similarly for considering it a TM_{11} mode propagating in the y direction exactly at cut-off.

10·05b Find the total charge on top plate and bottom plate. Determine an equivalent capacitance that would give this charge with a voltage equal to that between top and bottom at the center of the box.

10·05c Find the total current in the side walls. Determine an equivalent inductance in terms of this current and the magnetic flux linking a vertical path at the center of the box. What resonant frequency would be given by this inductance and the equivalent capacitance of Prob. b? Why is it different from the actual resonant frequency of the resonator?

10·06 ENERGY STORAGE, LOSSES, AND Q OF SIMPLE RESONATOR

The energy storage and energy loss in the rectangular resonator of the preceding article are of fundamental interest and will be calculated. Since the total energy passes between electric and magnetic fields, we may calculate it by finding the energy storage in electric fields at the instant when these are a maximum, for magnetic fields are then zero in the standing wave pattern of the resonator.

$$U = (U_E)_{\max} = \frac{\epsilon}{2} \int_0^d \int_0^b \int_0^a |E_y|^2 \, dx \, dy \, dz$$

Utilizing Eq. 10·05(5),

$$U = \frac{\epsilon}{2} \int_0^d \int_0^b \int_0^a E_0{}^2 \sin^2 \frac{\pi x}{a} \sin^2 \frac{\pi z}{d} \, dx \, dy \, dz$$

$$= \frac{\epsilon E_0{}^2}{2} \cdot \frac{a}{2} \cdot b \cdot \frac{d}{2} = \frac{\epsilon a b d}{8} E_0{}^2 \tag{1}$$

To obtain an approximation for power loss in the walls, we utilize the current flow in the ideal conductors as obtained from the tangential magnetic field at the surface. Referring to Fig. 10·05a,

Front: $J_y = -H_x\big|_{z=d}$ Back: $J_y = H_x\big|_{z=0}$

Left side: $J_y = -H_z\big|_{x=0}$ Right side: $J_y = H_z\big|_{x=a}$

Top: $J_x = -H_z, J_z = H_x$ Bottom: $J_x = H_z, J_z = -H_x$

If the conducting walls have surface resistivity R_s, the above currents will produce losses as follows:

$$W_L = \frac{R_s}{2} \left\{ 2 \int_0^b \int_0^a |H_x|_{z=0}{}^2 \, dx \, dy + 2 \int_0^d \int_0^b |H_z|_{x=0}{}^2 \, dy \, dz \right.$$

$$\left. + 2 \int_0^d \int_0^a \left[|H_x|^2 + |H_z|^2 \right] dx \, dz \right\}$$

In the above, the first term comes from the front and back, the second from left and right sides, and the third from top and bottom. Substituting from Eqs. 10·05(5) and (6) and evaluating the integrals,

$$W_L = \frac{R_s \lambda^2}{8\eta^2} E_0{}^2 \left[\frac{ab}{d^2} + \frac{bd}{a^2} + \frac{1}{2}\left(\frac{a}{d} + \frac{d}{a}\right) \right] \tag{2}$$

A Q of the resonator may be defined from the basic definition of Eq. 1·06(6),

$$Q = \frac{\omega_0 U}{W_L} \tag{3}$$

Substituting (1) and (2),

$$Q = \frac{\pi \eta}{4 R_s} \left[\frac{2b(a^2 + d^2)^{3/2}}{ad(a^2 + d^2) + 2b(a^3 + d^3)} \right] \tag{4}$$

Note that for a cube, $a = b = d$, this reduces to the expression

$$Q_{\text{cube}} = \frac{\sqrt{2}\,\pi}{6} \frac{\eta}{R_s} = 0.742 \frac{\eta}{R_s} \tag{5}$$

For an air dielectric, $\eta \approx 377$ ohms, and a copper conductor at 10,000 mc/sec, $R_s \approx 0.0261$ ohm, the Q is about 10,730. Thus we see the very large values of Q for such resonators as compared with those for lumped circuits (order of a few hundred) or even with resonant lines (order of a few thousand). In practice, some care must be used if Q's of the order of that calculated are to be obtained, since disturbances caused by the coupling system, surface irregularities, and other perturbations will act to increase the losses. Dielectric losses and radiation from small holes, when present, may be especially serious in lowering the Q.

Although the justification will not be given until the following chapter, it is worth noting here that the Q as calculated above is useful for estimating band width of a resonant cavity, as it was for a lumped circuit (Art. 1·10). If Δf is the distance between points on the response curve for which amplitude response is down to $1/\sqrt{2}$ of its maximum value,

$$\Delta f/f_0 \approx 1/Q \tag{6}$$

Thus, for the example above, a Q of 10,000 in a cavity resonant at 10,000 megacycles per second will yield a bandwidth between "half-power" points of 1 megacycle per second.

An equivalent series resistance for the cavity may be computed by utilizing the power loss and the total vertical current in the resonator walls, or an equivalent shunt conductance may be found from the loss and the voltage between top and bottom at the center. Although these are of limited usefulness, the latter will be found. Utilizing (2),

$$G = \frac{2W_L}{(E_0 b)^2} = \frac{R_s}{\eta^2}\left[\frac{2b(a^3 + d^3) + ad(a^2 + d^2)}{2b^2(a^2 + d^2)}\right] \tag{7}$$

PROBLEMS

10·06a Show that for resonance the same expression (1) for energy stored is obtained by calculating it from the magnetic fields when they are at their maximum.

10·06b For the mode of this article, plot the Q versus b/a for a square prism with $d = a$. Take air dielectric and copper conductor at 10,000 mc/sec. Why does Q decrease as b decreases?

10·06c Plot the equivalent conductance defined by (7) as a function of b/a under the same conditions as in Prob. b.

10·06d Show that, for any mode in any shape of resonator, the Q due to an imperfect dielectric filling the resonator is

$$Q_d = \frac{\omega\epsilon}{\sigma} = \frac{\epsilon'}{\epsilon''}$$

Note the value of this for a very good glass with $\epsilon' = 4$, $\epsilon'' = 0.004$.

10·06e Suppose that a perfect dielectric were available with $\epsilon' = 5$. How would the Q of a dielectric-filled cube compare with that of an air-filled one for the simple mode studied? Why are they different?

10·07 OTHER MODES IN THE RECTANGULAR RESONATOR

As has been noted, the particular mode studied for the rectangular box is only one of an infinite number of possible modes. If we adopt the point of view that a resonant mode is the standing wave pattern for incident and reflected wave guide modes, any one of the infinite number of possible wave guide waves might be used, with any integral number of half waves between shorting ends. It is recognized that this description of a particular field pattern is not unique, for it depends upon the axis chosen to be the "direction of propagation" for the wave guide modes. Thus (see Prob. 10·05a) the simple mode studied in past articles would be a TE_{101} mode if the z axis or x axis were considered the direction of propagation, but it would be a TM_{110} mode if the vertical (y) axis were taken as the propagation direction. In the following, a coordinate system will be chosen as in Fig. 10·05a, and field patterns will be obtained by superposing incident and reflected waves for various wave guide modes propagating in the z direction.

   A. The TE_{mnp} Mode. If we select the TE_{mn} mode of a rectangular wave guide (see Art. 9·03), addition of positively and negatively traveling waves for H_z gives

$$H_z = [Ae^{-j\beta z} + Be^{j\beta z}] \cos \frac{m\pi x}{a} \cos \frac{n\pi y}{b}$$

Since the normal component of magnetic field, H_z, must be zero at $z = 0$ and $z = d$, $B = -A$ and $\beta d = p\pi$ with p an integer. Let $C = -2jA$.

$$H_z = A[e^{-j\beta z} - e^{j\beta z}] \cos \frac{m\pi x}{a} \cos \frac{n\pi y}{b}$$

$$= C \cos \frac{m\pi x}{a} \cos \frac{n\pi y}{b} \sin \frac{p\pi z}{d} \tag{1}$$

Then, substituting in Eqs. 8·02(7) to (10), remembering that for the negatively traveling waves all terms multiplied by γ change sign,

$$H_x = -\frac{j\beta}{k_c{}^2} [Ae^{-j\beta z} - Be^{j\beta z}] \left(-\frac{m\pi}{a}\right) \sin \frac{m\pi x}{a} \cos \frac{n\pi y}{b}$$

$$= -\frac{C}{k_c{}^2} \left(\frac{p\pi}{d}\right) \left(\frac{m\pi}{a}\right) \sin \frac{m\pi x}{a} \cos \frac{n\pi y}{b} \cos \frac{p\pi z}{d} \tag{2}$$

Similarly combining terms for the other components,

$$H_y = -\frac{C}{k_c^2}\left(\frac{p\pi}{d}\right)\left(\frac{n\pi}{b}\right)\cos\frac{m\pi x}{a}\sin\frac{n\pi y}{b}\cos\frac{p\pi z}{d} \tag{3}$$

$$E_x = \frac{j\omega\mu C}{k_c^2}\left(\frac{n\pi}{b}\right)\cos\frac{m\pi x}{a}\sin\frac{n\pi y}{b}\sin\frac{p\pi z}{d} \tag{4}$$

$$E_y = -\frac{j\omega\mu C}{k_c^2}\left(\frac{m\pi}{a}\right)\sin\frac{m\pi x}{a}\cos\frac{n\pi y}{b}\sin\frac{p\pi z}{d} \tag{5}$$

where

$$k_c^2 = \left(\frac{m\pi}{a}\right)^2 + \left(\frac{n\pi}{b}\right)^2 \tag{6}$$

$$\beta = \left[\left(\frac{2\pi}{\lambda}\right)^2 - k_c^2\right]^{\frac{1}{2}} = \frac{p\pi}{d}$$

so

$$k = \frac{2\pi}{\lambda} = \left[\left(\frac{m\pi}{a}\right)^2 + \left(\frac{n\pi}{b}\right)^2 + \left(\frac{p\pi}{d}\right)^2\right]^{\frac{1}{2}} \tag{7}$$

B. *The TM_{mnp} Mode.* In a similar manner, positively and negatively traveling TM_{mn} modes in a rectangular wave guide may be combined to yield

$$E_z = D\sin\frac{m\pi x}{a}\sin\frac{n\pi y}{b}\cos\frac{p\pi z}{d} \tag{8}$$

$$E_x = -\frac{D}{k_c^2}\left(\frac{p\pi}{d}\right)\left(\frac{m\pi}{a}\right)\cos\frac{m\pi x}{a}\sin\frac{n\pi y}{b}\sin\frac{p\pi z}{d} \tag{9}$$

$$E_y = -\frac{D}{k_c^2}\left(\frac{p\pi}{d}\right)\left(\frac{n\pi}{b}\right)\sin\frac{m\pi x}{a}\cos\frac{n\pi y}{b}\sin\frac{p\pi z}{d} \tag{10}$$

$$H_x = \frac{j\omega\epsilon D}{k_c^2}\left(\frac{n\pi}{b}\right)\sin\frac{m\pi x}{a}\cos\frac{n\pi y}{b}\cos\frac{p\pi z}{d} \tag{11}$$

$$H_y = -\frac{j\omega\epsilon D}{k_c^2}\left(\frac{m\pi}{a}\right)\cos\frac{m\pi x}{a}\sin\frac{n\pi y}{b}\cos\frac{p\pi z}{d} \tag{12}$$

The quantity k_c^2 and resonant wavelength λ are as in (6) and (7).

C. *General Comments.* We note first that TM and TE modes of the same order m,n,p have identical frequencies. Such modes with different field patterns but the same resonant frequency are known as *degenerate* modes. Other cases of degeneracy may exist as in a cube, $a = b = d$, where orders 112, 121, and 211 of both TM and TE types have the same resonant frequency.

It is also apparent from (7) that, as the order of a mode becomes higher, the wavelength decreases or resonant frequency increases.   Put differently, it means that to be resonant at a given frequency, the box must be made bigger as the order increases.   This is to be expected, since more half-sine waves are to fit in each dimension.   Although we will not derive the general expression for Q, it turns out that Q increases at a given frequency as one goes to higher mode orders.   This too is logical, since the larger box has a greater volume-to-surface ratio, and energy is stored in the volume, whereas it is lost on the imperfectly conducting surface.   The high order modes are consequently useful in "echo boxes" where a high Q is desired so that the energy will decay at a very slow rate after being excited by a pulse.   Because modes become very close together in frequency as the order increases, it may be difficult to excite one mode only in such applications.

PROBLEMS

10·07a   Derive the expression for Q of a TE_{mmm} mode in a cube, $a = b = d$, and show that it increases as m increases, for a given dielectric and resonant frequency.

10·07b   Repeat Prob. a for a TM_{mmm} mode.

10·08   CIRCULAR CYLINDRICAL RESONATOR

For a circular cylindrical resonator, Fig. 10·08, there is a simple mode analogous to that first studied for the rectangular box, Art.

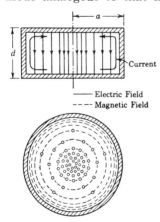

Fig. 10·08   Sections through a cylindrical cavity.

10·05.   The vertical electric field which exists has a maximum at the center and dies off to zero at the conducting side walls.   A circumferential magnetic field surrounds the displacement current represented by the time-varying electric field.   Neither component varies in the axial or circumferential direction.   Equal and opposite charges exist on the two end plates, and a vertical current flows in the side walls between them.   The mode may be considered a TM_{01} mode in a circular wave guide operating at cut-off (to give the constancy with respect to z), or it may be thought of as the standing wave pattern produced by inward and outward radially propagating waves of the radial transmission line type, Art. 9·11.   From either point of view we obtain the field components

$$E_z = E_0 J_0(kr) \tag{1}$$

$$H_\phi = \frac{jE_0}{\eta} J_1(kr) \tag{2}$$

$$k = \frac{p_{01}}{a} = \frac{2.405}{a} \tag{3}$$

Then the resonant wavelength is

$$\lambda = \frac{2\pi}{k} = 2.61a \tag{4}$$

The energy stored in the cavity at resonance may be found from the energy in the electric fields at the instant these have their maximum value. Take a and d, respectively, as radius and length of the cavity.

$$U = d \int_0^a \frac{\epsilon |E_z|^2}{2} 2\pi r \, dr = \pi\epsilon \, dE_0^2 \int_0^a rJ_0^2(kr) \, dr$$

This may be integrated by Eq. 3·28(5).

$$U = .\pi\epsilon \, dE_0^2 \frac{a^2}{2} J_1^2(ka) \tag{5}$$

If the walls are of imperfect conductors, the power loss may be calculated approximately.

$$W_L = 2\pi ad \frac{R_s}{2} |J_z|^2 + 2 \int_0^a \frac{R_s}{2} |J_r|^2 2\pi r \, dr$$

The first term represents losses on the side wall, the second on top and bottom. The current per unit width J_r on top and bottom is $\pm H_\phi$, and J_z on the side wall is the value of H_ϕ at $r = a$. Substituting from (2),

$$.W_L = \pi R_s \left[ad \frac{E_0^2}{\eta^2} J_1^2(ka) + 2 \int_0^a \frac{E_0^2}{\eta^2} rJ_1^2(kr) \, dr \right]$$

This may also be integrated by Eq. 3·28(5), recalling that $J_0(ka) = 0$ is the condition for resonance.

$$W_L = \frac{\pi a R_s E_0^2}{\eta^2} J_1^2(ka)[d + a] \tag{6}$$

The Q of the mode may then be obtained as usual from power losses and energy stored. An equivalent conductance may also be defined in terms of power losses and voltage at the center, or an equivalent resistance may be defined in terms of losses and the total current in the side walls.

$$Q = \frac{\omega U}{W_L} = \frac{\eta}{R_s} \frac{p_{01}}{2[a/d + 1]} \tag{7}$$

$$G = \frac{2W_L}{(E_0 d)^2} = \frac{R_s}{\eta^2} \frac{2\pi a}{d} [1 + a/d] J_1{}^2(p_{01}) \tag{8}$$

$$R = \frac{2W_L}{|2\pi a H_\phi(a)|^2} = R_s \frac{d}{2\pi a} [1 + a/d] \tag{9}$$

where $$p_{01} \approx 2.405$$

An infinite number of additional modes may be obtained for the cylindrical resonator by considering others of the possible wave guide modes for circular cylindrical guides as propagating in the axial direction with an integral number of half guide wavelengths between end plates. In this manner the standing wave pattern formed by the superposition of incident and reflected waves fulfills the boundary conditions of the conducting ends. Table 10·08 shows a TE_{11} mode, a TM_{01} mode, and a TE_{01} mode, each with one half guide wavelength between ends. The resonant wavelengths shown are obtained by solving the equation

$$d = \frac{p\lambda_g}{2} = \frac{p\lambda}{2}\left[1 - \left(\frac{\lambda}{\lambda_c}\right)^2\right]^{-\frac{1}{2}} \tag{10}$$

The integer p is unity for the above, and cut-off wavelength λ_c is obtained from Art. 9·05. Note that in the designations TE_{111}, TM_{011}, TE_{011}, the order of subscripts is not in the cyclic order of coordinates, r, ϕ, z, since it is common in circular waveguides to designate the ϕ variation by the first subscript.

Of the above modes, the TE_{011} is perhaps the most interesting since it has only circumferential currents in both the cylindrical wall and the end plates. Thus, if a resonator for such a wave is tuned by moving the end plate, one does not need a good contact between the ends and the cylindrical wall since no current flows between them. For both of the other modes shown (and in fact all except those of type TE_{0mp}) a finite current does flow between the cylinder and its ends so that any sliding contact must be good to prevent serious loss.

TABLE 10·08

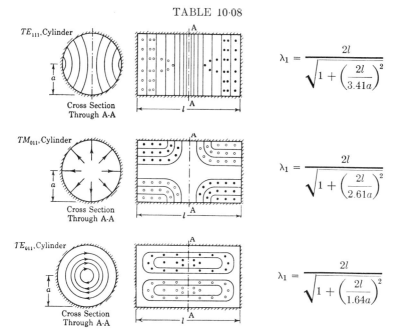

$$\lambda_1 = \frac{2l}{\sqrt{1 + \left(\dfrac{2l}{3.41a}\right)^2}}$$

$$\lambda_1 = \frac{2l}{\sqrt{1 + \left(\dfrac{2l}{2.61a}\right)^2}}$$

$$\lambda_1 = \frac{2l}{\sqrt{1 + \left(\dfrac{2l}{1.64a}\right)^2}}$$

As with the rectangular resonator, it would be found that higher wave orders (those having more variations with any or all coordinates r, ϕ, z) would require larger resonators to be resonant at a given wavelength. The Q would become higher because of the increased volume-to-surface ratio, but the modes would become close together in frequency so that it might be difficult to excite one mode only.

PROBLEMS

10·08a Give the field components and obtain expressions for energy storage, power loss, and Q for the TM_{011} cylindrical mode.

10·08b Repeat a for the TE_{011} mode.

10·08c An air-filled circular wave guide of radius 1 cm is to be made into a resonator for the TM_{021} mode at 30,000 mc/sec by placing end plates in the guide. Find the distance between end plates.

10·08d A circular cylindrical cavity of radius a and length d has a dielectric post of radius b and dielectric constant ϵ_2 extending from top to bottom. Obtain the solution for field components and the equation determining resonance, taking the simple mode analogous to that of Fig. 10·08.

10·09 WAVE SOLUTIONS IN SPHERICAL COORDINATES

Before considering the specific problem of a spherical cavity resonator, we shall look at the solutions of Maxwell's equations in spherical coordinates. We shall sketch here only those solutions with axial symmetry, $\partial/\partial\phi = 0$. The solutions with general ϕ variations are more involved, but have been given completely by Schelkunoff[2] and Stratton.[3] It is found that with axial symmetry the solutions separate into waves with components E_r, E_θ, H_ϕ and those with components H_r, H_θ, E_ϕ. These are called TM and TE types, respectively, the spherical surface r constant serving here as the transverse surface.

Consider then TM spherical modes with axial symmetry by setting $\partial/\partial\phi = 0$ in Maxwell's equations in spherical coordinates. The three curl equations containing E_r, E_θ, H_ϕ are

$$\frac{\partial}{\partial r}(rE_\theta) - \frac{\partial E_r}{\partial\theta} = -j\omega\mu(rH_\phi) \tag{1}$$

$$\frac{1}{r\sin\theta}\frac{\partial}{\partial\theta}(H_\phi\sin\theta) = j\omega\epsilon E_r \tag{2}$$

$$-\frac{\partial}{\partial r}(rH_\phi) = j\omega\epsilon(rE_\theta) \tag{3}$$

Equations (2) and (3) may be differentiated and substituted in (1), leading to an equation in H_ϕ alone.

$$\frac{\partial^2}{\partial r^2}(rH_\phi) + \frac{1}{r^2}\frac{\partial}{\partial\theta}\left[\frac{1}{\sin\theta}\frac{\partial}{\partial\theta}(rH_\phi\sin\theta)\right] + k^2(rH_\phi) = 0 \tag{4}$$

To solve this partial differential equation, we follow the product solution technique. Assume

$$(rH_\phi) = R\Theta \tag{5}$$

R is a function of r alone, Θ is a function of θ alone. If this is substituted in (4), the functions of r may be separated from the functions of θ, and these must then be separately equal to a constant if they are to equal each other for all values of r and θ. For a definitely ulterior motive, we label this constant $n(n + 1)$.

$$\frac{r^2R''}{R} + k^2r^2 = -\frac{1}{\Theta}\frac{d}{d\theta}\left[\frac{1}{\sin\theta}\frac{d}{d\theta}(\Theta\sin\theta)\right] = n(n + 1) \tag{6}$$

Thus there are two ordinary differential equations, one in r only, one in θ only. Let us consider that in θ first, making the substitution

[2] S. A. Schelkunoff, "Transmission Theory of Spherical Waves," *Trans. A.I.-E.E.*, **57**, 744–750 (1938).

[3] J. A. Stratton, *Electromagnetic Theory*, McGraw-Hill, 1941, Chapter VII.

$$u = \cos \theta \qquad \sqrt{1 - u^2} = \sin \theta \qquad \frac{d}{d\theta} = -\sin \theta \frac{d}{du}$$

Then

$$(1 - u^2) \frac{d^2\Theta}{du^2} - 2u \frac{d\Theta}{du} + \left[n(n + 1) - \frac{1}{1 - u^2} \right] \Theta = 0 \qquad (7)$$

The differential equation (7) is reminiscent of Legendre's equation (Art. 3·31) and is in fact a standard form. This form is

$$(1 - x^2) \frac{d^2y}{dx^2} - 2x \frac{dy}{dx} + \left[n(n + 1) - \frac{m^2}{1 - x^2} \right] y = 0 \qquad (8)$$

One of the solutions is written

$$y = P_n{}^m(x)$$

and the function defined by the above solution is called an associated Legendre function of the first kind, order n, degree m. These are actually related to the ordinary Legendre functions by the equation

$$P_n{}^m(x) = (1 - x^2)^{m/2} \frac{d^m P_n(x)}{dx^m} \qquad (9)$$

As a matter of fact, (8) could be derived from the ordinary Legendre equation by this substitution. A solution to (7) may then be written

$$\Theta = P_n{}^1(u) = P_n{}^1 (\cos \theta) \qquad (10)$$

And, from (9),

$$P_n{}^1 (\cos \theta) = -\frac{d}{d\theta} P_n (\cos \theta) \qquad (11)$$

Thus for integral values of n these associated Legendre functions are also polynomials consisting of a finite number of terms. By differentiations according to (9) in Eq. 3·31(8), the polynomials of the first few orders are found to be

$$P_0{}^1 (\cos \theta) = 0$$

$$P_1{}^1 (\cos \theta) = \sin \theta$$

$$P_2{}^1 (\cos \theta) = 3 \sin \theta \cos \theta \qquad (12)$$

$$P_3{}^1 (\cos \theta) = \tfrac{3}{2} \sin \theta (5 \cos^2 \theta - 1)$$

$$P_4{}^1 (\cos \theta) = \tfrac{5}{2} \sin \theta (7 \cos^3 \theta - 3 \cos \theta)$$

Other properties of these functions that will be useful to us, and which may be found from a study of the above, are

1. All $P_n{}^1$ (cos θ) are zero at $\theta = 0$ and $\theta = \pi$.
2. $P_n{}^1$ (cos θ) are zero at $\theta = \pi/2$ if n is even.
3. $P_n{}^1$ (cos θ) are a maximum at $\theta = \pi/2$ if n is odd, and the value of this maximum is given by

$$P_n{}^1(0) = \frac{(-1)^{-(n-1)/2}n!}{2^{n-1}\left[\left(\dfrac{n-1}{2}\right)!\right]^2} \quad n \text{ odd} \tag{13}$$

4. The associated Legendre functions have orthogonality properties similar to those of sinusoids and Bessel functions studied previously.

$$\int_0^\pi P_l{}^1 (\cos \theta)P_n{}^1 (\cos \theta) \sin \theta \, d\theta = 0 \quad l \neq n \tag{14}$$

$$\int_0^\pi [P_n{}^1 (\cos \theta)]^2 \sin \theta \, d\theta = \frac{2n(n+1)}{2n+1} \tag{15}$$

5. The differentiation formula is

$$\frac{d}{d\theta} [P_n{}^1 (\cos \theta)] = \frac{1}{\sin \theta} [nP_{n+1}{}^1 (\cos \theta) - (n+1) \cos \theta \, P_n{}^1 (\cos \theta)] \tag{16}$$

Note that only one solution for this second order differential equation (7) has been considered. The other solution becomes infinite on the axis, and so will not be required in problems such as those to be considered in this text, where the region of the axis is included in the solution.

To go back to the r differential equation obtainable from (6), substitute the variable $R_1 = R/\sqrt{r}$.

$$\frac{d^2R_1}{dr^2} + \frac{1}{r}\frac{dR_1}{dr} + \left[k^2 - \frac{(n+\frac{1}{2})^2}{r^2}\right] R_1 = 0$$

By comparing with Eq. 3·24(3) it is seen that this is Bessel's differential equation of order $(n + \frac{1}{2})$. A complete solution may then be written

$$R_1 = A_n J_{n+1/2}(kr) + B_n N_{n+1/2}(kr) \tag{17}$$

and
$$R = \sqrt{r} \, R_1$$

If n is an integer, these half-integral order Bessel functions reduce simply to algebraic combinations of sinusoids.† For example, the first few orders are

$$J_{1/2}(x) = \sqrt{\frac{2}{\pi x}} \sin x \qquad N_{1/2}(x) = -\sqrt{\frac{2}{\pi x}} \cos x$$

$$J_{3/2}(x) = \sqrt{\frac{2}{\pi x}} \left[\frac{\sin x}{x} - \cos x\right] \qquad N_{3/2}(x) = -\sqrt{\frac{2}{\pi x}} \left[\sin x + \frac{\cos x}{x}\right]$$

$$J_{5/2}(x) = \sqrt{\frac{2}{\pi x}} \left[\left(\frac{3}{x^2} - 1\right) \sin x \qquad N_{5/2}(x) = -\sqrt{\frac{2}{\pi x}} \left[\frac{3}{x} \sin x\right.\right.$$

$$\left. - \frac{3}{x} \cos x\right] \qquad\qquad \left. + \left(\frac{3}{x^2} - 1\right) \cos x\right]$$

$$(18)$$

The linear combination of the J and N functions into Hankel functions (Art. 3·22) represent waves traveling radially inward or outward, and boundary conditions will be as found previously for other Bessel functions:

1. If the region of interest includes the origin, $N_{n+1/2}$ cannot be present since it is infinite at $r = 0$.

2. If the region of interest extends to infinity, the linear combination of J and N into the second Hankel function, $H_{n+1/2}{}^{(2)} = J_{n+1/2} - jN_{n+1/2}$, must be used to represent a radially outward traveling wave.

The particular combination of $J_{n+1/2}(kr)$ and $N_{n+1/2}(kr)$ required for any problem may be denoted as $Z_{n+1/2}(kr)$, and now by combining correctly (17), (10), and (5), H_ϕ is determined. E_r and E_θ follow from (2) and (3) respectively.

$$H_\phi = \frac{A_n}{\sqrt{r}} P_n{}^1 (\cos \theta) Z_{n+1/2}(kr)$$

$$E_\theta = \frac{A_n P_n{}^1 (\cos \theta)}{j\omega \epsilon r^{3/2}} [n Z_{n+1/2}(kr) - kr Z_{n-1/2}(kr)] \qquad (19)$$

$$E_r = -\frac{A_n n Z_{n+1/2}(kr)}{j\omega \epsilon r^{3/2} \sin \theta} [\cos \theta \, P_n{}^1 (\cos \theta) - P_{n+1}{}^1 (\cos \theta)]$$

† Special notations for the spherical or half-integral order Bessel functions have been introduced and are useful if one has much to do with these functions. Thus Stratton, following Morse (*Vibration and Sound*, McGraw-Hill, 1936, p. 246) uses $j_n(x)$ to denote $(\pi/2x)^{1/2} J_{n+1/2}(x)$, and similar small letters denote other spherical Bessel and Hankel functions. Schelkunoff follows the definitions of spher-

The spherically symmetric TE modes may be obtained by the above and the principle of duality, Art. 9·13. We then replace E_r and E_θ by H_r and H_θ respectively, and H_ϕ by $-E_\phi$.

$$E_\phi = \frac{B_n}{\sqrt{r}} P_n{}^1 (\cos \theta) \, Z_{n+1/2} (kr)$$

$$H_\theta = -\frac{B_n P_n{}^1 (\cos \theta)}{j\omega\mu r^{3/2}} [n Z_{n+1/2} (kr) - kr Z_{n-1/2} (kr)] \tag{20}$$

$$H_r = \frac{B_n n Z_{n+1/2} (kr)}{j\omega\mu r^{3/2} \sin \theta} [\cos \theta \, P_n{}^1 (\cos \theta) - P_{n+1}{}^1 (\cos \theta)]$$

10·10 SPHERICAL RESONATORS

The general discussion of spherical waves from the preceding section will now be applied to the study of some simple modes in a hollow conducting spherical resonator. Since the origin is included within the region of the solution, the Bessel functions can only be those of first kind, $J_{n+1/2}$. For the lowest order TM mode, let $n = 1$ in Eq. 10·09(19) and utilize the definitions of Eqs. 10·09(12) and 10·09(18). Letting $C = A (\pi/2k)^{1/2}$, we then have

$$H_\phi = \frac{C \sin \theta}{kr} \left[\frac{\sin kr}{kr} - \cos kr \right] \tag{1}$$

$$E_r = -\frac{2j\eta C \cos \theta}{k^2 r^2} \left[\frac{\sin kr}{kr} - \cos kr \right] \tag{2}$$

$$E_\theta = \frac{j\eta C \sin \theta}{k^2 r^2} \left[\frac{(kr)^2 - 1}{kr} \sin kr + \cos kr \right] \tag{3}$$

The mode may be designated TM_{101}, the subscripts here giving variations in the order r, ϕ, and θ. Electric and magnetic field lines are sketched in Fig. 10·10a.

To obtain the resonance condition, we know that E_θ must be zero at the radius of the perfectly conducting shell, $r = a$. From (2), this requires

$$\tan ka = \frac{ka}{1 - (ka)^2} \tag{4}$$

ical Bessel functions given by Bateman (*Partial Differential Equations*, p. 386 Dover reprint, 1944, p. 386), though in a different notation, using $\hat{J}_n(x)$ to denote $(\pi x/2)^{1/2} J_{n+1/2}(x)$, and similarly for other Bessel and Hankel functions. Because of our limited need for spherical coordinates, we shall retain the original Bessel function forms so that standard recurrence formulas may be used.

Roots of this transcendental equation may be determined graphically, and the first is found at $ka \approx 2.74$, giving a resonant wavelength of

$$\lambda \approx 2.29a \tag{5}$$

The energy stored at resonance may be found from the peak energy in magnetic fields.

$$U = \int_0^a \int_0^\pi \frac{\mu}{2} \mid H_\phi \mid^2 2\pi r^2 \sin\theta \, d\theta \, dr$$

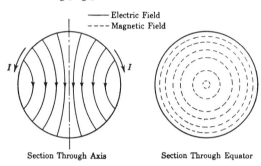

Section Through Axis　　　　Section Through Equator

Fig. 10·10a　Field patterns for simple TM_{101} mode in spherical resonator.

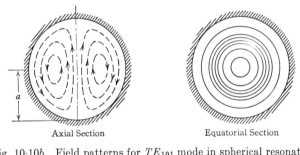

Axial Section　　　　Equatorial Section

Fig. 10·10b　Field patterns for TE_{101} mode in spherical resonator.

The value of H_ϕ is given by (1), and the result of the integration may be simplified by the resonance requirement (4).

$$U = \frac{2\pi\mu C^2}{3k^3}\left[ka - \frac{1 + (ka)^2}{ka}\sin^2 ka \right] \tag{6}$$

The approximate dissipation in conductors of finite conductivity is

$$W_L = \int_0^\pi \frac{R_s \mid H_\phi \mid^2}{2} 2\pi a^2 \sin\theta \, d\theta = \frac{4\pi R_s}{3} a^2 C^2 \sin^2 ka \tag{7}$$

So the Q of this mode is

$$Q = \frac{\eta}{2R_s(ka)^2}\left[\frac{ka}{\sin^2 ka} - \frac{1 + (ka)^2}{ka} \right] \approx \frac{\eta}{R_s} \tag{8}$$

The "dual" of the above mode is the TE_{101} mode, and its field components may be obtained by substituting in (1) to (3) E_ϕ for H_ϕ, $-H_r$ for E_r, and $-H_\theta$ for E_θ. The fields are sketched in Fig. 10·10b. Note that the resonance condition for this mode, obtained by setting $E_\phi = 0$ at $r = a$, requires

$$\tan ka = ka$$

Numerical solution of this yields $ka \approx 4.50$, or

$$\lambda \approx 1.395a \qquad (9)$$

PROBLEMS

10·10a Determine an equivalent conductance for the TM_{101} mode in terms of the conductor losses and a voltage between poles taken along the axis.

10·10b By utilizing solutions and definitions of Art. 10·09, write expressions for the components in a TE mode with $n = 2$.

Small-Gap Cavities and Coupling

10·11 SMALL-GAP CAVITIES

Because of their shielded nature and high Q possibilities, resonant cavities are ideal for use in many high-frequency tubes such as klys-

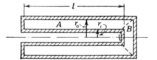

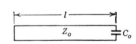

Fig. 10·11a Foreshortened coaxial line resonator.

Fig. 10·11b Approximate equivalent circuit for Fig. 10·11a.

trons, magnetrons, and microwave triodes.   When they are used with an electron stream, it is essential for efficient energy transfer that the electron transit time across the active field region be as small as possible. If resonators such as those studied in preceding articles were used, very thin cylinders or prisms would be required, so that impedance and Q would be low.   Certain special shapes are consequently employed which have a small gap in the region that is to interact with the electron stream.   Several examples of useful small-gap cavities will follow.

A. Foreshortened Coaxial Lines.   A resonator of the general form of Fig. 10·11a may be considered a coaxial line A terminated in the gap capacitance B (leading to the equivalent circuit of Fig. 10·11b) provided that the region B is small compared with wavelength.   The method is particularly useful when the region B is not uniform, but contains dielectrics or discontinuities, so long as a reasonable estimate of capacitance may be made.

For resonance, the impedance at any plane should be equal and opposite, looking in opposite directions. Selecting the plane of the capacitance for this purpose,

$$jZ_0 \tan \beta l = - \left(\frac{1}{j\omega_0 C} \right)$$

or

$$\beta l = \tan^{-1} \left(\frac{1}{Z_0 \omega C_0} \right) \tag{1}$$

If C_0 is small ($Z_0 \omega C_0 \ll 1$), the line is practically a quarter-wave in length. For larger values of C_0, the line is foreshortened from the quarter-wave value and would approach zero length if $Z_0 \omega C_0$ approached infinity.

B. Foreshortened Radial Lines. If the proportions of the resonator are more as shown in Fig. 10·11c, it is preferable to look at the problem

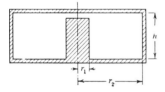   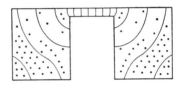

Fig. 10·11c Foreshortened radial line resonator.

Fig. 10·11d Resonator intermediate between foreshortened coaxial line and foreshortened radial line.

as one of a resonant radial transmission line (Art. 9·11) loaded or foreshortened by the capacitance of the post or gap. Then, for resonance, the inductive reactance of the shorted radial line looking outward from radius r_1 should be equal in magnitude to the capacitive reactance of the central post. Using the results and notation of Art. 9·11,

$$\frac{1}{\omega C} = - \frac{h}{2\pi r_1} Z_{01} \frac{\sin (\theta_1 - \theta_2)}{\cos (\psi_1 - \theta_2)}$$

or

$$\theta_2 = \tan^{-1} \left[\frac{\sin \theta_1 + (2\pi r_1/\omega C Z_{01} h) \cos \psi_1}{\cos \theta_1 - (2\pi r_1/\omega C Z_{01} h) \sin \psi_1} \right] \tag{2}$$

Once θ_2 is found, kr_2 is read from Fig. 9·11c or Fig. 9·11d.

C. Resonators of Intermediate Shape. In the coaxial line resonator of Fig. 10·11a the electric field lines would be substantially radial in the region far from the gap. In the radial line resonator of Fig. 10·11c the electric field lines would be substantially axial in the region far from the gap. For a resonator of the same general type, but with intermediate proportions, the field lines may be transitional between these extremes as indicated in Fig. 10·11d, and neither of the above approximations may yield good results. An exact approach will be outlined in the following chapter. Some useful design curves have been given in the literature.[4] Of course, if the capacitive loading at the center is great enough, the entire resonator will be relatively small compared with wavelength, and the outer portion may be considered a lumped inductance of value

$$L = \frac{\mu l}{2\pi} \ln \left(\frac{r_2}{r_1} \right) \tag{3}$$

Resonance is computed from this inductance and the known capacitance.

D. *Conical Line Resonator.* A somewhat different form of small-gap resonator, formed by placing a spherical short at radius a on a conical

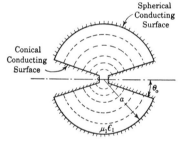

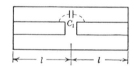

Fig. 10·11e   Conical line resonator.   Fig. 10·11f.

line as studied in Art. 9·14, is shown in Fig. 10·11e. Since this is a uniform line, formula (1) applies to this case as well. For the conical line, $\beta = k$ and

$$Z_0 = \frac{\eta}{\pi} \ln \cot \frac{\theta_0}{2} \tag{4}$$

In the limit of zero capacitance (the two conical tips separated by an infinitesimal gap), the radius a becomes exactly a quarter-wavelength. The field components in this case, obtained by forming a standing wave from Eqs. 9·14(5) and (6), are

$$E_\theta = \frac{C}{\sin \theta} \frac{\cos kr}{r} \tag{5}$$

$$H_\phi = \frac{C}{j\eta \sin \theta} \frac{\sin kr}{r} \tag{6}$$

[4] T. Moreno, *Microwave Transmission Design Data*, McGraw-Hill, 1948

The Q of the resonator in this limiting case may be shown to be

$$Q \approx \frac{\eta\pi}{4R_s} \frac{\ln \cot (\theta_0/2)}{\ln \cot (\theta_0/2) + 0.825 \csc \theta_0} \tag{7}$$

PROBLEMS

10·11a A coaxial line of radii 0.5 and 1.5 cm is loaded by a gap capacitance of 1 $\mu\mu$f. Find the length l for resonance at 3000 mc/sec.

10·11b A radial line of spacing $h = 1$ cm has a central post of radius 0.5 cm and capacitance 1 $\mu\mu$f. Find the radius r_2 for resonance at 3000 mc/sec.

10·11c Obtain expressions for the Q and the impedance referred to the gap for the resonator of Fig. 10·11a, neglecting losses in region B. Calculate values for a copper conductor and the data of Prob. a.

10·11d Find Q and impedance if in addition to copper losses there are losses in region B representable by a shunt resistance R_0. Repeat the numerical calculation of c, taking $R_0 = 10,000$ ohms.

10·11e By extension of the concepts of this article, show that the expression for resonant frequency for the resonator of Fig. 10·11f, having total gap capacity C_1, is

$$\beta l = \tan^{-1} \left(\frac{1}{2Z_0\omega C_1} \right)$$

10·11f For a cone angle θ_0 of 15° in Fig. 10·11e, find radius a for resonance at 3000 mc/sec if center capacitance is 1 $\mu\mu$f.

10·11g For the conical resonator with no loading capacitance, show that there is a value of θ_0 which gives maximum Q. Calculate the value of Q for a copper resonator designed for $\lambda = 15$ cm with this optimum angle.

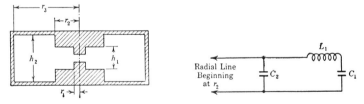

Fig. 10·11g An axially symmetric resonator and approximate equivalent circuit.

10·11h A radial cavity is loaded at the center by a section as shown in Fig. 10·11g. If r_2 is relatively small compared with wavelength, it is possible to represent approximately the region inside r_2 by a lumped-circuit equivalent, as shown. Here C_1 is the center post capacitance, L_1 is an inductance calculated from d-c formulas for the coaxial region of height h_1 between radii r_1 and r_2, and C_2 is approximately the capacitance calculated on the basis of parallel disks spaced h_1, and of radii r_1 and r_2. If $C_1 = 1$ $\mu\mu$f, $h_1 = 0.5$ cm, $h_2 = 1.0$ cm, $r_1 = 0.50$ cm, $r_2 = 1.0$ cm, find the approximate value of r_3 for resonance at $\lambda = 15$ cm.

10·12 COUPLING TO CAVITIES

The types of electromagnetic waves that may exist inside closed conducting cavities have been discussed without specifically analyzing ways of exciting these oscillations. Obviously they cannot be excited if the resonator is completely enclosed by conductors. Some means of coupling electromagnetic energy into and out of the resonator must be introduced from the outside. Some of these coupling methods have been implied in past articles. All are similar to those discussed in

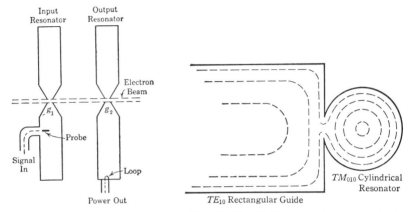

Fig. 10·12a Couplings to the cavities of a velocity modulation tube amplifier.

Fig. 10·12b Section showing approximate form of magnetic field lines in iris coupling between a guide and cavity.

Art. 9·06 for exciting waves in wave guides. The most straightforward methods are:

1. Introduction of a conducting probe or antenna in the direction of the electric field lines, driven by an external transmission line.

2. Introduction of a conducting loop with plane normal to the magnetic field lines.

3. Introduction of a pulsating electron beam passing through a small gap in the resonator, in the direction of electric field lines.

4. Introduction of a hole or iris between the cavity and a driving wave guide, the hole being located so that some field component in the cavity mode has a common direction to one in the wave mode.

For example, in a velocity modulation device of the klystron type, as pictured in Fig. 10·12a, the input cavity may be excited by a probe, the oscillations in this cavity producing a voltage across gap g_1 and causing a velocity modulation of the electron beam. The velocity modulation is converted to convection current modulation by a drifting action so that the electron beam may then excite electromagnetic oscillations in the second resonator by passing through the gap g_2. Power may be coupled out of this resonator by a coupling loop and a coaxial transmission line. Iris coupling between a TM_{010} mode in a cylindrical cavity and the TE_{10} mode in a rectangular wave guide is illustrated in Fig. 10·12b. Here the H_ϕ of the cavity and the H_x of the guide are in the same direction over the hole.

The rigorous approach to a quantitative analysis of cavity coupling will be given in the following chapter. Some comments and an approximate approach are, however, in order here. Let us concentrate on the loop coupling to a TM_{010} cylindrical mode as sketched in Fig. 10·12c. If a current is made to flow in the loop, all wave types will be excited which have a magnetic field threading the loop. The simple TM_{010} mode is one of these, and, if it is near resonance, certainly it will be excited most. However, this wave is known to fit the boundary conditions imposed by the perfectly conducting box alone. Other waves will have to be superposed to make the electric field zero along the perfectly conducting loop, but these will in general be far

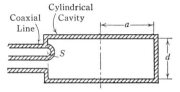

Fig. 10·12c　Magnetic coupling to a cylindrical cavity.

from resonance and so will contribute only a reactive effect. In fact, they may be thought of as producing the self-inductive reactance of the loop, taking into account the presence of the cavity as a shield.

The total induced voltage in the loop may be written

$$V_0 = j\omega\mu HS + j\omega L I_L \tag{1}$$

where H is an averaged magnetic field from the TM_{010} mode over the loop, S the area of the loop, I_L the loop current, and L the self-inductance of the loop in the presence of the cavity. If the simple mode is at resonance for the unperturbed condition, no reactive energy need be supplied to it, but only a power to account for the real losses in the cavity. The first term of (1) then represents a voltage in phase with current, and the real power input is

$$W_L = \tfrac{1}{2}I_L(j\omega\mu HS) \tag{2}$$

If we equate this to the expression for conductor losses, Eq. 10·08(6), with H obtained from Eq. 10·08(2) by taking H_ϕ at $r = a$, we have

$$\frac{1}{2}I_L j\omega\mu HS = \frac{\pi a R_s E_0{}^2}{\eta^2}(d+a)J_1{}^2(ka) = -\pi a R_s H^2(d+a)$$

or

$$H = \frac{-j\omega\mu S}{2\pi a(d+a)R_s}I_L \tag{3}$$

This equation enables us to find the level of excitation of the mode for a given loop current. Also, by substituting in (1), we may find the input impedance.

$$Z = \frac{V_0}{I_L} = \frac{(\omega\mu S)^2}{2\pi a(d + a)R_s} + j\omega L \tag{4}$$

PROBLEMS

10·12a   For the simple mode in a rectangular resonator perform an approximate analysis like the above leading to an expression for input impedance of a loop introduced at the center of a side wall.

10·12b   For the TM_{010} cylindrical mode, suppose that the coupling to the line is by means of a small probe of length d extending axially from the bottom center. Taking voltage induced in the probe as the probe length multiplied by electric field of the mode, find an expression for input admittance at resonance of the unperturbed mode, utilizing a procedure similar to the above.   The probe capacitance is C.

10·12c   Discuss the extension of the above approximate approach to other frequencies near resonance of the unperturbed mode by utilizing the Q in its relation to band width.   How would this enable one to find a new resonance defined as the frequency at which input impedance Z is real?

10·13   SMALL PERTURBATIONS IN IDEAL CAVITIES

Certain cavities may approximate the ideal shapes studied earlier except for small deviations such as screws, holes, and small regions of dielectric.   There is a powerful approximate method for studying such cases which we wish to illustrate by an example.   Like the methods utilized in studying the effects of small losses, it is a perturbation method in that the solution is assumed to deviate little from the ideal, and energy changes from the perturbation are calculated from the ideal solution.

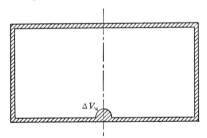

Fig. 10·13   Small perturbation in bottom of cylindrical cavity.

The example to be taken is that of a small perturbance in the bottom center of a cylindrical cavity with TM_{010} mode (Fig. 10·13), taking out a small volume ΔV. It is clear that some of the stored electric energy is removed by the process, and frequency must shift enough so that stored magnetic energy is changed by the same amount so that the balance of electric and magnetic energy is maintained. Field expressions are taken to be approximately the same as in Eqs.

10·08 (1) and (2), and the change in stored electric energy is approximately that of the volume removed.

$$\Delta U_E = - \frac{\epsilon E_0{}^2}{2} \Delta V \tag{1}$$

The change in stored magnetic energy represented by a change in frequency is approximately

$$\Delta U_H \approx 2\pi \sqrt{\mu\epsilon} \, \Delta f \frac{dU_H}{dk}$$

$$= 2\pi \sqrt{\mu\epsilon} \, \Delta f d \int_0^a \frac{d}{dk} \left[\frac{E_0{}^2}{2\eta^2} J_1{}^2(kr) \right] 2\pi r \, dr \tag{2}$$

Note that the perturbation does not have to be considered here since magnetic fields are small in this region. Evaluation of the integral gives

$$\Delta U_H = 2\pi d \sqrt{\mu\epsilon} \frac{\pi\epsilon E_0{}^2 a^2}{2} \frac{\Delta f}{f_0} ka J_1(ka) J_2(ka)$$

When this is equated to (1), an equation for frequency shift from that of the unperturbed mode is obtained.

$$\frac{\Delta f}{f_0} \approx - \frac{(\Delta V/V_0)}{(ka) J_1(ka) J_2(ka)} \approx -1.85 \frac{\Delta V}{V_0} \tag{3}$$

Note that frequency is decreased by the perturbance, as would be expected since it acts to increase the effective capacitance.

A similar thing may be done with small dielectric regions introduced into the cavity, but here one must decide if the E or thė D is substantially that of the unperturbed mode over the region of the dielectric.

PROBLEMS

10·13a Obtain the approximate expression for frequency shift if the small volume ΔV is taken from the side wall of the TM_{010} mode where magnetic field is large and electric field small.

10·13b Obtain the approximate expression for shift of resonant frequency of the TM_{010} mode if a thin dielectric plate of thickness t and constant ϵ_2 covers the bottom of the cavity. Calculate the shift for $a = 5$ cm, $d = 1$ cm, $t = 0.05$ cm and $\epsilon_2' = 5$.

10·13c Obtain the approximate expression for shift of resonant frequency of the TM_{010} mode if the dielectric is a thin cylinder of average radius b, thickness t, and dielectric constant ϵ_2 extending from top to bottom of the cavity. Calculate the shift for the dimensions of Prob. b with $b = 2.5$ cm, $t = 0.05$ cm, and $\epsilon_2' = 5$.

11 MICROWAVE NETWORKS

11·01 INTRODUCTION

In the last several chapters we have considered wave-propagating systems such as transmission lines and wave guides, and resonant wave systems of the cavity type. These are important elements in microwave systems, as has been implied in previous discussions, but now we want to be more specific about the manner in which they must be treated if they are combined into systems or "networks." A typical system of this type may use a cavity as the resonant element in coupling power from an electron stream. A coupling system may in turn excite the dominant mode of a wave guide which is to carry the power to an antenna. On the way it may pass through other cavities with associated coupling systems designed to act as filters, and will also have to encounter unavoidable bends and discontinuities as well as other discontinuities purposely added for matching, power monitering, or impedance measurement.

One approach to the analysis of such a system would be to solve the wave equation for each region with proper boundary or continuity conditions applied in passing from each region to the next. This would, of course, be a hopelessly complex procedure if it had to be repeated for each such system, and would be useless for engineering design. Moreover, it would reveal the distribution of fields everywhere in the system, which is more information than is wanted. One desires only to know the characteristics of each part of the system as a transducer or power transfer element over the frequency range of interest. Similar problems at low frequencies are handled by circuit or network theory, where, instead of giving detailed descriptions of the fields about a coil of wire or between conductors, over-all parameters such as inductance and capacitance or even more general impedance or transfer parameters are defined and utilized. In discussing the electromagnetic basis of conventional circuit theory in Chapter 5, those ideas perhaps seemed unsuitable for wave-type systems, but we shall

446

find that a very complete parallel can be set up, with many of the same techniques and theorems applying. The same terms, voltage, current, and impedance, are consequently used in order to stress this parallel, though they are used to represent field quantities and may not appear to be the same as in the definitions of these quantities employed in Chapter 5.

The important thing, however, is that there can be defined certain parameters which relate output quantities to input quantities for the microwave system just as for conventional networks, and these parameters may be found by measurement if they cannot be found by solution of the electromagnetic field equations. The parameters satisfy certain theorems analogous to classical network theorems so that some general things can be said about the behavior of all such systems which may be of help even if the specific problem cannot be solved. Moreover, the parameters of the over-all system may be found by suitable combination of the parameters of its components, much as a lumped-element network is formed from individual elements. The definitions, general theorems, and some examples for microwave networks will consequently be given in this chapter, with some comments about methods of determining the parameters of the system by measurement or by analysis.

Definitions and Network Theorems

11·02 DEFINITION OF A MICROWAVE NETWORK

Consistent with the preceding discussion, we shall mean by a microwave network a dielectric region surrounded by a good conductor of arbitrary shape having certain wave guide or transmission line inlets and outlets. The wave guides are assumed to support a finite number of non-cut-off modes. Examples are the cavity resonator coupled to a single transmission line (Fig. 11·02a), the rectangular wave guide with change of height (Fig. 11·02b), the E-plane T in rectangular wave guide (Fig. 11·02c), and the magic T or bridge (Fig. 11·02d). These may be said to be microwave networks with, respectively, one, two, three, and four wave guide terminals, or more often they are referred to as one-, two-, three-, and four-terminal pairs by analogy with lumped-element networks. (This assumes only one non-cut-off mode per guide.) In considering the defined arrangements as microwave networks, it will also be assumed that we are interested only in the behaviors of the dominant modes in certain of the guides when various load conditions are placed on the remaining guides, and not on the detailed solution of the electromagnetic field in the vicinity of the discontinuities.

Although we may excite only the dominant mode in any of the wave guide terminals, it is true that higher order modes will be excited in the vicinity of the junctions, and, although these modes may be cut off, they will have reactive energy which will affect the transmission between the propagating dominant modes of the various guides.   But, if we are interested only in the manner in which such transmission is

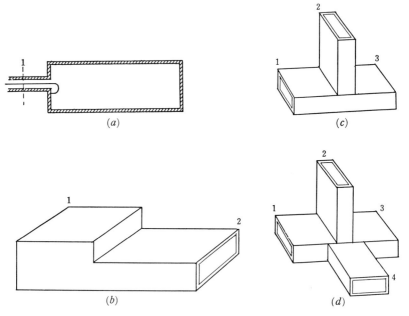

Fig. 11·02   Examples of microwave networks.   (a) Coupling from a line to a cavity (one-terminal pair).   (b) Discontinuity in rectangular guide (two-terminal pair).   (c) E-plane T (three-terminal pair).   (d) Magic T or microwave bridge (four-terminal pair).

affected, it can be expressed in terms of certain coefficients or equivalent circuits, and the details of the higher mode fields need not be described.   Thus, the microwave two-terminal pair of Fig. 11·02b may be represented by a T or π network just like a lumped-element two-terminal pair.   It is interesting to note that Carson[1] recognized the validity of this representation as early as 1924, though it has only been fully exploited within the last few years.[2]

[1] J. R. Carson, *A.I.E.E.*, **43**, 908–913 (Oct. 1924).

[2] C. G. Montgomery, R. H. Dicke, E. M. Purcell, *Principles of Microwave Circuits*, MIT Radiation Laboratory Series, Vol. 8, McGraw-Hill, 1948.

Finally, a combination of elements such as those in the example above is also a microwave network, fitting the definition of the first paragraph. An important part of the study will be concerned with the finding of network parameters for an over-all system when they are known for the individual components.

11·03   VOLTAGE, CURRENT, AND IMPEDANCE IN WAVE GUIDES

In discussing the microwave structure as a network, it is convenient to employ the usual terms, voltage, current, and impedance, in order to make easy use of the large body of applicable network theory. We have already seen in Art. 9·07 that certain simple problems may be solved by using only the field impedance (ratio of transverse E to transverse H), but in these there is a uniform discontinuity over an entire cross-sectional plane. For a problem such as that of Fig. 11·02b, where there is a change in height of a rectangular guide propagating the TE_{10} mode, a more general approach is required. One might feel intuitively that a good definition of voltage for this case would be obtained by taking the integral of electric field from top to bottom at the center of the guide, with a current defined as the total longitudinal current in the top (returning in the bottom). Then we might say that for a first approximation these defined voltages and currents should be continuous at the change of section. An exact treatment (to be discussed later) would show that, although the approximation of the last sentence is not too good, an equivalent circuit representing the exact transformation between input or output can be obtained with the stated definitions, but also other exact equivalent circuits could be obtained to fit an infinite number of possible definitions of voltage and current. Thus, the attempt to arrive at a proper definition of voltage and current by physical reasoning does not lead to anything wrong, but it is not particularly purposeful because of the lack of uniqueness of the definitions. Incidentally, it is clear that in a mode such as the TE_{01} in a circular guide, it would be difficult to apply the physical reasoning to decide upon sensible definitions anyway, since electric field lines form closed circles and there is no longitudinal current.

In spite of the lack of uniqueness, it is useful to make certain definitions and to employ the terms, as will be demonstrated in following articles. The following points may be made:

1. Voltage and current of a particular wave guide mode are *always* defined so that voltage is proportional to the strength of transverse electric field of the mode, with current proportional to the strength of transverse magnetic field.

2. Voltage and current are *usually* defined so that their product gives the power flow of the mode.

3. Voltage and current are *often* defined so that the ratio of voltage and current of a single traveling wave agrees with some preselected characteristic impedance Z_0. Thus Schelkunoff in his discussion[3] makes this impedance equal to the wave impedance, and others have defined Z_0 to be unity, so that all impedances are automatically normalized.

It is recognized that points 2 and 3 above resolve the lack of uniqueness inherent in 1, but other selections (such as the physical feelings mentioned in connection with the TE_{10} mode) might be substituted for either 2 or 3 or both. For reasons of convenience, we shall adopt all the above points in following discussions. From point 1, we then write transverse fields:

$$\bar{E}_t(x,y,z) = V(z)\bar{f}(x,y) \tag{1}$$

$$\bar{H}_t(x,y,z) = I(z)\bar{g}(x,y) \tag{2}$$

For a single traveling wave, for example,

$$\bar{E}_t(x,y,z) = V_0 e^{-j\beta z}\bar{f}(x,y) \tag{3}$$

$$\bar{H}_t(x,y,z) = I_0 e^{-j\beta z}\bar{g}(x,y) \tag{4}$$

The arbitrariness shows here by the manner in which any multiplicative constant is divided between the voltage V and the function $\bar{f}$ in the first expression, and similarly between I and $\bar{g}$ in the second. The arbitrariness is resolved by writing relations for points 2 and 3.

$$V_0 I_0 = 2W_T \tag{5}$$

$$\frac{V_0}{I_0} = Z_0 \tag{6}$$

As an example, take the TE_{10} mode in rectangular guide.

$$E_y = E_0 \sin\frac{\pi x}{a} = V_0 f(x) \tag{7}$$

$$H_x = -\frac{E_0}{Z_z}\sin\frac{\pi x}{a} = I_0 g(x) \tag{8}$$

Utilizing (5),

$$V_0 I_0 = 2b \int_0^a \frac{E_0^2}{2Z_z}\sin^2\frac{\pi x}{a}\, dx = \frac{ab E_0^2}{2Z_z}$$

---

[3] S. A. Schelkunoff, "Impedance Concept in Wave Guides," *Quart. Appl. Math.*, **2**, 1–15 (April 1944).

This result, combined with (6), gives current and voltage.

$$V_0 = E_0 \left(\frac{abZ_0}{2Z_z}\right)^{\frac{1}{2}} \qquad I_0 = \left(\frac{E_0}{Z_z}\right)\left(\frac{baZ_z}{2Z_0}\right)^{\frac{1}{2}} \tag{9}$$

and, by comparison with (7) and (8), the remaining functions are

$$f(x) = \left(\frac{2Z_z}{abZ_0}\right)^{\frac{1}{2}} \sin \frac{\pi x}{a} \qquad g(x) = -\left(\frac{2Z_0}{baZ_z}\right)^{\frac{1}{2}} \sin \frac{\pi x}{a} \tag{10}$$

As noted above, Z_0 can be made unity in order to normalize automatically all subsequent impedances.

PROBLEMS

11·03a Apply the above points to determine unique definitions of voltage and current of a single TE_{01} mode in circular cylindrical guide.

11·03b Apply the suggested physical definitions discussed in the first part of this article for determining voltage and current of the TE_{10} rectangular mode, and compare with (9).   How is the product VI related to power flow in this case?

11·03c From the relations of Arts. 8·13 and 8·14, show that the functions $\bar{f}$ and $\bar{g}$ are always related as follows:

$$\bar{g}(x,y) = \left(\frac{Z_0}{Z_z}\right) \bar{a}_z \times \bar{f}(x,y)$$

Show that the results for the rectangular guide satisfy this vector relation.

11·04   THE NETWORK FORMULATION

Consider as an example a general microwave network with three wave guide terminals as defined in Art. 11·02 and pictured in Fig. 11·04.   It is assumed that each of the wave guides supports one propagating mode only, and reference planes are at first chosen far enough from junctions so that all higher order (cut-off) modes have died out.†   The forms of the propagating or dominant modes are assumed to be known, so that field· is completely specified at each reference plane by giving two amplitudes, such as the voltage and current defined in the preceding article.   It is clear that it is not possible to specify independently all voltages and currents of the network.   The network formulation will tell us how many of these may be specified to determine the problem, and how the remaining

† The reference planes can actually be chosen by convenience at any place, but transmission line measurements to determine the network should not be made in the region where local waves are of importance, nor will the calculations from the network give *total* fields in that region.

ones are related to those specified.   The following three points will be cited in casting the problem in network form.

A. Uniqueness.   It has been shown[4] that there is one and only one steady state solution of Maxwell's equations within a region if tangential electric field is specified over the closed boundary surrounding that region, or if tangential magnetic field is specified over the closed boundary, or if tangential electric field is specified over some of the boundary and tangential magnetic field over the remainder.

B. Linearity.   Maxwell's equations are linear for linear media (μ, ϵ, and σ not functions of field strength) so that relations between various field quantities will be linear ones.

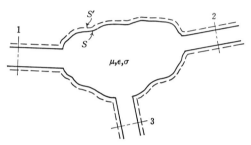

Fig. 11·04   General microwave network with three wave guide terminals.

C. Reciprocity.   An important reciprocity theorem will be given in some detail in the following article.   This too is of importance to the network formulation, as will be noted below.

In Fig. 11·04, consider the closed region bounded by the conducting surface S and reference planes 1, 2, 3.   If the conductor is first taken as perfectly conducting, the tangential electric field is known to be zero over the surface S.   Then, if voltages are given for each of the reference terminals, tangential electric fields are known there, and, by the statement of uniqueness given above, one and only one solution of Maxwell's equations is determined. $\bar{E}$ and $\bar{H}$ are then determinable for any point inside the region, so $\bar{H}$ may be computed at the reference planes so that the currents (amplitudes of the tangential magnetic field distributions) may be found there.   By the linearity argument, the relations must be linear ones and may therefore be written

$$I_1 = Y_{11}V_1 + Y_{12}V_2 + Y_{13}V_3$$

$$I_2 = Y_{21}V_1 + Y_{22}V_2 + Y_{23}V_3 \qquad (1)$$

$$I_3 = Y_{31}V_1 + Y_{32}V_2 + Y_{33}V_3$$

[4] J. A. Stratton, *Electromagnetic Theory*, McGraw-Hill, 1941, pp. 486–488.

Similarly, if currents are given for all reference planes, tangential magnetic fields are known there, and, with the known zero tangential electric field over S, the uniqueness argument again applies so that tangential electric fields and hence voltages could be found at the reference planes. Relations will again be linear.

$$V_1 = Z_{11}I_1 + Z_{12}I_2 + Z_{13}I_3$$

$$V_2 = Z_{21}I_1 + Z_{22}I_2 + Z_{23}I_3 \qquad (2)$$

$$V_3 = Z_{31}I_1 + Z_{32}I_2 + Z_{33}I_3$$

Forms (1) and (2) are identical with the forms that would be found relating voltages and currents at the terminals of a three-terminal pair lumped-element network. Here also the coefficients Y_{ij} and Z_{ij} are functions of frequency and are known as the admittance parameters and impedance parameters, respectively. As will be shown in the next article, application of the reciprocity theorem to a region without sources, and with proper definitions of voltages and currents, will require

$$Y_{ij} = Y_{ji} \qquad Z_{ij} = Z_{ji} \qquad (3)$$

Although the argument has been given for a perfectly conducting surface S, the forms above apply to an imperfectly conducting boundary also. A reasonably convincing way of seeing this comes from moving the bounding surface several depths of penetration within the conductor to S', Fig. 11·04. The electric field here is substantially zero, so that an imagined perfect conductor could be introduced along S' without changing the behavior of the system, and the argument would proceed as above. The conducting portion between S and S' will contribute to the parameters Y_{ij} or Z_{ij} since it is now part of the interior, and those coefficients will be complex because of the losses.

PROBLEMS

11·04a Supply the proof of the uniqueness theorem cited above. To do this, assume that there are two possible solutions, $(\bar{E}_1, \bar{H}_1)$ and $(\bar{E}_2, \bar{H}_2)$, and apply the Poynting theorem to the difference field $(\bar{E}_1 - \bar{E}_2, \bar{H}_1 - \bar{H}_2)$. Note Art. 3·03 for a typical uniqueness argument.

11·04b Suppose that an N-terminal pair has a load impedance Z_L connected to the terminals 1, and voltage generators connected to the other $N - 1$ terminals. Show that the following Thévenin equivalent circuits are valid *so far as calculations of effects in the load are concerned: A.* A voltage generator V_0 connected to Z_L through a series impedance Z_g. V_0 is the voltage produced at terminals 1 with these terminals open-circuited, and Z_g is the impedance seen looking into 1 with all voltage generators short-circuited (and any current generators open-circuited). B. A current generator I_0 connected across Z_L with internal admittance Y_g in parallel. I_0 is the current that would flow at terminals 1 if these terminals were shorted, and $Y_g = 1/Z_g$.

11·05 RECIPROCITY

A general form of the electromagnetic reciprocity theorem due to Lorentz states that fields $\bar{E}_a$, $\bar{H}_a$ and $\bar{E}_b$, $\bar{H}_b$ from two different sinusoidal sources a and b of the same frequency satisfy the condition

$$\nabla \cdot (\bar{E}_a \times \bar{H}_b - \bar{E}_b \times \bar{H}_a) = 0 \tag{1}$$

The medium should be isotropic but need not be homogeneous. Equation (1) is readily verified by expanding the indicated vector operations and substituting from Maxwell's equations in complex form. A volume integral of (1), with application of the divergence theorem, gives

$$\oint_S (\bar{E}_a \times \bar{H}_b - \bar{E}_b \times \bar{H}_a) \cdot \overline{dS} = 0 \tag{2}$$

The general reciprocity theorem may be applied to show the result 11·04(3) for a microwave network. Let us consider Fig. 11·04 with all reference planes but 1 and 2 closed by perfect conductors (shorted). Fields at 1 and 2 may be written [Eqs. 11·03(1)–(2)]

$$\bar{E}_{t1} = V_1 \bar{f}_1(x_1, y_1) \qquad \bar{H}_{t1} = I_1 \bar{g}_1(x_1, y_1) \tag{3}$$

$$\bar{E}_{t2} = V_2 \bar{f}_2(x_2, y_2) \qquad \bar{H}_{t2} = I_2 \bar{g}_2(x_2, y_2) \tag{4}$$

We assume also that *voltage and current are defined to have the same relation to power flow in both guides*, which requires that

$$\int_{S_1} (\bar{f}_1 \times \bar{g}_1) \cdot \overline{dS} = \int_{S_2} (\bar{f}_2 \times \bar{g}_2) \cdot \overline{dS} \tag{5}$$

Note that this is certainly satisfied if the second point of Art. 11·03 is adopted. The surface integral of (2) is zero along the conducting surfaces S of Fig. 11·04 (or S', if imperfectly conducting), and along the shorted planes. For planes 1 and 2, substitution of (3) and (4) gives

$$(V_{1a}I_{1b} - V_{1b}I_{1a}) \int_{S_1} (\bar{f}_1 \times \bar{g}_1) \cdot \overline{dS}$$
$$+ (V_{2a}I_{2b} - V_{2b}I_{2a}) \int_{S_2} (\bar{f}_2 \times \bar{g}_2) \cdot \overline{dS} = 0$$

If (5) is satisfied, this reduces to

$$V_{1a}I_{1b} - V_{1b}I_{1a} + V_{2a}I_{2b} - V_{2b}I_{2a} = 0$$

Relations between current and voltage are introduced from Eq. 11·04(1).

$$V_{1a}(Y_{11}V_{1b} + Y_{12}V_{2b}) - V_{1b}(Y_{11}V_{1a} + Y_{12}V_{2a})$$
$$+ V_{2a}(Y_{21}V_{1b} + Y_{22}V_{2b}) - V_{2b}(Y_{21}V_{1a} + Y_{22}V_{2a}) = 0$$

$$(V_{1a}V_{2b} - V_{1b}V_{2a})(Y_{12} - Y_{21}) = 0 \tag{6}$$

In this argument, the sources a and b are arbitrary so that the first factor need not be zero. Hence the second is zero.

$$Y_{21} = Y_{12} \tag{7}$$

The argument for the impedance coefficients may be supplied by placing "open circuits" at all but two of the terminals. This is done in the wave guides by placing a perfect short a quarter-wave in front of the reference planes. Moreover, since the numbering system is arbitrary, 1 and 2 may represent any two of the guides and the general relation 11·04(3) is valid.

In lumped-element networks, the reciprocity theorem is frequently stated: "The positions of an impedanceless generator and an impedanceless ammeter may be interchanged without affecting the ammeter reading." This also requires relations like 11·04(3) for the lumped-element network. The same wording may then be used if desired for the microwave network if one makes use of the extended definitions of voltage, current, and impedance.

PROBLEMS

11·05a　Verify (1) for the conditions stated.

11·05b　Complete the proof to show that $Z_{21} = Z_{12}$.

11·05c　For a lumped-element network, show that the statement of the reciprocity theorem in the last paragraph requires $Z_{21} = Z_{12}$. What similar word statement corresponds to $Y_{21} = Y_{12}$?

Wave Guide Junctions and Cavity Coupling

11·06　EQUIVALENT CIRCUITS FOR A TWO-TERMINAL PAIR

The microwave network with two wave guide terminals, as pictured in Fig. 11·02b, is of greatest importance since it includes the cases of discontinuities in a single guide or the coupling between two guides. Most filters, matching sections, phase-correction units, and many other components are of this type. There is a large body of literature on the lumped-element equivalents, frequently known as quadripoles, fourpoles, or four-terminal networks. The name two-terminal pair is preferred, since it stresses that voltage is meaningful for the input pair of terminals and for the output pair, but not for one terminal of the output and one of the input side.

From Art. 11·04, the equations for a two-terminal pair may be written in terms of either impedance or admittance coefficients.

$$V_1 = Z_{11}I_1 + Z_{12}I_2$$
$$V_2 = Z_{21}I_1 + Z_{22}I_2 \tag{1}$$

$$I_1 = Y_{11}V_1 + Y_{12}V_2$$
$$I_2 = Y_{21}V_1 + Y_{22}V_2 \tag{2}$$

Another convenient form expresses output quantities in terms of input quantities.

$$V_1 = \mathfrak{a}V_2 - \mathfrak{B}I_2$$
$$I_1 = \mathfrak{C}V_2 - \mathfrak{D}I_2 \tag{3}$$

The reciprocity relations (Art. 11·05) are expressed

$$Z_{21} = Z_{12} \qquad Y_{21} = Y_{12} \qquad \mathfrak{a}\mathfrak{D} - \mathfrak{B}\mathfrak{C} = 1 \tag{4}$$

A little algebra shows that the relations between the above forms for a network with reciprocity may be written

$$Y_{11} = \frac{Z_{22}}{\Delta(Z)} = \frac{\mathfrak{D}}{\mathfrak{B}}$$

$$Y_{12} = -\frac{Z_{12}}{\Delta(Z)} = -\frac{1}{\mathfrak{B}}$$

$$Y_{22} = \frac{Z_{11}}{\Delta(Z)} = \frac{\mathfrak{a}}{\mathfrak{B}} \tag{5}$$

$$\Delta(Z) = Z_{11}Z_{22} - Z_{12}{}^2$$

An infinite number of equivalent circuits may be derived which are equivalent to the above. Two important ones are the well-known T and π forms shown in Figs. 11·06a and b. They may be shown to be equivalent to (1) and (2), respectively, by setting down the circuit equations. Other interesting ones utilize ideal transformers and sections of transmission lines, two of which are pictured in Figs. 11·06c and d. These are of greatest importance for lossless microwave networks since the arbitrary reference planes in the input or output guides can be shifted in such a way that only an ideal transformer is left in the representation of Fig. 11·06c or an ideal transformer and shunt element in Fig. 11·06d. This will be explained in more detail when

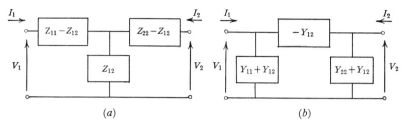

(a)   (b)

Fig. 11·06   (a) T equivalent circuit and (b) π equivalent circuit for a general two-terminal pair.

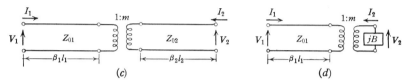

(c)   (d)

Fig. 11·06   (c) Equivalent circuit for a general two-terminal pair in terms of sections of transmission line and an ideal transformer.   (d) Similar equivalent circuit in terms of section of transmission line, transformer, and shunt element.

the measurement problem is discussed in the next article.   The quantites of Fig. 11·06c are related to the impedance parameters as follows:

$$\tan \beta_1 l_1 = \left[\frac{1 + c^2 - a^2 - b^2}{2(bc - a)}\right] \pm \sqrt{\left[\frac{1 + c^2 - a^2 - b^2}{2(bc - a)}\right]^2 + 1}$$

$$\tan \beta_2 l_2 = \frac{1 + a \tan \beta_1 l_1}{b \tan \beta_1 l_1 - c} \tag{6}$$

$$\frac{m^2 Z_{01}}{Z_{02}} = \frac{1 + a \tan \beta_1 l_1}{b + c \tan \beta_1 l_1}.$$

where $a = -\dfrac{jZ_{11}}{Z_{01}}$

$$b = \frac{Z_{11}Z_{22} - Z_{12}{}^2}{Z_{01}Z_{02}} \tag{7}$$

$$c = -j\frac{Z_{22}}{Z_{02}}$$

PROBLEM

11·06 Set up the relation between currents and voltages for Fig. 11·06d, and from these determine the impedance parameters in terms of Z_{01}, $\beta_1 l_1$, m and B.

11·07   DETERMINATION OF JUNCTION PARAMETERS BY MEASUREMENT

In certain cases where the geometrical configuration is relatively simple, techniques are available for the calculation of the parameters representing a microwave junction, and some of these will be discussed in later articles.   For many configurations actually used, the boundaries are not simple enough for such a calculation, and it is desirable to find the pertinent parameters by measurement.   The situation is not different from that encountered at low frequencies where one finds values of inductance, capacitance, and mutuals perhaps more often by measurement than by calculation from the known dimensions of the elements.   We wish to describe here some of the approaches to measurement for microwave elements.   There is an infinite number of

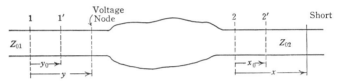

Fig. 11·07a   General two-terminal pair.

possible ways, as there is an infinite number of possible equivalent circuits.   The few approaches that can be discussed here are useful in themselves, and will suggest others.   The examples given will be for a two-terminal pair, as in the junction represented in Fig. 11·07a.

Most often the parameters of a junction are desired for determination of the impedance transfer through it, though the information may be expressed alternatively in terms of reflection coefficient or standing wave data.   If so, it is logical to determine the unknown parameters by impedance transformation measurements also.   Since there are three parameters in a two-terminal pair satisfying reciprocity, it is necessary to make three measurements of input impedance corresponding to known load impedances for each frequency of interest.   The load and input impedances might be measured, for example, by means of standing wave data on output and input guides, respectively (Chapter 1).   A particularly simple way is to place a good short at different positions along the output guide to produce the known load impedances.   These are then reactive (neglecting guide losses), and may be computed from a knowledge of the short positions with respect to the reference plane so that standing wave equipment on the output side is not needed.

From Eq. 11·06(1), load impedance $Z_L = -V_2/I_2$ produces input impedance $Z_i = V_1/I_1$ as follows:

$$Z_i = Z_{11} - Z_{12}{}^2/(Z_{22} + Z_L) \tag{1}$$

Algebraic elimination from three equations of the form of (1) shows that, if Z_{L1} produces Z_{i1}, Z_{L2} produces Z_{i2}, and Z_{L3} produces Z_{i3}, the impedance parameters are

$$Z_{11} = \frac{(Z_{i1} - Z_{i3})(Z_{i1}Z_{L1} - Z_{i2}Z_{L2}) - (Z_{i1} - Z_{i2})(Z_{i1}Z_{L1} - Z_{i3}Z_{L3})}{(Z_{i1} - Z_{i3})(Z_{L1} - Z_{L2}) - (Z_{i1} - Z_{i2})(Z_{L1} - Z_{L3})}$$

$$(2)$$

$$Z_{22} = \frac{(Z_{i1}Z_{L1} - Z_{i2}Z_{L2}) - Z_{11}(Z_{L1} - Z_{L2})}{(Z_{i2} - Z_{i1})} \tag{3}$$

$$Z_{12}{}^2 = (Z_{11} - Z_{ip})(Z_{22} + Z_{Lp}) \qquad p = 1, 2, 3 \tag{4}$$

If the network is lossless and if purely reactive terminations are used, input impedances will also be pure reactances, and Z's may be replaced by X's everywhere in the above equations. The form of (2) to (4) may also be shown to be valid for determination of admittance parameters Y_{11}, Y_{12}, and Y_{22} when pairs of input-output admittances $Y_{L1}Y_{i1}$, $Y_{L2}Y_{i2}$, $Y_{L3}Y_{i3}$ are measured. Z's are then replaced by Y's in the above. It is always a good idea to check for numerical errors by computing Z_{12} from all three pairs of data [$p = 1$, 2, 3, in (4)], though this checks nothing about the correctness of measurements. Note also that the sign of Z_{12} cannot be determined from impedance transformation measurements alone, since it does not enter into (1). For the same reason, it is of no interest if results are to be used only for impedance transformations by the network. For some purposes it may be necessary to know this sign, and, if so, an arrangement for measuring relative phase between input and output must be added. For simple configurations, the sign may sometimes be deduced by physical reasoning.

For regions that may be considered lossless, the representation of Fig. 11·06c is especially useful. This follows because a shift of the input reference plane from 1 to 1′ (Fig. 11·07a) by a distance $\beta_1 y_0 = \pi - \beta_1 l_1$ and a shift of output reference plane from 2 to 2′ by $\beta_2 x_0 = \pi - \beta_2 l_2$ gives as the equivalent circuit an ideal transformer with half-wave lines at input and output. But the latter give unity impedance transformation and so may be ignored, leaving only the ideal transformer representing the region between 2′ and 1′. A load impedance referred to 2′ is multiplied simply by $(1/m)^2$ to give the input impedance referred to 1′. A little thought shows that the parameters of this representation may be determined as follows: The output guide is perfectly terminated ($Z_L = Z_{02}$); the position of the minimum impedance point on the input guide corresponds to 1′, and the value of this minimum impedance gives m^2,

$$m^2 = \frac{Z_{02}}{Z_{\min}} \tag{5}$$

Similarly, if the network is reversed, the input guide terminated, and like measurements made on the output guide, the reference plane 2′ is obtained as well as a check on m^2.

An alternative procedure to the above has advantages in some cases. Weissfloch[5] has shown that for a lossless junction a plot of position of voltage minimum on the input guide as a function of position of a short on the output guide has the "S curve" form shown in Fig. 11·07b.

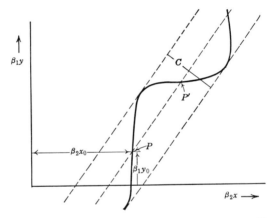

Fig. 11·07b Typical S curve obtained by measurement on Fig. 11.07a.

$\beta_1 y$ is the electrical distance of the minimum from the originally selected reference 1, and $\beta_2 x$ is the electrical distance of the short from 2. The form of the equation is

$$\tan \beta_1(y - y_0) = (Z_{02}/m^2 Z_{01}) \tan \beta_2(x - x_0) \tag{6}$$

The new reference planes 1′ and 2′ are given by the positions x_0, y_0 of the maximum slope of the S curve, point P of Fig. 11·07b. The value of this maximum slope is $Z_{02}/m^2 Z_{01}$. The turns ratio may also be determined in terms of the distance C between the envelope tangents.

$$m^2 Z_{01}/Z_{02} = \tan^2 (\pi/4 - \sqrt{2}\, C/4) \tag{7}$$

For the measurement, many points of input minimum are then measured as a short is moved along the output, and the curve determined. There is the advantage that the consistency of measurement and

[5] A. Weissfloch, *Hochfrequenztechnik u. Electroakustik*, **60**, 67–73 (Sept. 1942).

discrepancies caused by neglected losses may be told more easily than in the methods first described where only a few points are measured.

PROBLEM

11·07   If one selects the point of minimum slope, P' of Fig. 11·07b to determine x_0, y_0 and equates this slope to $Z_{02}/m^2 Z_{01}$, a second correct representation results. Show that transformations calculated by the latter are equivalent to those from the representation described above.

11·08   TRANSMISSION PARAMETERS AND CASCADED NETWORKS

The previous discussions have been given in terms of the voltages, currents, and impedances defined for microwave networks. It was noted that these definitions are not unique. Moreover, the imped-

Fig. 11·08a Incident and reflected wave convention.

ances are usually obtained by interpreting measured values of standing wave ratio or reflection coefficient. It is then evident that for some purposes it will be more convenient and direct to formulate the problem directly in terms of waves, so that the two independent quantities required for each wave guide terminal are an incident and a reflected wave instead of a voltage and a current. Several different formulations are possible here also, and by way of example the one in terms of transmission parameters will be described for a two-terminal pair.

Suppose that incident and reflected waves on the input guide are given in magnitude and phase at the chosen reference plane by $V_1{}^+$ and $V_1{}^-$ (Fig. 11·08a). Similarly, incident and reflected waves, looking into the terminals 2 are $V_2{}^+$ and $V_2{}^-$ By arguments similar to those previously given, we know that linear relations must relate input and output quantities.

$$
\begin{aligned}
V_2{}^- &= T_{11} V_1{}^+ + T_{12} V_1{}^- \\
V_2{}^+ &= T_{21} V_1{}^+ + T_{22} V_1{}^-
\end{aligned}
\tag{1}
$$

The parameters T_{11}, etc., are the *transmission parameters*, and are of course related to the impedance, admittance, or $\mathcal{ABCD}$ parameters already described. For example, since

$$
V_1 = V_1{}^+ + V_1{}^- \quad \text{and} \quad I_1 = \frac{V_1{}^+ - V_1{}^-}{Z_{01}}
\tag{2}
$$

and, similarly for V_2, I_2, comparison with Eq. 11·06(1) reveals

$$T_{11} = \frac{Z_{21}}{2Z_{01}} + \frac{Z_{02}}{2Z_{12}} \left(1 - \frac{Z_{11}}{Z_{01}}\right)\left(\frac{Z_{22}}{Z_{02}} - 1\right)$$

$$T_{12} = -\frac{Z_{21}}{2Z_{01}} + \frac{Z_{02}}{2Z_{12}} \left(1 + \frac{Z_{11}}{Z_{01}}\right)\left(\frac{Z_{22}}{Z_{02}} - 1\right)$$

$$T_{21} = \frac{Z_{21}}{2Z_{01}} + \frac{Z_{02}}{2Z_{12}} \left(1 - \frac{Z_{11}}{Z_{01}}\right)\left(\frac{Z_{22}}{Z_{02}} + 1\right) \tag{3}$$

$$T_{22} = -\frac{Z_{21}}{2Z_{01}} + \frac{Z_{02}}{2Z_{12}} \left(1 + \frac{Z_{11}}{Z_{01}}\right)\left(\frac{Z_{22}}{Z_{02}} + 1\right)$$

For a network satisfying reciprocity, it follows that

$$T_{11}T_{22} - T_{12}T_{21} = \frac{Z_{02}}{Z_{01}} \tag{4}$$

Then in this formulation, if reflection coefficients in input and output guides are defined as follows,

$$\rho_1 = \frac{V_1{}^-}{V_1{}^+} \qquad \rho_2 = \frac{V_2{}^+}{V_2{}^-} \tag{5}$$

the two are related by

$$\rho_1 = -\frac{T_{21} - T_{11}\rho_2}{T_{22} - T_{12}\rho_2} \tag{6}$$

In addition to the fact that wave quantities are here expressed directly, the greatest advantage of the present form comes from cascaded networks, as indicated in Fig. 11·08b. For, if the input ter-

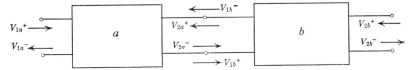

Fig. 11·08b Two cascaded two-terminal pairs.

minals of b are connected to the output terminals of a, $V_{2a}{}^-$ must equal $V_{1b}{}^+$ and $V_{2a}{}^+$ must equal $V_{1b}{}^-$. By elimination between two sets of equations of form (1), it may then be shown that the parameters of the composite network representing the combination of the two are

$$T_{11} = T_{11}{}^b T_{11}{}^a + T_{12}{}^b T_{21}{}^a$$

$$T_{12} = T_{11}{}^b T_{12}{}^a + T_{12}{}^b T_{22}{}^a$$

$$T_{21} = T_{21}{}^b T_{11}{}^a + T_{22}{}^b T_{21}{}^a \tag{7}$$

$$T_{22} = T_{21}{}^b T_{12}{}^a + T_{22}{}^b T_{22}{}^a$$

We do not have space for discussion of the matrix notation, which is the most convenient tool for handling such network relations,[6] but it is worth noting for those familiar with the notation that (7) expresses the fact that the transmission matrix for the over-all network is just the product of the matrices for the cascaded components,

$$\begin{bmatrix} T_{11}T_{12} \\ T_{21}T_{22} \end{bmatrix} = \begin{bmatrix} T_{11}{}^{b}T_{12}{}^{b} \\ T_{21}{}^{b}T_{22}{}^{b} \end{bmatrix} \begin{bmatrix} T_{11}{}^{a}T_{12}{}^{a} \\ T_{21}{}^{a}T_{22}{}^{a} \end{bmatrix} \tag{8}$$

where

$$\begin{bmatrix} V_2{}^{-} \\ V_2{}^{+} \end{bmatrix} = \begin{bmatrix} T_{11}T_{12} \\ T_{21}T_{22} \end{bmatrix} \begin{bmatrix} V_1{}^{+} \\ V_1{}^{-} \end{bmatrix}$$

In particular, if m like networks are cascaded, the transmission matrix of the over-all combination, T_{11}, etc., is just the mth power of the matrix of the individual networks, $T_{11}{}^{0}$, and the important Cayley-Hamilton theorem in the theory of matrices shows that the parameters are as follows, with reciprocity and $Z_{01} = Z_{02}$.

$$T_{11} = [\mu_1{}^{m}(\mu_2 - T_{11}{}^{0}) - \mu_2{}^{m}(\mu_1 - T_{11}{}^{0})]/(\mu_2 - \mu_1)$$

$$T_{12} = (\mu_2{}^{m} - \mu_1{}^{m})T_{12}{}^{0}/(\mu_2 - \mu_1)$$

$$T_{21} = (\mu_2{}^{m} - \mu_1{}^{m})T_{21}{}^{0}/(\mu_2 - \mu_1) \tag{9}$$

$$T_{22} = [\mu_1{}^{m}(\mu_2 - T_{22}{}^{0}) - \mu_2{}^{m}(\mu_1 - T_{22}{}^{0})]/(\mu_2 - \mu_1)$$

where　　$2\mu_{1,2} = [T_{11}{}^{0} + T_{22}{}^{0}] \pm \sqrt{(T_{11}{}^{0} + T_{22}{}^{0})^2 - 4}$

The transmission matrix parameters for several simple elements are given in Table 11·08. Note in particular the simplicity of the transformation along a section of uniform line or guide.

TABLE 11·08

TRANSMISSION PARAMETERS FOR SIMPLE ELEMENTS

	Transmission Line	Ideal Transformer	Series Element	Shunt Element
T_{11}	$e^{-\gamma l}$	$\frac{1}{2}(1/n + n)$	$1 - Z/2$	$1 - Y/2$
T_{12}	0	$\frac{1}{2}(1/n - n)$	$Z/2$	$-Y/2$
T_{21}	0	$\frac{1}{2}(1/n - n)$	$-Z/2$	$Y/2$
T_{22}	$e^{\gamma l}$	$\frac{1}{2}(1/n + n)$	$1 + Z/2$	$1 + Y/2$

[6] E. A. Guillemin, *The Mathematics of Circuit Analysis*, Wiley, 1949.

PROBLEMS

11·08a Show that the $\mathfrak{ABCD}$ constants (Art. 11·06) of cascaded networks are found from those of the individual networks by formulas exactly similar to those for the transmission parameters.

11·08b By a repeated use of (7), find the over-all transmission parameters when three networks, a, b, and c, are cascaded. Simplify for the case in which the middle one is a uniform transmission line.

11·08c Consider a disk-loaded wave guide in which disks which are equivalent to a per unit shunt susceptance B are placed an electrical distance βl apart in the guide. Write the transmission parameters for one section formed by a guide $\beta l/2$, the shunt element, and another length of guide $\beta l/2$. Write the parameters for N such sections.

11·08d For a lossless two-terminal pair considered as a filter, show that the pass-band occurs when

$$(T_{11} + T_{22})^2 > 4$$

Apply the above to find the filter characteristics in Prob. c.

11·08e A dielectric window is formed by two adjacent dielectric slabs, ϵ_1 of length l_1, and ϵ_2 of length l_2, placed with air (ϵ_0) on each side. Find the transmission parameters for the over-all unit. (Note that it is convenient to define all lines with unity Z_0, representing impedance changes by ideal transformers.) If there is only an outward propagating wave on the right, determine the conditions for no reflections to the left.

11·09 PROPERTIES OF A ONE-TERMINAL PAIR

Let us consider a closed region with one wave guide terminal (or, in the language of networks, a one-terminal pair), as in the cavity sketched in Fig. 11·02a. A reference plane 1 is selected far enough from the junction so that only the dominant mode in the guide is of importance, and we apply a form of the complex Poynting theorem,

$$\int_S (\bar{E} \times \bar{H}^*) \cdot \overline{dS} = (j\omega\epsilon - \sigma) \int_V \bar{E} \cdot \bar{E}^* \, dV - j\omega\mu \int_V \bar{H} \cdot \bar{H}^* \, dV \quad (1)$$

The surface integral on the left has a contribution only over S_1, for if the conductor is perfect, tangential $\bar{E}$ is zero over S, and if not, a surface S' is selected within the conductor where all fields are substantially zero, as in Art. 11·04. We select definitions of voltage and current so that the product gives power flow. Then

$$-VI^* = (j\omega - \sigma) \int_V \bar{E} \cdot \bar{E}^* \, dV - j\omega\mu \int_V \bar{H} \cdot \bar{H}^* \, dV$$

The minus sign enters because we are concerned with power flow into the network, and the integral of (1) utilizes an outward normal.

Defining voltage as the product of current and an input impedance Z,

$$-ZII^* = -2W_L + 4j\omega U_E - 4j\omega U_H$$

or
$$Z = R + jX = \frac{2W_L + 4j\omega(U_H - U_E)}{II^*} \tag{2}$$

where W_L is the average power loss in the region, U_E and U_H are *average* stored energies in electric and magnetic fields, respectively. Similarly for input admittance Y,

$$Y = G + jB = \frac{2W_L + 4j\omega(U_E - U_H)}{VV^*} \tag{3}$$

Certain properties of these impedance and admittance functions will be discussed below. Note that the comments apply to the function $Z_{ii}(\omega)$ of a general microwave network (Art. 11·04), since this would be the input impedance of a two-terminal pair formed by shorting all but the ith terminal. Similarly, the theorems apply to Y_{ii} and to some other combinations of the impedance or admittance functions.

   A. *Simple Properties of the Impedance Function.* A study of (2) shows several simple results expected from physical reasoning. Impedance is purely imaginary (reactive) if power loss is zero. When power loss is finite, it must be positive, so the real (resistance) part of Z is always positive. If stored electric and magnetic average energies are equal, reactance is zero and the network is said to be resonant. If average magnetic energy is greater than electric, the reactance is positive (inductive), and if electric energy is the greater, reactance is negative (capacitive). Similar results can be deduced for the admittance function.

   B. *Foster's Reactance Theorem for a Lossless Network.* In a lossless two-terminal pair where impedance is reactive, jX, the rate of change of reactance with angular frequency may be shown to be

$$\frac{dX}{d\omega} = \frac{4(U_E + U_H)}{II^*} \tag{4}$$

This result is derived by means of a variational form of the Poynting theorem (see Prob. 11·09b). It is evident that the average stored energy $(U_E + U_H)$ is positive, and II^* is positive, so the slope of the reactance versus frequency curve of a lossless two-terminal pair must always be positive. The reactance curve must go through a succession of zeros and poles as sketched in Fig. 11·09. Similarly, the susceptance versus frequency curve of a lossless two-terminal pair will be similar in form to Fig. 11·09, having always positive slope given by

$$\frac{dB}{d\omega} = \frac{4(U_E + U_H)}{VV^*} \tag{5}$$

These important results were first shown by Foster[7] for lumped-element networks. Some consequences in terms of equivalent circuits will be discussed in a later article.

C. Relations between Real and Imaginary Parts of Impedance Function. Certain relations between the resistance and reactance functions of frequency have been pointed out[8] for lumped-element networks.

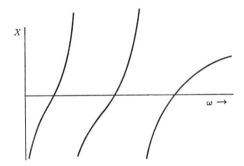

Fig. 11·09   Typical form of reactance versus frequency for a lossless one-terminal pair.

They have been derived from functional properties of the complex impedance considered a function of a complex "frequency" $\alpha + j\omega$, and, since it may be shown that these functional properties follow also from (2) or (3), the same forms are valid for the more general microwave networks. Typical relations are

$$R(\omega) = -\frac{2}{\pi} \int_0^\infty \frac{\eta X(\eta)\, d\eta}{\eta^2 - \omega^2} + R_0 \tag{6}$$

$$X(\omega) = \frac{2\omega}{\pi} \int_0^\infty \frac{R(\eta)\, d\eta}{\eta^2 - \omega^2} + X_0(\omega) \tag{7}$$

R_0 is a constant resistance, and $X_0(\omega)$ denotes the reactance function of any *lossless* two-terminal pair. A study of the complex network

[7] R. M. Foster, *Bell Sys. Tech. J.*, **3**, 259–267 (April 1924).

[8] H. W. Bode, *Network Analysis and Feedback Amplifier Design*, Van Nostrand, 1945.

functions is very similar to the study of potential fields by complex functions (Chapter 3), and in fact potential analogues such as electrolytic tanks[9] have provided most useful tools for the study of network functions.

PROBLEMS

11·09a Making use of Maxwell's equations in complex form, derive the form (1) of the complex Poynting theorem.

11·09b Suppose that a small variation $\delta\omega$ in frequency produces variations $\delta\bar{E}$ and $\delta\bar{H}$ in fields. Starting from Maxwell's equations, show that

$$\int_S (\bar{E} \times \delta\bar{H} - \delta\bar{E} \times \bar{H}) \cdot \overline{dS} = j\delta\omega \int_V (\mu H^2 - \epsilon E^2)\, dV$$

11·09c Apply the result of Prob. b to derive (4) for a lossless network with one wave guide input.

11·09d Consider a simple shunt circuit of R and C. Find resistance as a function of frequency, $R(\omega)$, and by substituting in (7) derive $X(\omega)$ and compare with the known reactance function of this simple circuit.

11·10 EQUIVALENT CIRCUITS FOR A CAVITY WITH SINGLE INPUT

In most of our discussion concerning the parameters that may be used to represent networks, it has been inferred that the frequency characteristics would be found by measurement, or perhaps calculated for certain simple specific cases. In Art. 11·09, however, we stated some things about the frequency characteristics of the one-terminal-pair class of networks, of which the cavity resonator with single input is an important example. We can carry this further, deriving detailed equivalent circuits with lumped inductances, capacitances, and resistances which will yield the frequency characteristics of the given network. This possibility comes from the fact that the frequency characteristics of a lossless network are completely specified once the poles (infinities of impedance or antiresonances) are stated with certain information about energy storage at those frequencies. Thus, if we construct lumped-element reactive networks having these same resonances and energy storages, we are assured that the response will be the same as for the original system at all frequencies. The extension to lossy networks is approximate, but, as in other cases where we have met low-loss (high-Q) networks, the approximations are excellent. Here, as elsewhere, we find that there are many possible representations. We shall study a few of the most common ones.

[9] W. W. Hansen and O. C. Lundstrom, *Proc. I.R.E.*, **33**, 528–534 (Aug. 1945).

A. Lossless Cavity. Let us begin by consideration of a lossless region. The input impedance is then purely reactive, and Eqs. 11·09(2) and (3) become

$$Z(\omega) = jX(\omega) = \frac{4j\omega(U_H - U_E)}{II^*} = \frac{VV^*}{4j\omega(U_E - U_H)} \tag{1}$$

If average stored energies in electric and magnetic fields are equal, X is zero (resonance) provided that current is finite at the input terminals, and is infinite (antiresonance) provided that voltage is finite at the input terminals. Because of the proof that the slope $dX/d\omega$ is positive, it follows that all zeros and poles must be simple (first order), resulting in the form of curve shown in Fig. 11·09. It is also important to note that the function $X(\omega)$, if extended mathematically to negative frequencies by the definition (1), must be an odd function of frequency. An important consequence coming from the theory of functions of a complex variable states that the function $X(\omega)$ can be expanded in a series of "partial fractions" about the poles, provided that the following summation is convergent.

$$X(\omega) = \sum_{n=1}^{\infty} \left[\frac{a_n}{\omega - \omega_n} + \frac{a_{-n}}{\omega - \omega_{-n}} \right] + \frac{a_0}{\omega} + f(\omega) \tag{2}$$

a_0/ω represents the pole at zero frequency, if any is present, and $f(\omega)$ is an arbitrary entire function (one with no singularities in the finite plane). Since the function is odd, $\omega_{-n} = -\omega_n$ and $a_n = a_{-n}$. Moreover, $f(\omega)$ can have only odd powers of ω, and, since it must behave at most like a simple pole at infinity, it is known to be proportional to the first power of ω. With these specializations, (2) becomes

$$X(\omega) = \sum_{n=1}^{\infty} \frac{2\omega a_n}{\omega^2 - \omega_n^2} + \frac{a_0}{\omega} + \omega L_\infty \tag{3}$$

In the above, a_n is known as the residue of the pole ω_n. It may be obtained in terms of the slope of the *susceptance* curve, which can in turn be related to energy storage through Eq. 11·09(5). For in the vicinity of ω_n, the nth term of (3) predominates and

$$B(\omega) = -\frac{1}{X(\omega)} \approx -\frac{\omega^2 - \omega_n^2}{2\omega a_n}$$

Differentiation shows that

$$\left. \frac{dB}{d\omega} \right|_{\omega = \omega_n} = -\frac{1}{a_n}$$

Then, utilizing Eq. 11·09(5),

$$a_n = - \frac{1}{(dB/d\omega)_{\omega=\omega_n}} = - \left[\frac{VV^*}{4(U_E + U_H)} \right]_{\omega=\omega_n} \tag{4}$$

The form of (3) suggests an equivalent circuit consisting of anti-resonant LC circuits added in series as shown in Fig. 11·10a, for the nth component of this circuit yields a reactance

$$X_n = - \frac{1}{[\omega C_n - 1/\omega L_n]} = - \frac{\omega/C_n}{\omega^2 - 1/L_n C_n}$$

By comparing with the above,

$$a_n = - \frac{1}{2C_n} \qquad \omega_n{}^2 = \frac{1}{L_n C_n} \qquad a_0 = - \frac{1}{C_0} \tag{5}$$

or
$$C_n = - \frac{1}{2a_n} \qquad L_n = - \frac{2a_n}{\omega_n{}^2} \qquad C_0 = - \frac{1}{a_0} \tag{6}$$

This representation, known as the first canonical form of Foster,[10] is then applicable to any lossless one-terminal pair for which the series in (3) is convergent. To find the circuit, we need to know the anti-resonances, with energy storage quantities at those frequencies, both of which quantities were studied for cavity resonators in the preceding chapter. The difficult part comes from the fact that the energy must be referred to the voltage in the input guide, see Eq. (4), and this requires some specific knowledge of the coupling network. The general representation may be useful for interpretation of measurements and for forming general conclusions even when this coupling problem cannot be solved.

B. *Effect of Losses.* The study of losses for practical cavity resonators in the last chapter was concerned with the calculation of a quality factor Q which expressed for a given mode the ratio of energy stored to energy lost per radian. For low-loss cavities, it might be expected that the equivalent circuit of Fig. 11·10a would be modified by adding a shunt conductance to each antiresonant element, as shown in Fig. 11·10b. The value of a given conductance G_n would be adjusted so that the Q calculated from the nth antiresonant circuit would agree with the known Q_n of the mode which it represents. That is,

$$G_n = \frac{\omega_n C_n}{Q_n} \tag{7}$$

[10] R. M. Foster, *Bell Sys. Tech. J.*, **3**, 259–267 (April 1924).

Justification for this procedure can be supplied by the theory of functions by making approximations appropriate to poles which are at a complex frequency near, but not exactly on, the real frequency axis.

If one accepts this modification of the lumped-circuit equivalent to

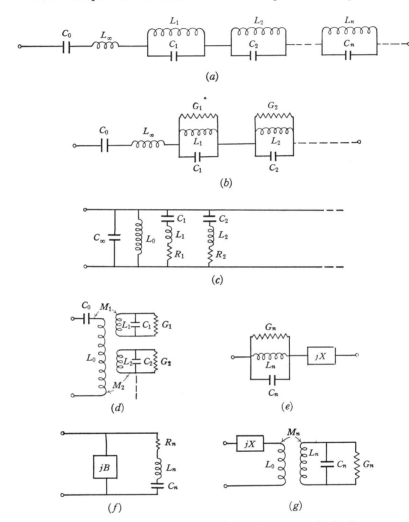

Fig. 11·10   Various equivalent circuits for one-terminal pairs.

account for losses, it is clear that the Q of a cavity, determined from energy calculations, is also useful for interpreting the frequency characteristics in the same manner as for a lumped circuit. This fact was stated without justification in Art. 10·06.

C. Second Foster Form. An expansion of the susceptance function about its poles yields a form similar to (3).

$$B(\omega) = \sum_{m=1}^{\infty} \frac{2\omega b_m}{\omega^2 - \omega_m^2} + \frac{b_0}{\omega} + \omega C_\infty \tag{8}$$

Where the residues b_m are given by

$$b_m = - \frac{1}{[dX/d\omega]_{\omega=\omega_m}} = - \left[\frac{II^*}{4(U_E + U_H)} \right]_{\omega=\omega_m} \tag{9}$$

When the series is convergent, this has the equivalent circuit of Fig. 11·10c (known as the second Foster canonical form) with

$$L_m = - \frac{1}{2b_m} \qquad C_m = - \frac{2b_m}{\omega_m^2} \qquad L_0 = - \frac{1}{b_0} \tag{10}$$

Figure 11·10c also shows series resistances added to each resonant circuit to account for small losses, and, as in the discussion above, these are selected to give the known Q for each mode.

$$R_m = \frac{\omega_m L_m}{Q_m} \tag{11}$$

D. Other Equivalent Circuits. Schelkunoff[11] has shown that other equivalent circuits may be derived by adding convergence factors to the series (3) or (8). These factors are necessary if the original series do not converge, the Mittag-Leffler theorem from the theory of functions telling how they may be formed to insure convergence. They may also be desirable in other cases where the original series converge, but do so slowly. For example, Schelkunoff has shown that the form with one term of the convergence factor is

$$X(\omega) = \sum_{n=1}^{\infty} 2\omega a_n \left[\frac{1}{\omega^2 - \omega_n^2} + \frac{1}{\omega_n^2} \right] + \frac{a_0}{\omega} + \omega L_0 \tag{12}$$

Note that, in addition to the convergence factor added in the series, the series inductance term has been modified, and inspection of (12) shows that L_0 is the entire series inductance of the circuit in the limit of zero frequency. The physical explanation of the above procedure is then that this low-frequency inductance has been taken out as a separate term rather than being summed from its contributions from the various modes. It is reasonable to expect that this would often

[11] S. A. Schelkunoff, *Proc. I.R.E.*, **32**, 83–90 (Feb. 1944).

help convergence. A specific example for loop coupling to a cavity will be given in a later article.

The equivalent circuit of Fig. 11·10d gives the form of reactance function (12) (loss elements G_n being neglected at first), provided that

$$\frac{M_n{}^2}{L_n} = -\frac{2a_n}{\omega_n{}^2} \qquad \frac{1}{L_nC_n} = \omega_n{}^2 \qquad (13)$$

Here one imagines the input guide coupled to the various natural modes of the resonator through transformers which gives a very natural way of looking at a problem of loop coupling to a cavity. Note, however, that one cannot determine the elements of the circuit uniquely since there are three elements, L_n, C_n, M_n, to be determined from the two basic quantities a_n and ω_n for each mode. One of the three may be chosen arbitrarily, perhaps by reference to physical feeling, but any choice will give a circuit which properly duplicates the behavior with respect to impedance at input terminals. Small losses are again accounted for by adding conductances G_n, calculated from form (7), to the circuits as shown in Fig. 11·10d.

E. Approximations in the Vicinity of a Single Mode. Finally, we note that when we are interested in operation in the vicinity of the natural frequency for one mode, other resonances being well separated, the dominant factor will be the one representing that mode. Other terms will vary only slowly with frequency over this range and may be lumped together as a constant impedance or admittance (predominantly reactive). The equivalent circuits of Figs. 11·10b, c, d then reduce to the simplified representations of Figs. 11·10e, f, g, respectively. This is an important practical case, enabling one to use simplified lumped-element circuit analysis for the study of cavity resonator coupling problems.

PROBLEM

11·10 Modify the form for $B(\omega)$, Eq. (8), to correspond to the form (12) with a convergence factor added, and find an equivalent circuit representation. *Hint:* Change the form of Fig. 11·10d by using T networks to replace the transformers, and look for the dual of this circuit.

11·11 EXAMPLES OF CAVITY EQUIVALENT CIRCUITS

Two examples will be given to clarify the calculation of element values in the equivalent circuits of the preceding article. It should be stressed again that the difficult part comes in solving enough of the coupling problem to refer the energy quantities within the resonator to defined voltage or current in the guide. In the first example, a uniform line is considered so that energy can be expressed directly in terms of the input current. In the second example, a reasonable approximation to the coupling problem can be made.

A. Open-Circuited Transmission Line. Let us consider a lossless open-circuited line of length l, inductance L per unit length, and capacitance C per unit length (Fig. 11·11a). We shall derive the second Foster form, Fig. 11·10c, starting from Eq. 11·10(8). For this calculation we need the natural modes having infinite susceptance at the

(a) (b)

Fig. 11·11 (a) Open-circuited ideal line and (b) equivalent circuit.

input. Current is then a maximum at the input, zero at $z = l$, and length must be an odd multiple of a quarter-wavelength.

$$I_m(z) = I_{0m} \cos \omega_m z \sqrt{LC} \tag{1}$$

$$\omega_m = \frac{2\pi}{\lambda_m \sqrt{LC}} = \frac{2\pi m}{4l \sqrt{LC}} \quad \text{(m odd)} \tag{2}$$

The sum of *average* U_E and U_H is equal to the total energy stored at resonance, which may be computed as maximum energy in magnetic fields.

$$U_E + U_H = (U_U)_{\max} = \int_0^l \frac{L I_{0m}^2}{2} \cos^2 \omega_m z \sqrt{LC} \, dz = \frac{l L I_{0m}^2}{4} \tag{3}$$

Substitution in Eq. 11·10(9) gives the residue for the mth mode,

$$b_m = -\frac{I_{0m}^2}{4(U_E + U_H)} = -\frac{1}{Ll}$$

Inductance and capacitance for the mth circuit are found from Eq. 11·10(10).

$$L_m = -\frac{1}{2b_m} = \frac{Ll}{2} \tag{4}$$

$$C_m = -\frac{2b_m}{\omega_m^2} = \frac{8Cl}{\pi^2 m^2} \tag{5}$$

This leads to the equivalent circuit of Fig. 11·11b, which is valid for all frequencies provided the equation for $B(\omega)$ obtained from Eq. 11·10(8) is convergent. The series is convergent in this case, and in fact can be shown to be equivalent to the following closed form.

$$B(\omega) = -\sum_{m \text{ odd}} \frac{2\omega}{Ll[\omega^2 - m^2\pi^2/4l^2LC]} = \sqrt{\frac{C}{L}} \tan \omega l \sqrt{LC} \quad (6)$$

The last expression can be recognized as the input susceptance for an open-circuited ideal line obtained from simple transmission line theory, as it should be.

B. Loop-Coupled Cavity. For a second example, we shall return to the loop-coupled cylindrical cavity discussed in Art. 10·12 from an energy point of view. In particular, we shall concern ourselves with behavior in the vicinity of resonance for the simple TM_{010} mode, all other resonances being well separated, so that one of the approximate forms of Fig. 11·10e, f, or g is appropriate. The form of Fig. 11·10g, arising from Eq. 11·10(12), is particularly useful because the self-inductance of the loop is separated out, and the remaining series may be thought of as representing more nearly the behavior of the unperturbed cavity. From the physical point of view, it is a natural equivalent circuit, since we picture the input line as being coupled to the cavity mode through a mutual which represents the loop.

The voltage at the loop terminals (computed with no self-inductance drop, as is appropriate for the zero current of antiresonance) is found approximately by taking magnetic field of the unperturbed mode flowing through the small loop of area S, as in Art. 10·12.

$$V = j\omega\mu HS \quad (7)$$

Energy stored in the mode from Eq. 10·08(5) may be written

$$(U_E + U_H) = (U_H)_{\max} = \tfrac{1}{2}\pi\mu dH^2a^2 \quad (8)$$

Substitution in Eq. 11·10(4) gives the residue for the mode.

$$a_1 = -\frac{VV^*}{4(U_E + U_H)_{w=w_1}} = -\frac{\omega_1^2\mu^2S^2}{2\pi a^2d} \quad (9)$$

Resonant frequency and Q are known from the analysis of Art. 10·08.

$$\omega_1 = p_{01}/a \sqrt{\mu\epsilon} \quad (10)$$

$$Q_1 = \frac{\eta p_{01}d}{2R_s(d + a)} \quad (11)$$

Here we meet the indeterminacy of the form selected, for we have three quantities, a_1, ω_1, Q_1, to determine four quantities, M_1, L_1, C_1, and G_1. As pointed out before, one of the four may be selected arbitrarily and the same input impedance will result. One choice is to leave the conductance G_1 as computed earlier from power loss and voltage across the center. This makes sense, for example, when an electron beam is to be shot across the center, in which case a beam admittance, calculated on the same basis, can simply be placed in parallel with G_1 in the equivalent circuit. Taking the value of G from Eq. 10·08(8),

$$G_1 = \frac{R_s}{\eta^2} \frac{2\pi a(d + a)}{d^2} J_1{}^2(p_{01}) \tag{12}$$

Application of Eqs. 11·10(7) and (13) then yields

$$C_1 = \frac{Q_1 G_1}{\omega_1} = J_1{}^2(p_{01}) \left(\frac{\pi a^2 \epsilon}{d}\right) \tag{13}$$

$$L_1 = \frac{1}{\omega_1{}^2 C_1} = \frac{\mu d}{\pi p_{01}{}^2 J_1{}^2(p_{01})} \tag{14}$$

$$M_1 = \left[-\frac{2a_1 L_1}{\omega_1{}^2}\right]^{1/2} = \frac{\mu S}{\pi a p_{01} J_1(p_{01})} \tag{15}$$

Input impedance, computed at resonance for the unperturbed mode $(\omega^2 L_1 C_1 = 1)$, can then be shown to yield the same result as was found in Eq. 10·12(4) by energy considerations.

$$Z = j\omega L_0 + \frac{\omega^2 M^2}{j\omega L_1 + 1/(G_1 + j\omega C_1)} \approx j\omega L_0 + \frac{(\omega \mu S)^2}{2\pi a R_s(d + a)} \tag{16}$$

PROBLEMS

11·11a Derive the equivalent circuit of Fig. 11.10a for a shorted length l of ideal line. Show that the series form for $X(\omega)$ converges to the usual expression for reactance of a shorted ideal line.

11·11b Derive the first Foster form for the open line and the second Foster form for the shorted line. Show that the series forms converge to proper expressions for reactance and susceptance, given that

$$\cot x = \frac{1}{x} + \sum_{n=1}^{\infty} \frac{2x}{x^2 + n^2\pi^2}$$

11·11c Show that the capacitance C_1 derived for the loop-coupled cavity is that which would be obtained by referring energy stored in electric fields to voltage at the center of the cavity. Compare the mutual M_1 to that which would be derived by referring induced voltage in the loop to total vertical current in the cavity wall.

11·11d   Derive an equivalent circuit similar to Fig. 11·11d for coupling to the TM_{010} cylindrical mode by a small probe of length s extending axially from the top at the center.   Assume that induced voltage is probe length times electric field of the unperturbed mode.

11·12   CAVITY WITH TWO OR MORE COUPLED GUIDES

In the equivalent circuit of Fig. 11·10d for a cavity coupled to a single guide, the input is coupled to each of the normal modes of the

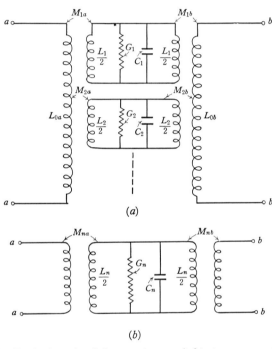

(a)

(b)

Fig. 11·12   (a) Equivalent circuit for a cavity coupled to two wave guide terminals, and (b) approximation in the vicinity of one resonant mode.

resonator by means of a mutual inductance associated with each mode.   It seems logical that this picture could be extended simply to yield one possible equivalent circuit for two couplings to the cavity by considering the two independently, supplying mutuals from each guide to the normal modes as in Fig. 11·12a.   Element values are computed for each as in Art. 11·10.   Justification for this procedure has been supplied by Schelkunoff[12] from complex function theory, and by Slater[13] by consideration of the normal modes.   It is evident

[12] S. A. Schelkunoff, *Proc. I.R.E.*, **32**, 83–90 (Feb. 1944).
[13] J. C. Slater, *Microwave Electronics*, Van Nostrand, 1950.

that this procedure assumes that direct coupling between input and output guides is negligible, though, if not, it might be accounted for by adding an additional mutual between input and output in the equivalent circuit. In most cases, the direct coupling is small, since such transducers usually have filter applications and coupling through the highly resonant cavity mode is the desired one.

In the vicinity of a resonance, the circuit simplifies to that of Fig. 11·12b. Note that, with an input guide and an output guide, we have a two-terminal pair, such as was discussed previously. The treatment here has added more information concerning the frequency characteristics of the parameters representing the network.

Extension of Figs. 11·12a, b to more than two inputs is obvious.

PROBLEMS

11·12a   Suppose that two well-separated loops, each of area 0.5 cm^2, are coupled to the TM_{010} cylindrical mode as for one loop in Art. 11·11. Draw the equivalent circuit, and calculate element values (except L_0) for an air-filled cavity resonant at 4000 mc/sec with $h = 1$ cm, $R_s = 0.02$.

11·12b   The Q of a cavity mode is sometimes measured by finding the curve of transmission versus frequency between two guides coupled to the cavity. Using the values of Prob. a, calculate from the equivalent circuit the transmission at resonance and at a frequency $f_0(1 + 1/Q)$, $Q \gg 1$, and compare with the ratio $\sqrt{2}:1$. Take both lines of 50 ohms impedance and assume self-inductances of loops tuned out.

Simple Discontinuities and Analytical Approaches

11·13   SIMPLE DISCONTINUITIES IN LINES AND GUIDES

For certain simple types of wave guide junctions where the types of higher order waves excited can be determined, continuity conditions can be applied and an exact or approximate equivalent circuit obtained by analysis. Among these are certain planar discontinuities such as diaphragms or changes of height in parallel-plane transmission lines, coaxial lines, and rectangular wave guides. The equivalent circuits here are particularly simple, consisting most often of shunt elements at the plane of the discontinuity, as will be shown.

As a first example, we consider the parallel-plane transmission line of Fig. 11·13a which changes in height from b to a at $z = 0$. In an approximate transmission line treatment, it is common to consider this as two lines of different characteristic impedance joined at $z = 0$. However, such a treatment considers only the *TEM* or principal transmission-line waves which have E_y and H_x with no variations in y. The perfect conductor portion from (2) to (3) requires that $E_y = 0$ here. If there were only principal waves, E_y would then have to be zero everywhere at $z = 0$ because of the lack of variations with y in the principal wave. There could then be no energy passing into the second line A regardless of its termination since the Poynting vector would then also be zero across the entire plane, $z = 0$. Physical reasoning shows that the above situation does not occur generally but only in such special cases as when line A is shorted a half wave from the discontinuity. The difficulty is met by the higher order waves which are excited at the discontinuity, so that E_y in the principal wave is not zero at $z = 0$, but *total* E_y (sum of principal and higher order components) is zero from (2) to (3) but not from (1) to (2). For the example of Fig. 11·13a the higher order waves excited are *TM* waves, since E_y, E_z, and H_x alone are required in the fringing fields. For spacings between planes not comparable to wave length, these waves are far below cut-off, so that their fields are localized in the region of the discontinuity. They may consequently be called *local* waves.

To show that the effect of the local waves on the transmission of the principal waves may be expressed as a lumped admittance placed at $z = 0$ in the transmission line equivalent circuit, as in Fig. 11·13a, consider that current at any value of z may be expressed as one part $I_0(z)$ from the principal wave and a contribution $I'(z)$ from all local waves.

$$I(z) = I_0(z) + I'(z) \tag{1}$$

Now *total* current must be continuous at the discontinuity $z = 0$, but current in the principal wave need not be, since the difference in principal wave currents may be made up by the local wave currents.

$$I_{0A}(0) + I_A'(0) = I_{0B}(0) + I_B'(0)$$

or $$I_{0B}(0) - I_{0A}(0) = I_A'(0) - I_B'(0) \tag{2}$$

However, total voltage in the line as defined from $- \int \bar{E} \cdot \overline{dl}$ between planes is only that in the principal wave, since a study of the local waves shows that their contribution is zero.

$$V(z) = V_0(z)$$

Continuity of total voltage across the discontinuity $z = 0$ then requires continuity of voltage in the principal wave.

$$V_{0A}(0) = V_{0B}(0) = V_0(0) \tag{3}$$

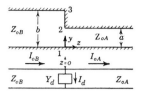

Fig. 11·13a   Step discontinuity in parallel-plane transmission line and exact equivalent circuit.

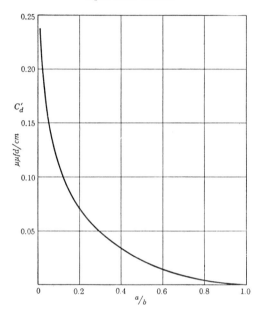

Fig. 11·13b   Curve of discontinuity capacitance for Fig. 11·13a.

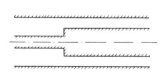

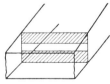

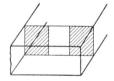

Fig. 11·13c   Typical discontinuity in coaxial line.

Fig. 11·13d   Capaci-
tive diaphragm in rec-
tangular guide.

Fig. 11·13e   Induc-
tive diaphragm in rec-
tangular guide.

Now, if an equivalent circuit is drawn *for the principal wave only,* its continuity of voltage but discontinuity of current may be accounted for by a lumped *discontinuity admittance* at $z = 0$, the current through this admittance being

$$I_{0B}(0) - I_{0A}(0) = I_d = Y_d V_0(0)$$

Or, from (2),

$$Y_d = \frac{I_A'(0) - I_B'(0)}{V_0(0)} \tag{4}$$

The complete analysis[14] reveals that, when local wave values are substituted in (4), numerical values of Y_d may be calculated which are independent of terminations so long as these are far enough removed from the discontinuity not to couple to the local wave fields. For Fig. 11·13a, with dimensions small compared with wavelength, this admittance turns out to be a pure capacitance, values of which are plotted versus step ratio a/b in Fig. 11·13b, in micromicrofarads per centimeter width of the plane. Analysis of a coaxial line discontinuity[15] such as Fig. 11·13c shows that a good approximation to discontinuity capacitance for this problem may be found by multiplying values from Fig. 11·13b by outer circumference. (If the step is in the outer conductor, values from Fig. 11·13b are multiplied by inner circumference.)

A diaphragm in a rectangular wave guide such as Fig. 11·13d excites both TM and TE modes (though with no E_x), but as energy is predominantly electric below cut-off, such a discontinuity is capacitive. An approximate value of the per unit susceptance is

$$\frac{B}{Y_0} = \frac{4b}{\lambda_g} \ln \csc \frac{\pi d}{2b} \tag{5}$$

When the diaphragm extends from the sides of the guide, as in Fig. 11·13e, the local waves excited are TE waves, energy is predominantly magnetic, and the discontinuity is said to be inductive. Approximate value of susceptance is

$$\frac{B}{Y_0} = -\frac{\lambda_g}{a} \cot^2 \frac{\pi d}{2a} \tag{6}$$

The above results and many others may be found in useful handbooks devoted to microwave elements.[16, 17]

[14] J. R. Whinnery and H. W. Jamieson, "Equivalent Circuits for Discontinuities in Transmission Lines," *Proc. I.R.E.*, **32**, 98–114 (Feb. 1944).

[15] Whinnery, Jamieson, and Robbins, "Coaxial Line Discontinuities," *Proc. I.R.E.*, **32**, 695–709 (Nov. 1944).

[16] T. Moreno, *Microwave Transmission Design Data*, McGraw-Hill, 1948.

[17] N. Marcuvitz, *Waveguide Handbook*, M.I.T. Rad. Lab. Series, Vol. 10 McGraw-Hill, 1951.

PROBLEMS

11·13a Determine the form of the proper local waves in the example of Fig. 11·13a. Show that voltage between planes, $-\int \bar{E} \cdot \overline{dl}$, is zero for each of these.

11·13b Imagine a parallel-plane transmission line with two steps such as the one in Fig. 11·13a. The first is from spacing b to spacing a; the second is removed from the first by a half-wavelength and is from spacing a back to b. The line to the right of b is perfectly terminated by its characteristic impedance, Z_{0B}. If it were not for the discontinuity capacitances, the line to the left of the first discontinuity would also be perfectly terminated. Calculate reflection coefficient in this line, taking into account the discontinuity capacitances from Fig. 11·13b. Take $a = 1$ cm, $b = 2$ cm, $\lambda = 12$ cm.

11·13c Using Fig. 11·13b, calculate an approximate discontinuity capacitance for the coaxial line of Fig. 11·13c. Take $r_1 = 0.5$ cm, $r_2 = 1$ cm, $r_3 = 1.2$ cm.

11·13d A rectangular wave guide of dimensions 0.900 by 0.400 inch propagating the TE_{10} mode at 9000 mc/sec feeds a horn. Standing wave ratio in the guide is measured as 2.5 with a voltage minimum 0.55 cm in front of the horn entrance. Find the dimensions and placing of a capacitive diaphragm in order to produce a match for waves approaching from the left.

11·13e Repeat Prob. d, using an inductive diaphragm.

11·14 THEORETICAL APPROACHES

Many of the powerful methods of boundary value problems have been applied to the analysis of wave guide junctions and discontinuities, resulting in equivalent circuits whose elements may be found by calculation. Some brief comments will be given concerning these. In principle, the problem is straightforward. Solutions of Maxwell's equations, most often expressed as a series of wave guide modes, are to be found for each of the basic regions. Amplitudes are then found by applying continuity of tangential electric and magnetic fields over surfaces separating the several regions. The obtaining of the equivalent circuit from the solution then proceeds somewhat as was illustrated for the simple shunt discontinuity in the preceding article.

A. Quasi-Static Methods. Often the region of the discontinuity is small compared with a wavelength. In such cases, useful approximations may be obtained by referring to the static field solutions of a similarly shaped region. This follows since the retardation terms may be neglected if the region is small compared with wavelength, and solutions of Laplace's equation then approximate wave solutions (in regard to space variations). As an example, consider the step in the parallel-plane line of Fig. 11·13a. The electrostatic solution of this problem is known (Art. 3·14), and a "fringing" or "excess" capacitance may be found as the excess of the total capacitance between electrodes over that which would exist if field lines were straight across.   Letting $\alpha = a/b$, this is

$$C_d = \frac{\epsilon}{\pi}\left[\left(\frac{\alpha^2+1}{\alpha}\right)\ln\left(\frac{1+\alpha}{1-\alpha}\right) - 2\ln\left(\frac{4\alpha}{1-\alpha^2}\right)\right]$$

$$\text{farads/meter width} \qquad (1)$$

Since the TEM mode has field lines straight across, it is clear that the above result must be consistent with the discontinuity capacitance defined in the preceding article when the distance between planes is small compared with wavelength.   The result plotted in Fig. 11·13b, although calculated by the series method to be described next, does agree with (1).   The series method, however, gives results also when the discontinuity region is not negligible compared with wavelength.

For other regions, such as the right-angle bend in a parallel-plane line shown in Fig. 11·14a, reasoning leads us to include an inductance which may be computed approximately from the static fields, as well as an excess capacitance term as in the preceding example.   The latter may be divided, leading to the approximate π equivalent circuit shown in Fig. 11·14b.

B. Series Methods.   The most obvious starting point in the exact solution of a problem such as the step in the parallel-plane line of Fig. 11·13a is the expression of field as a series of the wave guide modes. Thus utilizing previous solutions for the TEM and TM modes (TE modes are not excited by this discontinuity) for a parallel-plane line, the electric field E_y and the magnetic field H_x in the plane of the discontinuity may be written

$$E_A(y,0) = A_0 + \sum_m A_m \cos\frac{m\pi y}{a} \qquad (2)$$

$$H_A(y,0) = Y_{0a}A_0 + \sum_m Y_{ma}A_m \cos\frac{m\pi y}{a} \qquad (3)$$

$$E_B(y,0) = B_0 + \sum_n B_n \cos\frac{n\pi y}{b} \qquad (4)$$

$$H_B(y,0) = Y_{0b}B_0 + \sum_n Y_{nb}B_n \cos\frac{n\pi y}{b} \qquad (5)$$

$$Y_{ma} = -\frac{j\omega\epsilon a}{m\pi\sqrt{1-(2a/m\lambda)^2}} \qquad Y_{nb} = \frac{j\omega\epsilon b}{n\pi\sqrt{1-(2b/n\lambda)^2}} \qquad (6)$$

The first pair expresses fields in terms of the modes of the region to the right, and the second pair in terms of modes for the left-hand region. Y_{0a} and Y_{0b} are the wave admittances for the TEM modes in the two regions, and these depend upon the terminations of the regions. If we think of (4) as an expression for electric field in the

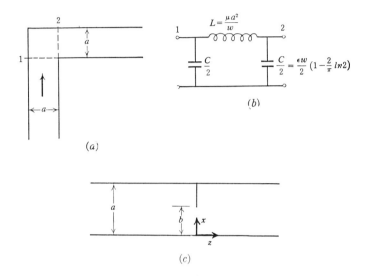

Fig. 11·14 (a) Corner discontinuity in parallel-plane line. (b) Approximate equivalent circuit valid if corner is small compared with wavelength. w is width normal to the paper. (c) Diaphragm in parallel-plane transmission line.

aperture as a Fourier series over the interval b, the usual formulas for Fourier coefficients give us

$$B_0 = \frac{1}{b} \int_0^a E(y,0) \, dy = \frac{a}{b} A_0 \tag{7}$$

$$B_n = \frac{2}{b} \int_0^a E(y,0) \cos \frac{n\pi y}{b} \, dy$$

$$= \frac{2}{n\pi} \sin \frac{n\pi a}{b} \left\{ A_0 + \frac{n^2 a^2}{b^2} \sum_m \frac{(-1)^m A_m}{m^2[(na/mb)^2 - 1]} \right\} \tag{8}$$

The interval in the integral is taken only from 0 to a, since electric field must be zero in the B region from a to b. The evaluations on the right are obtained by substituting (2) for the electric field from 0 to a. Similarly, (3) may be considered a Fourier expansion of magnetic field in the aperture over the interval a, and its coefficients may be found as follows.

$$Y_{0a}A_0 = \frac{1}{a} \int_0^a H(y,0)\, dy = Y_{0b}B_0 + \sum_n \frac{b}{n\pi a} Y_{nb}B_n \sin \frac{n\pi a}{b} \quad (9)$$

$$Y_{ma}A_m = \frac{2}{a} \int_0^a H(y,0) \cos \frac{m\pi y}{a}\, dy$$

$$= \sum_n Y_{nb}B_n \frac{2na}{m^2\pi b} \frac{(-1)^m \sin (n\pi a/b)}{[(na/mb)^2 - 1]} \quad (10)$$

The evaluations here were made by substituting the value from (5) in the integral. A study of (7) and (9) shows that voltage is continuous and current in the TEM wave discontinuous, as explained in the last article. The value of the discontinuity admittance is given as a series which contains the wave amplitudes A_m. Substitution between (8) and (10) yields an infinite number of simultaneous equations in the infinite number of amplitudes A_m. These are usually solved approximately by retaining only a finite number, and, by utilizing these results, a good value of the discontinuity admittance may be found. The method would converge slowly and so would not be of much use were it not for certain functions evaluated by Hahn,[18] which amount to the evaluation of the slowly converging parts of the summations such that the remaining series are rapidly converging. The method and tabulated functions given by Hahn are applicable to a wide variety of problems, in both rectangular and other coordinate systems.

    C. Integral Equation and Variational Formulations. If the formulas for coefficients B_0 and B_n from (7) and (8) are substituted back in (4), an integral equation in $E(y,0)$ is obtained, since it appears both inside and outside of the integral. It is possible to solve this directly in some cases. It may also be possible to proceed from the integral equation to a variational formulation. Thus, for the diaphragm in a parallel-plane line, Fig. 11·14c, the shunt susceptance representing the discontinuity can be put in the form

$$B = \frac{4\omega\epsilon}{\pi} \frac{\sum_n \left[\left(\frac{n\pi}{b}\right)^2 - \left(\frac{2\pi}{\lambda}\right)^2 \right]^{-\frac{1}{2}}}{\left[\int_0^a E(0,y)\, dy \right]^2} \left[\int_0^a E(0,y) \cos \frac{n\pi y}{b}\, dy \right]^2 \quad (11)$$

[18] W. C. Hahn, "A New Method for the Calculation of Cavity Resonators," *J. Appl. Phys.*, **12**, 62–68 (Jan. 1941).

This expression gives the exact value of susceptance if the exact field in the aperture is known from a solution of the integral equation, but it is even more useful in giving approximate values of susceptance by assuming reasonable forms for $E(0,y)$. It is a variational expression in that any approximation to the field yields a larger value for susceptance than the exact one. The assumption of a uniform field in (11), for example, gives for the diaphragm

$$B < \frac{4\omega\epsilon}{\pi^3} \sum_{n=1}^{\infty} \frac{\sin^2 (n\pi a/b)}{n^3 (a/b)^2 \sqrt{1 - (2b/n\lambda)^2}} \tag{12}$$

The series is rapidly convergent and may be used for calculation, though it may also be expressed in terms of the functions tabulated by Hahn.[18]

Schwinger[19] applied many of the powerful methods of mathematical physics to wave guide junctions, and in particular developed in detail the integral equation and variational formulations mentioned briefly above.

D. Relaxation Methods. When other analytical methods fail, one can always resort to numerical solutions of the differential equations subject to the boundary condition of the conductor. These methods are very tedious, even when rapid calculators are available, and may not be practical if field varies in all three dimensions. So, if the method is to be used, it is important to adopt a schedule of calculations which converges to the correct answer as quickly as possible. Southwell[20] has given the schedules for such rapidly converging calculations, called relaxation methods.

[19] N. Marcuvitz and J. Schwinger, *J. Appl. Phys.*, **22**, 806–819 (1951), and in unpublished work.

[20] R. V. Southwell, *Relaxation Methods in Theoretical Physics*, Oxford, 1946; *Relaxation Methods in Engineering Science*, Oxford, 1940.

12 RADIATION

12·01 THE PROBLEMS OF RADIATION ENGINEERING

Radiation of electromagnetic energy, to an engineer, is important in at least two cases. (1) It may be a desired end result if energy is to be transferred from a high-frequency transmitter to electromagnetic waves in space by means of some antenna system. (2) It may be a leakage phenomenon, adding undesired losses to an imperfectly shielded circuit or transmission line or to a cavity resonator with holes.

In order to perform an intelligent job of engineering in either of the above radiation problems, it is first desirable to have a good physical picture of radiation. In this picture radiation is not a mysterious and unknown link between transmitter and receiver, but a phenomenon following naturally from the excellent pictures of wave propagation, reflection, and excitation built up from familiarity with transmission lines and wave guides. It is desirable that this physical picture be concrete enough to give qualitative answers to specific questions that may arise in either of the above roles of radiation. It is, of course, also necessary to have methods available for obtaining quantitative design information about the amount of radiation and the effects on the radiating system. If radiation is the desired product, several or all of the following problems may arise in design of the radiating system:

1. The field strength at a known distance and in a known direction from the radiator excited by a given voltage may be desired. Often the relative field strength versus direction, i.e., the directivity pattern, is a sufficient answer for this problem.

2. The total power radiated from the antenna structure when excited by a known voltage or current may be desired. (The answer may often be expressed in terms of a radiation resistance.)

3. The input impedance of the radiator to the exciting voltage or current may be desired.

4. The resonant frequency and band width of the radiator may be ·

required. Band width questions are often answered if impedance versus frequency is known; however, it may be necessary sometimes to know the change in the radiation pattern with frequency.

5. The power dissipated in ohmic losses in the radiator, as compared to the power radiated, may be desired. The result may be expressed as a radiation efficiency.

6. The value of maximum gradient along the antenna may be required if corona difficulties are important.

If radiation is the leakage product, the problems are not essentially different, although a knowledge of power lost by radiation is usually sufficient. To assure ourselves that it is only in magnitude of importance that this differs from radiation as a desired product, it may be recalled that it is in the role of a leakage phenomenon that radiation was met previously. In Chapter 5, for the rigorous study of circuits, an energy loss term appeared which was not accounted for by ohmic dissipation, this term being the radiated energy. The term becomes more important as the circuit is made large compared with wavelength, suggesting the obvious conclusion that a well-designed antenna system is simply a circuit made purposely large compared with wavelength to increase the importance of radiation. Also, in the study of transmission lines, it was pointed out that the waves excited in space by the end effects of a transmission line, required for matching to these end effects, may take energy from the guided wave of the line. This too is radiation, and to obtain it as a major effect it is necessary only to accentuate these end effects or to match more closely to the waves in space. This latter point of view is excellent, and one that will be developed further.

An exact solution of the problem from Maxwell's equations would at once yield the answer to all the above problems. The approach to such an exact solution is straightforward, since it requires a solution of Maxwell's equations subject to the boundary conditions of the antenna system, which was the approach applied successfully to waveguiding systems and cavity resonators in previous chapters. For the antenna, the exciting source and the region at infinity must be included in the boundary conditions, and sometimes the effect of ground or couplings to adjacent antennas cannot be ignored. Because of these complications, but mostly because of the geometrical forms of practical antennas, the details of the exact solution cannot be carried through except in a few simple cases, such as for spherical, spheroidal, and conical antennas. Some of these solutions, which are of greatest usefulness in shedding light on the problems of input impedance and antenna gradients, will be discussed in a later part of the chapter.

However, approximate approaches to others of the problems are needed as well.

Fortunately, successful approximations to the problems of directivity and power radiated, which are two of the most important, have been available for many years. This comes about because fields at a great distance from the antenna are relatively insensitive to small changes in current distribution over the radiating system (at least for most practical antennas), so with a little experience some good approximations to current distribution can be made. Fields at any point can then be calculated in terms of these currents, and the Poynting theorem enables one to find the power radiated. This technique will be one of the first to be demonstrated in this chapter. By an extension, we shall find that it is also possible to make similar calculations when the field can be assumed over the aperture of an antenna. The assumed currents may also be used to compute a power loss in the conductors of known conductivity, so that an approximation to radiation efficiency may be had if desired, though for many practical antennas a sufficient answer is that power loss is negligible compared with that radiated.

12·02   SOME TYPES OF PRACTICAL RADIATING SYSTEMS

In order to give point to comments and analyses which follow, let us look for a moment at some of the typical systems that have been used as radiators. No attempt will be made to provide complete discussions of operation here, since the remainder of the chapter will be devoted to more thorough analyses of some of these systems. Nor does the list cover all types of radiators. The ones given are chosen as examples to make clearer the discussions of principles in sections to follow.

A. *"Dipole" Antennas.* Among the most common radiators is the dipole, which consists of a straight conductor (often a thin wire or circular cylinder of larger diameter) broken at some point where it is excited by a voltage derived from a transmission line, wave guide, or directly from a generator (Fig. 12·02a). In most cases, the exciting source is at the center, yielding a symmetrical dipole, though asymmetrical dipoles are used as well. If the arms are very short compared with wavelength, it is known as an infinitesimal dipole, or *Hertzian dipole.* Resonant dipoles, and especially the half-wave dipole with $2l$ approximately equal to a half-wavelength, are more common.

B. *Loop Antennas.* Radiation from a loop of wire excited by a generator has been discussed in Chapter 5, and such loop antennas are useful radiators, though often they have many turns (Fig. 12·02b). The field from a small loop is much like that from the small dipole

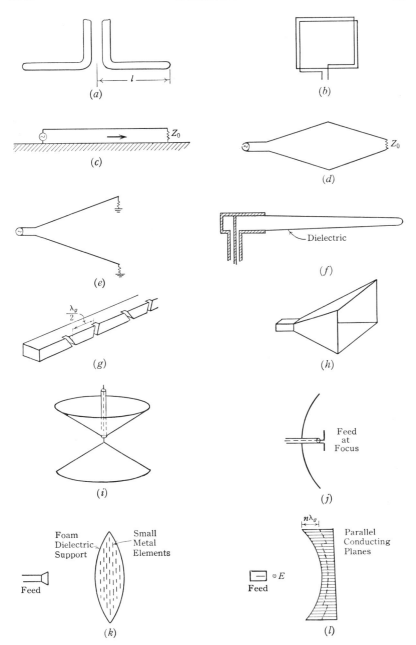

Fig. 12·02   Typical antennas.   (a) dipole, (b) loop, (c) Beverage, (d) rhombic,
(e) vee, (f) dielectric rod, (g) slot array, (h) pyramidal horn, (i) biconical horn,
(j) parabolic reflector, (k) artificial dielectric (l) metal lens.

of A, with electric and magnetic fields interchanged. Such a small loop is sometimes known for this reason as a *magnetic dipole*.

C. Thin-Wire "Wave" Antennas. In a wave antenna, the idea is to produce a traveling wave in one direction with a velocity of propagation about equal to the velocity of light, so that waves in space may be excited strongly in this direction as compared with other directions, yielding a high directivity. The Beverage wave antenna has a straight wire over earth, forming a transmission line which is terminated at the far end (Fig. 12·02c), and gives rise to the traveling wave as described above. A rhombic antenna is similar, but usually utilizes two conductors (Fig. 12·02d), and these are spread out at the center to give greater radiation. The V antenna (Fig. 12·02e) is like one half of the rhombic, though often it is used as a resonant antenna without the terminating resistances and is then more like the resonant dipoles of A.

D. Dielectric Rod Antennas. A length of dielectric rod (Fig. 12·02f) may be used as a radiator by exciting in it a propagating wave (Art. 9·09) of proper form. The dielectric rod wave guide, unlike the metal pipe guide, has fields outside the dielectric so that there may be radiation. If the rod is made long enough so that most of the energy is lost by radiation and dissipation before it reaches the end, the forward wave is the important one and there is then "end-fire" action, as in the wave antennas described above.

E. Slot Antennas. Although a wave guide or cavity completely closed by a perfect conductor cannot radiate, there will in general be radiation if holes or slots are provided in the walls. Fields excited in the slot from the interior in turn excite waves in space which may act to carry energy away. Such radiation is apt to be small if the holes are small compared with wavelength, and in such cases the radiation might be important as leakage in decreasing the Q of a cavity, but would not be of much use in constructing an antenna. However, if the slots are large, or if they are resonant even though small in some dimension, the fields may be built up to such an extent that radiation is appreciable and the slot becomes a useful antenna. In fact, as we shall see, the resonant half-wave slot has many similarities to a half-wave dipole, though electric and magnetic fields are interchanged. Antennas of the slot type are particularly useful in aircraft and ships where flush mounting is required. An example of the use of slots in a rectangular wave guide to form a "leaky wave guide" array is shown in Fig. 12·02g.

F. Electromagnetic Horns. The slot radiator is one of a class in which fields in an aperture excite waves in space. It is natural to attempt to shape the transition between the wave guide and the aperture to get a better match between the waves in the guide and the waves in space, particularly if broad band operation is desired because then resonant slots are undesirable.   The approach is much as in the acoustic horns used for sound.   Typical examples of resulting electromagnetic horns are the pyramidal horn of Fig. 12·02h and the biconical horn of Fig. 12·02i.   It is easy to achieve large apertures in these horns, which, as will be seen, give possibilities of obtaining very directive radiation patterns.

G. Arrays of Elements.   In a few applications it is desirable to radiate as uniformly as possible in all directions.   More often there are particular directions in which one wishes to concentrate the radiation. In these cases radiation in undesired directions at least wastes power, and may actually ruin performance, as in the case of returned echoes from side lobes in radar applications.   One approach to the directing of energy in desired directions is that of using a number of elements positioned and phased so that energy from the several elements adds in the desired directions, but cancels in undesired directions.   The example of the slot array has been given in Fig. 12·02g, and other examples will appear later.

H. Reflectors.   As an alternative to the use of arrays for directing energy, shaped reflectors may be used to reflect in desired directions the waves from primary sources such as dipoles, slots, or small horns. One of the simplest examples is the parabolic reflector with primary feed at the focus (Fig. 12·02j).   Geometrical optics will predict an exactly parallel beam from such a reflector if an infinitesimal source is placed at the focus.   Physical optics (or an electromagnetic-wave analysis) shows that there is always some spreading of the beam, and this decreases as aperture size is made greater.   To produce a beam width of 1 degree, an aperture of about 140 wavelengths is required.

I. Lens Directors.   Another approach to the directing of radiation, also suggested by optics, is that of using a lens system with the primary feed at the focus.   Although straightforward dielectric lenses of something like polystyrene may be used, they must be many wavelengths in diameter, and so are heavy and unwieldy at microwave frequencies. Two ingenious variations have consequently been used.   In one, artificial dielectrics have been constructed by embedding small metal disks, balls, or rods in a foam dielectric or other frame (Fig. 12·02k). These are excited by an electromagnetic field and respond much as the molecular dipoles of actual dielectrics.   Effective dielectric constants of around 225 have been obtained with a usefully light structure.[1]   Another variation was arrived at by looking at the lens from

---

[1] W. E. Kock, "Metallic Delay Lens," *Bell Sys. Tech. J.*, **27**, 58–82 (Jan. 1948).

the point of view of physical optics, where it is viewed as a means of delaying the various rays by just the right amount so that the over-all wave front comes from the lens with the phase of a plane wave. In a "metal-lens antenna," instead of delaying various parts of the rays by using a dielectric, sections of parallel-plane wave guide are used which we know to have a phase velocity *greater* than that of the plane wave. The outer parts of this lens are consequently longer than the center parts, giving a contour the opposite of that of a typical dielectric lens, as sketched in Fig. 12·02*l*. Since whole wavelengths contribute nothing from this point of view, these may be cut out, giving the typical stepped construction of practical metal-lens antennas[2] indicated by the dotted lines of the figure.

PROBLEM

12·02 For a dielectric or artificial dielectric lens of dielectric constant ϵ, set down the condition for total phase shift from the focus to a plane in front of the lens (Fig. 12·02*k*) to be a constant for all rays, taking the velocity of light in space over the path in air, and the velocity of a uniform plane wave in dielectric as applying to the dielectric part of the path. Similarly, set down the condition for the metal-lens antenna of Fig. 12·02*l*, writing phase velocity in the wave guide portion in terms of free-space wavelength and plate spacing *d*. In comparing the two expressions, what could be said to be the effective dielectric constant of the metal-lens antenna?

12·03 PHYSICAL PICTURES OF RADIATION

Radiation was first met in Chapter 5, when we found that a circuit large compared with wavelength has the possibility of losing energy because induced electric fields from time-varying currents and charges of the circuit may shift in phase as a result of the retardation over the circuit, and may have components in phase with current. This picture provides one approach to radiation. It is useful in analyzing antennas of the circuit type, such as the loop antenna of Fig. 12·02*b*, and it tells us something about why efficient radiators are usually large compared with wavelength, but it is unsatisfying in that it says nothing directly about the radiated field.

From a somewhat different point of view, we may think of the fields in space produced by currents and charges on the antenna as sources. We know that in a complete system there must at any instant be equal numbers of positive and negative charges, and, if these were static, fields at a great distance from the positive and negative sources would practically cancel. For example, the electrostatic field from a small

[2] W. E. Kock, "Metal Lens Antenna," *Proc. I.R.E.*, **34**, 828–836 (Nov. 1946).

dipole dies off as the inverse cube of distance. When the distance between positive and negative sources becomes comparable with wavelength, the phase shift or retardation in going the extra distance may keep the effects from canceling, and in fact will cause them to add up in one direction if distance between plus and minus sources is a half-wavelength. This picture also suggests why practical antennas are comparable with wavelength in size. It tells us something about the fields, and is especially useful in qualitative thinking about arrays (G of Art. 12·02).

In a manner somewhat similar to the above, we may think of the fields or wave fronts over the aperture of an antenna system as being the sources of radiation, and again add up the effects with proper phase to find the total field at a great distance. This is recognized as the Huygens principle, in which any part of a wave front can be considered a source of secondary waves which add up to produce the total field at a distance. The principle can be placed on an exact mathematical basis, and will be used for analysis of antennas with apertures in later articles.

When we consider the transmitting antenna, the receiving antenna, and the intermediate space as a complete system, a useful point of view can be borrowed from Chapter 11. That is, we may think of the system as a two-terminal pair or transducer with coupling between the transmitter and receiver through the time-varying fields or waves existing in the space. The displacement current of the space plays much the same part that conduction current would in a transducer in which mutual couplings existed through lumped elements. This is another qualitative picture that can be placed on an exact basis, and use will be made of it near the end of the chapter.

The most satisfying physical picture is also a wave picture, but one in which we visualize waves on the wave guide or transmission line feed as exciting waves in space through the mechanism of the antenna as an intermediate transition or matching mechanism. The design of the antenna is then one of exciting· the space waves in the desired direction, with an efficient match over the frequency range of interest. The picture is the only natural one for horns (Figs. 12·02h, i), wave antennas (Fig. 12·02c), or dielectric rod antennas (Fig. 12·02f), but it is also useful for qualitative thinking and analysis of many other types such as the dipole or other circuit type of antennas, where it would not at first appear so natural. It is a fairly modern point of view, and because of its importance it will be discussed in more detail in the following article.

12·04   WAVE CONCEPTS OF RADIATION

In following up the wave picture of radiation, let us use the specific example of the biconical antenna pictured in Fig. 12·04a, in which a source is applied between the apices A and B of two coaxial cones ending at $r = l$.   If the cone angle ψ is large, this will look like the biconical horn of Fig. 12·02i.   If the cone angle is small, it will look like the dipole antenna in Fig. 12·02a.   The fact that both types of antennas can be discussed from one model suggests at once that the wave picture, obvious for the horn antenna, may also give useful results for the dipole type.

If we were to attempt an exact solution of Fig. 12·04a, we would look for a solution of Maxwell's equations satisfying the boundary

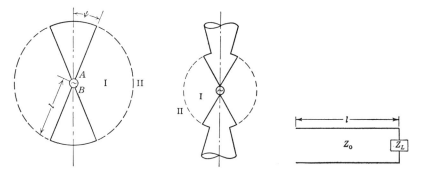

Fig. 12·04a Axial section through biconical antenna.

Fig. 12·04b Discontinuity in conical line.

Fig. 12·04c Equivalent circuit of biconical antenna.

conditions of the conducting cones, the source at the center, and the conditions at infinity.   It would be natural to divide the problem into two regions, $r < l$ and $r > l$, looking for individual solutions of the type we have called waves appropriate to the two regions.   Those appropriate to the former region would satisfy the boundary conditions at the cones, and would allow for the source at the center.   Those appropriate to the latter region would satisfy the condition at infinity.   Proper amounts of each would then be added to produce continuity of tangential field components over the common boundary, $r = l$, $\psi < \theta < \pi - \psi$, as well as zero tangential field E_θ over the perfectly conducting cap $r = l$, $0 < \theta < \psi$.

We have studied the TEM or principal wave of the biconical system in Art. 9·14 and found it to be like a transmission line mode along a uniform system.   This mode will certainly be excited by the source at the center because it is one with a finite voltage between cones, and, if the cones continued to infinity, it would be the only wave excited. However, if there were a discontinuity such as the abrupt change in cone angle pictured in Fig. 12·04b, other higher order modes would be excited just as in the changes in section of transmission lines discussed in Art. 11·13. From one point of view, the ending of the cones at $r = l$ in Fig. 12·04a is just a more grandiose discontinuity, and higher order modes will be excited on the conical system, as well as some waves in the space outside. This all seems very natural, but the interesting point, as shown by Schelkunoff[3] in an exact analysis of this problem, is that the effect of the higher order modes inside and outside may be represented in the principal wave's equivalent circuit as a lumped impedance at the end exactly as in the simple transmission line discontinuities discussed in Art. 11·13. This is pictured in Fig. 12·04c, with the impedance Z_L complex, since it includes the effect of energy carried away as radiation. Radiation in this picture is then regarded as an end effect, with the antenna as a guiding system from the exciting system to this end effect.

If the antenna is a thin-wire dipole (cone angle ψ small), we feel intuitively that there will not be a good match between the waves on the antenna and those in space, but instead most of the principal wave will be reflected at the end, forming a nearly perfect standing wave pattern on the antenna. In terms of the equivalent circuit Fig. 12·04c, the impedance Z_L will be very large compared with the characteristic impedance Z_0. This is true, and in fact, to obtain a good approximation to current distribution on a thin antenna, it may be sufficient to neglect the termination, in which case the open-circuited transmission line gives the perfectly sinusoidal standing wave pattern represented by complete reflection of the principal wave. Careful measurements on thin-wire antennas have, in fact, revealed current distributions very close to this perfect sinusoid. However, it cannot be strictly true, for this would mean that there were no waves in the space outside and no waves on the antenna except the TEM wave, perfectly reflected at the antenna end, giving a maximum of electric field and a zero of magnetic field there. But, with no waves outside, there would be a discontinuity at $r = l$ between the large tangential electric field of the principal wave inside and the zero field outside, so we know there must be fields outside, and of course we expect them from other pictures of radiation. When we study the spherical waves appropriate to the outer region, we find that they must have radial electric field

[3] S. A. Schelkunoff, "Antennas of Arbitrary Size and Shape," *Proc. I.R.E.*, **29**, 493–521 (Sept. 1941); S. A. Schelkunoff and C. B. Feldman, *Proc. I.R.E.*, **20**, 512–516 (Nov. 1942).

components; therefore continuity requires that there be higher order modes inside the antenna region to match these, since the TEM mode has no radial field.

An interesting point is raised here, as one of the first methods for calculation of radiation from a long thin dipole that we shall meet is the classical one of assuming a sinusoidal current distribution on the antenna and computing the fields outside by means of the retarded potentials. Here we consider the current distribution appropriate to the principal wave only; consequently, are we neglecting all higher order modes which by the above discussion means the neglect of all radiation? The answer is, of course, no, since radiation fields in this approach are computed from the current distribution as the source, and the total current is well approximated by the principal wave's current. Non-zero fields are computed in the external region, and these may be thought of as equal to the totality of all the external waves. The approximation can actually be considered the first step in a converging step-by-step method of which we shall later go to the second step. These steps are:

1. Assume only principal waves in region I.

2. Calculate corresponding higher order waves in region II.

3. Calculate higher order waves in region I to match radial field components of the region II higher order waves obtained in step 2.

4. Correct back and forth through as many succeeding steps as required.

We shall give more details of Schelkunoff's complete treatment of this problem in later articles. Before this, we shall go back to the other useful approximate methods of which the first is the calculation of radiation fields from assumptions regarding current distribution, as referred to above. The above discussion should give some feeling about the relation between these points of view.

Field and Power Calculations with Currents Assumed on the Antenna

12·05   THE SMALL CURRENT ELEMENT OR DIPOLE ANTENNA

In computing radiated power and the field distributions around an antenna when current distribution is assumed over the surface of the antenna's conductors, the simplest example is that of a linear element so short that current may be considered uniform over its length. Certain more complex antennas can be considered to be made up of a large number of such differential antennas with the proper magnitudes and phases of their currents. We shall consider only the case in which the current varies sinusoidally with time. Accordingly let it be expressed by $I_0 e^{j\omega t}$ or, better yet, by its peak value I_0 alone with the factor $e^{j\omega t}$ understood.

The direction of the current element will be selected as the z direction, and at the origin of a set of spherical coordinates (Fig. 12·05a). Its length is h, and it is understood that h is very small compared with wavelength. By continuity, equal and opposite time-varying charges must exist on the two ends $\pm h/2$, so the element is frequently called a small dipole or *Hertzian dipole*.

Now one way of finding fields once current is given is through the retarded potentials studied in Chapter 4. Article 4·17 gives a form

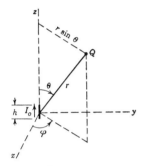

Fig. 12·05a Small current element at origin of spherical coordinates.

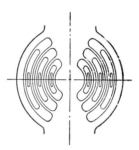

Fig. 12·05b Axial section showing electric field lines in first order symmetrical *TM* waves.

of $\bar{A}$ suitable for present purposes. Since current vector points in the z direction, the vector potential can be only in the z direction. For any point Q at radius r, $\bar{A}$ of Art. 4·17 becomes simply

$$A_z = \mu \frac{h I_0}{4\pi r} e^{-j(\omega r/v)} \tag{1}$$

Or, in the system of spherical coordinates,

$$A_r = A_z \cos\theta = \mu \frac{h I_0}{4\pi r} e^{-jkr} \cos\theta$$

$$A_\theta = -A_z \sin\theta = -\mu \frac{h I_0}{4\pi r} e^{-jkr} \sin\theta \tag{2}$$

where $k = \omega/v = \omega \sqrt{\mu\epsilon} = 2\pi/\lambda$. There is no ϕ component of $\bar{A}$, and there are no variations with ϕ in any expressions because of the symmetry of the structure about the axis. The electric and magnetic field components may be found directly from the components of $\bar{A}$ by use of the other equations listed in Art. 4·17. Thus,

$$H_\phi = \frac{I_0 h}{4\pi} e^{-jkr} \left[\frac{jk}{r} + \frac{1}{r^2} \right] \sin \theta$$

$$E_r = \frac{I_0 h}{4\pi} e^{-jkr} \left[\frac{2\eta}{r^2} + \frac{2}{j\omega\epsilon r^3} \right] \cos \theta \tag{3}$$

$$E_\theta = \frac{I_0 h}{4\pi} e^{-jkr} \left[\frac{j\omega\mu}{r} + \frac{1}{j\omega\epsilon r^3} + \frac{\eta}{r^2} \right] \sin \theta$$

For the region very near the element (r small) the most important term in H_ϕ is that varying as $1/r^2$. The important terms in E_r and E_θ are those varying as $1/r^3$. Thus, in this region near the element, magnetic field is very nearly in phase with current and H_ϕ may be identified as the usual induction field obtained from Ampère's law. Electric field in this region may be identified with that calculated for an electrostatic dipole. (By continuity, $I_0/j\omega$ represents the charge on one end of the dipole.) As the important components of electric and magnetic field in this region are 90° out of time phase, so these components represent no time average energy flow according to the Poynting theorem.

At very great distances from the source, the only terms important in the expressions for E and H are those varying as $1/r$.

$$H_\phi = \frac{jkI_0 h}{4\pi r} \sin \theta \ e^{-jkr}$$

$$E_\theta = \frac{j\omega\mu I_0 h}{4\pi r} \sin \theta \ e^{-jkr} = \eta H_\phi \tag{4}$$

$$\eta = \sqrt{\frac{\mu}{\epsilon}} \approx 120\pi \quad \text{ohms for space.}$$

At great distances from the source, any portion of a spherical wave surface is essentially a plane wave, so the above characteristics typical of uniform plane waves might be expected. E_θ and H_ϕ are in time phase, related by η, and at right angles to each other and the direction of propagation. The Poynting vector is then completely in the radial direction. The time average flow of energy is of interest. The time average of the products of any two sinusoids of equal frequency and of the same phase is one-half the product of their magnitudes. So time average P_r,

$$P_r = \frac{\eta k^2 I_0{}^2 h^2}{32\pi^2 r^2} \sin^2 \theta \quad \text{watts/meter}^2$$

The total energy flow out must be the total surface integral of the Poynting vector over any surrounding surface. For simplicity this surface may be taken as a sphere of radius r. From Fig. 12·05a,

$$W_{av} = \int_S \bar{P} \cdot \overline{dS} = \int_0^\pi P_r 2\pi r^2 \sin\theta \, d\theta$$

$$= \frac{\eta k^2 I_0^2 h^2}{16\pi} \int_0^\pi \sin^3\theta \, d\theta$$

$$W_{av} = \frac{\eta \pi I_0^2}{3}\left(\frac{h}{\lambda}\right)^2 = 40\pi^2 I_0^2 \left(\frac{h}{\lambda}\right)^2 \quad \text{watts} \tag{5}$$

A radiation resistance may be defined as the resistance which would dissipate the same amount of power with this same constant current flowing.

$$R_r = \frac{2W_{av}}{I_0^2} = 80\pi^2 \left(\frac{h}{\lambda}\right)^2 \quad \text{ohms} \tag{6}$$

It is interesting and important to note that the field of the small dipole has the same form as the first order TM spherical wave studied in Art. 10·09. From Eqs. 10·09(19) with $n = 1$ and the Bessel function taken as the second Hankel form which is appropriate to a region extending to infinity,

$$H_\phi = A_1 r^{-\frac{1}{2}} P_1^{\ 1}(\cos\theta) H_{\frac{3}{2}}^{(2)}(kr)$$

$$E_\theta = \frac{A_1}{j\omega\epsilon r^{\frac{3}{2}}}[H_{\frac{3}{2}}^{(2)}(kr) - kr H_{\frac{1}{2}}^{(2)}(kr)] P_1^{\ 1}(\cos\theta) \tag{7}$$

$$E_r = -\frac{A_1 H_{\frac{3}{2}}^{(2)}(kr)}{j\omega\epsilon r^{\frac{3}{2}}\sin\theta}[\cos\theta P_1^{\ 1}(\cos\theta) - P_2^{\ 1}(\cos\theta)]$$

But, from the relations of Art. 10·09 it may be shown that

$$H_{\frac{3}{2}}^{(2)}(kr) = \sqrt{\frac{2}{\pi kr}}\, e^{-jkr}\left(\frac{j}{kr} - 1\right)$$

$$P_1^{\ 1}(\cos\theta) = \sin\theta$$

With these substitutions and the identification of A_1 with

$$I_0 h k^{\frac{3}{2}}/4j\sqrt{2\pi},$$

(7) and (3) are identical. The electric field lines for this mode are sketched in Fig. 12·05b.

PROBLEMS

12·05a   An inspection of (3) shows that there are other in-phase parts than those considered in forming the power flow above.   Taking into account all terms, show that the result (5) is correct.   *Suggestion:* Use the form

$$W = \tfrac{1}{2}\text{Re} \oint (\bar{E} \times \bar{H}^*) \cdot \overline{dS}$$

12·05b   Study the $n = 2$ *TM* wave and show that it corresponds to a quadrupole field, i.e., field from two small current elements at right angles.

12·06   THE LONG STRAIGHT ANTENNA

If the antenna length is appreciable compared with wavelength, which is true of practical antennas, current may not be considered

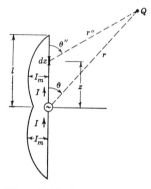

constant over the length.   The antenna can, however, be broken into a large number of the differential elements of the type analyzed in Art. 12·05 and the fields from all of these superposed.   Although fields or potentials, which are proportional to current, may be superposed, power, which varies as square of current, may not.   Thus, to use the integration method employed in Art. 12·05, which we shall call the Poynting method, will require that the total $\bar{E}$ and $\bar{H}$ be first evaluated at each point of the large enclosing sphere.

Fig.   12·06   Long   straight dipole antenna.

The   long   dipole   of   Fig.   12·06 with voltage applied at its midpoint is shown with an assumed sinusoidal distribution of current.   The standing wave has zero current at the ends, and is selected with distance between zero and a maximum equal to a quarter free-space wavelength. A qualitative discussion of this assumption has been given in Art. 12·04.

$$I = \begin{cases} I_m \sin [k(l - z)] & z > 0 \\ I_m \sin [k(l + z)] & z < 0 \end{cases} \tag{1}$$

From Eq. 12·05(4) the contributions to H_ϕ and E_θ at a great distance r'' from a differential element dz are

$$dE_\theta = \eta dH_\phi = \frac{j\eta kI\,dz}{4\pi r''} e^{-jkr''} \sin \theta''$$

r'' is the distance from any element to Q, whereas r is the distance from the origin to Q.   These   may   be   taken   so   large   that   the   difference between r and r'' is important only as it affects phase, and is completely insignificant in its effect upon magnitude. Similarly, the difference between θ and θ'' will be negligibly small. In the phase difference,

$$r'' = \sqrt{r^2 + z^2 - 2rz \cos \theta} \cong r - z \cos \theta$$

Otherwise,

$$\frac{1}{r''} \cong \frac{1}{r} \qquad \theta'' \cong \theta$$

$$E_\theta = \eta H_\phi = \int_{-l}^{+l} dE_\theta$$

$$= \frac{j\eta k I_m}{4\pi r} \sin \theta e^{-jkr} \left\{ \int_{-l}^{0} e^{jkz \cos \theta} \sin [k(l + z)\, dz \right.$$

$$\left. + \int_{0}^{l} e^{jkz \cos \theta} \sin [k(l - z)]\, dz \right\}$$

The integral

$$\int e^{ax} \sin (bx + c)\, dx = \frac{e^{ax}}{a^2 + b^2} [a \sin (bx + c) - b \cos (bx + c)]$$

so

$$E_\theta = \eta H_\phi = \frac{j\eta k I_m}{4\pi r} \sin \theta e^{-jkr} \left\{ \frac{2}{k \sin^2 \theta} [\cos (kl \cos \theta) - \cos kl] \right\}$$

$$= \frac{j\eta I_m}{2\pi r} e^{-jkr} \left[\frac{\cos (kl \cos \theta) - \cos kl}{\sin \theta} \right] \tag{2}$$

Total $\bar{E}$ and $\bar{H}$ at long distances from the antenna are also at right angles to each other and the direction of propagation, in time phase, and related by η. So, as with the differential antenna of Art. 12·05, the time average Poynting vector is half the product of field magnitudes.

$$P_r = \frac{1}{2} | E_\theta || H_\phi | = \frac{\eta I_m^2}{8\pi^2 r^2} \left[\frac{\cos (kl \cos \theta) - \cos kl}{\sin \theta} \right]^2 \tag{3}$$

Total power radiated from the long dipole in free space,

$$W = \int_S \bar{P} \cdot d\bar{S} = \int_0^\pi P_r 2\pi r^2 \sin \theta\, d\theta$$

$$= \frac{\eta I_m^2}{4\pi} \int_0^\pi \frac{[\cos (kl \cos \theta) - \cos kl]^2}{\sin \theta}\, d\theta \quad \text{watts} \tag{4}$$

Since current varies along the antenna, the value of radiation resistance depends upon the current used to define it. Suppose for this case that radiation resistance is defined in terms of maximum current, wherever it may occur.

$$R_r = \frac{2W}{I_m{}^2} = \frac{\eta}{2\pi} \int_0^\pi \frac{[\cos{(kl \cos{\theta})} - \cos{kl}]^2 \, d\theta}{\sin{\theta}} \tag{5}$$

Taking $\eta = 120\pi$, this integral may be shown to have the following result.

$$R_r = 60\{C + \ln 2kl - Ci(2kl) + \tfrac{1}{2} \sin 2kl[Si(4kl) - 2Si(2kl)]$$
$$+ \tfrac{1}{2} \cos 2kl[C + \ln (kl) + Ci(4kl) - 2Ci(2kl)]\} \text{ ohms} \tag{6}$$

where $C = 0.5772 \cdots$ and the following functions (sine and cosine integrals) are tabulated.

$$Si(x) = \int_0^x \frac{\sin x}{x} \, dx \qquad Ci(x) = -\int_x^\infty \frac{\cos x}{x} \, dx \tag{7}$$

PROBLEM

12·06   Perform the integration (5) leading to (6).   (*Hint:* Substitute $u = \cos \theta$, separate denominator by partial fractions, and note $\lim\limits_{x\to 0} Ci(x) = C + \ln x$.)

12·07   THE HALF-WAVE DIPOLE; ANTENNA GAIN

The most important special case of the long center-fed antenna is that of the *half-wave dipole* in which $l = \lambda/4$.   Field intensity, power density, and radiation resistance then become, from Eqs. 12·06(2), (3), and (6), respectively,

$$|E_\theta| = \frac{60I_m}{r} \left[\frac{\cos \left(\dfrac{\pi}{2} \cos \theta \right)}{\sin \theta} \right] \text{ volts/meter} \tag{1}$$

$$P_r = \frac{15I_m{}^2}{\pi r^2} \left[\frac{\cos \left(\dfrac{\pi}{2} \cos \theta \right)}{\sin \theta} \right]^2 \text{ watts/meter}^2 \tag{2}$$

$$R_r = 73.09 \quad \text{ohms} \tag{3}$$

Polar plots of the bracketed parts of the field and power density expressions are shown in Fig. 12·07.   The field pattern for the infinitesimal dipole of Art. 12·05 is also shown for comparison.   The radiation resistance given in (3) is also a good approximation to the input impedance of practical half-wave dipoles, since these are nearly resonant and the maximum of current, to which radiation resistance is referred, appears at the central input terminals.

In looking at the polar plots in Fig. 12·07, it is evident that radiated fields are a maximum in the plane perpendicular to the antenna and are zero along the axis of the antenna. We say then that this antenna has a certain *directivity* as compared with an imagined isotropic radiator which radiates equally in all directions. This is, of course, an advantage if we desire to have the signal radiated in the plane of the maximum, since there is less power required to produce a given field in the desired direction than there would be for the isotropic radiator.

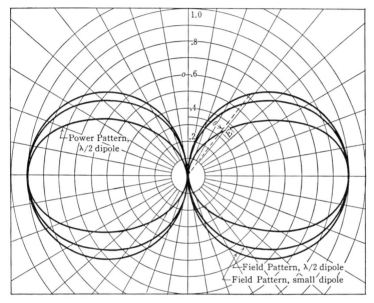

Fig. 12·07   Polar plots of field and power density for a half-wave dipole, and of field for an infinitesimal dipole in plane of dipole.

The amount of the saving is frequently expressed as the *gain* of the antenna, defined as the ratio of power required from the isotropic radiator to produce the given intensity in the desired direction to that required from the actual antenna.

$$g = \frac{4\pi r^2 P_r}{W} \tag{4}$$

As defined, gain may be given for any direction from the antenna, but it is most often given as its maximum value. For the half-wave dipole, this maximum direction is for $\theta = \pi/2$.

$$g_{\max} = 4\pi r^2 \times \frac{15 I_m{}^2}{\pi r^2} \times \frac{2}{I_m{}^2 \times 73.09} \approx 1.64 \tag{5}$$

For the infinitesimal dipole of Art. 12·05, the gain is

$$g_{max} = 4\pi r^2 \times \frac{\eta I_0^2 h^2}{8r^2\lambda^2} \times \frac{3\lambda^2}{\eta\pi I_0^2 h^2} = \frac{3}{2} \tag{6}$$

It is interesting to note that directivity pattern and gain are not very different for the half-wave and infinitesimal dipoles, but of course radiation resistances are very different.

PROBLEMS

12·07a Considering gain as defined by (4) a function of direction, plot curves of gain versus θ for the half-wave and infinitesimal dipoles.

12·07b Compare the currents that would be required in a half-wave dipole and a small dipole of height 0.05λ to produce 100 watts of radiated power from each.

12·08   ANTENNAS ABOVE PERFECT EARTH

If the earth near an antenna must be taken into account, two very difficult problems can result: (1) effect of earth conductivity, (2) effect of earth curvature.   It is common to assume that the earth is plane and

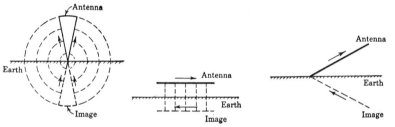

Fig. 12·08a Cone above plane conducting earth and image cone.

Fig. 12·08b Horizontal wire above plane conducting earth and image wire.

Fig. 12·08c Inclined wire above plane conducting earth and image wire.

perfectly conducting, not alone because it avoids these two difficulties, but also because it gives answers which agree well with actual results in many practical cases.   If earth is so assumed, it is then possible to account for it by imaging the antenna in the earth.   For example, given a single cone with axis vertical above earth (Fig. 12·08a), the boundary condition of zero electric field tangential to the earth may be satisfied by removing the earth and utilizing a second cone as an image of the first.   The problem then reduces to that of the biconical antenna studied previously.   Note that current is in the *same vertical* direction at any instant in the two cones.   Given a single wire above earth and parallel to it, as in Fig. 12·08b, our knowledge of symmetry in the transmission line problem tells us that the condition of electric field lines normal to the earth is met by removing the earth and placing the image with current in the *opposite horizontal* direction. Generalizing from these two cases, we guess that current direction in the image will be selected so that vertical components are in the same direction, horizontal components in opposite directions at any instant. An example is shown in Fig. 12·08c.

The technique of replacing the earth by the antenna image, of course, gives only the proper value of field above the earth plane. The proper value below the perfectly conducting earth plane should be zero. For example, given a long straight vertical antenna above earth, excited at the base, the image reduces the problem to that solved in Art. 12·06. Field strength for maximum current I_m in the antenna is given exactly by Eq. 12·06(2) for all points above the earth $(0 < \theta < \pi/2)$, but is zero for all points below $(\pi/2 < \theta < \pi)$. Thus, for power integration, the integral of Eq. 12·06(4) extends only from 0 to $\pi/2$, and radiation resistance is just half that for the corresponding complete dipole.

$$W = \frac{\eta I_m{}^2}{4\pi} \int_0^{\pi/2} \frac{[\cos (kl \cos \theta) - \cos kl]^2}{\sin \theta}\, d\theta \quad \text{watts} \qquad (1)$$

Thus, for a quarter-wave vertical antenna above earth, the radiation resistance is just half that of the half-wave dipole of Eq. 12·07(3).

$$R_r = 36.54 \quad \text{ohms} \qquad (2)$$

PROBLEMS

12·08a Prove by a study of the resulting vector potential the *same vertical direction, opposite horizontal direction* rule for image currents given in the preceding article.

12·08b Simpson's rule is useful for evaluation of the radiation integrals. If the area to be evaluated is divided into $2m$ even-numbered portions by $(2m + 1)$ lines spaced an equal distance Δ apart, and values of the function at these lines are $f_0, f_1, \cdots, f_{2m+1}$, then the area under the curve is approximately

$$I = \frac{\Delta}{3}[(f_0 + f_{2m}) + 4(f_1 + f_3 + \cdots + f_{2m-1}) + 2(f_2 + f_4 + \cdots + f_{2m-2})]$$

Evaluate the integral of Eq. 12·08(1) for a vertical quarter-wave antenna above earth, $kl = \pi/2$, using $m = 3$ in Simpson's rule. Calculate the radiation resistance and compare with (2).

12·09 SYSTEMIZATION OF POYNTING CALCULATIONS

In using the Poynting integration for calculation of radiated power from antennas, many of the same mathematical approximations are introduced each time the method is employed. Short cuts are soon

discovered and are extremely time saving. It will be desirable therefore to place these on a systematic basis. Schelkunoff has given this
systemization in the literature.[4]

In the Poynting method, field is usually calculated at a great distance
from the radiator. The following assumptions are then justified.

1. Differences in radius vector to different points of the radiator are
absolutely unimportant in their effect on *magnitudes*.

2. Differences in direction of the radius vector to different points on
the radiator are negligible.

3. All field components decreasing with distance faster than $1/r$

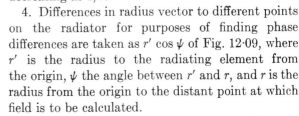

are completely negligible compared with those
decreasing as $1/r$.

4. Differences in radius vector to different points
on the radiator for purposes of finding phase
differences are taken as $r' \cos \psi$ of Fig. 12·09, where
r' is the radius to the radiating element from
the origin, ψ the angle between r' and r, and r is the
radius from the origin to the distant point at which
field is to be calculated.

Consider the vector potential at point P, distance
r from the origin of a radiating system made up of
current elements arranged in any manner what-
soever, the element a shown at radius r' from the
origin being one of these.

Fig. 12·09 Coor-
dinates of general
current element at
a and distant point
P with respect to
origin O.

$$\bar{A} = \mu \int_V \frac{\bar{i}_a e^{j\omega\left(t - \frac{r''}{v}\right)}}{4\pi r''}\, dV'$$

By the assumptions listed above, and $e^{j\omega t}$ understood,

$$\bar{A} = \mu \frac{e^{-jkr}}{4\pi r} \int_V \bar{i}_a e^{jkr' \cos \psi}\, dV' \tag{1}$$

The function of r is now completely outside the integral; the integral
itself is only a function of the antenna configuration, current distribution assumption, and direction in which field is to be calculated.
Define this integral as the radiation vector $\bar{N}$.

$$\bar{N} = \int_V \bar{i}_a e^{jkr' \cos \psi}\, dV' \tag{2}$$

Then

$$\bar{A} = \mu \frac{e^{-jkr}}{4\pi r} \bar{N} \tag{3}$$

[4] S. A. Schelkunoff, "A General Radiation Formula," *Proc. I.R.E.*, **27**, 660–666
(Oct., 1939).

In the most general case, $\bar{A}$, and hence $\bar{N}$, may have components in any direction. In spherical coordinates, employing the unit vectors,

$$\bar{A} = \mu \frac{e^{-jkr}}{4\pi r} [\bar{a}_r N_r + \bar{a}_\theta N_\theta + \bar{a}_\phi N_\phi]$$

A study of the equation $\bar{B} = \nabla \times \bar{A}$ in spherical coordinates (Art. 2·39) shows that the only components which do not decrease faster than $1/r$ are

$$H_\theta = -\frac{1}{\mu r} \frac{\partial}{\partial r} (rA_\phi) = \frac{jk}{4\pi r} e^{-jkr} N_\phi \tag{4}$$

$$H_\phi = \frac{1}{\mu r} \frac{\partial}{\partial r} (rA_\theta) = -\frac{jk}{4\pi r} e^{-jkr} N_\theta$$

An examination of

$$\bar{E} = -\frac{j\omega}{k^2} \nabla(\nabla \cdot \bar{A}) - j\omega \bar{A}$$

shows that the only components of $\bar{E}$ which do not decrease faster than $1/r$ are

$$E_\theta = -\frac{j\omega\mu}{4\pi r} e^{-jkr} N_\theta \qquad E_\phi = -\frac{j\omega\mu}{4\pi r} e^{-jkr} N_\phi \tag{5}$$

The Poynting vector $\bar{E} \times \bar{H}$ has a time average value

$$P_r = \frac{1}{2} \times \frac{\eta}{2\lambda r} \times \frac{1}{2\lambda r} [|N_\theta|^2 + |N_\phi|^2] \tag{6}$$

Total time average power radiated is

$$W = \int_0^\pi \int_0^{2\pi} P_r r^2 \sin \theta \, d\theta \, d\phi$$

$$= \frac{\eta}{8\lambda^2} \int_0^\pi \int_0^{2\pi} [|N_\theta|^2 + |N_\phi|^2] \sin \theta \, d\theta \, d\phi \tag{7}$$

The expression is independent of r, as it should be.

The Poynting vector $\bar{P}$ gives the actual power density at any point. However, to obtain a quantity which gives the information of direction only, define K, radiation intensity, as the power radiated in a given direction per unit solid angle. This is the average value of P on a sphere of unit radius.

$$K = \frac{\eta}{8\lambda^2} [|N_\theta|^2 + |N_\phi|^2] \tag{8}$$

and

$$W = \int_0^\pi \int_0^{2\pi} K \sin \theta \, d\theta \, d\phi \tag{9}$$

A plot of K against direction may then define the radiation pattern. If should be recognized that this is a power radiation pattern and not a field strength radiation pattern.

Currents All in One Direction. If current in a radiating system flows all in one direction, this may be taken as the direction of the axis of a set of spherical coordinates. $\bar{A}$ (hence $\bar{N}$) can have a z component only. Then

$$N_\phi = 0 \qquad N_\theta = -N_z \sin \theta \qquad (10)$$

$$K = \frac{\eta}{8\lambda^2} \, | \, N_z \, |^2 \sin^2 \theta$$

Circularly Symmetric Currents. If all current in some radiating system is circularly symmetric about an axis, this axis may be taken as the axis of a set of spherical coordinates. $\bar{A}$ (hence $\bar{N}$) can have a ϕ component only. Then

$$K = \frac{\eta}{8\lambda^2} \, | \, N_\phi \, |^2$$

and

$$W = 2\pi \int_0^\pi K \sin \theta \, d\theta \qquad (11)$$

Useful Relations for Spherical Coordinates. It sometimes may be desirable to calculate N_θ and N_ϕ from the cartesian components N_x, N_y, N_z,

$$N_\theta = (N_x \cos \phi + N_y \sin \phi) \cos \theta - N_z \sin \theta \qquad (12)$$

$$N_\phi = -N_x \sin \phi + N_y \cos \phi$$

The angle ψ appearing in the equation for radiation vector (2) may be found as follows, if θ, φ are the angular coordinates of the distant point P, and θ', φ' are angular coordinates of the variable point a on the element, Fig. 12·09.

$$\cos \psi = \cos \theta \cos \theta' + \sin \theta \sin \theta' \cos (\phi - \phi') \quad (13)$$

Fig. 12·10 Thin wire of length l supporting a progressive wave.

12·10 PROGRESSIVE WAVE ON A STRAIGHT WIRE

As an example of the application of the general relations derived in the preceding article, let us consider a straight wire extending from $z = 0$ to $z = l$, excited by a single traveling wave of current, assumed to be unattenuated and with phase velocity equal to $1/\sqrt{\mu\epsilon}$ (Fig. 12·10). As all current is in the z direction, the radiation vector of Eq. 12·09(2) will have only a z component.

The special forms of Eqs. 12·09(10) then apply.

$$N_z = I_0 \int_0^l e^{-jkz'} e^{jkz' \cos \theta} \, dz'$$

$$= \frac{I_0[1 - e^{-jkl(1 - \cos \theta)}]}{jk(1 - \cos \theta)}$$

$$|N_z| = \frac{2I_0 \sin [(kl/2)(1 - \cos \theta)]}{k(1 - \cos \theta)} \tag{1}$$

$$K = \frac{\eta |N_z|^2}{8\lambda^2} \sin^2 \theta = \frac{I_0^2 \eta}{2\lambda^2} \frac{\sin^2 [(kl/2)(1 - \cos \theta)]}{k^2(1 - \cos \theta)^2} \sin^2 \theta \tag{2}$$

Also, since there is symmetry about the axis,

$$W = 2\pi \int_0^\pi K \sin \theta \, d\theta = 2\pi \int_0^\pi \frac{I_0^2 \eta}{2\lambda^2} \frac{\sin^2 [(kl/2)(1 - \cos \theta)]}{k^2(1 - \cos \theta)^2} \sin^3 \theta \, d\theta$$

$$W = 30I_0^2 \int_0^\pi \frac{\sin^3 \theta \sin^2 [(kl/2)(1 - \cos \theta)]}{(1 - \cos \theta)^2} \, d\theta$$

If the above integral is evaluated,[5]

$$W = 30I_0^2 \left[1.415 + \ln \frac{kl}{\pi} - Ci \, 2kl + \frac{\sin 2kl}{2kl} \right] \tag{3}$$

From the general discussion of wave antennas in Art. 12·02, it might be expected that this single traveling wave would produce a maximum of radiation in the direction of wave propagation. Actually, radiation is zero at $\theta = 0$ as seen from (2), but only because radiation from each element of current is zero in that direction. A study of the form of (2) would reveal that lobes near $\theta = 0$ will be the largest, and those near $\theta = \pi$ will be small.

PROBLEMS

12·10a   Plot the form of radiation intensity as a function of θ for $kl = \pi, 2\pi, 4\pi$. Find the direction and value of maximum gain for $kl = \pi$.

12·10b   Apply the generalized method of Art. 12·09 to the long antenna with sinusoidal current, showing that the same results as in Art. 12·06 are obtained for power radiated. Show in particular that the radiation intensity of a half-wave dipole is

$$K = \frac{15}{\pi} I^2 \frac{\cos^2 [(\pi/2) \cos \theta]}{\sin^2 \theta}$$

[5] Stratton, *Electromagnetic Theory*, p. 445.

12·11 SMALL CIRCULAR LOOP ANTENNA

We wish now to apply the generalized forms to a circular loop antenna, assumed small in circumference compared with a wavelength, and with constant current about the circumference. Because of the symmetry about the axis (Fig. 12·11), we may use the special forms of Eq. 12·09(11), and N_ϕ may be computed at $\phi = 0$ since it is independent of angle. The coordinates of the element of the antenna are ϕ' and $\theta' = \pi/2$.

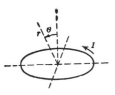

Fig. 12·11 Circular loop carrying current.

Loop radius is a.   Then, from Eq. 12·09(13),

$$\cos \psi = \sin \theta \cos \phi'$$

$$N_\phi = I \int_0^{2\pi} e^{jka \sin \theta \cos \phi'} \cos \phi' \, a \, d\phi'$$

$$\approx I \int_0^{2\pi} [1 + jka \sin \theta \cos \phi'] \cos \phi' \, a \, d\phi' = jk\pi I a^2 \sin \theta \quad (1)$$

The radiation intensity,

$$K = \frac{\eta}{8\lambda^2} k^2 \pi^2 I^2 a^4 \sin^2 \theta = \frac{\eta}{32} (ka)^4 I^2 \sin^2 \theta \tag{2}$$

The power radiated,

$$W = 2\pi \int_0^\pi K \sin \theta \, d\theta = \frac{\pi\eta}{12} (ka)^4 I^2 \tag{3}$$

The radiation resistance,

$$R_r = \frac{2W}{I^2} = \frac{\pi\eta}{6} (ka)^4 = 20\pi^2 (ka)^4 \quad \text{ohms} \tag{4}$$

This is the same as the result found in Art. 5·13 by a consideration of induced fields about the circuit.   The relation between the two methods of radiation calculation will be discussed in the following article.

PROBLEMS

12·11a   What current is required to radiate 100 watts from a loop of circumference equal to 0.1 wavelength?

12·11b   Compare the form of the radiation intensity from the small loop with that from the small dipole.   Compare the variation of electric and magnetic fields with angle in the radiation field.   (Note that these may be derived simply from the radiation vector.)   On the basis of this comparison, explain why the small loop is frequently called a magnetic dipole.

12·11c   Find the maximum gain of the small loop antenna.

12·12   THE INDUCED EMF METHOD

We have seen that a Poynting integration of distant fields gave the same result for power radiated from a small loop antenna as was found by a consideration of retardation of the induced fields in Chapter 5. This verifies that the power loss found there does leave the circuit as radiation, but also suggests that the method might be useful in antenna calculations. It has been so used, and is called the induced emf method. The calculation for the loop in Art. 5·13 may then be considered one example of the method. Before considering another, several things may be said.

First, it is important to note that, for a given assumption of current, one should expect the same result by the two methods. Certainly the fields are fixed and are determined by the same equations in the two cases. Moreover, in the induced emf method, radiated power is computed by integrating over the conductor surface the product of surface current density and in-phase component of induced electric field, and this actually amounts to finding the average Poynting flow through a surface taken along the conductor, since surface current density is equal to tangential magnetic field. The average Poynting flow should be the same through this surface as through the large exterior sphere utilized in the other method, since there are no sources between.

There are some conceptual difficulties in the method, somewhat like those discussed earlier (Art. 12·04) for other methods. In the present method, the difficulties arise mainly with the applied field. For we know that total field, applied and induced, must add to zero along the antenna surface if it is taken as perfectly conducting. For various forms of applied field, distributed over the antenna as when excited by a wave from a distant antenna, or localized near a gap when excited from a transmission line, the induced field should then take on correspondingly different forms so that field is properly zero along the conductor. However, we take no account of this, assuming a given current distribution (which fixes the distribution of induced field), and applying the results to antennas having a variety of excitation with practically useful results. Apparently integrated effects come out nearly the same for the different forms of applied field.

There are also practical limitations to the usefulness of the method. It is seldom easier to perform the integrations for this method than for the Poynting method of previous articles, and yet it tells nothing about the form of the distant field. Because it is concerned with conditions near the antenna, it seems that it might tell us more about antenna impedance, yet it is difficult to carry out for other than

filamentary currents, and we have found earlier that reactive calculations for such filamentary paths yield infinite results. It has, however, been applied as a step in more powerful methods of finding
antenna impedance, and has been extended to give mutual effects
between radiators. It is also of importance in adding to one's concepts
of radiation. The form for radiation resistance given in Eq. 5·11(7)
assumed a constant current. Let us
consider as another example a form
useful for straight wire antennas such
as the dipole pictured in Fig. 12·12
with variations in current magnitude
considered. If current on the antenna

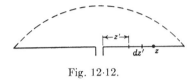

Fig. 12·12.

has a distribution $I = I_0 f(z)$, where $f(z)$ is assumed real, vector
potential at any point z is given as

$$A_z = \mu I_0 \int_{-l}^{l} \frac{f(z')e^{-jk|z-z'|}}{4\pi|z-z'|}\,dz' \qquad (1)$$

Radiated power is obtained by integrating the component of electric
field tangential to the antenna and in phase with current. We are
interested then in the real part of E_z, which is the negative of applied
field E_0.

$$W = \frac{1}{2}\int_{-l}^{l}|I||E_0|\,dz = -\frac{1}{2}\int_{-l}^{l}|I|\,\mathrm{Re}\,(E_z)\,dz \qquad (2)$$

Referring to Eq. 4·17(7),

$$\mathrm{Re}\,(E_z) = -j\omega\left[\mathrm{Im}(A_z) + \frac{1}{k^2}\,\mathrm{Im}\left(\frac{\partial^2 A_z}{\partial z^2}\right)\right] \qquad (3)$$

And, from (1),

$$\mathrm{Im}\,(A_z) = -\frac{j\mu I_0}{4\pi}\int_{-l}^{l}\frac{f(z')\,\sin k|z-z'|}{|z-z'|}\,dz' \qquad (4)$$

This integral can be evaluated for certain forms of $f(z)$. However, it
is sometimes easier to proceed by series methods. If the sine term of
(4) is expressed as a power series, it can be shown that

$$\mathrm{Im}\,(A_z)$$
$$= -\frac{2\mu jk I_0}{4\pi}\left[\alpha_0 - \frac{k^2}{3!}(z^2\alpha_0 + \alpha_2) + \frac{k^4}{5!}(z^4\alpha_0 + 6z^2\alpha_2 + \alpha_4) + \cdots\right] \qquad (5)$$

$$\alpha_n = \int_0^l (z')^n f(z')\,dz' \qquad (6)$$

Substitution in (2) and (3) yields

$$W = \frac{\eta k^2 I_0^2}{3\pi} \left[\alpha_0^2 - \frac{k^2}{5} \alpha_0\alpha_2 + \frac{k^4}{140} (\alpha_0\alpha_4 + 3\alpha_2^2) + \cdots \right] \quad (7)$$

We may define a radiation resistance in terms of I_0.

$$R_r = \frac{2W}{I_0^2} = 80k^2 \left[\alpha_0^2 - \frac{k^2}{5} \alpha_0\alpha_2 + \frac{k^4}{140} (\alpha_0\alpha_4 + 3\alpha_2^2) + \cdots \right] \quad (8)$$

For a half-wave dipole $l = \lambda/4$, and $f(z)$ is taken as $\cos kz$. From (6),

$$\alpha_0 = \int^{\lambda/4} \cos kz'\, dz' = \frac{1}{k}$$

$$\alpha_2 = \int_0^{\lambda/4} (z')^2 \cos kz'\, dz' = \frac{[(\pi/2)^2 - 2]}{k^3} \cong \frac{0.467}{k^3}$$

$$\alpha_4 = \int_0^{\lambda/4} (z')^4 \cos kz'\, dz' = \frac{[(\pi/2)^4 - 12(\pi/2)^2 + 24]}{k^5} \cong \frac{0.479}{k^5}$$

Substitution in (8) then gives a radiation resistance of about 73.2 ohms, which checks the previously derived result.

Arrays of Elements

12·13   SUPERPOSITION OF EFFECTS AND MUTUAL INTERACTIONS

If there are several complete radiators operating together, currents might be assumed over the entire group, and a complete calculation made for total vector potential $\bar{A}$ (or for the total radiation vector, $\bar{N}$). However, as a practical thing, the synthesis of special antennas is often accomplished by putting together elements for which, as isolated antennas, calculations have already been made. Not only may some labor be saved in calculating such cases, but it is also possible in this way to determine the effects of various changes or additions to a structure and thus to attain a desired and special radiation pattern in space. The problem then is to know how to superpose the separate and known radiation characteristics to yield the over-all radiation characteristics of the combination.

If calculations for the potentials or fields from each of the radiators operating separately are already available, the fields may be superposed to obtain total fields, and, from these, total power by a Poynting integration. Suppose that, in a case with two separate radiators, the component fields are known as $E_{\phi 1}$, $H_{\phi 1}$, etc., due to radiator 1, and

$E_{\phi 2}$, $H_{\phi 2}$ due to radiator 2. The Poynting theorem as written in Eq. 7·03(12) then gives an average value of P_r,

$$P_r = \tfrac{1}{2} \operatorname{Re} \left[\{E_{\theta 1}H_{\phi 1}{}^* - E_{\phi 1}H_{\theta 1}{}^*\} + \{E_{\theta 2}H_{\phi 2}{}^* - E_{\phi 2}H_{\theta 2}{}^*\} \right. \\ \left. + \{E_{\theta 2}H_{\phi 1}{}^* + E_{\theta 1}H_{\phi 2}{}^* - E_{\phi 1}H_{\theta 2}{}^* - E_{\phi 2}H_{\theta 1}{}^*\} \right] \qquad (1)$$

The first term is the power due to the first radiator alone; the second is that due to the second radiator alone; the third term is a mutual power due to interaction of fields from the two. The mutual term would be obtained in the induced emf method from components of induced fields from charges and changing magnetic effects of the first radiator in phase with currents of the second radiator, and vice versa. It must be emphasized that current distribution assumptions over all radiators are still required for either method, and these may be difficult to make when it is necessary to consider the mutual interaction of several radiators. The induced emf method gives some clue to this mutual effect upon current distribution, and Carter[6] has by this method calculated mutual effects of parallel linear radiators, interpreting the problem of finding relative current distributions between several such radiators as a circuit problem.

Especially important is the problem of identical radiators with

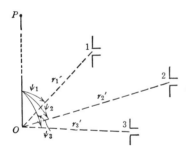

Fig. 12·13 Coordinate system for a general array.

similar current distributions (though magnitudes and phases of currents in individual radiators need not be the same). The radiation vector for one of these alone may be calculated as $\bar{N}_0$. Differences in the distances from the radiators to a far removed point where field is to be calculated is again important only as it affects phase differences, and not as it affects magnitude or direction. Thus the total radiation vector for the system of radiators, if these all have the same orientation, may be written

$$\bar{N} = \bar{N}_0(C_1 e^{jkr_1' \cos \psi_1} + C_2 e^{jkr_2' \cos \psi} + \cdots) \qquad (2)$$

C_1, C_2, etc., are complex numbers giving the relative magnitudes and phases of currents in the several individual radiators; r_1', r_2', etc., are radii from the common origin to the reference origin of the individual radiators; ψ_1, ψ_2, etc., are the angles between r_1', r_2' and the direction of the radius from the common origin to the point at which field is to be calculated (Fig. 12·13). It follows that the total radiation intensity

[6] P. S. Carter, *Proc. I.R.E.*, **20**, 1004–1041 (June 1932).

may be written in terms of the radiation intensity K_0 for one radiator alone.

$$K = K_0 \left| C_1 e^{jkr_1' \cos \psi_1} + C_2 e^{jkr_2' \cos \psi_2} + \cdots \right|^2 \tag{3}$$

The use of these forms will be clearer from the examples to follow.

PROBLEMS

12·13a A section of parallel-wire transmission line when properly terminated may be approximately considered as two wires along which waves are propagating, the currents being opposite in phase at any point along the line. Neglect the radiation from the termination and the mutual effect between the termination and the lines, and compute the radiated power from the line by the method described in Art. 12·13. Use results for a single wire with traveling wave from Art. 12·10.

12·13b Given a radiator with horizontal current elements only of radiation intensity K_0, show that, if this is placed at a height h above earth which may be assumed plane and perfectly conducting,

$$K = 4K_0 \sin^2 (kh \cos \theta)$$

The vertical direction is taken as the axis, $\theta = 0$.

12·13c How is the result of Prob. 12·13b revised if the $\theta = 0$ axis is taken horizontal and the vertical direction defines $\phi = 0$?

12·13d What conclusions similar to those of Prob. 12·13b can be derived for antennas with vertical current elements only, if placed with their reference origin a distance h above earth?

12·14   EXAMPLE: ARRAY OF TWO HALF-WAVE DIPOLES

Consider two half-wave dipoles separated by a quarter-wavelength and fed by currents equal in magnitude and 90° out of time phase, as in Fig. 12·14a. For a single dipole (Prob. 12·10b),

$$K_0 = \frac{15}{\pi} I^2 \frac{\cos^2 [(\pi/2) \cos \theta]}{\sin^2 \theta}$$

For the two dipoles with the origin as shown in Fig. 12·14a,

$$r_1' = 0 \qquad r_2' = \frac{\lambda}{4} \qquad \theta_2' = \frac{\pi}{2} \qquad \phi_2' = 0$$

so
$$\cos \psi_2' = \sin \theta \cos \phi$$

If
$$I_2 = I_1 e^{-j(\pi/2)}$$

Then
$$K = K_0 \left| 1 + e^{-j(\pi/2)} e^{j(\pi/2)(\sin \theta \cos \phi)} \right|^2$$

$$= 4K_0 \cos^2 \left[\frac{\pi}{4} (\sin \theta \cos \phi - 1) \right]$$

A horizontal radiation intensity pattern is plotted in Fig. 12·14b.

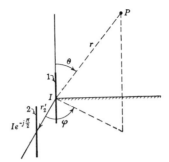

Fig. 12·14a   Combination of two half-wave dipoles.

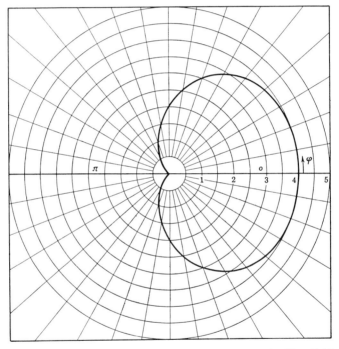

Fig. 12·14b   Polar plot of relative power intensity radiation for Fig. 12·14a in the plane $\theta = \pi/2$.

PROBLEM

12·14   Plot radiation intensity patterns for the following half-wave dipole arrays in vertical and horizontal planes.

(a) Two parallel dipoles fed in phase with equal currents and placed $\lambda/2$ apart.

(b) Four parallel dipoles fed in phase with equal currents and spaced $\lambda/2$ apart

(c) Two dipoles placed end to end, fed in phase with equal currents.

(d) Same as (c) but with four dipoles.

(e) Same as (d) but with a perfectly conducting reflecting plane parallel to the dipoles at distance $\lambda/4$.

12·15 THE RHOMBIC ANTENNA

The rhombic antenna[7, 8] has four wire elements which form the boundary of a rhombus in space, as shown in Fig. 12·15.

The antenna is fed at O and terminated at A by the proper resistance; therefore energy travels along the wires only from O toward A, no reflected waves traveling back from A toward O. This may be analyzed as a system of combined elements, the elements having energy traveling along them in only one direction. Since the elements do not have the same orientation, addition must be by components.

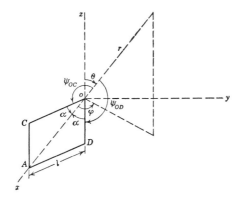

Fig. 12·15 Rhombic antenna and selected coordinate system.

The radiation vector for a single wire with energy traveling at the velocity of light in only one direction, Ie^{-jkl}, has only the direction of the wire (Art. 12·10).

$$N_s = \frac{I[1 - e^{-jkl(1- \cos \psi)}]}{jk(1 - \cos \psi)} = \frac{I}{jk} f(\psi) \tag{1}$$

The subscript s denotes the direction of the wire, and ψ is the angle between the wire and the radius vector to the distant point (r, θ, ϕ) at which field is desired. The angles ψ for the various elements, in terms of the coordinates shown in Fig. 12·15, are found to be

$$\cos \psi_{OC} = \cos \psi_{DA} = \sin \theta \cos (\phi + \alpha) \tag{2}$$

$$\cos \psi_{OD} = \cos \psi_{CA} = \sin \theta \cos (\phi - \alpha)$$

The currents at O for OC and OD are 180° out of phase. They may be taken as I and $-I$. The currents at the beginning of CA and DA

[7] Donald Foster, *Proc. I.R.E.*, **25**, 1327–1353 (Oct. 1937).
[8] Bruce, Beck, Lowry, *Proc. I.R.E.*, **23**, 24–46 (Jan. 1935).

(at C and D respectively) are then Ie^{-jkl} and $-Ie^{-jkl}$. Components of radiation vector may now be added, taking into account the differences in phase with respect to the common origin O.

$$r_{OC}' = r_{OD}' = 0 \qquad r_{CA}' = r_{DA}' = l$$

So
$$N_x = \cos \alpha [N_1 + N_2 + N_3 e^{jkl \cos \psi_{OC}} + N_4 e^{jkl \cos \psi_{OD}}]$$

$$N_y = \sin \alpha [-N_1 + N_2 + N_3 e^{jkl \cos \psi_{OC}} - N_4 e^{jkl \cos \psi_{OD}}]$$

$$N_z = 0$$

where
$$N_1 = \frac{I}{jk} f(\psi_{OC}) \qquad N_2 = -\frac{I}{jk} f(\psi_{OD})$$

$$N_3 = \frac{Ie^{-jkl}}{jk} f(\psi_{OD}) \qquad N_4 = -\frac{I}{jk} e^{-jkl} f(\psi_{OC})$$

and $f(\psi)$ is defined by (1).

Define also

$$S = S(\psi_{OC}\psi_{OD}) = \frac{[1 - e^{-jkl(1-\cos \psi_{OC})}][1 - e^{-jkl(1-\cos \psi_{OD})}]}{(1 - \cos \psi_{OC})(1 - \cos \psi_{OD})} \tag{3}$$

Then
$$N_x = \frac{IS \cos \alpha}{jk} [\cos \psi_{OC} - \cos \psi_{OD}]$$

$$= -\frac{2IS}{jk} \sin \theta \sin \phi \sin \alpha \cos \alpha \tag{4}$$

Similarly,

$$N_y = -\frac{2IS}{jk} \sin \alpha (1 - \sin \theta \cos \phi \cos \alpha) \tag{5}$$

The components of radiation vector in spherical coordinates may be written in terms of the cartesian components N_x and N_y [Eq. 12·09(12)].

$$N_\theta = (N_x \cos \phi + N_y \sin \phi) \cos \theta = -\frac{2IS}{jk} \sin \alpha \sin \phi \cos \theta \tag{6}$$

$$N_\phi = (-N_x \sin \phi + N_y \cos \phi) = -\frac{2IS}{jk} \sin \alpha [\cos \phi - \sin \theta \cos \alpha] \tag{7}$$

The radiation intensity is [Eq. 12·09(8)],

$$K = \frac{\eta}{8\lambda^2} [|N_\theta|^2 + |N_\phi|^2]$$

$$= \frac{4I^2 \eta}{8\lambda^2 k^2} |S|^2 [\sin^2 \phi \cos^2 \theta + (\cos \phi - \sin \theta \cos \alpha)^2] \sin^2 \alpha \tag{8}$$

By trigonometric substitutions in the quantity in brackets,

$$K = \frac{4I^2\eta^2}{8\lambda^2 k^2} \mid S \mid^2 \{[1 - \sin\theta\cos(\phi + \alpha)][1 - \sin\theta\cos(\phi - \alpha)]\} \sin^2\alpha$$

$$= \frac{4I^2\eta}{8\lambda^2 k^2} \mid S \mid^2 [1 - \cos\psi_{OC}][1 - \cos\psi_{OD}] \sin^2\alpha \tag{9}$$

S, defined by (3), has a magnitude,

$$\mid S \mid = \frac{4\sin[(kl/2)(1 - \cos\psi_{OC})]\sin[(kl/2)(1 - \cos\psi_{OD})]}{(1 - \cos\psi_{OC})(1 - \cos\psi_{OD})}$$

For air, $\qquad \eta = 120\pi \qquad$ and $\qquad k = \dfrac{2\pi}{\lambda}$

so

$$K = \frac{240I^2}{\pi}\sin^2\alpha\,\frac{\sin^2[(kl/2)(1 - \cos\psi_{OC})]\sin^2[(kl/2)(1 - \cos\psi_{OD})]}{(1 - \cos\psi_{OC})(1 - \cos\psi_{OD})} \tag{10}$$

where ψ_{OC} and ψ_{OD} are defined by (2).

From this expression for radiation intensity, it is seen that, for large values of $kl/2$, K may become zero many times (each time $\cos\psi_{OC}$, $\cos\psi_{OD}$ are unity, or when $(kl/2)(1 - \cos\psi) = n\pi$). The radiation pattern may then have many lobes. By properly proportioning the angle α and the length l, these lobes may be changed in relative magnitude and the directivity pattern altered greatly.

If a horizontal rhombic antenna is located at height h above a plane earth which may be considered perfectly conducting, the result of Prob. 12·13b may be applied directly to find total radiation intensity.

$$K = 4K_0\sin^2(kh\cos\theta) \tag{11}$$

K_0 is the radiation intensity for a single rhombic by (10).

PROBLEMS

12·15a For a rhombic with $l = 3.5\lambda$, $\alpha = 24°$, plot a vertical radiation intensity pattern (in plane $\phi = 0$) and a horizontal pattern (in plane $\theta = \pi/2$).

12·15b How is the vertical pattern revised if the rhombus is placed 2λ above earth?

12·16 LINEAR ARRAYS

An especially important class of arrays is that in which the elements are arranged along a straight line, with an equal spacing between

elements, as indicated in Fig. 12·16a.   Let the line be the z axis, with
the basic spacing d and coefficients $a_0, a_1, \cdots a_{N-1}$ representing

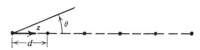

Fig. 12·16a   Coordinate system for a
linear array.

the relative currents in elements at
$z = 0, d, \cdots, (N-1)d$.   (Note
that any of the elements can be
missing, in which case the coefficient
is zero, so the elements need only
be of commensurate spacing instead
of equal spacing.)   If the elements have a radiation vector $\bar{N}_0$,
Eq. 12·13(2) becomes for this case

$$\bar{N} = \bar{N}_0[a_0 + a_1 e^{jkd \cos \theta} + \cdots a_{N-1} e^{j(N-1)kd \cos \theta}] = \bar{N}_0 S(\theta) \quad (1)$$

Where $S(\theta)$ may be called the space factor of the array,

$$S(\theta) = \sum_{n=0}^{N-1} a_n e^{jnkd \cos \theta} \quad (2)$$

The radiation intensity from Eq. 12·13(3) is then

$$K = K_0 \left| S \right|^2 \quad (3)$$

Broadside Array.   If all currents in the linear array are equal in
magnitude and phase, it is evident from physical reasoning that the
contributions to radiation will add in phase in the plane perpendicular
to the axis of the array ($\theta = \pi/2$).   For this reason, the array is called
a *broadside array*.   Moreover, it is evident that, if the total length l is
long compared with wavelength, the phase of contributions from
various elements will change rapidly as angle is changed slightly from
the maximum, so the maximum in this case would be expected to be
sharp.   To see this from (2), let all $a_n = a_0$.

$$S(\theta) = a_0 \sum_{n=0}^{N-1} e^{jnkd \cos \theta} = a_0 \frac{1 - e^{jNkd \cos \theta}}{1 - e^{jkd \cos \theta}} \quad (4)$$

The summation above is effected by the rule for a geometric progres-
sion.   Then

$$\left| S \right|^2 = a_0{}^2 \frac{\sin^2 \frac{1}{2} (Nkd \cos \theta)}{\sin^2 \frac{1}{2} (kd \cos \theta)} \quad (5)$$

Relation (4) is plotted as a function of ($kd \cos \theta$) in Fig. 12·16b for
$N = 10$.   Note that the peak of the main lobe occurs at $kd \cos \theta = 0$
(or $\theta = \pi/2$) as expected.   The width of the main lobe may be

described by giving the angles at which radiation goes to zero. If we set these angles as $\theta = \pi/2 \pm \Delta/2$,

$$Nkd \cos\left(\frac{\pi}{2} \pm \frac{\Delta}{2}\right) = \mp 2\pi$$

$$\Delta = 2 \sin^{-1}\left(\frac{\lambda}{Nd}\right) \approx \frac{2\lambda}{l} \tag{6}$$

The last approximation is for large N. So we see that the beam becomes narrow as l/λ becomes large, as predicted.

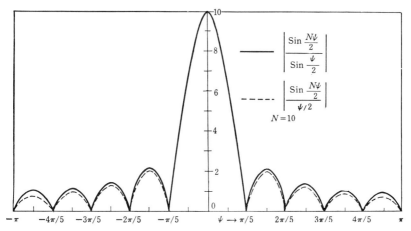

Fig. 12·16b   Plot of space factor and approximation with 10 elements. ψ is $kd \cos \theta$ for a broadside array and $(1 - kd \cos \theta)$ for an end-fire array.

If N is large, the denominator of (5) remains small over several of the lobes near the main lobe. Over this region it is then a good approximation to set the sine equal to the angle in the denominator.

$$|S|^2 \approx N^2 a_0^2 \frac{\sin^2 \frac{1}{2}(Nkd \cos \theta)}{(\frac{1}{2} Nkd \cos \theta)^2} \tag{7}$$

This approximation is compared as a dotted curve with the accurate curve for $N = 10$ in Fig. 12·16b, and is found to agree well over several maxima. Thus, for large N, this universal form applies near $\theta = \pi/2$ and the first secondary maximum is observed to be about 0.045 of the absolute maximum, or 13.5 db below.

The gain of an array is usually expressed as though the elements were isotropic radiators. The gain is of course modified if actual elements having some directivity are employed, but, for high-gain arrays, the modification is small. (Note that it is not correct to multiply gain of the array by gain of a single element.)   For the array,

$$g = \frac{4\pi \left| S_{\max} \right|^2}{2\pi \int_0^\pi \left| S \right|^2 \sin \theta \, d\theta} \tag{8}$$

The high-gain broadside array gives most of its contribution to the integral in the denominator near $\theta = \pi/2$, where the approximate expression (7) applies.

$$\int_0^\pi \left| S \right|^2 \sin \theta \, d\theta = \frac{2N^2 a_0^2}{Nkd} \int_0^{Nkd} \frac{\sin^2 \psi/2}{(\psi/2)^2} \, d\psi \rightarrow \frac{4N^2 a_0^2}{Nkd} \cdot \frac{\pi}{2}$$

From (8),

$$g \approx \frac{N^2 a_0^2}{N^2 a_0^2 \pi} \times Nkd = \frac{2l}{\lambda} \qquad \left(\text{large } \frac{l}{\lambda} \right) \tag{9}$$

End-Fire Arrays. If the elements of the array are progressively delayed in phase just enough to make up for the retardation of the waves, it would be expected that the radiation from all elements of the array could be made to add up in the direction of the array axis. Such an array is called an *end fire array.* To accomplish this, let

$$a_n = a_0 e^{-jnkd} \tag{10}$$

Then in (2)

$$S = a_0 \sum_{n=0}^{N-1} e^{-jnkd(1-\cos \theta)} = a_0 \frac{1 - e^{-jNkd(1-\cos \theta)}}{1 - e^{-jkd(1-\cos \theta)}} \tag{11}$$

$$\left| S \right|^2 = \frac{\sin^2 \frac{1}{2}[Nkd(1-\cos \theta)]}{\sin^2 \frac{1}{2}[kd(1-\cos \theta)]} a_0^2 \tag{12}$$

By comparison with (5), it is recognized that the plot of Fig. 12·16b made for a broadside array may be utilized for the end-fire also if the abscissa is interpreted as $kd(1 - \cos \theta)$. The pattern as a function of θ of course looks different, but the ratio of secondary to primary maxima is the same.   It may also be shown to follow that the formula for gain (9) applies also to an end-fire array with large l/λ. To obtain the angular width of the main lobe, let $\Delta/2$ be the angle at which S goes to zero.

$$Nkd \left(1 - \cos \frac{\Delta}{2} \right) = 2\pi$$

$$\Delta \approx 2 \sqrt{\frac{2\lambda}{l}} \tag{13}$$

Polynomial Formulation of Arrays.   If we let

$$\zeta = e^{j\psi} = e^{jkd\cos\theta} \tag{14}$$

equation (2) may be written as a polynomial in ζ.

$$S = \sum_{n=0}^{N-1} a_n \zeta^n \tag{15}$$

Schelkunoff[9] has shown that useful results may be obtained by considering the properties of this complex polynomial relation between S and ζ. The location of the zeros of S in the ζ plane are especially important.

Note first that real θ corresponds to values of ζ on the unit circle with phase angles between $-kd$ and kd. All, a part, or none of the $N-1$ zeros of S may occur in this part of the unit circle. When they do so occur, they correspond to true zeros of the pattern, or "cones of silence." The broadside array, Eq. (5), has its zeros spread out uniformly over the entire unit circle except for the missing one at $\psi = 0$ (Fig. 12·16c), where the very large main lobe builds up. One approach to the synthesis of arrays is then that of positioning zeros on this picture so that they are close together where the pattern is to be of small amplitude, and farther apart where it is to build up to a relatively large value. Potential analogues to the complex function are useful in this synthesis procedure.

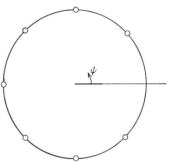

Fig. 12·16c Location of zeros of polynomial representing a uniform broadside array.

PROBLEMS

12·16a Set up the exact formula for gain of an array of elements which are not isotropic radiators. Show that it is not correct to set tne gain equal to the gain of the element alone multiplied by the gain of the array. Explain physically why, for high-gain array, the over-all gain is nearly that of the array.

12·16b Derive formula (9) for the approximate gain of an end-fire array with large l/λ.

12·16c Show the location of the zeros of S in the ζ plane for the end-fire array.

[9] S. A. Schelkunoff, "A Mathematical Theory of Linear Arrays," *Bell Sys. Tech. J.*, **22**, 80–107 (Jan. 1943).

12·17   LIMITATIONS ON DIRECTIVITY

If we limit ourselves to linear arrays with currents in phase, it can be shown that the uniform array (one with all currents of equal amplitude) gives more gain than arrays with non-uniform excitations. However, still greater gains are possible in principle if one goes to excitations of other phases.   Arrays having more gain than the uniform array are known as *super-gain arrays*.

In terms of the picture in the ζ plane, as given in the preceding article, we see that for an element spacing less than a half-wavelength ($kd = \pi$) the range of real θ covers only a part of the unit circle.   The uniform array, however, has its zeros spread over all the unit circle, so some are "invisible."   Schelkunoff has shown that arbitrarily high

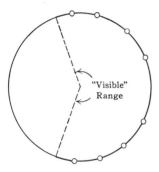

Fig. 12·17   Positioning   of zeros of polynomial to produce a super-gain array.

gain for a given antenna size is possible in principle by moving the zeros into the range of real θ, properly distributed to give the desired directivity (Fig. 12·17).   The trouble here is that a monstrous lobe builds up in the "invisible" range from which the zeros have been eliminated, which might seem to be of no concern, but it turns out to represent reactive energy and so is of importance.   It is surprising to find the rapidity with which this limitation takes over.   For high-gain broadside arrays, no significant increase in gain is possible over that of the uniform array before the reactive energy becomes impossibly large.[10]   For end-fire arrays, a modest increase is possible, and has been utilized in practice.[11]   Another way of stating the above limitation is that currents of the elements become huge for a given power radiated and fluctuate in phase from one element to the next so that it would be impossible to feed such an array.

A more direct physical picture is provided by looking at the problem from a wave point of view.   Imagine that we are attempting to produce a high-gain broadside array with a thin pancake pattern near the equator.   We may imagine the distant fields (H_ϕ and E_θ) of this pattern expanded in a series of the spherically symmetrical TM modes of the type studied in Art. 10·09.   If the pattern is to be sharp, it is clear that we shall require waves of very high order to represent this

[10] L. J. Chu, *J. Appl. Phys.*, **19**, 1163–1175 (Dec. 1948).
[11] W. W. Hansen and J. R. Woodyard, *Proc. I.R.E.*, **26**, 333–345 (March 1938)

pattern (order of $2\pi/\Delta$ for a narrow beam of angle Δ). A study of the Hankel functions shows that these change character at a radius such that n is of the order kr, becoming rapidly reactive for radii less than this value. Hence, the antenna boundary must extend approximately to this radius if excessive reactive power is to be avoided. That is

$$\frac{2r}{\lambda} \approx \frac{n}{\pi} \approx \frac{2}{\Delta} \tag{1}$$

which gives a relation between angle and length equivalent to that for a uniform broadside array, Eq. 12·16(6). The phenomenon is a cut-off of the type found in sectoral horns, Art. 9·12, where it was found that reactive effects caused an effective cut-off when the cross section became too small to support the required number of half-wave variations in the pattern. The rapidity with which the limitation takes over must again be stressed. For an array 50 wavelengths long, a halving in size from that of the uniform array would require reactive power 10^{59} times the radiated power.

It should not be inferred from the above discussion that uniform arrays are always best. Often the side-lobe level (13.5 db) is higher than can be tolerated. These can be reduced at a sacrifice in gain. Dolph[12] has given the procedure for finding the array of a given number of elements which gives the lowest side lobes for a prescribed antenna gain, or highest gain for a prescribed side-lobe level. The polynomial $S(\zeta)$ in Eq. 12·16(15) has in this case the form of a Tchebycheff polynomial.

PROBLEMS

12·17a By studying the properties of the spherical-wave functions, verify the statements made above that wave orders up to at least $2\pi/\Delta$ will be required to represent thin patterns of angle Δ and that energy is predominantly reactive for radii less than $n\lambda/2\pi$. Demonstrate that at this transition radius, the number of sinusoidal variations in the pattern just fits the number of wavelengths about the spherical surface.

12·17b Consider the following polynomials representing five element arrays with spacing $kd = \pi/2$.

$$S_1(\zeta) = (\zeta - e^{j2\pi/5})(\zeta - e^{-j2\pi/5})(\zeta - e^{j4\pi/5})(\zeta - e^{-j4\pi/5})$$

$$S_2(\zeta) = (\zeta - e^{j\pi/5})(\zeta - e^{-j\pi/5})(\zeta - e^{j2\pi/5})(\zeta - e^{-j2\pi/5})$$

The first is a uniform array and the second a "super-gain" array, since it has all zeros in the visible range. Multiply out to display the relative element currents and comment on the comparison. Plot $|S(\theta)|$ versus θ for both arrays and compare.

[12] C. L. Dolph, *Proc. I.R.E.*, **34**, 335–348 (June 1946).

Field and Power Calculations with Fields Assumed over a Surface

12·18 FORMULATION IN TERMS OF EQUIVALENT CURRENTS

For wire antennas of the type discussed in previous articles, it is fairly natural to assume a current distribution over the antenna. When this is done, radiation can be calculated, as has been outlined. For others of the examples of Art. 12·02, such as the electromagnetic horns, slot antennas, or parabolic reflectors, it would be difficult to make good approximations to current over the radiators. For these types, however, it is possible to make reasonable approximations to field over an aperture, and it turns out that radiation can be calculated from this starting point as well. This is not unexpected, for Huygens' principle states that any wave front can be considered the source of secondary waves which add up to produce distant wave fronts. The following formulations can be considered precise statements of this general principle.

Of the several possible ways of formulating the equations for use with assumptions of field distributions near the source, the method chosen for the initial study is broken into steps, and it is possible to form relatively sound physical pictures for each of these steps.[13] A neater but less revealing mathematical formulation will be given later in the article. The present study takes advantage of the techniques developed in past studies and follows these stages:

1. Once the fields arising from the source are assumed over some known surface, it is possible to replace the currents and charges of the real source by imaginary current sheets over the surface where fields are assumed, these being selected to produce the fields assumed at that surface with the actual source removed. (The kinds and amounts of currents required are discussed later in this article.)

2. The problem from this point on is of the same type as that worked previously: from some given distribution of currents, fields may be found and the radiated energy calculated by Poynting's theorem.

Suppose, for an example, that the field to the right of the conducting plane, region B of Fig. 12·18a, is desired. If the exact current and charge sources in region A to the left of the plane, the sources which actually produce the electromagnetic energy, were known, we could theoretically solve for the desired field, subject to the boundary conditions of the leaky plane. The mathematics would not be pleasant. However, if the field at the surface of the opening arising from those

[13] S. A. Schelkunoff, *Bell Sys. Tech. J.*, **15**, 92–112 (1936); *Phys. Rev.*, **56**, 308–316 (1939).

sources were known exactly, it would do just as well, as far as region B is concerned, to replace the actual currents and charges of region A by fictitious currents and charges lying in the surface of the opening, provided these could be made to produce the same fields at the opening. For, with the conditions over the opening unchanged, and all other boundaries of region B unchanged, the proper solution to Maxwell's equations in region B would be unchanged.

In general, the field that must be produced along the selected surface may have normal and tangential components of electric field, and normal and tangential components of magnetic field. However, at any boundary it is necessary only to know the tangential magnetic and

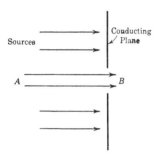

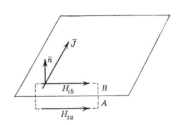

Fig. 12·18a   Conducting plane
with aperture.

Fig. 12·18b.

electric fields, for then Maxwell's equations will provide the normal components (Art. 4·12). Let us consider then what fictitious currents must be placed over the opening in the absence of the actual sources to give the same fields in region B that the true sources in region A were causing. The problem is easy and old to us in the case of the tangential magnetic field. For, as indicated in Fig. 12·18b, a surface current density J on a given surface will result in a discontinuity of magnetic field components tangential to the surface and normal to $\bar{J}$. That is, the difference between tangential H on one side of the sheet and that on the other,

$$H_{tb} - H_{ta} = J$$

Thus, if the current sheet over the opening in the plane is to replace completely the effect of the sources in A which are producing a given H_t tangent to the boundary, there must be a current density $\bar{J}$ on this sheet, given by $J = H_t$ in magnitude. The direction will be included if we write

$$\bar{J} = \bar{n} \times \bar{H} \qquad (1)$$

where $\bar{n}$ is the unit vector normal to the surface pointing into the region B, and $\bar{H}$ is the total magnetic field. Such a current sheet will wipe out the tangential magnetic field on the A side of the surface (just as though there were no sources in A) but will leave a tangential field as before of magnitude $J = H_t$ on the B side. Thus the current sheet is exactly as effective as the source, which is now assumed absent, in producing tangential magnetic field at the boundary.

Now, the replacing of the sources in so far as they produce tangential electric field would be just as quickly done if only there were such a thing as magnetic currents. Then we could write that the magnetic surface current density $\bar{M}$ is

$$\bar{M} = -\bar{n} \times \bar{E} \qquad (2)$$

Also, by analogy with the magnetic vector potential, which for surface currents is written

$$\bar{A} = \mu \int_S \frac{\bar{J}e^{-jkr}}{4\pi r} \, dS \qquad (3)$$

there could be defined an electric vector potential, say,

$$\bar{F} = \epsilon \int_S \frac{\bar{M}e^{-jkr}}{4\pi r} \, dS \qquad (4)$$

Maxwell's equations, if there were such things as magnetic current i_m and magnetic charge ρ_m, would be

$$\nabla \cdot \bar{D} = \rho_e$$

$$\nabla \cdot \bar{B} = \rho_m$$

$$\nabla \times \bar{E} = -\bar{\imath}_m - \frac{\partial \bar{B}}{\partial t} \qquad (5)$$

$$\nabla \times \bar{H} = \bar{\imath}_e + \frac{\partial \bar{D}}{\partial t}$$

and the fields at any distance from the source currents would be obtained from the two vector potentials $\bar{A}$ and $\bar{F}$.

$$\bar{E} = -j\omega\bar{A} - \frac{j\omega}{k^2} \nabla(\nabla \cdot \bar{A}) - \frac{1}{\epsilon} \nabla \times \bar{F} \qquad (6)$$

$$\bar{H} = -j\omega\bar{F} - \frac{j\omega}{k^2} \nabla(\nabla \cdot \bar{F}) + \frac{1}{\mu} \nabla \times \bar{A} \qquad (7)$$

Although the above forms of the augmented Maxwell's equations would be directly applicable if magnetic currents and charges were found in nature, that is not the point for the present discussion. We are using these names and symbols as equivalents, respectively, for tangential electric field and normal magnetic field at a surface. The intermediate quantities need not appear, since we could substitute $-(\bar{n} \times \bar{E})$ for $\bar{M}$ in (4) and $(\bar{n} \times \bar{H})$ for $\bar{J}$ in (3), so potentials would be given directly in terms of tangential field components. The advantage of the procedure is in the opportunity it gives to build physical pictures by analogies between the electric and magnetic sources. Stratton and Chu[14] have derived important basic forms in terms of the fields on a surface by directly integrating Maxwell's equations. A typical form is

$$\bar{E}' = -\frac{1}{4\pi} \int_S \{ -j\omega\mu(\bar{n} \times \bar{H})\psi + (\bar{n} \times \bar{E}) \times \nabla\psi + (\bar{n} \cdot \bar{E})\nabla\psi \} \, dS$$

(8)

$$\bar{H}' = \frac{1}{4\pi} \int_S \{ -j\omega\epsilon(\bar{n} \times \bar{E})\psi - (\bar{n} \times \bar{H}) \times \nabla\psi - (\bar{n} \cdot \bar{H})\nabla\psi \} \, dS \quad (9)$$

$\bar{E}'$ and $\bar{H}'$ are fields at any point inside the surface S, $\bar{E}$ and $\bar{H}$ are the fields on the surface, r is the distance from the differential element dS to the point at which $\bar{E}'$ and $\bar{H}'$ are being evaluated, and $\psi = e^{-jkr}/r$. The above forms assume fields continuous over a closed surface. As we shall see, it is often expedient to assume fields only over an aperture, taking fields zero outside and thus introducing a discontinuity which Stratton and Chu take into account by adding contributions $\bar{E}''$ and $\bar{H}''$ resulting from charges on the discontinuity. These are given by the following integrals taken about the contour of the discontinuity.

$$\bar{E}'' = \frac{1}{4\pi j\omega\epsilon} \oint (\nabla\psi)\bar{H} \cdot \overline{dl} \tag{10}$$

$$\bar{H}'' = -\frac{1}{4\pi j\omega\mu} \oint (\nabla\psi)\bar{E} \cdot \overline{dl} \tag{11}$$

Because contour integrals as in (10) and (11) do not appear in the earlier formulation in terms of equivalent currents, the two methods would not appear to be equivalent. They are, however, as the terms

[14] J. A. Stratton and L. J. Chu, *Phys. Rev.*, **56**, 99–107 (1939); also Stratton's *Electromagnetic Theory*.

are implicit in that formulation because it is consistent with the continuity equation. In following examples, we shall use the first formulation because of the advantages in breaking the calculation into steps.

It should be stressed that the method would be exact if the exact fields over a complete closed surface surrounding the distant field point (and therefore including infinity) were known exactly. This is seldom the case, but we can often make good enough approximations to obtain useful results, as will be demonstrated in following articles.

If we are concerned only with the radiation field, the usual approximations appropriate to great distances can be employed, and the general formulation of Art. 12·09 extended. A magnetic radiation vector $\bar{L}$ may be related to vector potential $\bar{F}$ as $\bar{N}$ was to $\bar{A}$. Thus, consistent with the assumptions listed previously,

$$\bar{F} = \epsilon \frac{e^{-jkr}}{4\pi r} \bar{L} \tag{12}$$

where
$$\bar{L} = \int_V \bar{i}_m e^{jkr' \cos \psi} \, dV' \tag{13}$$

If electric and magnetic field components are now written in the usual way in terms of these two vector potentials, the only components not decreasing faster than $(1/r)$ are

$$E_\theta = -j \frac{e^{-jkr}}{2\lambda r} \left(\eta N_\theta + L_\phi \right) \qquad H_\phi = \frac{E_\theta}{\eta} \tag{14}$$

$$E_\phi = j \frac{e^{-jkr}}{2\lambda r} \left(-\eta N_\phi + L_\theta \right) \qquad H_\theta = -\frac{E_\phi}{\eta} \tag{15}$$

So the radiation intensity,

$$K = \frac{\eta}{8\lambda^2} \left[\left| N_\theta + \frac{L_\phi}{\eta} \right|^2 + \left| N_\phi - \frac{L_\theta}{\eta} \right|^2 \right] \tag{16}$$

12·19 ELEMENTAL PLANE WAVE SOURCE

The radiation vector and radiation intensity may be calculated for a differential surface element on a uniform plane wave. Such an element might be considered the elemental radiating source in radiation calculations from field distributions, as was the differential current element for radiation calculations from current distributions.

The plane wave source, that is, one that produces $\bar{E}$ and $\bar{H}$ of constant direction, normal to each other, and in the ratio of magni-

tudes η over the area of interest may be replaced by equivalent electric
and magnetic current sheets over that area, Fig. 12·19.

If

$$\bar{E} = \bar{a}_x E_x \quad \text{and} \quad \bar{H} = \bar{a}_y H_y = \bar{a}_y \frac{E_x}{\eta} \tag{1}$$

the equivalent current sheets are

$$J_x = -H_y = -\frac{E_x}{\eta} \quad M_y = -E_x \tag{2}$$

If this is a source of infinitesimal area
dS (actually it need only be small
compared with wavelength for following results to hold), the radiation
vectors $\bar{N}$ and $\bar{L}$ become simply

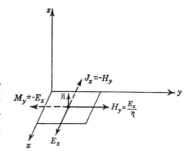

$$N_x = -\frac{E_x dS}{\eta} \quad L_y = -E_x dS$$

Fig. 12·19 Small plane wave
source and equivalent current
sheets.

The components in spherical coordinates:

$$N_\theta = -\frac{E_x dS}{\eta} \cos \phi \cos \theta \quad N_\phi = \frac{E_x dS}{\eta} \sin \phi \tag{3}$$

$$L_\theta = -E_x dS \sin \phi \cos \theta \quad L_\phi = -E_x dS \cos \phi$$

According to Eq. 12·18(16) the radiation intensity in this case may be
given by

$$K = \frac{E_x{}^2 (dS)^2}{\eta 8\lambda^2} [(-\cos \phi \cos \theta - \cos \phi)^2 + (\sin \phi + \sin \phi \cos \theta)^2]$$

$$K = \frac{E_x{}^2 (dS)^2}{2\eta\lambda^2} \cos^4 \frac{\theta}{2} \tag{4}$$

PROBLEM

12·19 From (2) we see that the plane wave source is equivalent to crossed
electric and magnetic infinitesimal dipoles. Find the fields for the latter, utilizing
duality and the known results for the electric dipole in Art. 12·05. By superposition, find fields for the two crossed dipoles and show that the pattern is consistent with that found above.

12·20 CIRCULAR APERTURE OR PARABOLIC REFLECTOR

Consider next a circular aperture illuminated by a uniform plane
wave polarized with electric and magnetic fields as shown in Fig.

12·20a.   We assume that field sources outside this circular aperture are negligible, so the problem is best represented by transmission through a circular hole in an absorbing screen.   However, the results may also apply approximately to a paraboloid of revolution in which

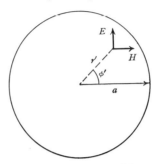

Fig. 12·20a   Circular aperture illuminated by uniform plane wave.

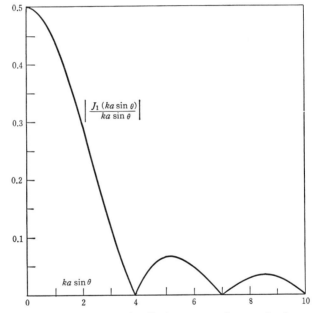

Fig. 12·20b   Approximate form of radiation pattern from a circular aperture for small θ.

one attempts to obtain a uniform plane wave illumination in the plane of the aperture from an approximate point source placed at the focus, though in practice this exact uniformity is not obtained.

We may utilize the results of the last article for radiation intensity from any small element of the plane wave, adding up contributions from various elements as explained in Art. 12·13. For an element at r', ϕ', as shown in Fig. 12·20a, the angle ψ is given by

$$\cos \psi = \sin \theta \cos (\phi - \phi')$$

Then utilizing the result from Eq. 12·19(4),

$$K = \frac{E_0{}^2}{2\eta\lambda^2} \cos^4 \frac{\theta}{2} \left| \int_0^{2\pi} \int_0^a e^{jkr' \sin \theta \cos (\phi-\phi')} r' \, dr' \, d\phi' \right|^2$$

$$= \frac{E_0{}^2}{2\eta\lambda^2} \cos^4 \frac{\theta}{2} \left| 2\pi \int_0^a J_0(kr' \sin \theta) r' \, dr' \right|^2 \tag{1}$$

The ϕ' integration was effected by means of the integral

$$\int_0^{2\pi} e^{jq \cos \phi} \, d\phi = 2\pi J_0(q)$$

The remaining integration utilizes Eq. 3·28(3).

$$K = \frac{2E_0{}^2\pi^2 a^4}{\eta\lambda^2} \cos^4 \frac{\theta}{2} \left| \frac{J_1(ka \sin \theta)}{(ka \sin \theta)} \right|^2 \tag{2}$$

For small θ the bracketed part of the expression governs the pattern and is plotted in Fig. 12·20b. Width of main beam between zeros is approximately

$$\Delta \approx 2\theta_0 = 2 \times \frac{3.83\lambda}{2\pi a} = \frac{1.22\lambda}{a} \tag{3}$$

This corresponds to a gain of approximately

$$g \approx \left(\frac{2\pi a}{\lambda}\right)^2 \qquad ka \gg 1 \tag{4}$$

Note that this can be written in the form

$$g = \frac{4\pi}{\lambda^2} \times \text{area} \tag{5}$$

which can be shown to be generally applicable to large apertures of any shape with uniform illumination.

Equations (3) and (4) are useful in the design of paraboloid reflectors, though a practical parabolic reflector may differ from this ideal in several respects. The feed system placed at the focus to illuminate the paraboloid necessarily disturbs the radiation pattern somewhat. Also, the feed is not a point source; therefore it produces variations in phase and amplitude over the circular aperture not accounted for above. Sometimes the illumination is purposely decreased near the edges to diminish the side lobes caused by diffraction at the edges. Most often illumination is not uniform in angle about the axis, so that the beam is wider in one plane than in another at right angles. Finally, radiation and diffraction effects from the supports may be of importance.

PROBLEMS

12·20a   When a half-wave dipole is used as the feed for a parabolic antenna, the radiated pattern from the system is known to be broader in the E plane (parallel to the dipole) than in the H plane (perpendicular to the dipole).   On the basis of what has been given, explain qualitatively why this is expected.   What happens if the feed system itself is made too directive?

12·20b   Suppose that all radiation was confined to a cone of angle Δ given by (3) and was of constant amplitude over this cone.   Give the gain and compare with (4).

12·20c   For $ka = 10$, give beam angle, gain, and plot K versus θ.

12·20d   Assuming that ka is large and that all significant radiation occurs in a region of small θ, derive the approximate formula for gain (4), starting from (2). Given the integral,

$$\int \frac{1}{x} J_1{}^2(\alpha x)\, dx = -\frac{1}{2} [J_0{}^2(\alpha x) + J_1{}^2(\alpha x)]$$

12·20e   Find the expression for radiation intensity for a rectangular aperture of dimensions a and b with uniform illumination.   By assumptions appropriate to large apertures, verify formula (5) for this shape.

12·21   RESONANT SLOT ANTENNA

Another important class of radiators in which the emphasis is on the field in the aperture is that of the slot antenna mentioned quali-

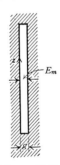

tatively in Art. 12·02.   Let us consider the case of the resonant slot antenna (approximately a half-wave long in an infinite plane conductor.[15]   Referring to Fig. 12·21, the electric field E_x across the gap is assumed to be the only significant aperture field, and this is assumed to be uniform in x and to have a half-sine distribution in z with its maximum at the center.   By reference to Eq. 12·18(2), the magnetic current sheet equivalent to this would be found to lie in the z direction and to be equal to E_x.

Fig.   12·21
Resonant
half-wave
slot.

$$M_z = E_x = E_m \cos kz \qquad (1)$$

However, to account for the infinite plane conductor, the above value must be doubled, which amounts to an imaging of the magnetic current in the infinite plane.   The necessity for this is not at first obvious, but it follows after careful study.

[15] N. Begovich, *Proc. I.R.E.*, **38,** 803–806 (July 1950).

If gap width g is taken as small, the equation for magnetic radiation vector, Eq. 12·18(13), becomes

$$L_z = \int_{-\lambda/4}^{\lambda/4} 2gE_m \cos kz' \, e^{jkz' \cos \theta} \, dz' \tag{2}$$

The integral is evaluated as in Art. 12·06.

$$L_z = \frac{4gE_m \cos [(\pi/2) \cos \theta]}{k \sin^2 \theta} \tag{3}$$

Then, utilizing Eq. 12·18(15), fields are

$$E_\phi = -\eta H_\theta = \frac{je^{-jkr}gE_m}{\pi r} \left[\frac{\cos [(\pi/2) \cos \theta]}{\sin \theta} \right] \tag{4}$$

We should note here that this is of the same form as the expression for fields about a half-wave dipole antenna (Art. 12·07) except for the interchange in electric and magnetic fields. Another difference arises in that expression (4) applies to only one side of the plane. If radiation is allowed in the backward direction, fields must be reversed there since normal electric field and tangential magnetic field are discontinuous at the conducting plane because of currents and charges there.

The power radiated corresponding to (4), counting both sides, is

$$W = \frac{2\pi(gE_m)^2}{2\pi^2 \eta} \int_0^\pi \frac{\cos^2 [(\pi/2) \cos \theta]}{\sin \theta} \, d\theta \tag{5}$$

This may be interpreted in terms of a radiation conductance defined in terms of the maximum gap voltage.

$$(G_r)_{\text{slot}} = \frac{2W}{(gE_m)^2} = \frac{2}{\pi \eta} \int_0^\pi \frac{\cos^2 [(\pi/2) \cos \theta]}{\sin \theta} \, d\theta \tag{6}$$

By comparing with the expression for radiation resistance of the half-wave dipole, Eq. 12·06(5), we find

$$(G_r)_{\text{slot}} = \frac{4(R_r)_{\text{dipole}}}{\eta^2} \approx 0.00205 \quad \text{mho} \tag{7}$$

The reciprocity between results for the slot and dipole can also be shown to follow from *Babinet's principle*, which is an extension of the principle of duality discussed in Art. 9·13.

PROBLEMS

12·21a Prove that the image of a magnetic current in a perfectly conducting plane requires horizontal currents in the same direction for source and image. In what sense is the field for this problem the dual of the field for the half-wave dipole?

12·21b Find the approximate radiation conductance if the slot is fed from a wave guide entering from the back so that shielding prevents radiation in the backward direction.

12·21c For the open end of a coaxial line of radii a and b, set up the problem of determining power radiated, assuming the electric field of the TEM mode as the only important field in the aperture. Make approximations appropriate to a line small in radius compared with wavelength, and show that the equivalent radiation resistance of the open end is

$$R = \frac{3\eta}{2\pi^3} \left[\frac{\lambda^2 \ln (b/a)}{\pi (b^2 - a^2)} \right]^2$$

Calculate the value for $a = 0.3$ cm, $b = 1$ cm, $\lambda = 30$ cm. What standing wave ratio would this produce in the line?

12·21d In Prob. c, assume the magnetic field of the TEM mode at the open end of sufficient magnitude to account for the energy calculated above. Show that a recalculation of power radiated including effects from this magnetic field leads to only a small correction to the first calculation. Take radii small compared with wavelength.

12·22 ELECTROMAGNETIC HORNS

The electromagnetic horns discussed qualitatively in Art. 12·02 are of interest both as directive radiators in themselves, and also as feed systems for reflectors or directive lens systems. In the horn, there is a gradual flare from the wave guide or transmission line to a larger aperture. This large aperture is desired to obtain directivity, and also to produce more efficient radiation by providing a better match to space. Usually, a fair approximation to aperture field may be made by studying the fields in the feeding system and the possible modes in the horn structure. This then makes possible approximate radiation calculations starting from these fields, by the methods discussed in preceding articles. The steps may be difficult because of difficulties in evaluating certain integrals, but as there are no new principles the details will not be covered here. Much is given in the literature.[16, 17] In utilizing theoretical results for practical horns, it should be remembered that the side-lobe structure especially will be different because of higher order modes, edge effects, and radiation from external surfaces and supports not accounted for in the assumptions for fields. Because of variations across the aperture, the gain will always be somewhat less than for the ideal large aperture with uniform illumi-

---

[16] L. J. Chu, *J. Appl. Phys.*, **11**, 603–610 (1940).

[17] W. L. Barrow and L. J. Chu, *Proc. I.R.E.*, **27**, 51–64 (1939); *Trans. A.I.E.E.*, **58**, 333–338 (1939).

nation, Eq. 12·20(5).

$$g < \frac{4\pi}{\lambda^2} \times \text{area} \tag{1}$$

For horns of rectangular apertures and moderate flare angles, the following results worked out by Chu[18] for radiation from the open end of a rectangular wave guide will be of help in estimating patterns. The coordinate system is as in Fig. 12·22.

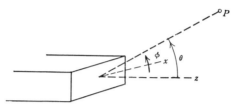

Fig. 12·22   Coordinate system for radiation from rectangular guide.

TM_{mn} *Modes.*   Field components in the radiation field are

$$E_\theta = \frac{mn\beta_{mn}\pi^3 ab}{4\lambda^2 rk_{cmn}{}^2} \sin \theta \left[1 + \frac{k}{\beta_{mn}} \cos \theta + \rho \left(1 - \frac{k}{\beta_{mn}} \cos \theta \right) \right]$$
$$\Psi_{mn}(\theta,\phi) \tag{2}$$

where

$$\Psi_{mn}(\theta,\phi)$$
$$= \left[\frac{\sin \left(\frac{1}{2} ka \sin \theta \cos \phi + \frac{m\pi}{2} \right)}{\left(\frac{1}{2} ka \sin \theta \cos \phi \right)^2 - \left(\frac{m\pi}{2} \right)^2} \right] \left[\frac{\sin \left(\frac{1}{2} kb \sin \theta \sin \phi + \frac{n\pi}{2} \right)}{\left(\frac{1}{2} kb \sin \theta \sin \phi \right)^2 - \left(\frac{n\pi}{2} \right)^2} \right]$$
$$\tag{3}$$

and ρ is the complex reflection coefficient in the guide, referred to the end.

TE_{mn} *Modes.*   With the same definition as (3),

$$E_\theta = - \frac{\eta(\pi ab)^2 \sin \theta}{2\lambda^3 rk_{cmn}{}^2} \left[1 + \frac{\beta_{mn}}{k} \cos \theta + \rho \left(1 - \frac{\beta_{mn}}{k} \cos \theta \right) \right]$$
$$\left[\left(\frac{m\pi}{a} \sin \phi \right)^2 - \left(\frac{n\pi}{b} \cos \phi \right)^2 \right] \Psi_{mn}(\theta,\phi) \tag{4}$$

[18] Given in S. Silver, *Microwave Antenna Theory and Design*, McGraw-Hill, 1949, Chapter 10.

$$E_\phi = - \frac{\eta(\pi ab)^2 \sin\theta \sin\phi \cos\phi}{2\lambda^3 r}$$
$$\left[\cos\theta + \frac{\beta_{mn}}{k} + \rho\left(\cos\theta - \frac{\beta_{mn}}{k}\right)\right]\Psi_{mn}(\theta,\phi) \quad (5)$$

The important special case of the TE_{10} mode is obtained by putting $m = 1$, $n = 0$ in (4) and (5).

Antenna Impedance by Approximate Solution of the Boundary-Value Problem

12·23   THE SPHERICAL ANTENNA

As we have seen in past articles, it is possible to tell much about the pattern of an antenna, its directivity properties, and the total power radiated by making reasonable assumptions concerning the currents of the radiator, or the fields over a surface surrounding the radiator. The methods considered do not tell much about the input impedance of the antenna, or antenna surface gradients. For these quantities it is necessary to go back to the field equations, attempting to obtain solutions which have greater validity in the immediate vicinity of the radiator. As we have mentioned, this is straightforward in principle but difficult to complete except in cases where the configuration is simple. The most generally useful results obtained in this manner are those of Schelkunoff, to be described later in the section. We shall start here with the simpler example of two hemispherical conductors with a gap at the equator across which a voltage is applied uniformly in azimuth, say by the driving system shown in Fig. 12·23a. (Perturbing effects of feeding transmission lines will be neglected in the analysis.) In this and other analyses using straightforward solution of Maxwell's equations subject to boundary conditions, we shall concentrate on the important problem of antenna impedance, but should stress that such solutions actually give answers to all of the problems discussed in Art. 12·01.

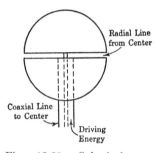

Fig. 12·23a Spherical antenna and possible driving system.

Labels in figure: Radial Line from Center; Coaxial Line to Center; Driving Energy

Superposition of TM Waves to Match Boundary Conditions. A study of the fields of Fig. 12·23a suggests solutions in spherical coordinates, uniform in azimuthal angle ϕ, and with field components E_r,

E_θ, and H_ϕ. Such solutions have been given as the spherical TM waves of Eq. 10·09(19). No single one of these will satisfy the boundary conditions of the spherical antenna, as the lowest order mode has been identified with the small dipole solution (Art. 12·05), and higher order modes correspond to higher order multipoles. So, as in similar static problems, we attempt a solution formed by a series of the modes with coefficients chosen to satisfy the appropriate boundary conditions.

The boundary conditions to be satisfied on the surface of the spherical antenna (assuming perfect conductivity for the sphere in the first approximation) are:

1. $E_\theta = 0$ at $r = a$, except across gap.
2. $E_\theta =$ applied field across gap, $\theta = (\pi/2) - \alpha$ to $(\pi/2) + \alpha$.

The distribution of E_θ across the gap is not known, but its integral across the gap (which is the same as the integral from 0 to π since E_θ is elsewhere zero) must be equal to the applied voltage.

$$V_0 = \int_{(\pi/2)-\alpha}^{(\pi/2)+\alpha} E_\theta a \, d\theta = \int_0^\pi E_\theta a \, d\theta \tag{1}$$

Now, if the exact distribution of E_θ across the gap were known, the function E_θ at $r = a$ could be expanded in a series. This series would be written in associated Legendre polynomials so that it might be compared directly with previous TM wave solutions. Known functions may be expanded in terms of these functions in a manner similar to that used to expand functions in a Fourier series, a series of Bessel functions, Art. 3·30, or a series of ordinary Legendre polynomials, Art. 3·32. The formula for the coefficients follows from the orthogonality properties of Eqs. 10·09(14) and 10·09(15).

$$f(\theta) = \sum_{n=1}^\infty b_n P_n^1 (\cos \theta) \tag{2}$$

where $$b_n = \frac{2n+1}{2n(n+1)} \int_0^\pi f(\theta) P_n^1 (\cos \theta) \sin \theta \, d\theta \tag{3}$$

The exact form of the $f(\theta)$ to be expanded, i.e., E_θ, is not known except that it is zero everywhere but at the gap. If the gap is truly small, we may approximate the answer to the integral (3) by assuming that $P_n^1 (\cos \theta)$ and $\sin \theta$ do not vary appreciably across the gap. That is, assume that $P_n^1 (\cos \theta)$ is approximately constant at its maximum value given by Eq. 10·09(13) and that $\sin \theta$ is constant at its maximum value of unity over the gap.   Then

$$b_n = \frac{2n + 1}{2n(n + 1)} P_n{}^1(0) \int_{(\pi/2) - \alpha}^{(\pi/2) + \alpha} E_\theta \, d\theta$$

The latter integral may be found directly from (1).

$$b_n = \frac{(2n + 1)P_n{}^1(0) V_0}{2n(n + 1)a}$$

and   (4)

$$E_\theta\big|_{r=a} = \sum_{n=1}^{\infty} b_n P_n{}^1(\cos \theta)$$

The above is exactly correct for an infinitesimal gap, but for any gap of finite size it will not give correct coefficients for the highest harmonics that vary appreciably over the region of the gap.

For the wave solution in the space surrounding the antenna, we are to add an infinite number of the TM waves found in Eq. 10·09(19). Following previous reasoning, the Bessel function solution should be the Hankel function of the second kind since the region surrounding the antenna extends to infinity.   Then E_θ at $r = a$ from Eq. 10·09(19) may be written

$$E_\theta\big|_{r=a} = \frac{j}{\omega \epsilon a^{3/2}} \sum_{n=1}^{\infty} A_n P_n{}^1(\cos \theta)[ka H_{n-1/2}{}^{(2)}(ka) - n H_{n+1/2}{}^{(2)}(ka)]$$

(5)

By comparing (5) with (4), A_n may be evaluated.

$$A_n = \frac{\omega \epsilon a^{3/2} b_n}{j[ka H_{n-1/2}{}^{(2)}(ka) - n H_{n+1/2}{}^{(2)}(ka)]}$$ (6)

In (4) b_n is defined, so A_n, the arbitrary coefficients of the solution, are completely determined in terms of applied voltage and the antenna dimensions.   Field at any point is now expressed in a series of TM waves with determined coefficients.   Thus, if desired, the field distribution at any radius could be mapped and thus the radiation pattern obtained.   However, we shall go directly to the calculation of antenna impedance.   It is at least evident, though, that E_θ and H_ϕ in the radiation field at large distances are zero along the axis and a maximum at $\theta = \pi/2$, since all odd $P_n{}^1(\cos \theta)$ (the only ones excited) are zero at $\theta = 0$, maximum at $\theta = \pi/2$.

Input Admittance of Antenna. The magnetic field H_ϕ is now determined since the coefficients A_n are known by (6) and (4).

$$H_\phi = \sum_{n=1}^{\infty} \frac{A_n}{r^{1/2}} P_n^{\ 1}\ (\cos\ \theta) H_{n+1/2}^{(2)}(kr) \qquad (7)$$

Surface current density is given in terms of the magnetic field at the conductor surface.

$$\bar{J} = \bar{n} \times \bar{H}$$

or
$$J_\theta = -H_\phi\big|_{r=a}$$

Thus total current flow on the antenna at any angle θ is

$$I_\theta = 2\pi a \sin\ \theta J_\theta = -2\pi a \sin\theta\ H_\phi\big|_{r=a} \qquad (8)$$

The total current flow away from the gap, at $\theta = \pi/2$, from (7) and (8)

$$I = -I_\theta\big|_{\theta=\pi/2}$$

$$= 2\pi a \sum_{n=1}^{\infty} \frac{P_n^{\ 1}(0)A_n}{a^{1/2}}\ H_{n+1/2}^{(2)}(ka) \qquad (9)$$

A_n as defined by (4) and (6) is proportional to V_0, so the ratio of I to V_0 may be written as an admittance.

$$Y = \frac{I}{V_0} = \sum_{n=1}^{\infty} Y_n$$

where
$$Y_n = \frac{j\pi(2n+1)[P_n^{\ 1}(0)]^2}{n(n+1)\eta}\left[\frac{1}{\dfrac{n}{ka} - \dfrac{H_{n-1/2}^{(2)}(ka)}{H_{n+1/2}^{(2)}(ka)}}\right] \qquad (10)$$

As usual, $\eta = \sqrt{\mu/\epsilon}$.

The form of (10) is particularly interesting, because it represents total admittance as the sum of a number of admittances, one for each harmonic solution corresponding to a given n. This is of the form for the admittance of a group of circuits in parallel. Each circuit then corresponds to a given harmonic solution and has admittance characteristics determined by (4). $P_n^{\ 1}(0)$ is defined by Eq. 10·09(13), and the $H_{n+1/2}^{(2)}$ functions by Eq. 10·09(18) and the usual definition for Hankel functions, $H_n^{(2)}(x) = J_n(x) - jN_n(x)$. Thus this admittance characteristic may be calculated. Its conductance and susceptance parts are plotted against ka for air dielectric ($\eta = 120\pi$)

in Figs. 12·23b and c.   Note that there are no even harmonics since $P_n{}^1(0) = 0$ for n even.   This is as would be expected because $P_n{}^1(\cos\theta)$ for n even are all odd functions with respect to the equator and should not be stimulated by a configuration symmetrical with respect to the equator.

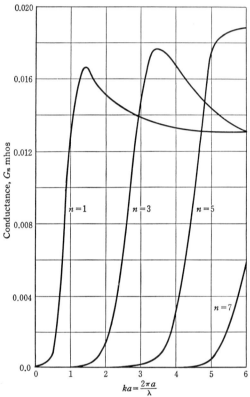

Fig. 12·23b   Conductance of individual spherical TM wave orders.

The higher harmonics may be readily approximated.

$$Y_n \cong \frac{j\pi(2n+1)[P_n{}^1(0)]^2}{\eta n^2(n+1)} ka \quad \text{if } ka \lll n$$

A study of this equation will show that, if an infinite number of n's are present, the total Y does not converge since finite contributions to susceptance are added by the higher n's forever.   However, this is only true for an infinitesimal gap, for which an infinite susceptance term might be expected.   When the gap is finite a point will be reached at which the coefficients b_n (and hence Y_n) will begin to decrease, approaching zero as n approaches infinity. This occurs for harmonic solutions which vary appreciably in the P_n^1 (cos θ) function over the region of the gap. Consequently, the actual total admittance cannot be obtained until the width of the gap is known. However,

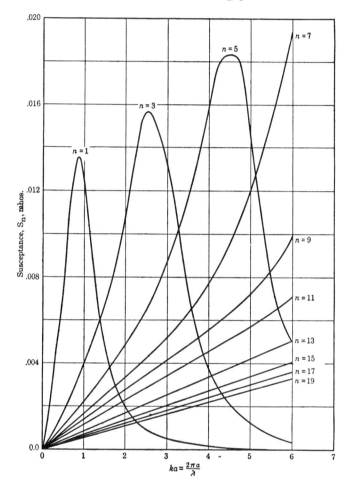

Fig. 12·23c　Susceptance of individual spherical TM wave orders.

the form of the curve and the order of magnitude of admittance will be changed little by missing the point by a few n's above which contributions to Y from Y_n should cease. Consequently, a representative curve for $\eta = 120\pi$ is plotted in Fig. 12·23d, using up to $n = 19$. The conductance or real part does converge and so the curve for conductance should be quite accurate.

These conclusions from the admittance curves are of importance.

1. Admittance of any mode, Y_n, is zero at zero frequency.

2. For low frequencies ($ka \ll n$) admittance is mainly a susceptance proportional to frequency, thus representing a pure capacitance: the capacitance between the hemispheres.

3. Input admittance is capacitive at any frequency; there are no resonant points as there are in thin antennas.

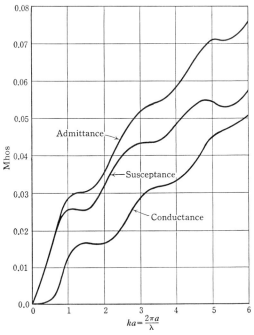

Fig. 12·23d Total admittance, conductance, and susceptance for spherical antenna.

4. Admittance curves have several fairly flat regions, indicating that the antenna has broad-band possibilities.

PROBLEMS

12·23a Show that admittances in a given mode in air approach these values at low and high frequencies.

$$Y_n \to jkaK_n \qquad ka \ll n$$

$$Y_n \to K_n \qquad ka \gg n$$

where
$$K_n = \frac{(2n + 1)[P_n^1(0)]^2}{120n(n + 1)} \text{ mhos}$$

12·23b   Calculate voltage required to radiate 100 watts at the first flat point on the admittance-frequency curve, Fig. 12·23d.

12·23c   Find the point of maximum gradient E_r in the antenna, and calculate approximately its value in terms of applied voltage.   Take ka in the vicinity of unity.   (*Suggestion:* Calculate only that in the predominant wave mode.)

12·23d   Write the complete series for field H_ϕ at any radius r.   Make approximations appropriate to the far-zone field by using asymptotic forms for the Hankel functions of kr, and investigate the problem of plotting the antenna pattern from the series.

12·23e   Calculate, by taking only a few terms of the series at $ka = 1$, the approximate power lost on the antenna if the conductor has a finite surface resistivity R_s.   Compare with the power radiated and note the high efficiency of the device in this respect.

12·24   SPHEROIDAL ANTENNAS

Stratton and Chu[19] have given solutions not only for spherical antennas but also for prolate spheroidal antennas.   Such a solution includes all spheroidal shapes between the sphere just studied and a thin wire (Fig. 12·24a).

The assumptions of Stratton and Chu are those used in the spherical antenna of the previous articles.   Axial symmetry is assumed, and voltage is applied across a very small gap at the center.   Results are quite similar in nature but different in magnitude from the results for the sphere.   Input admittance may again be expressed as the sum of a large number of input admittances, one for each harmonic mode of oscillation of the antenna.   However, for large eccentricities (large ratios of length to diameter) the resonances of each of these modes are very sharp, as contrasted to the broad resonances of the sphere.   At a given order of resonance ($n = 1, 3, 5$, etc.) the other modes are correspondingly less important than in the sphere, so the resonant mode practically determines the antenna characteristics in the neighborhood of resonance.

In the limit of an infinitesimally thin wire, the nth mode becomes resonant slightly below $L = n\lambda/2$.   These are true resonances in that the susceptance component of Y_n actually goes through zero and becomes inductive for frequencies above resonance, whereas for the sphere it is always positive (capacitive).   At frequencies much higher than resonance, susceptance in the nth mode approaches zero and conductance approaches a small but constant value.   This constant value is zero in the limiting case of an infinitesimally small wire, the value

[19] J. A. Stratton and L. J. Chu, *J. Appl. Phys.*, **12**, 230–248 (March 1941).

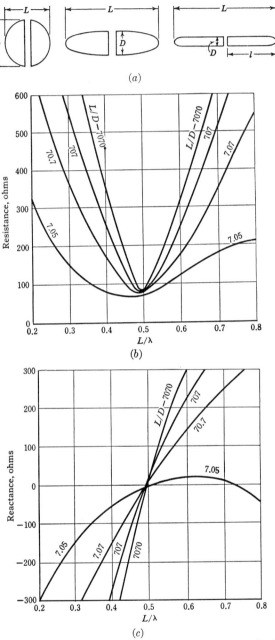

Fig. 12·24   (a) Transition from sphere to thin spheroidal wire dipole; (b) resistance and (c) reactance of spheroidal antennas fed at the center. From Stratton and Chu.

found in Prob. 12·23a in the limiting case of a sphere, and something between for medium eccentricities.

These characteristics are shown in the curves for input impedance in the vicinity of the first resonance, as plotted by Stratton and Chu, Figs. 12·24b and c. Again it must be realized that the harmonics cannot be combined exactly until the exact distribution of applied field across the gap is known, yet the form of the curves is accurate and magnitudes are nearly correct unless the gap is infinitesimal (in which case an infinite input capacitance must result). The $L/D = 1$ curve is of course the case of the sphere calculated earlier.

A study of the curves shows many features associated with past antenna knowledge. The radiation resistance for $L/\lambda = 0.5$ (a half-wave dipole) is found to be about 72 ohms, near the value calculated previously. This varies little for any eccentricity. The condition for zero reactance occurs at something less than a half-wavelength for long thin wires (about 0.49λ or 98 per cent of the antenna length). For fatter wires this condition of zero reactance actually may occur for L greater than a half-wavelength (or at a higher frequency than before). In the limit of the sphere there is no place at which input reactance is zero; there is always a capacitive component.

The increase in broadness of the impedance curve is evident for the fatter antennas, thus making available the wide band width required for television antennas.

Finally, Stratton and Chu have plotted the actual current distribution along the antenna for a thin spheroid (large L/D) and found it to vary little from the sinusoidal distribution usually assumed in the conventional methods of calculating antennas.

We will be able to compare some of these results with those obtained by Schelkunoff in the later articles.

12·25 THE BICONICAL ANTENNA

Another antenna of simple enough shape to make possible an approximate wave solution is the biconical antenna (Fig. 12·04a) used as an example for qualitative discussion in Art. 12·04. The wave solutions required are similar to those utilized for the spherical antenna (Art. 12·23) except that a TEM wave is required in the region of the antenna, $r < l$, and the form of the TM waves is modified there, as will be noted below. A series of TM modes for the external region is then written, and a series of TM modes appropriate to the inner region plus the spherical TEM mode is written for $r < l$. The unknown amplitudes of the series are to be evaluated by making tangential fields continuous across the common boundary at $r = l$. The procedure has been carried through approximately for cones of any angle by Tai[20] and Smith.[21]   We shall concentrate, however, on the approximate solution appropriate to small angles given by Schelkunoff, since this is particularly rich in physical pictures.

Form of Solutions.   The form of solutions for the outer region (Fig. 12·04a) is exactly that for the spherical wave types developed in Art. 10·09.   That is, axial symmetry ($\partial/\partial\phi = 0$) will be assumed and only the TM wave components H_ϕ, E_r, and E_θ will be excited; the axis ($\theta = 0, \pi$) is included in this region, so only the $P_n{}^1$ (cos θ) functions are required, and n must be an integer; the region extends outward to infinity, so the second Hankel function will be used for the Bessel function solution.   Equation 10·09(19) may then be used directly for the region $r > l$ with $Z_{n+1/2}$ read as $H_{n+1/2}{}^{(2)}$.

For the region between the cones, $r < l$, there is the principal wave, and to this must be added higher order TM waves similar to those in the space outside the antenna.   The TM waves for this region will, however, be somewhat different in form.   The Bessel function solution in this region can contain only a $J_{n+1/2}$ term since $N_{n+1/2}$ becomes infinite at $r = 0$.   For future purposes note that all field components in these higher order waves then disappear at $r = 0$ since $J_{n+1/2}(0) = 0$. Moreover, a second Legendre function solution is required for this region to account for the two boundary conditions of the cones at $\theta = \psi$ and $\pi - \psi$.   This second solution is usually denoted $Q_n{}^1$ (cos θ). Its value of infinity on the axis does not trouble us because the axis is excluded from the dielectric region over which the wave solution is to apply by the conducting cones.   Thus with the Bessel function read as $J_{n+1/2}$ and an extra associated Legendre function, the TM waves applicable to the region $r < l$ will be similar to Eq. 10·09(19).   The order n (probably better written ν) is in general not an integer because of the presence of the cones.†   This is in fact determined by the boundary conditions $E_r = 0$ at $\theta = \psi$, $\pi - \psi$.

Exact Equivalent Circuit.   The total current flow in the cones is proportional to H_ϕ.

$$I(r) = 2\pi r \sin \psi H_\phi\big|_{\theta=\psi} \tag{1}$$

Since H_ϕ in the region of the cones is made up of contributions from the principal and complementary waves, so is I.

[20] C. T. Tai, *J. Appl. Phys.*, **20**, 1076–1084 (Nov. 1949).

[21] P. D. P. Smith, *J. Appl. Phys.*, **19**, 11–23 (Jan. 1948).

† It is then possible to use $P_\nu{}^m$ ($-$ cos θ) as a second independent solution in place of $Q_\nu{}^m$ (cos θ), as is done by Schelkunoff; he also gives equations in terms of the ordinary Legendre functions rather than the associated, since the two are related by the simple derivative.

$$I(r) = I_0(r) + I'(r) \qquad (2)$$

I_0 denotes the current from fields in the principal wave, I' from the higher order waves. The latter is zero at $r = 0$, because the higher order wave components disappear at the origin. Total current flow into the antenna at $r = 0$ is then only that in the principal wave.

$$I(0) = I_0(0) \qquad (3)$$

Now define a total voltage between the two conical conductors as the integral of E_θ over a surface $r =$ constant.

$$V(r) = -r \int_{\psi}^{\pi - \psi} E_\theta \, d\theta$$

A study of this integral for the higher order wave components of E_θ would reveal that the net integral is zero for all such waves at any radius and has a contribution only for the principal wave. The corresponding situation is readily seen in the higher order waves between parallel planes or rectangular wave guides, where the sinusoids representing transverse electric fields yield just as much negative as positive contribution to the integral of electric field, and so give a net integral of zero.

$$V(r) = V_0(r) \qquad (4)$$

Finally, if total current is zero at the end of the antenna with $r = l$, (2) then requires

$$I(l) = 0 \qquad \text{or} \qquad I_0(l) = -I'(l) \qquad (5)$$

Thus, if an equivalent transmission line circuit is drawn to represent the behavior of the principal wave, current in this wave at the end must have the value given by (5). We can assure that this value will be obtained from the equivalent circuit by placing an impedance Z_L across the line at $r = l$ where

$$Z_L = \frac{V_0(l)}{-I'(l)} \qquad (6)$$

Thus the behavior of the principal wave is exactly described by the equivalent circuit of Fig. 12·04c, where Z_L is defined by (6). Moreover, since input current in the principal wave is exactly the total input current by (3), and voltage in the principal wave is total voltage everywhere by (4), the input impedance calculated from this principal wave equivalent circuit is the total input impedance. Of course it is not necessary that total current be zero at the end of the antenna in order for the equivalent circuit to be of use. For a finite $I(l)$, $I(l) - I'(l)$ is the current to be accounted for by the lumped impedance.

Input Impedance of Biconical Antenna. In order to calculate Z_L in the equivalent circuit of Fig. 12.04c, Schelkunoff has shown two methods. In the first method, the complex Poynting flow of power from an infinitesimal biconical antenna is computed, and this is interpreted in terms of an input impedance. By comparing the result with

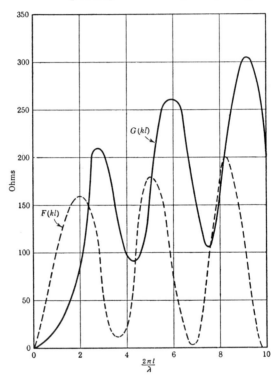

Fig. 12·25a.

the expression for input impedance in the equivalent circuit with $Z_0 \to \infty$, Z_L is identified as

$$Z_L = \frac{Z_0{}^2}{G(kl) + jF(kl)} \qquad (7)$$

Characteristic impedance of the TEM wave from Art. 9·14 is

$$Z_0 = \frac{\eta}{\pi} \ln \cot \frac{\psi}{2}$$

G (kl) and $F(kl)$ are functions of the electrical length and are plotted in Fig. 12·25a.

The second method shown by Schelkunoff follows from a more direct study of the higher order waves. The matching operation of the wave solutions is carried through approximately, in a manner applicable to cones of high characteristic impedance. The steps are as follows.

1. It is assumed that field at a large distance from the antenna is of the same form as that found previously (Art. 12·06) for a dipole antenna. This function of θ is expanded in a series of Legendre polynomials in cos θ by the rules used in Art. 12·23.

2. By noting the limiting case of the wave solutions, Eq. 10·09(19), for large values of kr, the unknown coefficient of the nth order term may be evaluated by comparing with the corresponding term in the series from step 1. Coefficients are of course proportional to principal wave current or voltage. Thus the field in the region $r > l$ is in reality taken as that field found previously from the integration of effects from the assumed sinusoidal distribution of current, but now expanded as a sum of TM waves.

3. Now it is next noted that the TM wave solutions inside the cone region approach exactly the corresponding waves in the space outside as $Z_0 \rightarrow \infty$. Thus, for matching of E_r across the boundary, the coefficients of corresponding wave orders inside and outside must be equal in the limit of $Z_0 = \infty$ since there is no E_r component in the principal wave. For large but finite values of Z_0, the coefficients inside may then be taken as equal to those outside to a first approximation. Coefficients of higher order waves inside the antenna region are then obtained in terms of the principal wave current or voltage. Thus step 3 of the converging step-by-step method sketched in Art 12·04 is performed, at least approximately.

4. Since coefficients for H_ϕ of the higher order waves are now determined, current in the cones due to these is given by (1). Once this current is determined and written in terms of voltage in the principal wave at $r = l$, Z_L is given by (6). The method again gives the same form as in (7), and

$$G(kl) = \sum_{m=0}^{\infty} b_m J_{2m+3/2}{}^2 (kl)$$

$$F(kl) = - \sum_{m=0}^{\infty} b_m J_{2m+3/2} (kl) N_{2m+3/2} (kl)$$

where $$b_m = \frac{30\pi kl(4m + 3)}{(m + 1)(2m + 1)} \tag{8}$$

Curves showing the resistance and reactance components of input impedance for biconical antennas as a function of length and characteristic impedance are shown in Figs. 12·25b and c. These are calculated from ordinary transmission line theory for the equivalent circuit Fig. 12·04c with Z_L defined by the above. These important practical points follow.

1. Input resistance in the neighborhood of the first resonance is close to the value 73 ohms for a half-wave dipole (Art. 12·07) regardless of the size of the antenna.

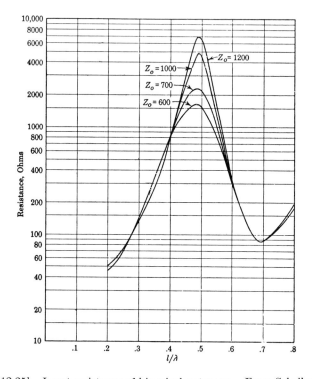

Fig. 12·25b   Input resistance of biconical antennas.   From Schelkunoff.

2. Resonance occurs for the antenna somewhat shorter than the corresponding integral number of half-waves, this shortening being greater for the lower characteristic impedances. A curve of shortening versus Z_0 for the first three resonances is given in Fig. 12·25d.

3. Resonance is sharper for high characteristic impedances, again demonstrating the broad band input impedance properties of the fatter antennas.

4. In the neighborhood of the second resonance (high driving-point-impedance antennas) input resistance is a definite function of Z_0 as shown by Fig. 12·25b.

Current Distribution along the Antenna. It is of importance to study current distribution from this analysis (as was done by Stratton and Chu for the thin spheroids) in order to check the approximations of sinusoidal current distribution commonly made on thin-wire antennas.

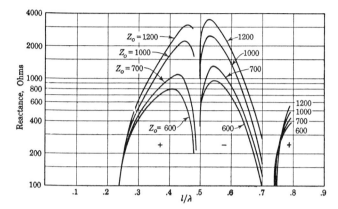

Fig. 12·25c Input reactance of biconical antenna. From Schelkunoff.

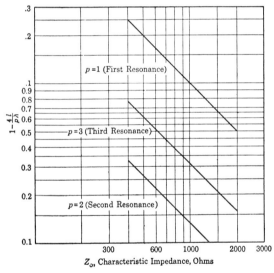

Fig. 12·25d· Per unit foreshortening of biconical antenna. From Schelkunoff.

As has been noted, in the limit of infinitesimal cone angles (infinite Z_0), the higher order waves in the antenna region become negligible compared with the principal TEM wave, so the sinusoidal distribution becomes exact. Schelkunoff has also plotted current distribution for a biconical antenna of 1000 ohms characteristic impedance. His curves show that the real part of current is very close to that in the principal wave. The imaginary part is noticeably different, but magnitude of total current still compares well with that in the principal wave. The deviation will, of course, become more marked as the antenna impedance decreases.

PROBLEMS

12·25a   Consider a biconical antenna with $l = \lambda/4$. From the approximate value of power radiated from a half-wave dipole in Art. 12·07, find the expression for the appropriate value of resistance to use for Z_L to account for this radiated power, if the reactive part of this is neglected. For a thin antenna $\psi = 0.1°$, and a thick antenna $\psi = 5°$, find the values of this resistance. Assuming that the resistance does not vary appreciably with frequency over a small range, plot input impedance of the antenna over a small range about the resonant length $l = \lambda/4$ for the two antennas. What conclusion do you draw on impedance band width of thick antennas versus slender ones?

12·25b   For the first antiresonant point, $l/\lambda \approx 0.5$, calculate the power radiated in terms of maximum current on the antenna by Eq. 12·06(6). From the equivalent circuit for the antenna, considering that this maximum current is that of the principal wave, find the voltage at the end in terms of the current and Z_0. From this, find the terminating impedance in terms of Z_0 for this case, assuming Z_L real. Note that, since the line is a half-wave long, this is also the input resistance, and compare with the antiresonant peaks given in Fig. 12·25b.

12·25c   Expand the field of a dipole antenna calculated approximately in Art. 12·06 in a series of spherical transverse magnetic waves.

12·25d   If current in the higher order waves approaches zero as $Z_0 \to \infty$, the terminating impedance Z_L in the equivalent circuit approaches infinity. It seems that the possibility of accounting for radiation in the equivalent circuit is then excluded. Demonstrate that such reasoning is faulty.

12·26 THIN DIPOLE ANTENNAS OF GENERAL SHAPE

Schelkunoff has extended results of the analysis based on the biconical antenna to antennas of other shape. The method is approximate, but, if antennas are not of too great diameter to length ratio,

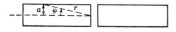

Fig. 12·26a Cylindrical dipole interpreted as a non-uniform transmission line.

these approximations are easy to accept on a physical basis. It is assumed that the same equivalent circuit applies (Fig. 12·04c), but the shape of the antenna is taken into account by considering the antenna as a non-uniform transmission line. For example, if the antenna is cylindrical (Fig. 12·26a), the capacity and inductance per unit length may be obtained approximately at any radius by con-

TABLE 12·26

Antenna Shape	Thin Cylinders	Thin Spheroids	Diamond Shaped Longitudinal Section
Average characteristic impedance	$120\left(\ln\dfrac{2l}{a}-1\right)$	$120\ln\dfrac{l}{a}$	$120\ln\dfrac{2l}{a}$
Per-unit shortening at first resonance	$\dfrac{27.08}{Z_{0a}}$	$\dfrac{5040}{(Z_{0a}+83)^2}$	$\dfrac{27.08}{\pi Z_{0a}}$
Per-unit shortening at second resonance	$\dfrac{39.92}{Z_{0a}}$	$\dfrac{25.68}{Z_{0a}}$	$\dfrac{30.82}{Z_{0a}}$

sidering the values for a cone that would just pass through this radius. For small ratios of a/r (a = antenna radius, r = distance along antenna from center),

$$L \cong \frac{\mu}{\pi}\ln\frac{2}{\psi} = \frac{\mu}{\pi}\ln\frac{2r}{a} \qquad C \cong \frac{\pi\epsilon}{\ln(2r/a)} \qquad (1)$$

Thus L and C, and hence Z_0, are functions of r.

As a first approximation, all previous curves plotted for the biconical antennas may be used, with characteristic impedance taken as an average value over the length defined by

$$Z_{0a} = \frac{1}{l}\int_0^l Z_0(r)\,dr \qquad (2)$$

Formulas for the average characteristic impedance for cylindrical, spheroidal, and diamond-shaped longitudinal-sectioned wires are given in Table 12·26.

A better approximation may be had by utilizing non-uniform transmission line theory to transfer the load impedance, obtained from the biconical analysis, to the input. Schelkunoff has supplied particularly useful equations for this purpose appropriate to lines with only slight non-uniformities. Curves of input resistance and reactance for the cylindrical antenna, calculated in this manner, are shown in

Figs. 12·26*b* and *c*. Non-uniform transmission line theory shows also that there is a correction to resonant length due to the antenna shape which may be either in the same direction or the opposite direction to the correction from the terminating reactance. Approximate formulas for net length at first and second resonances are listed in Table 12·26.

For any of the antenna types above plane perfectly conducting earth, the image (Art. 12·08) is used to give a corresponding free-space con-

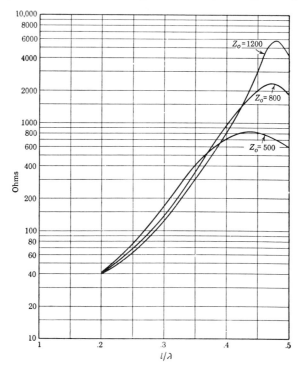

Fig. 12·26*b*   Input resistance for cylindrical dipole antenna.   From Schelkunoff.

figuration for which the impedance may be found by the above methods. Impedance of the actual antenna is then half that calculated for the antenna and its image, as demonstrated in Fig. 12·26*d* for a cylindrical antenna above earth.

PROBLEM

12·26   Plot on a Smith transmission line chart the locus of impedance for a cylindrical dipole of 800 ohms characteristic impedance, a biconical antenna of 700 ohms characteristic impedance, and of the spherical antenna of Art. 12·23, all referred to a 70-ohm line.   Comment on the comparison.

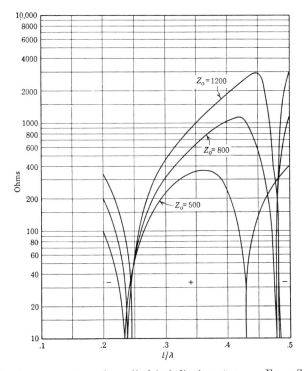

Fig. 12·26c   Input reactance for cylindrical dipole antenna.   From Schelkunoff.

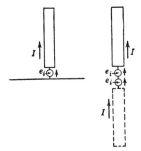

Fig. 12·26d   Use of image for determining impedance of antenna above plane
conducting earth.

Receiving Antennas and Reciprocity

12·27   A TRANSMITTING-RECEIVING SYSTEM

The discussion in previous articles has generally inferred that the
radiating system was to be used as a transmitting antenna, exciting
waves in space from some source of high-frequency energy. The same
devices useful for transmission are also useful for reception, and it

will be seen that the quantities already calculated (such as the pattern, antenna gain, and input impedance for transmission) are the useful parameters in the design of a receiving system also. This might at first seem surprising, since the two problems have some noticeable differences. In the transmitting antenna, a generator is generally applied at localized terminals, and waves are set up which go out in space approximately as spherical wave fronts. In the receiving antenna, a wave coming in from a distant transmitter approximates a portion of a uniform plane wave, and so sets up an applied electric field on the antenna system quite different from that associated with the localized sources in the transmitting case. As a consequence, the induced fields must be different in order that total field shall meet the boundary conditions of the antenna, and the current distribution will in general be different for the same antenna on transmission or reception. The currents set up on the receiving antenna system by the plane wave will convey useful power to the load (probably through a transmission line or guide), but will also produce re-radiation or scattering of some of the energy back into space. The mechanism of this scattering is exactly the same as that discussed in preceding sections for radiation from a transmitting antenna, but the form may be different for a given antenna because of the different current distribution.

Thus, we seem to have somewhat different pictures of the mechanism of transmitting and receiving electromagnetic radiation. Reciprocity theorems related to those already discussed (Art. 11·05) provide ties between the two phenomena such as the following:

1. The antenna pattern for reception is identical with that for transmission.

2. The input impedance of the antenna on transmission is the internal impedance of the equivalent generator representing a receiving system.

3. An effective area for the receiving antenna can be defined and by reciprocity is related to the gain previously defined (Art. 12·07). Several of these points will be discussed in this and following articles. An excellent treatment in more detail has been given by Silver.[22]

We wish to begin the discussion by considering the transmitting and receiving antennas with intermediate space (Fig. 12·27a) as a system in which energy is to be transferred from the first to the second. We select terminals in the feeding guide where voltage and current may be defined in the manner explained in Art. 11·03, and similarly select a

---

[22] S. Silver, *Microwave Antenna Theory and Design*, M.I.T. Radiation Laboratory Series, Vol. 12, McGraw-Hill, 1949, Chapter 2.

reference in the guide from the receiving antenna. The region between, including both antennas, the space, and any intermediate conductors and dielectric (assumed linear) may be represented as a two-terminal pair or transducer as indicated in Fig. 12·27b. That is,

$$V_1 = Z_{11}I_1 + Z_{12}I_2 \tag{1}$$

$$V_2 = Z_{21}I_1 + Z_{22}I_2 \tag{2}$$

The systems discussed in Chapter 11, for which proofs of the above were given, were assumed to be closed by conducting boundaries, whereas the present system extends to infinity. However, the

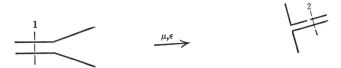

Fig. 12·27a   A system of transmitting and receiving antennas.

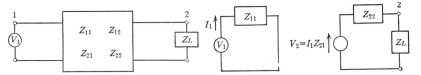

Fig. 12·27b   Equivalent representation for Fig. 12.27a.

Fig. 12·27c   Approximate equivalent circuit neglecting reaction of receiver back on transmitting system.

theorems given there can be extended to regions extending to infinity because of the manner in which fields die off there.[23]

The present system is specialized in another respect in that the coupling impedance Z_{12} in (1) is very small for a large separation between transmitter and receiver. It may then be neglected in (1), and the impedance coefficient Z_{11} is just the input impedance of the transmitting antenna calculated by itself.

$$V_1 \approx Z_{11}I_1 \approx Z_A I_1 \tag{3}$$

The coupling term in (2) cannot be neglected, since this coupling is the effect being studied. However, (2) can be represented by the usual equivalent circuit of Thévenin's theorem (Prob. 11·04b) in which an equivalent voltage generator $I_1 Z_{21}$ is connected to the load impedance Z_L through an antenna impedance Z_{22} (which is essentially the input impedance of antenna 2 if driven as a transmitter). Thus, because of the small coupling, the reaction of the receiving antenna on

[23] W. K. Saunders, *Proc. Nat. Acad. Sci.*, **38**, 342–348, April, 1952.

the transmitting antenna can be neglected and the equivalent circuit separated as in Fig. 12·27c.

The equivalent circuit will be discussed again later. For the moment, we shall discuss transmission over the system from another point of view. For this purpose, an *effective area* of the receiving antenna is defined so that the useful power removed by the receiving antenna is given by this area multiplied by the average Poynting vector (power density) in the oncoming wave.

$$W_r = A_{er}P_{av} \tag{4}$$

Like antenna gain defined previously, this is in general a function of direction about the antenna, and of the condition of match in the guide. When not otherwise specified, it will be assumed to be the value for a matched load and for the maximum direction. The power density at the receiver is the power density of an isotropic radiator $(W_t/4\pi r^2)$ multiplied by gain of the transmitting antenna in the given direction.

$$W_r = W_t \frac{A_{er}g_t}{4\pi r^2} \tag{5}$$

W_t is the power transmitted, r is the distance between transmitter and receiver, g_t is gain of the transmitting antenna, and A_{er} is the effective area of the receiving antenna. As will be noted in the next article, the gain of a given antenna is proportional to the above-defined effective area for that antenna,

$$g = \frac{4\pi}{\lambda^2} A_e \tag{6}$$

Therefore (5) may be written in either of the following forms given by Friis.[24] Subscripts r and t refer to receiving and transmitting antennas, respectively.

$$\frac{W_r}{W_t} = \frac{g_r g_t \lambda^2}{(4\pi r)^2} = \frac{A_{er}A_{et}}{\lambda^2 r^2} \tag{7}$$

PROBLEM

12·27 Calculate power received corresponding to a transmitted power of 100 watts and a distance between transmitter and receiver of 10^3 meters under the following conditions:

a. Gain of transmitting antenna = 1.5; effective area of receiver = 0.40 meter.^{2}

b. Gain of both antennas = 2; wavelength = 0.10 meter.

c. Effective area of both antennas = 1 meter^2; wavelength = 0.03 meter.

[24] H. T. Friis, *Proc. I.R.E.*, **34**, 254–256 (May 1946).

12·28   RECIPROCITY RELATIONS

From the equivalent circuit of Fig. 12·27c, we can obtain a different form for the power delivered to the receiving antenna. For this purpose, let us assume that there is a conjugate match,

$$Z_L = Z_{22}{}^* = R_{r2} - jX_{r2} \tag{1}$$

which is known to be the condition for maximum power transfer from the equivalent generator to the load. The power delivered to the load under this condition is

$$W_r = \frac{|I_1 Z_{21}|^2}{8R_{r2}} \tag{2}$$

If the transmitting antenna has input resistance R_{r1}, transmitted power is

$$W_t = \tfrac{1}{2}|I_1|^2 R_{r1} \tag{3}$$

so

$$\frac{W_r}{W_t} = \frac{|Z_{21}|^2}{4R_{r1}R_{r2}} \tag{4}$$

By comparing (4) with Eq. 12·27(5),

$$|Z_{21}|^2 = \frac{R_{r1}R_{r2}g_1 A_{e2}}{\pi r^2} \tag{5}$$

If we now reverse the roles of transmitting and receiving antennas, we find for the transfer impedance in the reverse direction

$$|Z_{12}|^2 = \frac{R_{r2}R_{r1}g_2 A_{e1}}{\pi r^2} \tag{6}$$

By the reciprocity argument of Art. 11·05 (modified so that it applies to a region extending to infinity), Z_{12} and Z_{21} are equal, so we conclude

$$\frac{g_1}{g_2} = \frac{A_{e1}}{A_{e2}} \tag{7}$$

The antennas in the above argument were arbitrary, so it follows from (7) that the defined effective area of any antenna is proportional to the gain of that antenna. The constant of proportionality can be found by solving the problem for one of the simple shapes, such as the small dipole[25] or the small loop antenna. The result is as given in Eq. 12·27(6). Note that this is the same relation between gain and *actual* area of large apertures with uniform plane wave illumination

[25] D. O. North, *RCA Review*, **6**, 332–343 (Jan. 1942).

found in Eq. 12·20(5) (and Prob. 12·20e). Thus, for large apertures with uniform illumination, the effective area is equal to the actual aperture area, as might be expected. For small antennas, this relation does not hold. In fact, for an infinitesimal dipole, we found the gain to be 1.5, so the effective area is

$$(A_e)_{\text{dipole}} = \frac{\lambda^2}{4\pi} g = \frac{3}{8\pi} \lambda^2 \tag{8}$$

which is finite and sizable even though antenna size is infinitesimal.

Another relation following from reciprocity, which is probably more important in practice, is that the pattern of a given antenna is the same for transmission or reception. This is useful because the pattern

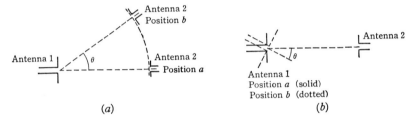

(a)   (b)

Fig. 12·28   Possible systems for pattern measurement.

may then be calculated or measured in the easiest way and then be used for both transmission or reception designs. To show this, imagine, as in Fig. 12·28a, that antenna 2 is moved about the arc of a circle to measure the pattern of antenna 1. Let $\theta = 0$ be the angle of maximum response (position a) and angle θ (position b) be a general position. Also, for simplicity we assume that 1 watt is radiated in all the measurements to be described. Then, if 1 is transmitting and 2 receiving, the power received in position b, as compared with position a, by (4) is

$$\frac{W_{2b}}{W_{2a}} = \frac{|Z_{21}|_b^2}{|Z_{21}|_a^2} \tag{9}$$

If 2 is transmitting and 1 receiving, the power received for the two positions is related by

$$\frac{W_{1b}}{W_{1a}} = \frac{|Z_{12}|_b^2}{|Z_{12}|_a^2} \tag{10}$$

Because of reciprocity $|Z_{12}|_a = |Z_{21}|_a$, and similarly for b, so the ratios (9) and (10) are the same. Thus, the same relative power pattern will be measured with antenna 1 transmitting or receiving.

It is, of course, important to remember that the reciprocity relation may be violated if the transmission path contains a medium such as the ionosphere, which may not have strictly bilateral properties. It is obvious that frequency must be kept constant when receiver and transmitter are interchanged. Also, if there are obstacles or other secondary radiators in the field, they must keep their same position relative to the system when the interchange is made. (See Prob. 12·28c).

PROBLEMS

12·28a   Calculate the effective area for a half-wave dipole antenna. Compare with that for the infinitesimal dipole.

12·28b   Calculate the effective area for the small loop antenna.

12·28c   If the antennas are in free space, the pattern of 1 may be measured, as was described in Fig. 12·28a, by moving antenna 2 about the arc of a circle, or, as in Fig. 12·28b, by rotating 1 about an axis to give the same relative position. Explain why the same results might not be obtained by the two methods if there are fixed obstacles in the transmission path.

12·28d   For the data of Prob. 12·27b and the radiation resistance of both antennas equal to 50 ohms, calculate $\mid Z_{12} \mid$. Now, allowing separation r to vary, find the separation for which Z_{12} becomes comparable to Z_{11}.

12·29   EQUIVALENT CIRCUIT OF THE RECEIVING ANTENNA

For a study of the circuit problem in matching the antenna to a receiver, the second part of the equivalent circuit of Fig. 12·27c is useful and is repeated in Fig. 12·29a. In this the internal impedance of the generator, Z_{22}, is essentially the input impedance of the same antenna if driven at the same terminals.

$$Z_{22} \approx Z_{i2} \tag{1}$$

This follows by the same argument given for antenna (1) in Art. 12·27, meaning that reaction back through Z_{21} is negligible *when the antenna is driven.*

The voltage generator in Fig. 12·29a is given from Eq. 12·27(2) as $I_1 Z_{21}$, but transmitter current and transfer impedance are not convenient parameters for most calculations, so other forms in terms of the power density of the oncoming wave are preferable. By substitution from Eq. 12·27(4) and Eq. 12·28(2), we can find this voltage in terms of the average Poynting vector or power density of the oncoming wave, P_{av}, the radiation resistance of the receiving antenna

R_{r2}, and the effective area A_{e2}. (This effective area is calculated on the assumption of a matched load, but may be a function of the orientation of the antenna with respect to the oncoming wave.)

$$V_a = I_1 Z_{21} = (8R_2 A_{er} P_{av})^{1/2} \qquad (2)$$

The equivalent circuit is useful, for example, in computing the transfer of power from the antenna to the useful load through a transmission line which may have discontinuities, matching sections, or filter elements. All these may be lumped together as a transducer, as explained in the preceding chapter (Fig. 12·29b), and the problem from

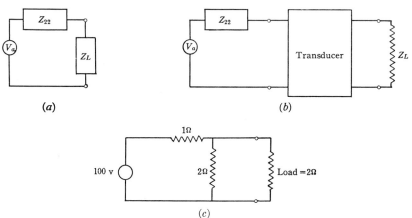

(a)   (b)

(c)

Fig. 12·29 (a) Equivalent circuit of receiving antenna for power transfer calculations. (b) Circuit for receiving antenna coupled to the load through a transducer.

here on is a standard circuit calculation. It must be emphasized, as in any Thévenin equivalent circuit, that the equivalent circuit was derived to tell what happens in the load under different load conditions, and significance cannot be automatically attached to a calculation of power loss in the internal impedance of the equivalent circuit. In the present case, it is tempting to interpret this as the power re-radiated or scattered by currents on the receiving antenna, and one would conclude that as much power is scattered under a condition of perfect match as is absorbed in the load. This conclusion is not true, except in special cases where the current distribution may be the same for reception as for transmission.

PROBLEMS

12·29a To demonstrate that a power calculation in the internal impedance of a Thévenin equivalent circuit does not necessarily represent the power lost internally, consider a generator of constant voltage 100 volts coupled to a resistance load of

2 ohms through the series-parallel resistances shown in Fig. 12.29c.   Calculate the actual power lost in the generator, and compare with that calculated by taking load current flowing through the internal impedance of a Thévenin equivalent circuit.

12·29b   An antenna having an input impedance on transmission of $70 + j30$ ohms is used on reception by connecting directly to a 50-ohm transmission line which is perfectly matched to a pure resistance load.   The effective area is 0.40 meter.[2]   Find the power transfer to the load if the antenna is in a plane wave field of 100 microvolts per meter.   Compare this with the power that could be obtained with a conjugate match to the antenna impedance.

APPENDIX

SOME USEFUL REFERENCES

I. Electromagnetic Theory

Attwood, *Electric and Magnetic Fields*, Wiley, 3rd ed., 1949.

Maxwell, *A Treatise on Electricity and Magnetism*, Oxford, 3rd ed., 1892.

Page and Adams, *Electrodynamics*, Van Nostrand, 1940.

Schelkunoff, *Electromagnetic Waves*, Van Nostrand, 1943.

Skilling, *Fundamentals of Electric Waves*, Wiley, 2nd ed., 1948. (Introductory; higher mathematics not required.)

Smythe, *Static and Dynamic Electricity*, McGraw-Hill, 2nd ed., 1950.

Stratton, *Electromagnetic Theory*, McGraw-Hill, 1941.

Weber, *Electromagnetic Fields*, Vol. I, "Mapping of Fields," Wiley, 1950.

II. Applications to Special Problems

Jordan, *Electromagnetic Waves and Radiating Systems*, Prentice-Hall, 1950.

Montgomery, Dicke, and Purcell, *Principles of Microwave Circuits*, McGraw-Hill, 1948.

Pierce, *Theory and Design of Electron Beams*, Van Nostrand, 1949.

Pierce, *Traveling-Wave Tubes*, Van Nostrand, 1950.

Schelkunoff, *Advanced Antenna Theory*, Wiley, 1952.

Schelkunoff and Friis, *Antennas: Theory and Practice*, Wiley, 1952.

Silver, *Microwave Antenna Theory and Design*, McGraw-Hill, 1949.

Slater, *Microwave Electronics*, Van Nostrand, 1950.

III. Mathematical Tables and Texts

Dwight, *Tables of Integrals and Other Mathematical Data*, Macmillan, rev. ed., 1947.

Jahnke and Emde, *Tables of Functions*, Dover, 1943.

Peirce, *A Short Table of Integrals*, Ginn, 1929.

Bateman, *Partial Differential Equations of Mathematical Physics*, Dover, 1944.

Bewley, *Two-Dimensional Fields in Engineering*, Macmillan, 1948.

Churchill, *Fourier Series and Boundary Value Problems*, McGraw-Hill, 1941.

Gray, Matthews, and MacRobert, *A Treatise on Bessel Functions and Their Applications in Physics*, Macmillan, 1931.

Hobson, *Spherical and Ellipsoidal Harmonics*, Cambrige, 1931.

Margenau and Murphy, *The Mathematics of Physics and Chemistry*, Van Nostrand, 1943.

McLachlan, *Bessel Functions for Engineers*, Oxford, 1934.

Schelkunoff, *Applied Mathematics for Engineers and Scientists*, Van Nostrand, 1948.

Sokolnikoff, J. S., and Sokolnikoff, E. S., *Higher Mathematics for Engineers and Physicists*, McGraw-Hill, 2nd ed., 1941.

Watson, *A Treatise on Bessel Functions*, Macmillan, 2nd ed., 1944.

IV. Electric Circuit Theory

Gardner and Barnes, *Transients in Linear Systems Studied by the Laplace Transformation*, Wiley, 1942.

Guillemin, *Communication Networks*, Vols. 1 and 2, Wiley, 1935.

Guillemin, *The Mathematics of Circuit Analysis*, Wiley, 1949.

V. Mathematical Physics

Joos, *Theoretical Physics*, Blackie, 1934.

Slater and Frank, *Introduction to Theoretical Physics*, McGraw-Hill, 1933.

INDEX